Biology

Study Workbook A

PEARSON

Boston, Massachusetts   Chandler, Arizona   Glenview, Illinois   Upper Saddle River, New Jersey

Photo Credits: p 1 ©istockphoto.com/Linda Fleurin; p 13 ©Comstock/Jupiter Images; p 27 ©Julian Gutt/AFP/Getty Images/NewsCom; p 29 ©istockphoto.com/John Woodworth; p 45 © Jeff Rotman/www.jeffrotman.com; p 65 ©George McCarthy/Nature Picture Library; p 79 Geoff Dann/©DK Images; p 95 ©SIME s.a.s / eStock Photo; p 97 ©istockphoto.com/Andrey Prokhorov; p 113 © simple stock shots/Age Fotostock; p 127 Watering can (earthenware), English School, (16th century) / © Museum of London, UK, / The Bridgeman Art Library International; p 141 Kike Calvo/V&W/Image Quest Marine; p 157 © Joe McDonald/CORBIS; p 159 ©istockphoto.com/Andrey Prokhorov; p 177 blickwinkel/Alamy; p 191 t. ©Pearson Education, Photo by Heather Wright; b. ©aliciahh/istockphoto.com; p 211 EYE OF SCIENCE / SPL/Photo Researchers, Inc.; p 225 BL: ©arlindo71/istockphoto.com, BM: Kenneth Eward/BioGrafx/Photo Researchers, Inc., BR: PR NEWSWIRE, TL: Biophoto Associates / Photo Researchers, Inc.; p 227 Sebastian Kaulitzki/Fotolia; p 245 ©David Parker / Photo Researchers, Inc.; p 247 ©istockphoto.com/Lorraine Benjamin; p 265 ©Chris Johns/National Geographic Image Collection; p 283 ©Pearson Education. Photo by Heather Wright; p 297 © Mark Hamblin/age footstock; p 311 © Marvin Dembinsky Photo Associates / Alamy; p 313 ©istockphoto.com/Joe Biafore; p 323 © Peter Cade/Getty Images; p 339 © Nigel Cattlin / Visuals Unlimited; p 355 © Vienna Report Agency/Sygma/Corbis; p 375 © Ted Mead/PhotoLibrary; p 391 ©Martin Perez/istockphoto.com; p 393 ©istockphoto.com/alle12; p 405 ©Kelly McGann Hebert; p 419 © O. LOUIS MAZZATENTA /National Geographic Society; p 435 ©Anastasiya Maksymenko/istockphoto.com; p 451 © 2002 Masa Ushioda/Image Quest 3-D; p 463 ©Ariadne Van Zandbergen/africanpictures.net; p 465 ©istockphoto.com/Svetlana Prikhodko; p 481 CLS Design/Shutterstock; p 497 © Private Collection/Bridgeman Art Library; p 511 © The Schlesinger Library/Radcliffe; p 527 ©Libby Chapman/istockphoto.com; p 543 ©Nicholas Monu/istockphoto.com; p 559 © Christopher Wheeler

ISBN-13: 978-0-13-368719-4
ISBN-10:   0-13-368719-8
14 15 16 17   V031 16

Contents

Study Workbook A

This workbook is designed to be used in conjunction with *Miller & Levine Biology*. As students work through each lesson, they will acquire the skills they need to study biology more effectively.

This study workbook can be used to
- preview a chapter
- learn key vocabulary terms
- master difficult concepts
- review for chapter and unit tests
- practice 21st Century Skills

Ensure your students are on the pathway to Biology mastery with *Study Workbook A*!

Start with the Big Idea
Gauge your students prior knowledge using the guiding questions provided at the beginning of every chapter of *Workbook A*. Ask them to fill in the first column of the graphic organizer before they read the chapter. Remind them to fill in the second column after they finish each lesson. Use their responses to discuss the Big Idea and answer the Essential Question.

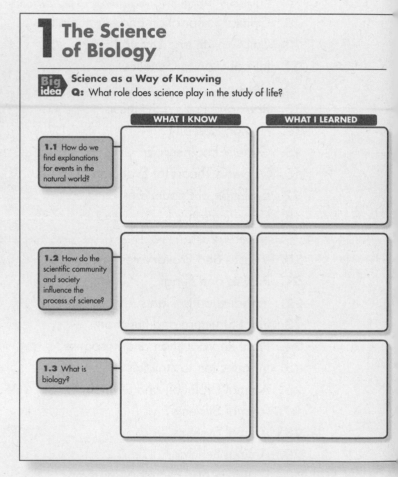

1 The Science of Biology

Big idea Science as a Way of Knowing
Q: What role does science play in the study of life?

WHAT I KNOW	WHAT I LEARNED
1.1 How do we find explanations for events in the natural world?	
1.2 How do the scientific community and society influence the process of science?	
1.3 What is biology?	

review Each Lesson
Go through the Lesson
Objectives with students before
they read a lesson and use the
Lesson Summary as a preview.
Remind your students use this
page for a quick review before
a test or quiz.

3.4 Cycles of Matter

Lesson Objectives

- Describe how matter cycles among the living and nonliving parts of an ecosystem.
- Describe how water cycles through the biosphere.
- Explain why nutrients are important in living systems.
- Describe how the availability of nutrients affects the productivity of ecosystems.

Lesson Summary

Recycling in the Biosphere Matter, unlike energy, is recycled within and between ecosystems. Elements pass from one organism to another and from one part of the biosphere to another through **biogeochemical cycles**, which are closed loops powered by the flow of energy.

The Water Cycle Water moves between the ocean, the atmosphere, and land.
- ▶ Evaporation is the process in which water changes from a liquid to a gas.
- ▶ Transpiration is the process in which water evaporates from the leaves of plants.

Nutrient Cycles The chemical substances that an organism needs to survive are called **nutrients**. Like water, nutrients pass through organisms and the environment.
- ▶ **Carbon Cycle:** Carbon is a key ingredient of all organic compounds. Processes involved in the carbon cycle include photosynthesis and human activities such as burning.
- ▶ **Nitrogen Cycle:** Nitrogen is needed by all organisms to build proteins. Processes involved in the nitrogen cycle include nitrogen fixation and denitrification.
  - • In **nitrogen fixation**, certain bacteria convert nitrogen gas into ammonia.
  - • In **denitrification**, other soil bacteria convert nitrogen compounds called nitrates back into nitrogen gas.
- ▶ **Phosphorus Cycle:** Phosphorus is needed for molecules such as DNA and RNA. Most of the phosphorus in the biosphere is stored in rocks and ocean sediments. Stored phosphorus is gradually released into water and soil, where it is used by organisms.

Test Student
Understanding
Have students complete the
different workbook activities
to help them remember the
key concepts of a lesson. The
questions are written in a
variety of formats.

Summary of Mendel's Principles

For Questions 16–20, complete each statement by writing the correct word or words.

16. The units that determine the inheritance of biological characteristics are _____.

17. A form of a gene is a(n) _____.

18. If two or more forms of a gene exist, some may be dominant and others may be _____.

19. The offspring of most sexually reproducing organisms have two copies of each gene. One came from each _____.

20. Alleles from different genes usually _____ independently from each other when gametes form.

For Questions 21–25, match the term with its description.

_____ 21. Determine traits

_____ 22. Can be two of these in one gene

_____ 23. Allele that is expressed

_____ 24. Where genes come from

_____ 25. What genes do during gamete formation

A. parents

B. alleles

C. dominant

D. segregate

E. genes

An Overview of Photosynthesis

For Questions 11–13, write the letter of the correct answer on the line at the left.

_____ 11. What are the reactants of the photosynthesis reaction?

A. chlorophyll and light   C. carbohydrates and oxygen

B. carbon dioxide and water   D. high-energy electrons and air

_____ 12. What are the products of the light-dependent reactions?

A. chloroplasts and light   C. oxygen and ATP

B. proteins and lipids   D. water and sugars

_____ 13. Where do the light-independent reactions occur?

A. stroma   C. chlorophyll

B. thylakoids   D. mitochondria

Work with Graphic Organizers

In addition to working with different types of questions, students will be able to use graphic organizers to structure their thoughts.

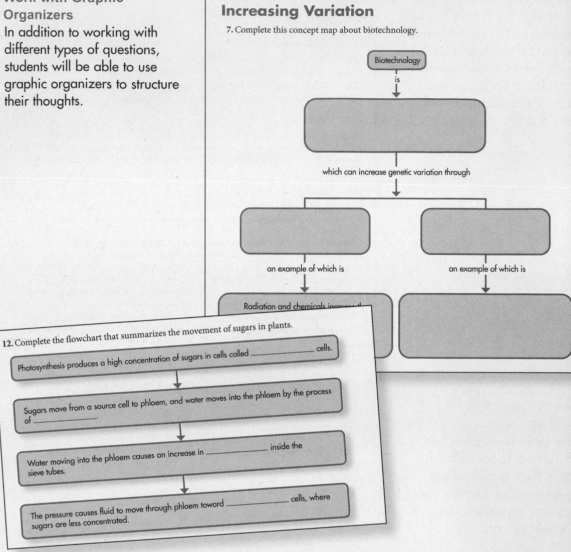

Increasing Variation

7. Complete this concept map about biotechnology.

Biotechnology

is

which can increase genetic variation through

an example of which is

an example of which is

Radiation and chemicals increase...

12. Complete the flowchart that summarizes the movement of sugars in plants.

Photosynthesis produces a high concentration of sugars in cells called _____ cells.

Sugars move from a source cell to phloem, and water moves into the phloem by the process of _____.

Water moving into the phloem causes an increase in _____ inside the sieve tubes.

The pressure causes fluid to move through phloem toward _____ cells, where sugars are less concentrated.

Use Visuals

Students will also be able to work with a variety of visuals to reinforce concepts, answering questions and drawing their answers.

5. **VISUAL ANALOGY** In the visual analogy of the growing town, what does the library represent? Identify two characteristics that make it a good choice for this analogy.

_____
_____
_____
_____

17. **THINK VISUALLY** The four circles below represent the nucleus of a cell going through mitosis. Draw four chromosomes as they go through each phase. Label each phase and describe what is happening to the DNA.

Apply the Big Idea Each lesson ends with a question that brings students back to the Big Idea. This gives them an opportunity to apply what they've learned.

Apply the Big idea

39. Some housecats have orange fur with darker orange stripes. The traits of these *tabby* cats are usually seen in male cats. *Tortoiseshell* cats have patches of many different colors. "Torties," as they are called, are almost always female. What does this tell you about the way cellular information about color and sex are passed on in cats?

_____

_____

_____

_____

Apply the Big idea

8. The left side of the heart is larger and more muscular than the right side. Also, artery walls are thicker than those of veins. Explain how those differences in structure are important to function.

_____

_____

_____

_____

Review the Vocabulary Students will have an opportunity to review key vocabulary using crossword puzzles, matching, fill-ins, and labeling activities.

Chapter Vocabulary Review

Crossword Puzzle *Complete the puzzle by entering the term that matches each numbered description.*

Across

1. a specific characteristic
4. physical traits
6. the separation of alleles during formation of sex cells
9. containing two identical alleles for a trait
11. the likelihood of an event occurring
12. scientific study of heredity
13. the union of male and female sex cells

Down

2. one form of a gene
3. the offspring of a cross between parents with different, true-breeding traits
4. word that describes a trait controlled by two or more genes
5. containing two different alleles for a trait
7. genetic makeup
8. a phenotype in which both alleles are expressed
10. reproductive cell, egg or sperm

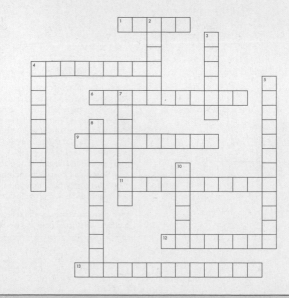

21st Century Skills

At the end of each chapter in the workbook, students are given an opportunity to revisit the Chapter Mystery. This time, the mystery topic is discussed in terms of 21st Century themes, and students practice skills such as

- Information and Media Literacy
- Systems Thinking
- Problem Identification, Formulation, and Solution
- Creativity and Intellectual Curiosity
- Interpersonal and Collaborative Skills
- Self-Direction
- Social Responsibility

CHAPTER MYSTERY

STONE AGE STORYTELLERS

21st Century Learning

In the Chapter Mystery, you learned about Iceman, who died 5300 years ago. His body is the oldest naturally preserved mummy ever recovered. Many plant materials were preserved along with Iceman. It's very unusual for plant materials to survive that long.

Iceman of the Future?

The environmental conditions where Iceman died were unique. The glacial ice he was found in helped to preserve him and many of his belongings for thousands of years before hikers discovered him in 1991. Consider what might happen to a climber today who died on a mountaintop and whose body became trapped in ice. The article below is a fictional broadcast account of the discovery of Iceman II in the year 3008.

Afternoon Mindcast, January 8, 3008—Hikers on Pike's Glacier literally stumbled upon a major anthropological discovery this morning. When Klendon Deel, 85, tripped over something in the trail, his hiking companion and mother, Mender Yayv Akong, 122, helped him up and then looked for the partially hidden obstacle. It turned out to be an ancient electronic device called a "Hype-Odd," which was used for listening to music aurally. But the most amazing part of the discovery was the skeletal hand still clutching the device.

Akong and Deel beamed the authorities, and within an hour scientists had uncovered the remains of an adult male human. Preliminary tests indicate the man died in February or March of 2016. At that time the glacier did not cover the mountain, which is in an area that was then called "Colorado."

Scientists say that unfortunately most of the man's soft tissue disintegrated through the 100-Year Heat Wave of the 22nd century, the Crustal Shocks of the 24th century, and the Kelvin Ice Age of the 29th century. But according to spokesbeing Nkavrjdn*w, the skeleton, nails, hair, and many of the belongings were all remarkably well preserved. "The lead scientist studying the find is particularly fascinated with the objects remaining in the man's pack," Nkavrjdn*w says. "For example, she thinks she has found what is left of an ancient apple. While the actual fruit is gone, a stem and a pile of seeds remained in the pack."

In addition, a clear bottle was found in the pack. Scientists are planning on doing tests to try to determine what the bottle contained. The only marking they could find on the bottle was a small triangular shape composed of three arrows. Scientists are unsure what this mysterious symbol meant.

21st Century Skills Pondering Plant Products

The skills used in this activity include **information and media literacy, communication skills, creativity and intellectual curiosity,** and **social responsibility.**

Synthetic materials, such as nylon and plastic, tend to be more durable than plant-based materials, such as cotton and paper. Because of this, many modern products are made out of synthetic materials. However, most synthetic materials are made from nonrenewable resources. Use library and Internet resources to compare plant-based materials to synthetic materials. For example, visit the Web sites of companies that manufacture plastic, nylon, paper, or cotton fabric. Consider the following questions:

- How do the costs of plant products compare with those of synthetic products?
- What sort of business opportunities are there in manufacturing products out of plant materials instead of synthetic materials?

With a group, come up with a new plant-based product. Identify potential customers for the product and discuss how you would market the product to them.

1 The Science of Biology

 Big idea **Science as a Way of Knowing**

Q: What role does science play in the study of life?

WHAT I KNOW	WHAT I LEARNED
1.1 How do we find explanations for events in the natural world?	SAMPLE ANSWER: *Asking questions about events in the natural world can yield answers. Answers can also be found in books, journals, and online.*	SAMPLE ANSWER: *After posing questions and making observations, scientists may make inferences that can lead to a hypothesis. Data from experiments can be used as evidence to support, refute, or revise the hypothesis.*
1.2 How do the scientific community and society influence the process of science?	SAMPLE ANSWER: *The needs of society can spur scientific inquiry.*	SAMPLE ANSWER: *Science and scientists operate in the context of the scientific community and society at large. Often, questions that involve society cannot be answered by science alone.*
1.3 What is biology?	SAMPLE ANSWER: *Biology is the study of living things.*	SAMPLE ANSWER: *Biology is the science that employs scientific methodology to study living things.*

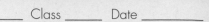

1.1 What Is Science?

Lesson Objectives
- State the goals of science.
- Describe the steps used in scientific methodology.

Lesson Summary

What Science Is and Is Not Science is an organized way of gathering and analyzing evidence about the natural world. The goals of science are to provide natural explanations for events in the natural world and to use those explanations to make useful predictions. Science is different from other human works in the following ways:

▶ Science deals only with the natural world.

▶ Scientists collect and organize information about the natural world in an orderly way.

▶ Scientists propose explanations that are based on evidence, not belief.

▶ They test those explanations with more evidence.

Scientific Methodology: The Heart of Science Methodology for scientific investigation involves:

▶ Making an **observation**. Observation involves the act of noticing and describing events or processes in a careful, orderly way. Scientists use their observations to make inferences. An **inference** is a logical interpretation based on what scientists already know.

▶ Suggesting hypotheses. A **hypothesis** is a scientific explanation for a set of observations that can be tested in ways that support or reject it.

▶ Testing the hypothesis. Testing a hypothesis often involves designing an experiment. Whenever possible, a hypothesis should be tested by a **controlled experiment**—an experiment in which only one variable (the **independent variable**, or manipulated variable) is changed. The variable that can change in response to the independent variable is called the **dependent variable**, or responding variable. The **control group** is exposed to the same conditions as the experimental group except for one independent variable.

▶ Collecting, recording, and analyzing **data**, or information gathered during the experiment.

▶ Drawing conclusions based on data.

What Science Is and Is Not

1. What is science?
   Science is an organized way of gathering and analyzing evidence about the natural world.

2. What are the goals of science?
   The goals of science are to investigate and understand nature, to explain events in nature, and to use those explanations to make useful predictions.

Scientific Methodology: The Heart of Science

Questions 3–10 refer to spontaneous generation, the idea that life can arise from nonliving matter. Spontaneous generation was accepted by many in the scientific community up until the mid-nineteenth century. A series of simple experiments tested the validity of this idea.

3. Evidence used to support spontaneous generation was the observation that foods over time become covered in maggots or fungal and bacterial growth. The inference behind spontaneous generation is that there is no "parent" organism. Write this inference as a hypothesis using an if–then sentence that suggests a way of testing it.

If an organism appears on rotting food with no visible connection to a parent, then

the organism is arising spontaneously from the food.

4. In 1668, Francesco Redi proposed a different hypothesis to explain the specific example of maggots that appear on spoiled food. He had observed that maggots appear on meat a few days after flies have been seen on the food. He inferred that the flies had left behind eggs too small to see. Redi's experiment is shown below. What conclusion can you draw from Redi's experiment?

Maggots form only when flies come in contact with meat, therefore spontaneous

generation of maggots does not occur.

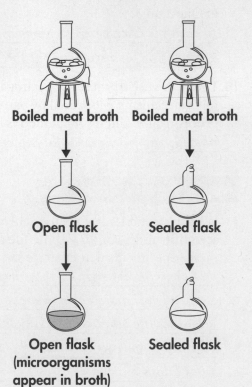

Uncovered jars — Several days pass. — Maggots appear

Covered jars — Several days pass. — No maggots appear

5. In the late 1700s, Lazzaro Spallanzani designed a different experiment to show that life did not arise spontaneously from food. He inferred that some foods spoil because of growing populations of microorganisms. Fill in the information requested below.

Boiled meat broth   Boiled meat broth

Open flask   Sealed flask

Open flask (microorganisms appear in broth)   Sealed flask

Independent variable:
boiled meat broth

Dependent variable:
exposure to air

Controlled variables (identify three):
same food source, same boiling, same type of

flask, same time

6. **THINK VISUALLY** Critics of Spallanzani said that he showed only that organisms cannot live without air. In 1859 Louis Pasteur designed an experiment to address that criticism, an experiment that reproduced Spallanzani's results.

Draw in the third and final steps in the experiment. Use an arrow to show the path of travel of the microorganisms. Shade the broth in the flask(s) in which microorganisms grew.

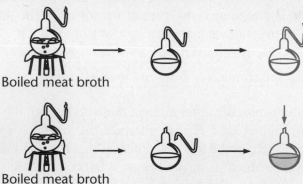

Boiled meat broth

Boiled meat broth

7. How did Pasteur solve Spallanzani's problem of limiting exposure to air?

   He used a flask with a bent neck that allowed air, but not the microorganisms in the air, to get to the broth.

8. What purpose did boiling the meat broth serve in both the Spallanzani and Pasteur experiments?

   Boiling the broth ensured that there were no living organisms in the broth at the beginning of the experiment.

9. How do the Redi, Spallanzani, and Pasteur experiments disprove the hypothesis you wrote in Question 3?

   In each instance where organisms were thought to arise spontaneously, an alternate explanation was provided for the appearance of the organisms.

10. Today, we use a process of heating liquids to prevent spoiling by bacteria and other microorganisms, pioneered by one of the three scientists mentioned above. What is that process called and for what food is it used?

    pasteurization, used for foods derived from milk

Apply the Big idea

11. What facts did Redi's, Spallanzani's, and Pasteur's experiments establish? What broader scientific understanding about life did the experiments explore? How does the example of these experiments demonstrate science as a way of knowing?

    The experiments showed that flies produce maggots and that air carries microorganisms. However, the experiments point to the broader idea that life comes from life.

    Scientists use careful observations and controlled experiments to understand what is happening in specific instances, then apply the understanding gained to larger questions about biology.

1.2 Science in Context

Lesson Objectives

- Explain how scientific attitudes generate new ideas.
- Describe the importance of peer review.
- Explain what a scientific theory is.
- Explain the relationship between science and society.

Lesson Summary

Exploration and Discovery: Where Ideas Come From Scientific methodology is closely linked to exploration and discovery. Good scientists share scientific attitudes, or habits of mind, that lead them to exploration and discovery. New ideas are generated by curiosity, skepticism, open-mindedness, and creativity.

- Ideas for exploration can arise from practical problems.
- Discoveries in one field of science can lead to new technologies; the new technologies give rise to new questions for exploration.

Communicating Results: Reviewing and Sharing Ideas Communication and sharing of ideas are vital to modern science. Scientists share their findings with the scientific community by publishing articles that undergo peer review. In peer review, scientific papers are reviewed by anonymous, independent experts. Publishing peer-reviewed articles in scientific journals allows scientists to

- share ideas.
- test and evaluate each other's work.

Once research has been published, it enters the dynamic marketplace of scientific ideas. New ideas fit into scientific understanding by leading to new hypotheses that must be independently confirmed by controlled experiments.

Scientific Theories In science, the word **theory** applies to a well-tested explanation that unifies a broad range of observations and hypotheses and that enables scientists to make accurate predictions about new situations.

- No theory is considered absolute truth.
- Science is always changing; as new evidence is uncovered, a theory may be reviewed or replaced by a more useful explanation.

Science and Society Using science involves understanding its context in society and its limitations. Understanding science

- helps people make decisions that also involve cultural customs, values, and ethical standards.
- can help people predict the consequences of their actions and plan the future.

Scientists strive to be objective, but when science is applied in society, it can be affected by **bias**, a point of view that is personal rather than scientific.

Exploration and Discovery: Where Ideas Come From

1. Describe how new ideas are generated.

New ideas are generated by curiosity, skepticism, open-mindedness, and creativity.

2. How are science and technology related?

Discoveries in science can lead to new technologies, and new technologies can give rise

to new questions for scientific exploration.

3. It took hundreds of years of discussion and the experiments of Louis Pasteur in the nineteenth century for the larger scientific community to accept that spontaneous generation of life was not a valid scientific concept. Referring to the diagram, describe how modern methods of communication have changed the scientific process.

Access to information of all

kinds has changed dramati-

cally because of computers

and the Internet. Not only do

scientists have broad access

to all sorts of information to

inspire them, but they can

also get almost immediate

feedback on their work from

other scientists.

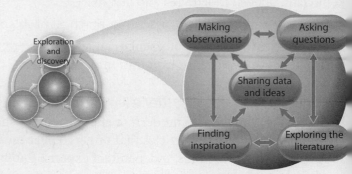

Adapted from *Understanding Science*, UC Berkeley, Museum of Paleontology

Communicating Results: Reviewing and Sharing Ideas

4. **THINK VISUALLY** Use lesson concepts to complete the diagram to show the outcome of communication among scientists. Why are "New Ideas" placed at the center of the diagram?

New ideas are generated as a result of all types of

scientific communication.

5. Of the four types of communication you added, identify the one that is critical to ensuring communication among the scientific community.

publication

Adapted from *Understanding Science*, UC Berkeley, Museum of Paleontology

New Ideas

Scientific Theories

6. A typical dictionary will have different definitions for the word *theory*. It will include a definition that describes how scientists use the term, but it will also define *theory* as speculation, or an assumption, or a belief. Are these common definitions of *theory* synonyms (words similar in meaning) or antonyms (words opposite in meaning) to the definition of a scientific theory? Explain your thinking.

They are antonyms, because scientific theories are built from well-tested ideas that

are supported by evidence, and not beliefs or untested assumptions.

_____

_____

For Questions 7–11, identify whether each statement is a hypothesis or a theory. For a hypothesis, write an "H" on the line. For a theory, write a "T."

_____**H**_____ **7.** The rate that grass grows is related to the amount of light it receives.

_____**T**_____ **8.** All life is related and descended from a common ancestor.

_____**T**_____ **9.** The universe began about 15 billion years ago.

_____**H**_____ **10.** New tennis balls bounce higher than old tennis balls.

_____**H**_____ **11.** Caffeine raises blood pressure.

Science and Society

12. How can bias affect the application of science in society? What role does a good understanding of science play in this phenomenon?

Bias can make a scientist misinterpret or misapply data to fit a personal agenda.

Understanding science allows us to fairly apply science in ways that benefit

humanity.

_____

Apply the Big idea

13. What is it about science, as a way of knowing, that makes it self-correcting?

Scientific information at some point is shared with a larger community whose mem-

bers maintain a healthy degree of skepticism as well as offer different perspectives

and interpretations.

_____

1.3 Studying Life

Lesson Objectives

- List the characteristics of living things.
- Identify the central themes of biology.
- Explain how life can be studied at different levels.
- Discuss the importance of a universal system of measurement.

Lesson Summary

Characteristics of Living Things **Biology** is the study of life. Living things share these characteristics: They are made of cells and have a universal genetic code; they obtain and use materials and energy to grow and develop; they reproduce; they respond to signals in their environment (**stimuli**) and maintain a stable internal environment; they change over time.

Big Ideas in Biology The study of biology revolves around several interlocking big ideas:

- ▶ **Cellular basis of life.** Living things are made of cells.
- ▶ **Information and heredity.** Living things are based on a universal genetic code written in a molecule called **DNA**.
- ▶ **Matter and energy.** Life requires matter that provides raw material, nutrients, and energy. The combination of chemical reactions through which an organism builds up or breaks down materials is called **metabolism**.
- ▶ **Growth, development, and reproduction.** All living things reproduce. In **sexual reproduction**, cells from two parents unite to form the first cell of a new organism. In **asexual reproduction**, a single organism produces offspring identical to itself. Organisms grow and develop as they mature.
- ▶ **Homeostasis**. Living things maintain a relatively stable internal environment.
- ▶ **Evolution.** Taken as a group, living things evolve, linked to a common origin.
- ▶ **Structure and function.** Each major group of organisms has evolved structures that make particular functions possible.
- ▶ **Unity and diversity of life.** All living things are fundamentally similar at the molecular level.
- ▶ **Interdependence in nature.** All forms of life on Earth are connected into a **biosphere**—a living planet.
- ▶ **Science as a way of knowing.** Science is not a list of facts but "a way of knowing."

Fields of Biology Biology includes many overlapping fields that use different tools to study life. These include biotechnology, global ecology, and molecular biology.

Performing Biological Investigations Most scientists use the metric system as a way to share quantitative data. They are trained in safe laboratory procedures. To remain safe when you are doing investigations, the most important rule is to follow your teacher's instructions.

Characteristics of Living Things

1. Complete the graphic organizer to show the characteristics living things share.

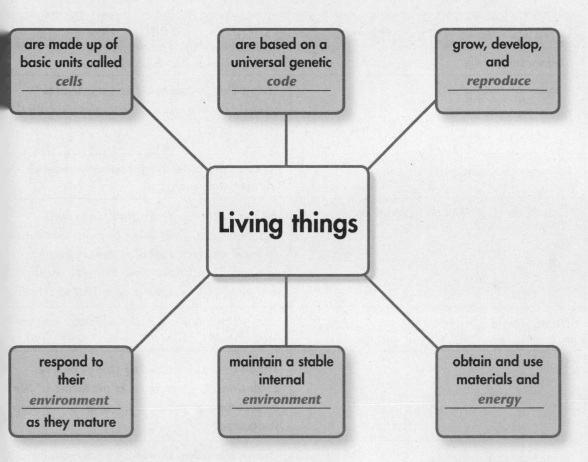

are made up of basic units called _____cells_____

are based on a universal genetic _____code_____

grow, develop, and _____reproduce_____

Living things

respond to their _____environment_____ as they mature

maintain a stable internal _____environment_____

obtain and use materials and _____energy_____

2. The genetic molecule common to all living things is _____DNA_____.

3. The internal process of _____homeostasis_____ enables living things to survive changing conditions.

4. Living things are capable of responding to different types of _____stimuli_____.

5. Living things have a long history of _____evolutionary_____ change.

6. The continuation of life depends on both _____asexual reproduction_____ and _____sexual reproduction_____.

7. The combination of chemical reactions that make up an organism's _____metabolism_____ help to organize raw materials into living matter.

Big Ideas in Biology

8. Complete the table of Big Ideas in Biology. The first row is filled in for you.

Big Idea	Description
Cellular basis of life	Living things are made of cells.
Information and heredity	*Living things are based on a universal genetic code written in a molecule called DNA.*
Matter and energy	Life requires matter that provides raw materials, nutrients, and energy.
Growth, development, and reproduction	*All living things reproduce. In sexual reproduction, cells from two parents unite to form the first cell of a new organism. In asexual reproduction, a single organism produces offspring identical to itself.*
Homeostasis	Living things maintain a relatively stable internal environment.
Evolution	*Taken as a group, living things evolve. Evolutionary change links all forms of life to a common origin more than 3.5 billion years ago.*
Structure and function	Each major group of organisms has evolved structures that make particular functions possible.
Unity and diversity of life	All living things are fundamentally similar at the molecular level.
Interdependence in nature	All forms of life on Earth are connected into a biosphere—a living planet.
Science as a way of knowing	*Science is not a list of facts, but "a way of knowing." Scientists use observations, questions, and experiments to explain the natural world.*

9. Pick two of the big ideas from the chart and describe how the ideas interlock.

Examples could show how the cellular basis of life links to a shared genetic code or growth, development, and reproduction; how homeostasis links to structure and function; how unity and diversity of life links to evolution.

_____

_____

Fields of Biology

0. Biology is made up of many overlapping fields, each of which uses different tools to gather information about living things. Fill out the table below with information about two fields of biology—one that appeals to you, and one that does not. Include a description of each field and the tools scientists in the field use, as well as your impressions of each.

Field of Biology	Description of Field	Why It Does or Does Not Appeal to Me
	Answers will vary.	

Performing Biological Investigations

11. Describe the system of measurement most scientists use when collecting data and doing experiments.

   Most scientists use the metric system, which is a decimal system of measurement

   with units based on certain physical standards and scaled to multiples of 10.

12. Why do scientists need a common system of measurement?

   Researchers need to replicate one another's experiments, and most experiments

   involve measurements.

13. What is the most important safety rule for you to follow in the laboratory?

   Always follow your teacher's instructions.

Apply the Big idea

14. Your teacher is doing a long-term experiment by having you and your classmates grow plants at home. You are testing the hypothesis that plant growth is affected by the amount of water a plant receives. All the data will be compiled in three weeks. Why isn't it a good idea to use the 8-ounce measuring cup from your kitchen or the 12-inch ruler you have on your desk?

   It's important that all students use the same system of measurement so results can

   be compared. If someone uses liquid ounces and inches, they will need to convert

   these to the metric system, which may introduce errors. Also, the measurement may

   be less precise since those measures use fractions and not decimals for partial units.

Chapter Vocabulary Review

For Questions 1–8, complete each statement by writing the correct word.

1. The act of noticing and describing events or processes in a careful, orderly way is called __observation__.

2. The information gathered during an experiment is called __data__.

3. A(n) __inference__ is a logical interpretation based on what scientists already know.

4. A(n) __hypothesis__ is a scientific explanation for a set of observations that can be tested in ways that support or reject it.

5. A(n) __theory__ is a well-tested explanation that unifies a broad range of observations and hypotheses.

6. In __asexual__ reproduction, the new organism has a single parent.

7. A(n) __stimulus__ is a signal to which an organism responds.

8. __Science__ is an organized way of gathering and analyzing evidence about the natural world.

For Questions 9–17, write the letter of the definition that best matches each term on the line provided.

Term

__B__ 9. biology

__E__ 10. bias

__C__ 11. homeostasis

__G__ 12. metabolism

__D__ 13. DNA

__A__ 14. control group

__H__ 15. independent variable

__I__ 16. dependent variable

__F__ 17. biosphere

Definition

A. in an experiment, the group exposed to the same conditions as the experimental group except for one independent variable

B. the study of life

C. living things maintaining a relatively stable internal environment

D. a molecule containing the universal genetic code

E. a point of view that is personal rather than scientific

F. a living planet

G. the combination of chemical reactions through which an organism builds up or breaks down materials

H. in an experiment, the variable that is manipulated

I. in an experiment, the responding variable

CHAPTER MYSTERY

HEIGHT BY PRESCRIPTION

In the Chapter Mystery, you read about parents who had their healthy son injected with HGH hormones in the hope the treatment would increase his height. You also read that there is no evidence that treatment will make a child grow taller.

21st Century Learning

Should Pharmaceuticals Be Advertised on Television?

Today, medical consumers often make the final decision about their or their child's treatment. It was not always like that. Not that long ago, patients were far more accepting of treatments prescribed by their doctor. They listened to the doctor's advice and did not demand a particular treatment. Why have the roles of doctor and patient changed today? One reason has to do with pharmaceutical advertising on television and in magazines. Drug ads are aimed at consumers, not doctors. Is it a good idea to advertise prescription drugs on television? Two viewpoints are presented below.

Want some fries with that?

By: The Opinionator

I was watching TV last night, and I counted 14 ads for drugs. That's right, 14! I think things have gotten a bit out of hand. I mean, I'm all in favor of informed consumers, but I think this goes far beyond that.

I did some research this morning. Turns out that of all the people who go to their doctor and say, "Please write me a prescription for Drug X," 80% of them get it! Apparently, the doctor is just following the patients' orders.

Here's the thing. All drugs, all medicines, can be dangerous under certain circumstances. Doctors know if a patient should be taking a particular drug or not, and how much the patient should take. Doctors, not patients, should be making the decisions about medical treatments and what drug a patient should take.

Responses to "Want some fries with that?"

Posted at 9:17 by Dragonfly

Believe it or not, this humble blogger still reads newspapers. I read an OpEd piece in the paper this morning that was all about how dangerous TV ads for drugs are. Here's a link to it. I couldn't find one point in the OpEd that I agreed with. What's wrong with letting people know what's out there? Nothing. Doctors are still the gatekeepers. They still have to write the prescription. If a drug is dangerous for people who have kidney problems, and you have kidney problems, your doctor won't write the prescription. But you probably wouldn't ask for it because you heard that little voice at the end of the ad say, "Do not take Drug X if you have kidney problems." Doctors can't possibly keep up with all the medical journals and stuff they get. TV advertising lets doctors know about new medications, too. So when it comes to drug ads, I say bring 'em on.

Continued on next page ▶

21st Century Themes Science and Civic Literacy

Answer the following questions.

1. What is the main point made by the first blogger?

   Doctors, not patients, should be making the decisions about medical treatments.

2. How does the second blogger address the first blogger's point of view?

   The second blogger says that doctors do make the decisions because they decide whether or not to write the prescription.

3. What argument does second blogger use to support his or her viewpoint?

   TV ads let both patients and doctors know about possible treatments.

4. Which blogger do you agree with? Give reasons for your answer.

   SAMPLE ANSWER: *I agree with the first blogger because sometimes patients are so demanding that the doctor feels too pressured and just writes the prescription.*

   SAMPLE ANSWER: *I agree with the second blogger because I think people have the right to know about all treatments available to them.*

5. More than 200 medical school teachers, as well as 39 medical and senior citizens' groups, have supported an end to all medical advertising aimed at consumers. They want to ban these ads on television, on the radio, in newspapers and magazines, and online. Does this change the opinion you expressed in the previous answer? Why or why not?

   Students who agreed with the first blogger may say that the new information reinforces their opinion. Some students who agreed with the second blogger may say the new information caused them to change their minds because the instructors and groups are experts.

21st Century Skills Evaluating Sources of Information

The skills used in this activity include **social responsibility, critical thinking and systems thinking, information and media literacy,** and **communication skills.**

Use Internet resources to find additional arguments in favor of and against advertising pharmaceuticals to consumers. "DTCA" (which stands for "direct to consumer advertising") might be a helpful keyword to use in your search. Make two lists, one containing arguments that support DTCA for drugs and one containing reasons for opposing drug DTCA. Then, for each source, evaluate the accuracy of the Web site and the usefulness of the information. HINT: Sites with URLs that end in ".gov" or ".edu" are usually fairly reliable. Sites put up by organizations or individuals who have a financial interest in the issue may be biased.

Evaluate students' work based on their having an adequate number of arguments for both points of view, they used reliable online sources for each argument, and their blog entry clearly presents their viewpoint, with supporting arguments.

2 The Chemistry of Life

Big idea **Matter and Energy**

Q: What are the basic chemical principles that affect living things?

WHAT I KNOW	WHAT I LEARNED
2.1 What is the matter in organisms made of?	SAMPLE ANSWER: **Matter is made up of atoms.**	SAMPLE ANSWER: **Atoms have three subatomic particles: protons, neutrons, and electrons.**
2.2 Why are the properties of water important to organisms?	SAMPLE ANSWER: **Many parts of an organism's body contain water.**	SAMPLE ANSWER: **Some of the most important biological fluids contain water. Also, water's high heat capacity protects living things both internally and externally from drastic temperature changes.**
2.3 How do organisms use different types of carbon compounds?	SAMPLE ANSWER: **Carbon is the primary element found in living things.**	SAMPLE ANSWER: **Organisms use carbon compounds to form four types of molecules: lipids, carbohydrates, nucleic acids, and proteins.**
2.4 How do chemicals combine and break apart inside living things?	SAMPLE ANSWER: **A lot of what that happens in an organism is based on chemical reactions.**	SAMPLE ANSWER: **Enzymes are proteins that speed up chemical reactions that take place in cells.**

2.1 The Nature of Matter

Lesson Objectives

🔑 Identify the three subatomic particles found in atoms.

🔑 Explain how all of the isotopes of an element are similar and how they are different.

🔑 Explain how compounds are different from their component elements.

🔑 Describe the two main types of chemical bonds.

Lesson Summary

Atoms The **atom** is the basic unit of matter, made up of three subatomic particles.

▶ Protons have a positive charge and neutrons carry no charge. Strong forces bind protons and neutrons together in the **nucleus**.

▶ An **electron** is a negatively charged particle that has only about 1/1840 the mass of a proton. Electrons constantly move around the space surrounding the atom's nucleus.

▶ Because an atom has the same number of protons and electrons, if it is electrically neutral.

Elements and Isotopes A chemical **element** is a pure substance that consists entirely of one type of atom.

▶ Atoms of the same element that differ in the number of neutrons are called **isotopes**. Isotopes are identified by their mass number, the total number of protons and neutrons in the nucleus. Because they have the same number of electrons in each atom, all isotopes of an element have the same chemical properties.

▶ Radioactive isotopes have unstable nuclei and break down at a constant rate.

Chemical Compounds A chemical **compound** is a substance formed by the chemical combination of two or more elements in definite proportions. The physical and chemical properties of a compound are usually very different from those of the elements from which it is formed. Scientists use formulas to show the ratio of elements that make up a compound.

Chemical Bonds The atoms in compounds are held together by chemical bonds. Electrons that are available to form bonds are called valence electrons.

▶ An **ionic bond** forms when one or more electrons are transferred from one atom to another, forming **ions**. An atom that loses electrons becomes positively charged. An atom that gains electrons becomes negatively charged.

▶ A **covalent bond** forms when electrons are shared rather than transferred. The structure formed by atoms joined by covalent bonds is called a **molecule**. The molecule is the smallest unit of most compounds.

▶ When molecules are close together, a slight attraction can form between the oppositely charged portions of nearby molecules. These intermolecular forces of attraction are called **van der Waals forces**.

Atoms

1. **THINK VISUALLY** The diagram shows a model of a carbon atom, with an atomic number of 6. Complete the diagram by drawing in the rest of the atomic particles, including their charges. Label all particles and the nucleus.

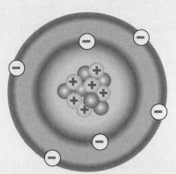

Diagrams should contain six protons, six electrons, and six neutrons. Check that students have correctly labeled each type of subatomic particle.

Elements and Isotopes

2. **THINK VISUALLY** The diagrams show models of carbon isotopes. Complete the diagrams by drawing in the rest of the atomic particles, including their charges.

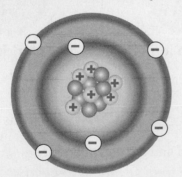

Nonradioactive carbon-13

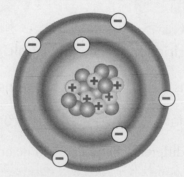

Radioactive carbon-14

Use your completed diagrams to answer Questions 3–4.

3. Identify two differences between carbon-12 and carbon-14.

   Carbon-14 is radioactive, carbon-12 is not. Carbon-14 has two more neutrons than carbon-12.

4. Identify two ways in which carbon-12, carbon-13, and carbon-14 are alike.

   They have the same number of protons and electrons and they are chemically similar.

For Questions 5–7, complete each statement by writing the correct word or words.

5. A chemical element is a pure substance that consists entirely of one type of ____*atom*____.

6. Atoms of the same element that differ in the number of neutrons they contain are called ____*isotopes*____.

7. An atom is made up of protons, neutrons, and ____*electrons*____.

Chemical Compounds

8. What is a chemical compound?

   A chemical compound is a substance formed by the chemical combination of two or more elements in definite proportions.

9. What do the formulas for table salt, NaCl, and water, H_2O, indicate about these compounds?

   In table salt, sodium and chlorine combine in a 1:1 ratio; in water, hydrogen and oxygen combine in a 2:1 ratio.

Chemical Bonds

10. Sea salt contains calcium chloride ($CaCl_2$), an ionic compound similar to table salt. One atom of calcium (atomic number 20) bonds to two atoms of chlorine (atomic number 17). Fill in the number of protons and electrons in each ion.

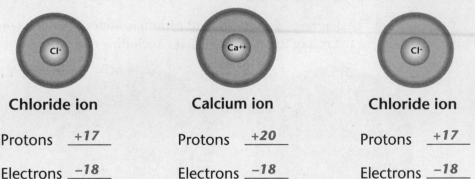

Chloride ion	Calcium ion	Chloride ion
Protons _+17_	Protons _+20_	Protons _+17_
Electrons _−18_	Electrons _−18_	Electrons _−18_

11. What is the difference between an ionic bond and a covalent bond?

    In an ionic bond, electrons are transferred from one atom to another. In a covalent bond, electrons are shared between atoms.

Apply the Big idea ▸

12. How are chemical bonds important in metabolism?

    Metabolism includes all of the processes in the body that break down or build substances. These substances break down because chemical bonds are broken and form because chemical bonds are made.

2.2 Properties of Water

Lesson Objectives

- Discuss the unique properties of water.
- Differentiate between solutions and suspensions.
- Explain what acidic solutions and basic solutions are.

Lesson Summary

The Water Molecule Water molecules (H_2O) are polar because of an uneven distribution of electrons, creating a slight negative (–) charge in the oxygen atom and a slight positive (+) charge in each hydrogen atom. The attraction between a hydrogen atom of one water molecule and the oxygen atom of another water molecule is called a **hydrogen bond**.

- **Cohesion** is an attraction between molecules of the same substance. It causes water molecules to be drawn together, producing surface tension.

- **Adhesion** is an attraction between molecules of different substances. It causes capillary action, an effect that causes water to rise in a narrow tube against the force of gravity.

Solutions and Suspensions A **mixture** is a material composed of two or more elements or compounds that are physically mixed together but not chemically combined. A **solution** is a mixture in which all the components are evenly spread out: the substance dissolved is the **solute**; the substance that causes the dissolving is the **solvent**. Mixtures of water and undissolved materials are **suspensions**.

Acids, Bases, and pH A water molecule (H_2O) can split apart to form a hydrogen ion (H^+) and a hydroxide ion (OH^-).

- The **pH scale** measures the concentration of hydrogen ions in a solution. The scale ranges from 0 to 14. Pure water has a pH of 7.

- An **acid** is any compound that forms H^+ ions in solution. Acidic solutions have pH values below 7. A **base** is a compound that forms OH^- ions in solution. Basic, or alkaline, solutions have pH values above 7.

- **Buffers** are weak acids or bases that can react with strong acids or bases to prevent sudden changes in pH.

The Water Molecule

For Questions 1–4, write True or False on the line provided.

True	1.	Water is a polar molecule.
False	2.	Hydrogen bonds are an example of adhesion.
False	3.	Covalent bonds give water a low heat capacity.
False	4.	A hydrogen bond is stronger than a covalent bond.

Solutions and Suspensions

5. Complete the table.

Substance	Definition	Example(s)
Mixture	Physical combination of two or more substances	Cinnamon sugar
Solute	*Substance that is dissolved*	Salt in saltwater
Solvent	*Substance in which solute dissolves*	*Water in saltwater*
Suspension	Mixture of water and nondissolved substance	Blood
Solution	*Mixture in which all substances are evenly distributed*	*Saltwater*

Acids, Bases, and pH

6. What makes pure water neutral?

It has an equal number of positive hydrogen ions and negative hydroxide ions.

7. What does the pH scale measure?

concentration of hydrogen ions (H^+) in solution

8. On the pH scale, indicate which direction is increasingly acidic and which is increasingly basic.

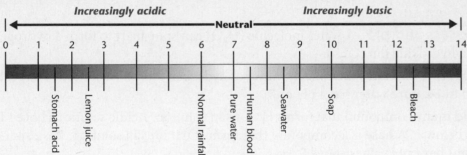

9. Identify two solutions that have more H^+ ions than OH^- ions.

SAMPLE ANSWER: *rainfall, lemon juice*

10. Identify two solutions that have more OH^- ions than H^+ ions.

SAMPLE ANSWER: *human blood, seawater*

11. How would you buffer a solution that has a pH of 12?

add a weak acid to decrease the pH

Apply the Big idea

12. Why are buffers important to living things?

Buffers react with strong acids or bases to prevent sharp, sudden changes in pH. In

living things, controlling pH is important for maintaining homeostasis.

2.3 Carbon Compounds

Lesson Objectives

Describe the unique qualities of carbon.

Describe the structures and functions of each of the four groups of macromolecules.

Lesson Summary

The Chemistry of Carbon Organic chemistry is the study of compounds with bonds between carbon atoms. Carbon atoms have four valence electrons, allowing them to form strong covalent bonds with many other elements, including hydrogen, oxygen, phosphorus, sulfur, and nitrogen. Living organisms are made up of molecules made of carbon and these other elements.

➤ One carbon atom can bond to another to form chains and rings.

➤ Carbon can form millions of different large and complex structures.

Macromolecules Many of the carbon molecules in living things are so large they are called macromolecules. Macromolecules form by polymerization, in which smaller units called **monomers** join together to form **polymers**. Biochemists sort the macromolecules in living things into groups based on their chemical composition.

➤ **Carbohydrates** (starches and sugars) are composed of carbon, hydrogen, and oxygen. Carbohydrates are the main energy source for living things. Plants and some animals also use carbohydrates for structural purposes. Molecules with one sugar monomer are **monosaccharides**. A disaccharide is made of two monosaccharides.

➤ **Lipids** (fats, oils, and waxes) are made mostly of carbon and hydrogen atoms. Lipids can be used to store energy and form parts of biological membranes and waterproof coverings. Steroids manufactured by the body are lipids as well.

➤ **Nucleic acids** contain hydrogen, oxygen, nitrogen, carbon, and phosphorus. They are polymers of **nucleotides**. A nucleotide has three parts: a 5-carbon sugar, a phosphate ($-PO_4$) group, and a nitrogenous base. Nucleic acids store and transmit hereditary (genetic) information. There are two kinds of nucleic acids: DNA (deoxyribonucleic acid) and RNA (ribonucleic acid).

➤ **Proteins** are made up of nitrogen, carbon, hydrogen, and oxygen. Proteins are polymers of **amino acids**. An amino acid molecule has an amino group ($-NH_2$) on one end and a carboxyl group ($-COOH$) on the other end. Proteins control the rate of reactions, regulate cell processes, form cellular structures, carry substances into or out of cells, and help fight disease.

• More than 20 different amino acids are found in nature. Any amino acid can bond with any other.

• Covalent bonds called peptide bonds link amino acids together to form a polypeptide.

• Amino acids are assembled into polypeptide chains according to instructions coded in DNA.

The Chemistry of Carbon

1. How many valence electrons does each carbon atom have?
   Each carbon atom has four valence electrons.

2. What gives carbon the ability to form chains that are almost unlimited in length?
   A carbon atom can bond to other carbon atoms.

Macromolecules

For Questions 3–5, complete each statement by writing the correct word or words.

3. Many of the molecules in living cells are so large they are called *macromolecules*.

4. *Polymerization* is the process that forms large organic molecules.

5. When two or more *monomers* join together, a polymer forms.

6. Create a table in which you compare the components and functions of the following macromolecules: carbohydrates, lipids, nucleic acids, and proteins.

Macromolecule	Components	Functions
Carbohydrate	carbon, hydrogen, and oxygen	main source of energy; structural purposes
Lipid	mostly carbon and hydrogen	stores energy; forms parts of biological membranes and waterproof coverings
Nucleic acid	hydrogen, oxygen, nitrogen, carbon, and phosphorus	stores and transmits genetic information
Protein	nitrogen, hydrogen, carbon, and oxygen	controls rate of reactions, regulates cell processes, forms cellular structures, carries substances into or out of cell, fights disease

Apply the Big idea

7. How did organic compounds get their name? How is the word related to its meaning?
   Organic means "living." The four major groups of organic compounds are molecules that are produced by organisms using energy and the raw material of nonliving matter.

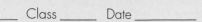

2.4 Chemical Reactions and Enzymes

Lesson Objectives

- Explain how chemical reactions affect chemical bonds.
- Describe how energy changes affect how easily a chemical reaction will occur.
- Explain why enzymes are important to living things.

Lesson Summary

Chemical Reactions Everything that happens in an organism is based on chemical reactions. A **chemical reaction** is a process that changes one set of chemicals into another set of chemicals.

- The elements or compounds that enter into the reaction are the **reactants**.
- The elements or compounds produced by the reaction are the **products**.
- Chemical reactions involve changes in the chemical bonds that join atoms in compounds.

Energy in Reactions Some chemical reactions release energy; others absorb energy.

- Chemical reactions that release energy often occur on their own.
- Chemical reactions that absorb energy require a source of energy. The energy needed to get a reaction started is called the **activation energy**.

Enzymes An **enzyme** is a protein that acts as biological catalyst. A **catalyst** is a substance that speeds up the rate of a chemical reaction. Catalysts work by lowering a reaction's activation energy.

- In an enzyme-catalyzed reaction, the reactants are known as **substrates**. Substrates bind to a part of an enzyme called the active site and remain bound to the enzyme until the reaction is complete, when the products are released.
- Temperature, pH, and regulatory molecules can affect the activity of enzymes.

Chemical Reactions

1. What is a chemical reaction?

   It is a process that changes one set of chemicals into another set of chemicals.

2. Complete the table about chemicals in a chemical reaction.

Chemicals in a Chemical Reaction	
Chemicals	**Definition**
Reactants	*the elements or compounds that enter into a chemical reaction*
Products	*the elements or compounds that are produced by a chemical reaction*

Energy in Reactions

3. **THINK VISUALLY** The graphs below show the amount of energy present during two chemical reactions. One of the reactions is an energy-absorbing reaction, the other is an energy-releasing reaction. Label the type of reaction for each, label the energy level for the reactants and products, then draw an arrow on each to show the energy of activation.

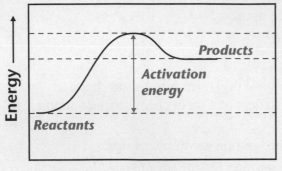

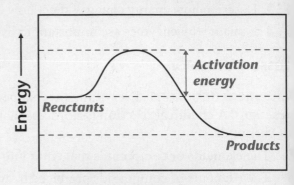

Type of reaction: *energy-absorbing reaction*

Type of reaction: *energy-releasing reaction*

4. What is released or absorbed whenever chemical bonds form or are broken?

energy

5. What is the energy of activation?

energy needed to start a chemical reaction

6. Of the two reactions shown, which one is more likely to start spontaneously and why?

energy-releasing reaction because it may not need energy to start the reaction, an energy-absorbing reaction always does

Enzymes

7. How does the addition of a catalyst affect the energy of activation of a chemical reaction?

It lowers the energy of activation, making the reaction occur faster.

8. What type of catalysts affect biochemical reactions?

enzymes

9. What makes proteins the ideal types of compounds to act as enzymes?

Proteins are large molecules that are able to bend into many different shapes. This enables the formation of active sites with specific shapes for specific substrates.

Use the diagram to answer Questions 10–11.

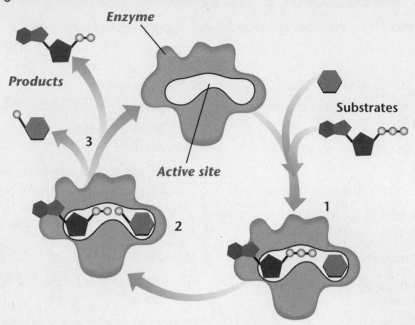

Enzyme

Products

Active site

Substrates

3

2

1

10. THINK VISUALLY Label the enzyme, the active site, and the products in the diagram.

11. Write what is happening at each numbered part of the diagram.

(1) *Substrates bind to enzyme.* _____

(2) *Substrates are converted into products.* _____

(3) *Products are released.* _____

For Questions 12–13, refer to the Visual Analogy comparing the action of enzymes to a lock and key.

12. VISUAL ANALOGY How is a substrate and its enzyme like a lock and its key?

Just as only a certain key will fit into

a lock, only a certain substrate will fit

into the active site of an enzyme.

_____

13. What is being unlocked in this analogy?

the bonds in the reactants _____

Apply the Big idea

14. In terms of an organism and how it interacts with its environment, what is the benefit of having controls on the chemical reactions that take place in its body?

Conditions vary in the environment, for example when food is available or when

seasonal changes occur. Such controls enable the organism to respond to different

conditions.

Chapter Vocabulary Review

Crossword Puzzle *Use the clues below to fill in the spaces in the puzzle with the correct words.*

Across

1. element or compound that enters into a chemical reaction
4. process that changes one set of chemicals into another
7. positively charged subatomic particle
8. substance formed by the chemical combination of elements
11. positively or negatively charged atom
12. carbon compound that stores and transmits genetic information
14. the center of an atom
16. bond formed when electrons are shared between atoms
17. macromolecule formed when monomers join together

Down

2. negatively charged subatomic particle
3. compound that forms hydroxide ions in solution
5. bond formed when one or more electrons are transferred from one atom to another
6. monomer of nucleic acid
9. monomer of protein
10. compound that forms hydrogen ions in solution
13. atom of an element that differs in the number of neutrons compared with other atoms of the same element
15. basic unit of matter

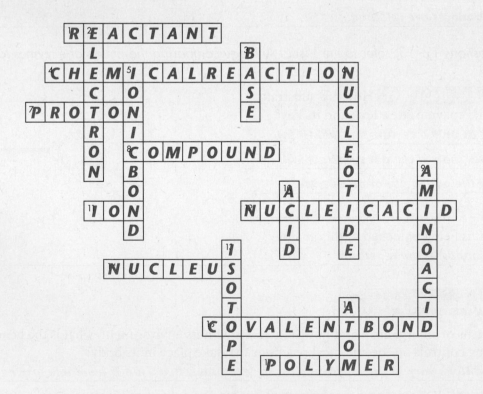

CHAPTER
MYSTERY

THE GHOSTLY FISH

In the Chapter Mystery, you learned about a fish whose body produces an "antifreeze" protein. Several other species of fish, as well as species of insects and plants, produce similar proteins. The proteins' structure and chemical makeup are different, but all function as an effective "antifreeze."

21st Century Learning

Marketing a Natural "Antifreeze"

A protein able to prevent organic matter from freezing could have enormous commercial value. As with other inventions and innovations, a company that develops such a protein—or devises a unique method for producing such a protein—should have the right to patent it. A patent is a government order that grants an inventor exclusive rights to the use of the invention. In other words, a patent prevents anyone other than the inventor from profiting from the invention. A patent application may be hundreds of pages long. That's why every application must start with a brief description of the invention. This brief description is called an abstract. An abstract that might be written for a patent application for an antifreeze production process is shown below.

Abstract

Description of invention: A method for synthesizing a protein that lowers the freezing temperature of water. Such proteins are not unusual in nature. Called "antifreeze proteins" (AFPs) or "Ice Structuring Proteins" (ISPs), they are produced in certain species of fish, plants, and insects. One AFP, produced in nature by fish but commercially by genetically modified yeast, is already being used in frozen products such as ice cream and sherbet.

The method described herein produces a type of insect-derived AFP. Fish-derived AFPs can reduce the freezing point of water by as much as 1.5° Celsius. This insect-derived AFP reduces the freezing point of water to −10° C. The process uses genetically modified algae to produce a threonine- and cysteine-rich 9 kDa protein that is produced naturally by the spruce budworm (*Choristoneura fumiferana*).

Continued on next page ▶

21st Century Themes Science and Economic Literacy

1. What is the inventor trying to patent?

a method for synthesizing a protein that lowers the freezing temperature of water

2. What commercial application does AFP already have? How is this AFP produced commercially?

One AFP is used in frozen products such as ice cream and sherbet. It is produced commercially by genetically modified yeast.

3. Why do you think the patent applicant wants to use insect-derived AFP rather than fish-derived AFP?

The insect-derived AFP reduces the freezing point of water to −10° C. Fish-derived AFPs can reduce the freezing point of water by only 1.5° Celsius.

4. Why would this process need algae?

The process uses genetically modified algae to produce a protein.

5. Why did the patent applicant research the spruce budworm?

This budworm naturally produces the protein needed in the process.

21st Century Skills AFP Ad Campaign

The skills used in this activity include **information and media literacy, critical thinking and systems thinking,** and **creativity and intellectual curiosity.**

Work with a partner to use Internet or library resources to research the effects of extreme cold on the human body. Think about how these reactions would change if the body contained the AFP described in the patent application. What safety concerns would have to be addressed if a person had to ingest an AFP? What are the commercial applications for an AFP treatment that is safe for humans to ingest? Who would want to use it? Choose one type or group of potential users.

Create an ad campaign aimed specifically at that group of people and designed to convince them to get the AFP treatment.

Evaluate students' ad campaigns based on the correct choice for the AFP application; the accuracy of the information it contains, including an explanation of why the AFP is safe to use; and its visual appeal to its potential audience.

3 The Biosphere

Big idea ▸ **Matter of Energy, Interdependence in Nature**
Q: How do Earth's living and nonliving parts interact and affect the survival of organisms?

WHAT I KNOW	WHAT I LEARNED
3.1 How do we study life?	SAMPLE ANSWER: *Biologists study life by observing many different kinds of life forms.*	SAMPLE ANSWER: *Modern ecologists use three methods to study life: observation, experimentation, and modeling.*
3.2 How do different organisms get the energy they need to survive?	SAMPLE ANSWER: *Plants use sunlight for their energy. Other animals eat food to get energy.*	SAMPLE ANSWER: *Autotrophs can capture energy from sunlight or chemicals and convert it into forms that living cells can use. Heterotrophs must acquire energy from other organisms.*
3.3 How does energy move through an ecosystem?	SAMPLE ANSWER: *Energy moves through ecosystems when one organism ingests another organism.*	SAMPLE ANSWER: *Energy flows through an ecosystem in a one-way stream, from primary producers to various consumers.*
3.4 Why is the cycling of matter important to life on Earth?	SAMPLE ANSWER: *Organisms need certain kinds of matter in order to grow and perform life processes.*	SAMPLE ANSWER: *Living organisms are composed mostly of four elements: oxygen, carbon, hydrogen, and nitrogen. The availability of these elements depends on how quickly they are cycled through the environment.*

3.1 What Is Ecology?

Lesson Objectives

- Describe the study of ecology.
- Explain how biotic and abiotic factors influence an ecosystem.
- Describe the methods used to study ecology.

Lesson Summary

Studying Our Living Planet **Ecology** is the scientific study of interactions among organisms and between organisms and their environment.

- ▶ Earth's organisms live in the **biosphere**. The biosphere consists of the parts of the planet in which all life exists.
- ▶ Ecologists may study different levels of ecological organization:
  - Individual organism
  - An assemblage of individuals that belong to the same species and live in the same area is called a **population**.
  - An assemblage of different populations that live together in an area is referred to as a **community**.
  - An **ecosystem** includes all the organisms that live in a particular place, together with their physical environment.
  - A group of ecosystems that have similar climates and organisms is called a **biome**.

Biotic and Abiotic Factors Ecosystems include biotic and abiotic factors.

- ▶ A **biotic factor** is any living part of an environment.
- ▶ An **abiotic factor** is any nonliving part of an environment.

Ecological Methods Ecologists use three basic methods of research: observation, experimentation, and modeling:

- ▶ Observation often leads to questions and hypotheses.
- ▶ Experiments can be used to test hypotheses.
- ▶ Modeling helps ecologists understand complex processes.

Studying Our Living Planet

1. What is ecology?

   It is the scientific study of interactions among organisms and between organisms and

   their environment.

2. What does the biosphere contain?

   It contains all the organisms and physical environments of Earth.

3. How are human economics and ecology linked?

Economics has to do with human "houses" and interactions based on money and
trade. Ecological interactions have to do with nature's "houses" and are based on
energy and nutrients. Humans depend on ecological processes to provide nutrients
that can be bought or traded.

Jse the diagram to answer Questions 4–5.

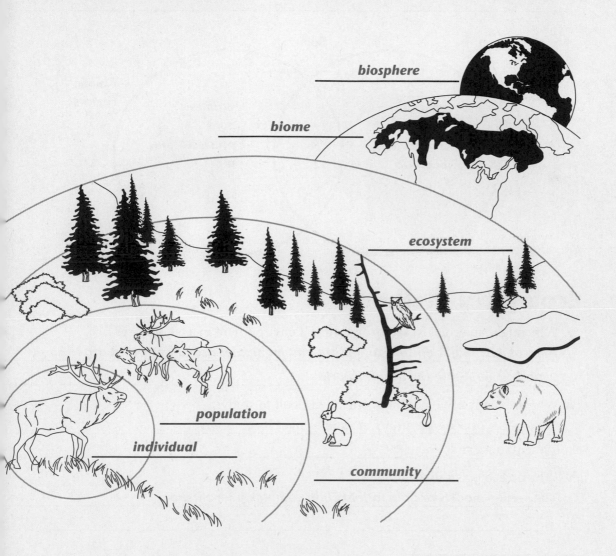

biosphere

biome

ecosystem

population

individual

community

4. Label each level of organization on the diagram.

5. Explain the relationship between ecosystems and biomes.

An ecosystem describes all of the organisms that live in a place, together with
their physical environment. A group of ecosystems that share similar climates and
organisms is considered a biome.

Biotic and Abiotic Factors

6. Use the terms in the box to fill in the Venn diagram. List parts of the environment that consist of biotic factors, abiotic factors, and some components that are a mixture of both.

air	heat	precipitation
animals	mushrooms	soil
bacteria	plants	sunlight

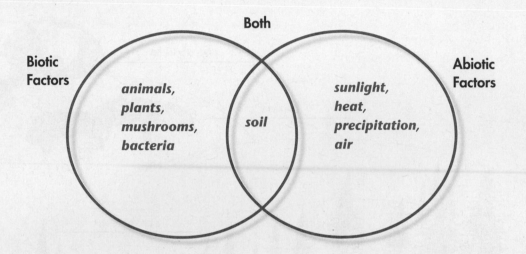

Both

Biotic Factors

animals, plants, mushrooms, bacteria

soil

sunlight, heat, precipitation, air

Abiotic Factors

Ecological Methods

7. Why might an ecologist set up an artificial environment in a laboratory?
An ecologist might do that to imitate and manipulate conditions that organisms would encounter in the natural world.

8. Why are many ecological phenomena difficult to study?
They occur over long periods of time or over large areas.

9. Why do ecologists make models?
They make models to gain insights into complex phenomena.

Apply the Big idea

10. What makes a planet living? Explain your answer by comparing Earth with Mars.
Earth is a living planet because it contains organisms. Life exists on Earth on the land, in the water, and in the atmosphere. Earth's environments can be described based on biotic and abiotic factors. In contrast, Mars is a planet void of life. Mars can be described based only on abiotic factors such as sunlight, heat, wind, soil type, and so on.

3.2 Energy, Producers, and Consumers

Lesson Objectives
- Define primary producers.
- Describe how consumers obtain energy and nutrients.

Lesson Summary

Primary Producers Sunlight is the main energy source for life on Earth. Organisms that can capture energy from sunlight or chemicals and use that energy to produce food are called **autotrophs**, or **primary producers**.

- The process in which autotrophs capture light energy and use it to convert carbon dioxide and water into oxygen and sugars is called **photosynthesis**.
- The process in which autotrophs use chemical energy to produce carbohydrates is called **chemosynthesis**.

Consumers Organisms that rely on other organisms for their energy and food are called **heterotrophs**. Heterotrophs are also referred to as consumers. There are many different types of heterotrophs:

- **Herbivores**, such as cows, obtain energy by eating only plants.
- **Carnivores**, such as snakes, eat only animals.
- **Omnivores**, such as humans, eat both plants and animals.
- **Detritivores**, such as earthworms, feed on dead matter.
- **Decomposers**, such as fungi, break down organic matter.
- **Scavengers**, such as vultures, consume the carcasses of other animals.

Primary Producers

1. What do autotrophs do during photosynthesis?

   They use light energy to power chemical reactions that convert carbon dioxide and water into oxygen and energy-rich carbohydrates such as sugars and starch.

2. Can some organisms survive without energy from the sun? Explain your answer.

   Yes, some deep-sea ecosystems do not depend on the sun for their energy source. Primary producers can harness chemical energy from inorganic molecules such as hydrogen sulfide to produce carbohydrates through chemosynthesis.

3. Can organisms create their own energy? Explain your answer. *No, primary producers harness energy from the sun or chemicals to produce carbohydrates. They do not produce their own energy. Other organisms obtain their energy from primary producers.*

Consumers

4. Complete the table about types of heterotrophs.

Types of Heterotrophs		
Type	**Definition**	**Examples**
Herbivore	*Heterotroph that obtains energy by eating only plants*	cows, rabbits
Carnivore	Heterotroph that eats animals	*snakes, dogs, owls*
Omnivore	*Heterotroph that eats both plants and animals*	humans, bears, pigs
Detritivore	*Heterotroph that feeds on detritus*	*mites, earthworms, snails, crabs*
Decomposer	*Heterotroph that breaks down organic matter*	*bacteria, fungi*
Scavenger	Heterotroph that consumes the carcasses of dead animals but does not typically kill them itself	*vulture, hyena*

5. What is a consumer?

A consumer is any organism that relies on other organisms for energy and nutrients.

6. How would you categorize a consumer that usually catches and eats prey, but also eats dead animal carcasses? *a carnivore*

Apply the Big idea

7. What role do producers play in establishing Earth as a living planet? *Energy enters the biotic portion of Earth's ecosystems through primary producers. Primary producers convert nonliving, abiotic factors, such as sunlight or chemicals, into carbohydrates. In this way, producers make the energy accessible to other organisms on the planet. Photosynthetic producers also give off oxygen, a gas that is required by most other organisms, during photosynthesis.*

3.3 Energy Flow in Ecosystems

Lesson Objectives

- Trace the flow of energy through living systems.
- Identify the three types of ecological pyramids.

Lesson Summary

Food Chains and Food Webs Energy flows through an ecosystem in one direction from primary producers to various consumers.

- A **food chain** is a series of steps in which organisms transfer energy by eating and being eaten. Producers, such as floating algae called **phytoplankton**, are at the base of every food chain.
- A **food web** is a network of all the food chains in an ecosystem. Food webs are very complex. Small disturbances to one population can affect all populations in a food web. Changes in populations of **zooplankton**, small marine animals that feed on algae, can affect all of the animals in the marine food web.

Trophic Levels and Ecological Pyramids Each step in a food chain or food web is called a **trophic level**. Producers make up the first trophic level. Consumers make up higher trophic levels. Each consumer depends on the trophic level below it for energy.

An **ecological pyramid** is a diagram that shows the relative amounts of energy or matter contained within each trophic level in a food chain or food web. Types of ecological pyramids are pyramids of energy, pyramids of biomass, and pyramids of numbers:

- Pyramids of energy show relative amounts of energy available at different trophic levels.
- Pyramids of **biomass** show the total amount of living tissue at each trophic level.
- A pyramid of numbers shows the relative numbers of organisms at different trophic levels.

Food Chains and Food Webs

1. Complete the table about feeding relationships.

Feeding Relationships	
Relationship	**Description**
Food Chain	*A series of steps in which organisms transfer energy by eating and being eaten*
Food Web	*A network of complex interactions formed by the feeding relationships among the various organisms in an ecosystem*

Use the food chain to answer Questions 2–4.

2. Draw arrows between the organisms to show how energy moves through this food chain. Write *producer*, *herbivore*, or *carnivore* under each organism.

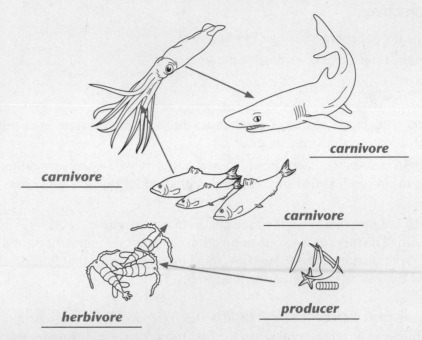

carnivore

carnivore

carnivore

herbivore

producer

3. Explain how energy flows through this food chain. **Phytoplankton are photosynthetic organisms. They use energy from the sun to create carbohydrates. The zooplankton eats the phytoplankton to obtain energy. The small fish eat the zooplankton. The squid eats the small fish. The shark eats the squid.**

4. What would happen to this food chain if a disturbance caused a serious decline in the shark population? **If the shark numbers declined, there would be no natural predator to control the number of squids. Therefore the squid population might increase. The larger population of squid would then eat more fish than the typical population would have. Eventually the squid would run out of fish to eat and start to die out.**

5. **VISUAL ANALOGY** What role does energy play in the diagram, and how is it represented? **Energy is both taken in and recycled by the decomposers and the primary producers. The recycling machines represent the mechanisms by which those organisms convert energy from the forms they use (the house and building blocks) to the forms into which they recycle it (building blocks, ship and bridge).**

Decomposers

Primary Producers

Trophic Levels and Ecological Pyramids

Write True or False on the line provided.

False   **6.** Primary consumers always make up the first trophic level in a food web.

True   **7.** Ecological pyramids show the relative amount of energy or matter contained within each trophic level in a given food web.

False   **8.** On average, about 50 percent of the energy available within one trophic level is transferred to the next trophic level.

False   **9.** The more levels that exist between a producer and a given consumer, the larger the percentage of the original energy from producers is available to that consumer.

Use the diagram to answer Questions 10–17.

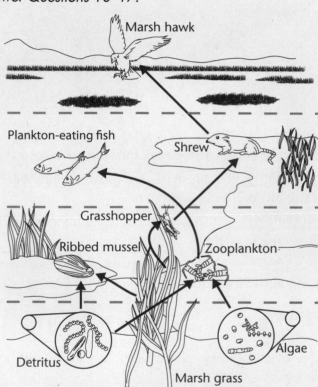

Match the organism with its trophic level. A trophic level may be used more than once.

Organism		Trophic Level
A	**10.** algae	**A.** primary producer
B	**11.** grasshopper	**B.** first-level consumer
A	**12.** marsh grass	**C.** second-level consumer
D	**13.** marsh hawk	**D.** third-level consumer
C	**14.** plankton-eating fish	
B	**15.** ribbed mussel	
C	**16.** shrew	
B	**17.** zooplankton	

18. Complete the energy pyramid by writing the source of the energy for the food web and how much energy is available to first-, second-, and third-level consumers.

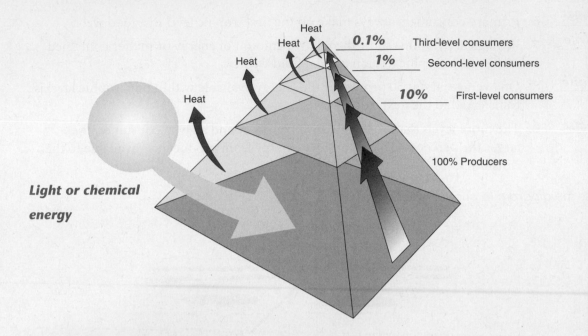

For Questions 19–21, complete each statement by writing the correct word or words.

19. A pyramid of _____**biomass**_____ illustrates the relative amount of living organic matter available at each trophic level in an ecosystem.

20. A pyramid of _____**numbers**_____ shows the relative numbers of individual organisms at the trophic levels in an ecosystem.

21. A pyramid of _____**energy**_____ shows the relative amounts of energy available at the trophic levels of a food chain or food web.

Apply the Big idea

22. Identify which type of ecological pyramid best traces the flow of matter through an ecosystem. Explain your answer.

Biomass pyramids show the amount of organic material at each trophic level;

thus, they are the best type of ecological pyramid to use in order to model the flow

of matter through an ecosystem. A numbers pyramid would not as accurately display

this kind of information because a larger producer, such as a tree, which contains a

great deal of matter, would be able to feed hundreds or thousands of small first-level

consumers, such as wood-eating insects.

3.4 Cycles of Matter

Lesson Objectives

- Describe how matter cycles among the living and nonliving parts of an ecosystem.
- Describe how water cycles through the biosphere.
- Explain why nutrients are important in living systems.
- Describe how the availability of nutrients affects the productivity of ecosystems.

Lesson Summary

Recycling in the Biosphere Matter, unlike energy, is recycled within and between ecosystems. Elements pass from one organism to another and from one part of the biosphere to another through **biogeochemical cycles**, which are closed loops powered by the flow of energy.

The Water Cycle Water moves between the ocean, the atmosphere, and land.

- Evaporation is the process in which water changes from a liquid to a gas.
- Transpiration is the process in which water evaporates from the leaves of plants.

Nutrient Cycles The chemical substances that an organism needs to survive are called **nutrients**. Like water, nutrients pass through organisms and the environment.

- **Carbon Cycle:** Carbon is a key ingredient of all organic compounds. Processes involved in the carbon cycle include photosynthesis and human activities such as burning.
- **Nitrogen Cycle:** Nitrogen is needed by all organisms to build proteins. Processes involved in the nitrogen cycle include nitrogen fixation and denitrification.
  - In **nitrogen fixation**, certain bacteria convert nitrogen gas into ammonia.
  - In **denitrification**, other soil bacteria convert nitrogen compounds called nitrates back into nitrogen gas.
- **Phosphorus Cycle:** Phosphorus is needed for molecules such as DNA and RNA. Most of the phosphorus in the biosphere is stored in rocks and ocean sediments. Stored phosphorus is gradually released into water and soil, where it is used by organisms.

Nutrient Limitation A nutrient that, in short supply, can limit the productivity of an ecosystem is called a **limiting nutrient**.

Recycling in the Biosphere

For Questions 1–3, write True if the statement is true. If the statement is false, change the underlined word or words to make the statement true.

carbon	1. The four elements that make up over 95 percent of the body in most organisms are oxygen, <u>sulfur</u>, nitrogen, and hydrogen.
True	2. Matter moves through an ecosystem in <u>cycles</u>.
lightning	3. Chemical and physical processes include the formation of clouds and precipitation, <u>"burning" food</u>, and the flow of running water.

4. **VISUAL ANALOGY** The illustration draws an analogy between the way energy drives matter to cycle in an ecosystem and the way water causes a waterwheel to turn. Give an example of another analogy that could be used to show the relationship between energy and the cycles of matter.

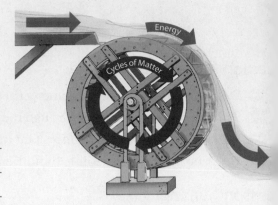

> *Possible analogies include wind causing a windmill to turn or a foot pushing a bicycle pedal around and around.*

5. Explain why Earth is considered a closed system.

> *Earth is a closed system because matter does not enter and matter does not escape. The materials used by organisms cannot be lost; they are recycled.*

6. How might building a new highway affect the cycles of matter?

> *When a new highway is being built, trees and other plants are cleared. The removal of plants limits the food, energy, and habitats available to other organisms, like animals. The removal of plants and animals stops nutrients from being recycled.*

The Water Cycle

7. What role do plants play in the water cycle?

> *Plants absorb groundwater through their roots. That water re-enters the atmosphere in the form of water vapor when it evaporates from the leaves of plants during transpiration. This transpired water then continues the cycle.*

8. **THINK VISUALLY** Draw a diagram explaining the water cycle. Label the processes involved as biological or physical/chemical.

> *Drawings should include the following: Physical/Chemical processes: Water evaporates from bodies of water and then condenes into clouds in the atmosphere. Water falls to the surface as precipitation. Surface runoff goes to rivers and oceans. Water seeps into the ground and becomes groundwater. Biological Processes: Groundwater is absorbed by plant roots. Plant leaves release water vapor into the atmosphere through transpiration.*

Nutrient Cycles

9. Complete the chart about the carbon cycle.

Processes That Cause Carbon to Move into the Atmosphere		Processes That Cause Carbon to Move out of the Atmosphere	
Process	**Description**	**Process**	**Description**
Respiration	**the release of CO_2 by an organism after breaking down carbohydrates into usable energy**	Photosynthesis	**the use of sunlight and CO_2 to produce carbohydrates**
Volcanic Activity	the release of CO_2 and other gases into the atmosphere through vents in Earth's crust	SAMPLE ANSWER: **Dissolving**	SAMPLE ANSWER: CO_2 **dissolves in rainwater and oceans.**

For Questions 10–12, write the letter of the correct answer on the line at the left.

B   **10.** The carbon in coal, oil, and natural gas came from

     A. the combustion of fossil fuels.

     B. the remains of dead organisms.

     C. carbon-fixing bacteria in swamp soil.

     D. carbon dioxide dissolved in ocean water.

A   **11.** How does most of the carbon in an organism's body return to the environment after the organism dies?

     A. Decomposers break the body down into simpler compounds.

     B. Heat from the sun causes the carbon in the body to evaporate.

     C. Geological processes cause the body to turn into a fossil fuel.

     D. Rainwater dissolves the carbon in the body and carries it to the ocean.

A   **12.** Human processes mainly contribute to the

     A. release of carbon dioxide into the atmosphere.

     B. decrease of the total amount of carbon found on Earth.

     C. depletion of carbon dioxide reserves in the atmosphere.

     D. increase in the amount of carbon contained in rock materials.

Write True if the statement is true. If the statement is false, change the underlined word or words to make the statement true.

_____True_____ **13.** Nitrogen, in the form of ammonia, <u>nitrate</u>, and nitrite, is found in the soil.

_____ammonia_____ **14.** Nitrogen fixation is the process in which certain bacteria convert nitrogen gas into <u>nitrates</u>.

_____True_____ **15.** <u>Denitrification</u> is the process by which some soil bacteria convert nitrates into nitrogen gas.

_____proteins_____ **16.** All organisms require nitrogen to make amino acids, which in turn are used to build <u>carbohydrates</u>.

_____True_____ **17.** Phosphate is released as <u>rocks and sediments</u> wear down.

_____True_____ **18.** Plants absorb phosphate from the <u>soil</u> or from water.

_____Nitrogen_____ **19.** <u>Phosphorus</u> is the most abundant gas in the atmosphere.

_____Carbon dioxide_____ **20.** <u>Organic phosphate</u> is taken up by producers during photosynthesis and released by cellular respiration.

_____True_____ **21.** <u>Phosphorus</u> forms part of the important life-sustaining molecules such as DNA and RNA.

_____soil_____ **22.** Plants absorb phosphorus from <u>the atmosphere</u> or water.

23. List and describe the biological steps in the nitrogen cycle.

Bacteria convert nitrogen gas into ammonia during nitrogen fixation. Other soil bacteria convert ammonia into nitrates and nitrites. Primary producers use nitrates and nitrites to make proteins and nucleic acids. Consumers eat producers and reuse nitrogen to make compounds. Decomposers release nitrogen from waste and dead organisms. Bacteria convert nitrates into nitrogen gas during denitrification.

24. What is atmospheric nitrogen fixation, and how does it affect organisms?

Atmospheric nitrogen fixation is the process in which lightning converts nitrogen gas in the atmosphere into usable compounds. It makes nitrogen available to organisms.

25. How do humans add nitrogen to the biosphere?

Humans add nitrogen to the biosphere by using fertilizers that contain nitrogen.

26. Which parts of the phosphorus cycle are geological processes?

Geological activity turns marine sediments into rock and washes the phosphates from the rock into the ocean.

Nutrient Limitation

*Use the diagram of the interlocking nutrients to answer
Question 27.*

27. **VISUAL ANALOGY** The visual analogy compares
interlocking gears to the major nutrients—
potassium, phosphorus, and nitrogen. What other
"gears" would be affected if these gears stopped
working together?

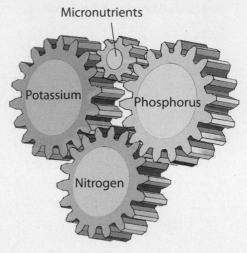

Micronutrients

Potassium

Phosphorus

Nitrogen

Plants and other organisms can also be added to

this analogy. Without potassium, phosphorus and

nitrogen, plants would not be able to live and

thrive. Plants produce oxygen and carbohydrates.

Without these "gears," animals and most living

things would not survive.

_____

_____

28. If a nutrient were in short supply in an ecosystem, how might it affect an organism?
   SAMPLE ANSWER: *It would limit an organism's growth.*

29. When is a substance a limiting nutrient?
   A substance is a limiting nutrient when it is scarce or cycles very slowly and limits an

   ecosystem.

Apply the Big idea

30. Compare and contrast the flow of energy through an environment with the flow of matter
   through that same environment.
   Matter moves through an environment differently than the way in which energy

   moves. Energy is captured by producers and then passed in a linear progression from

   one trophic level to the next. At each level, much of the energy escapes the ecosystem

   as heat. Unlike this one-way flow of energy, matter is recycled within and between

   ecosystems. Elements pass from one organism to another and among parts of the non-

   living environment through closed loops called biogeochemical cycles.

   _____

   _____

   _____

   _____

   _____

Chapter Vocabulary Review

Match the term with its definition.

Term

  D   1. nutrient

  B   2. chemosynthesis

  C   3. consumer

  A   4. ecosystem

  H   5. photosynthesis

  F   6. ecology

  E   7. primary producer

  G   8. biosphere

Definition

A. all the organisms in one area and their physical environment

B. a process in which producers use chemical energy to make carbohydrates

C. an organism that feeds on other organisms

D. a chemical substance that an organism needs to survive

E. an organism that uses chemical or light energy to produce its own food supply

F. the study of the biosphere

G. the portion of Earth and its atmosphere that contains organisms

H. a process in which producers use light energy to make carbohydrates

For Questions 9–12, complete the analogies.

SAMPLE ANSWERS

9. omnivore : human :: carnivore : ___*lion*___

10. detritivore : earthworm :: herbivore : ___*cow*___

11. autotroph : heterotroph :: phytoplankton : ___*zooplankton*___

12. biotic factor : elephant :: abiotic factor : ___*precipitation*___

13. What is the difference between a food chain and a food web?

A food chain is a series of steps in which organisms transfer energy by eating and being eaten. A food web is a network of several interacting food chains.

Complete each statement by writing the correct word or words.

14. There are several hundred squirrels living in an oak forest. The squirrels make up a(n) ___*population*___.

15. Fungi and some kinds of bacteria are ___*decomposers*___ that obtain nutrients by chemically breaking down organic matter.

16. Ecologists measure ___*biomass*___ in grams of organic matter per unit area.

17. In a process known as ___*denitrification*___, some types of soil bacteria obtain energy by converting nitrates into nitrogen gas.

CHAPTER
MYSTERY

CHANGES IN THE BAY

Rhode Island's Narragansett Bay is not the only ecosystem that suffers from changes in abiotic factors such as temperature. This is happening within many biomes and ecosystems around the world.

21st Century Learning

Rising Temperatures in a Lake

The northwest coniferous forest is a small biome along the coast of the northwestern United States. It experiences seasonal variations in temperature and precipitation. Close to Seattle, Washington, is Lake Washington, which is a freshwater ecosystem in peril from decades of sewage dumping and rising water temperatures. The following is a brief summary of an environmental report on Lake Washington.

ENVIRONMENTAL REPORT: Lake Washington Status

PREPARED BY: Environmental Sub-Committee

SUMMARY: While it has been more than 40 years since sewage has been dumped into Lake Washington, problems still exist in this freshwater ecosystem. The lake's overall temperature has increased by 0.5°C in the past 40 years. Its upper layer, which is 9 meters deep, has experienced a temperature increase of 1.25°C. These rising temperatures are negatively affecting the ecosystem's food chain. Zooplankton numbers are declining. These microscopic organisms eat algae, which are at the base of the food chain. Zooplankton are also prey for salmon. Higher temperatures are generating more frequent algal blooms, which are starting to create eutrophic conditions in the lake. Eutrophication is a condition in which a body of water is very high in nutrients, but low in oxygen. Salmon populations are also declining due to these conditions. Spring turnover in the lake, a process by which warmer surface water sinks and mixes with deep, cold water, is occurring a month later than in the past. The result is that some fish that prefer colder water are migrating into deeper waters, where they encounter more predatory species than they would shallow water. Studies indicate that global warming is the major contributor to the rising temperatures.

Continued on next page ▶

21st Century Themes — Science and Global Awareness, Science and Civic Literacy

1. What abiotic factor is changing the ecosystem of Lake Washington, and how has this factor changed over time?

Temperature is the abiotic factor that is changing the ecosystem. Both the top layer

temperature and the overall temperature of the lake are increasing.

2. Explain how this change has affected the mixing of warm and cold water in the lake. How does this in turn affect fish?

The warmer temperatures have delayed the yearly springtime mixing of warm and co

water in the lake. Consequently, some fish that prefer colder water migrate to deeper

water layers that are cooler but that hold larger populations of predatory fish specie.

3. This report suggests that global warming is a primary contributor to the increased temperature in the lake. What does this suggest about other lake ecosystems in the northwest coniferous forest?

Other lakes in the northwest coniferous forest may also have increased water

temperatures. Their fish, algae, and zooplankton populations may also be in danger.

Seasonal turnover may also be later, as it is in Lake Washington.

4. Briefly describe a food chain in Lake Washington.

Algae are at the bottom of the food chain and are eaten by zooplankton. Salmon eat

the zooplankton.

5. If the zooplankton population is decreasing in Lake Washington, what do you think is happening to the salmon population? Explain your answer.

The salmon are not able to find as much food, and their numbers are decreasing.

21st Century Skills — Lake Presentation

The skills used in this activity include **critical thinking and systems thinking; problem identification, formulation, and solution; communication; information literacy;** and **leadership and responsibility.**

Working with a small group, research information about Lake Washington's past issues with sewage disposal and current trends in increasing water temperature. Or, conduct research about a body of water in your community or state. You may find it helpful to start your research at the Web sites of federal and state environmental agencies. Visiting your local public library and inquiring at government offices can offer valuable information, too. Find evidence about the relationship between global warming and these rising temperatures. Prepare a presentation describing the information that you find. In your presentation, provide at least one example and show the effects of changing conditions on this ecosystem. Present your findings to the class in an oral report, using figures, tables, and illustrations.

Evaluate students' presentations by their inclusion of descriptions and past and current data about the body of water, including charts, graphs, and/or diagrams. Evaluation should also depend on the reliability of the sources students use.

4 Ecosystems and Communities

Big Idea Interdependence in Nature

Q: How do abiotic and biotic factors shape ecosystems?

WHAT I KNOW	WHAT I LEARNED
4.1 What factors affect global climate?	SAMPLE ANSWER: *The global climate is affected by how much sunlight reaches Earth.*	SAMPLE ANSWER: *The global climate is shaped by many factors, including solar energy, latitude, and the transport of heat by winds and ocean currents.*
4.2 How do organisms interact with one another?	SAMPLE ANSWER: *Some organisms are predators. Others are prey.*	SAMPLE ANSWER: *Organisms have roles, or niches, in a community. These roles govern how organisms interact with other organisms.*
4.3 How do ecosystems change over time?	SAMPLE ANSWER: *Ecosystems become more complex over time.*	SAMPLE ANSWER: *Disturbances cause ecosystems to change. Some disturbances allow the ecosystem to become more diverse. Other disturbances cause species to leave.*
4.4 What are the characteristics of the major biomes?	SAMPLE ANSWER: *Biomes are shaped by average temperature and precipitation.*	SAMPLE ANSWER: *Biomes are described in terms of abiotic factors like climate and soil type, and biotic factors like plant and animal life.*
4.5 What are the characteristics of aquatic ecosystems?	SAMPLE ANSWER: *Aquatic ecosystems can be either saltwater or freshwater.*	SAMPLE ANSWER: *An aquatic ecosystem can be described by the water's depth, temperature, flow, and amount of dissolved nutrients.*

4.1 Climate

Lesson Objectives

⊂▪⊃ Differentiate between weather and climate.

⊂▪⊃ Identify the factors that influence climate.

Lesson Summary

Weather and Climate Weather is the condition of Earth's atmosphere at a particular time and place. Climate is the average condition of temperature and precipitation in a region over long periods.

▶ Climate can vary over short distances.

▶ These variations produce **microclimates**.

Factors That Affect Climate Climate is affected by solar energy trapped in the biosphere, by latitude, and by the transport of heat by winds and ocean currents.

▶ Temperature on Earth stays within a range suitable for life due to the greenhouse effect. The **greenhouse effect** is the trapping of heat by gases in the atmosphere.

▶ Earth's curvature causes different latitudes to receive less or more intense solar energy. The unequal distribution of the sun's heat on Earth's surface results in three main climate zones: polar, temperate, and tropical.

▶ Unequal heating of Earth's surface also causes winds and ocean currents. Winds and currents move heat and moisture through the biosphere.

Weather and Climate

1. How is weather different from climate?

   Weather is the day-to-day condition of Earth's atmosphere at a particular time

   and place, whereas climate is the average year-to-year condition of temperature and

   precipitation in a particular region.

   _____

   _____

2. What causes microclimates to form?

   Microclimates are caused by small differences in environmental conditions within a

   region.

   _____

3. In the Northern Hemisphere, why are the south-facing sides of buildings often warmer and drier than the north-facing sides?

   because the south-facing sides of buildings receive more sunlight

   _____

Factors That Affect Climate

VISUAL ANALOGY For Questions 4–5, refer to the Visual Analogy comparing the Earth's atmosphere to a greenhouse.

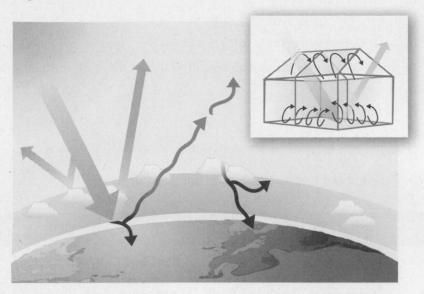

4. What is the source of radiation for both the Earth's atmosphere and the greenhouse?

sunlight

5. What happens to sunlight that hits Earth's surface?

Some sunlight is reflected back by Earth's surface, some escapes as heat into space, some is trapped as heat by the greenhouse gases, and some is absorbed by Earth's surface.

For Questions 6–9, write the letter of the correct answer on the line at the left.

_____A_____ **6.** What effect do carbon dioxide and methane have on Earth's temperature?

    A. They trap heat in the atmosphere.

    B. They release heat from the atmosphere.

    C. They block heat from entering the ocean.

    D. They block heat from reaching Earth's surface.

_____D_____ **7.** How would the temperature on Earth change without the greenhouse effect?

    A. The temperature at the equator would be warmer.

    B. The temperature would stay the same.

    C. It would be 30°C warmer.

    D. It would be 30°C cooler.

_____A_____ 8. What causes solar radiation to strike different parts of Earth's surface at an angl
that varies throughout the year?

    A. Earth's tilted axis

    B. Earth's erratic orbit

    C. the moon's orbit around Earth

    D. solar flares on the sun's surface

_____A_____ 9. In which location is the sun almost directly overhead at noon all year?

    A. the equator

    B. the South Pole

    C. the North Pole

    D. North America

10. Complete the table about Earth's three main climate zones.

Main Climate Zones		
Climate Zone	**Location**	**Climate Characteristics**
Polar zones	Areas around North and South poles	*Cold areas*
Temperate zones	Between the polar zones and the tropics	*Ranges from hot to cold, depending on the season*
Tropical zones	Near the equator	*Almost always warm*

For Questions 11–14, write True if the statement is true. If the statement is false, change the underlined word or words to make the statement true.

_____True_____ 11. Patterns of heating and cooling result in <u>ocean currents</u>.

_____True_____ 12. Warm air is <u>less</u> dense than cool air.

_____True_____ 13. Surface water moved by <u>winds</u> results in ocean currents.

_____cold_____ 14. Deep ocean currents are caused by the sinking of <u>warm</u> water near the poles.

Apply the Big idea

15. Describe how a change in the temperature of an ocean current might affect the climate of
a nearby coastal area.

Should a cold-water current begin to become warmer, the water in the current will

absorb less heat from the surrounding air. This will cause the climate of the nearby

coastal area to become warmer. The reverse would be true for a warm-water current

that begins to become cooler.

4.2 Niches and Community Interactions

Lesson Objectives
- Define niche.
- Describe the role competition plays in shaping communities.
- Describe the role predation and herbivory play in shaping communities.
- Identify the three types of symbiotic relationships in nature.

Lesson Summary

The Niche Every species has its own **tolerance**, or a range of conditions under which it can grow and reproduce. A species' tolerance determines its **habitat**, the place where it lives.

- A **niche** consists of all the physical and biological conditions in which a species lives and the way the species obtains what it needs to survive and reproduce.
- An organism's niche must contain all of the resources an organism needs to survive. A **resource** is any necessity of life, such as water, nutrients, light, food, or space.

Competition Competition occurs when organisms try to use the same limited resources.

- Direct competition between species often results in one species dying out. This is the basis of the **competitive exclusion principle**. This principle states that no two species can occupy exactly the same niche in exactly the same habitat at the same time.
- Competition helps to determine the number and type of species in a community.

Predation, Herbivory, and Keystone Species Predator-prey and herbivore-plant interactions help shape communities.

- **Predation** occurs when one organism (the predator) captures and eats another (the prey).
- **Herbivory** is an interaction that occurs when an animal (the herbivore) feeds on producers (such as plants).
- Sometimes changes in the population of a single species, often called a **keystone species**, can cause dramatic changes in the structure of a community.

Symbioses **Symbiosis** occurs when two species live closely together in one of three ways: mutualism, commensalism, or parasitism.

- In **mutualism**, both species benefit from the relationship.
- In **parasitism**, one species benefits by living in or on the other and the other is harmed.
- In **commensalism**, one species benefits and the other is neither helped nor harmed.

The Niche

1. What is a niche?

A niche is the full range of physical and biological conditions in which an organism

lives and the way in which the organism uses those conditions.

2. Give an example of resources a squirrel might need.

SAMPLE ANSWER: *food (acorns), space in a tree, water, air*

3. Three different warbler species live in the same tree. One species feeds at the top of the tree, the second species feeds in the middle part of the tree, and the third species feeds at the bottom of the tree. Do all three species occupy the same niche? Explain.

No, the warblers occupy different niches because the warblers are feeding at different

locations in the tree. Therefore, they are not in competition with one another.

Competition

For Questions 4–8, write True if the statement is true. If the statement is false, change the underlined word or words to make the statement true.

___True___ 4. Competition occurs when organisms attempt to use the same <u>resources</u>.

___intraspecific___ 5. Competition between members of the same species is known as <u>interspecific</u> competition.

___species___ 6. The competitive exclusion principle states that no two <u>organisms</u> can occupy exactly the same niche in exactly the same habitat at exactly the same time.

___True___ 7. If two species of bacteria are grown in the same culture, one species will always <u>outcompete</u> the other.

___True___ 8. Members of the same species tend to <u>divide</u> resources instead of competing over them.

Predation, Herbivory, and Keystone Species

Write the letter of the correct answer on the line at the left.

___C___ 9. A lion eating a zebra is an example of
  A. herbivory.   C. predation.
  B. habitat destruction.   D. a keystone species.

___A___ 10. A cow eating grass is an example of
  A. herbivory.   C. habitat destruction.
  B. predation.   D. a keystone species.

___D___ 11. A keystone species is one that
  A. eats a mixture of plants and animals.
  B. is introduced into a community after a major disturbance.
  C. causes the amount of diversity in a community to decrease.
  D. helps to stabilize the populations of other species in the community.

Symbioses

2. Complete the table about main classes of symbiotic relationships.

Main Classes of Symbiotic Relationships	
Class	**Description of Relationships**
Mutualism	*Both species benefit from the relationship.*
Commensalism	*One member of the association benefits and the other is neither helped nor harmed.*
Parasitism	*One organism lives on or inside another organism and harms it.*

Match the example with the type of relationship. A relationship type may be used more than once.

Example

Type of Relationship

_____C_____ **13.** a tick living on the body of a deer

    A. mutualism

_____A_____ **14.** a bee eating a flower's nectar and picking up the flower's pollen

    B. commensalism

_____B_____ **15.** a barnacle living on a whale's skin

    C. parasitism

_____C_____ **16.** a tapeworm living in a person's intestines

_____A_____ **17.** an aphid providing food to an ant in exchange for protection

Apply the Big idea

18. How do keystone species illustrate the interdependence of organisms living in a community? Give an example.

SAMPLE ANSWER: *A change in a keystone species can cause dramatic changes to other species in the community. Sea otters are a keystone species in the Pacific coast community. When the number of sea otters dropped, the other species in the community were affected. Without the sea otters to eat them, the number of sea urchins increased. The sea urchins are herbivores that eat kelp. The increase in sea urchins caused the kelp population to decrease.*

4.3 Succession

Lesson Objectives

- Describe how ecosystems recover from a disturbance.
- Compare succession after a natural disturbance with succession after a human-caused disturbance.

Lesson Summary

Primary and Secondary Succession The series of predictable changes that occurs in a community over time is called **ecological succession**. Over the course of succession, the number of different species usually increases.

▶ **Primary succession** begins in areas with no remnants of an older community. It occurs on bare rock surfaces where no soil exists. The first species to live in an area of primary succession are called **pioneer species**.

▶ **Secondary succession** occurs when a disturbance changes a community without completely destroying it.

Climax Communities A climax community is a mature, relatively stable ecosystem.

▶ Secondary succession in healthy ecosystems following natural disturbances often reproduces the original climax community.

▶ Ecosystems may or may not recover from extensive human-caused disturbances.

Primary and Secondary Succession

1. What is ecological succession?

   It is a series of predictable changes that occur in a community over time.

2. What is primary succession?

   It is succession that occurs on surfaces where no soil exists.

3. When a disturbance changes a community without removing the soil, what type of succession follows?

   secondary succession

4. Describe the process of succession in an ecosystem.

   In the process of succession, older inhabitants die out, and new organisms move in.

5. Why does secondary succession typically proceed faster than primary succession?

   Soil is already in place, thus a larger range of plant species can colonize the area.

6. Use the Venn diagram to compare the two types of ecological succession.

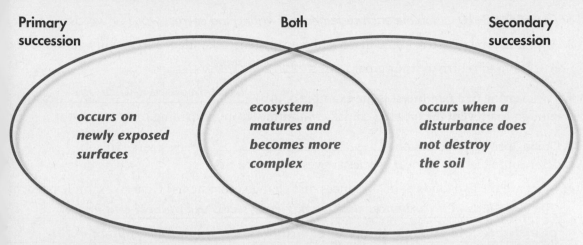

Primary succession

occurs on newly exposed surfaces

Both

ecosystem matures and becomes more complex

Secondary succession

occurs when a disturbance does not destroy the soil

7. The panels show changes taking place in an ecosystem after a volcano erupts and covers an area with rock and ash. Number each panel in the order that changes occur. Then, under each panel, write a description of the changes taking place.

1

A volcano has erupted and covered the area with rocks and ash. No organisms live in the area.

3

As the soil deepens, larger plants move into the area. The community becomes more complex.

4

More species move into the area. The soil grows deep enough for trees to be able to grow.

2

Pioneer species, such as lichen and certain grasses, begin to move into the area. As they die, their bodies decay and mix with weathered rock. Soil begins to form.

Climax Communities

For Questions 8–10, complete each statement by writing the correct word or words.

8. After a natural disaster occurs in a healthy ecosystem, secondary succession will cause the ecosystem to return to its original _____*climax community*_____.

9. The clearing of a rain forest is the example of a(n) _____*human-caused disturbance*_____ drastic enough to prevent the original climax community from reforming.

10. During primary succession, _____*chance*_____ plays a large role in determining which pioneer species arrives in an area first.

11. What are the two kinds of disturbances that change ecosystems? Give an example of each.

   The two kinds of disturbances that change ecosystems are natural and human

   disturbances. An example of a natural disturbance is a volcanic eruption. An

   example of a human disturbance is a farmer clearing a field.

   _____

Apply the Big idea

12. Many biotic and abiotic factors determine how quickly ecological succession can cause a climax community to develop in an area. Complete the graphic organizer by adding two factors that contribute to the development of a climax community.

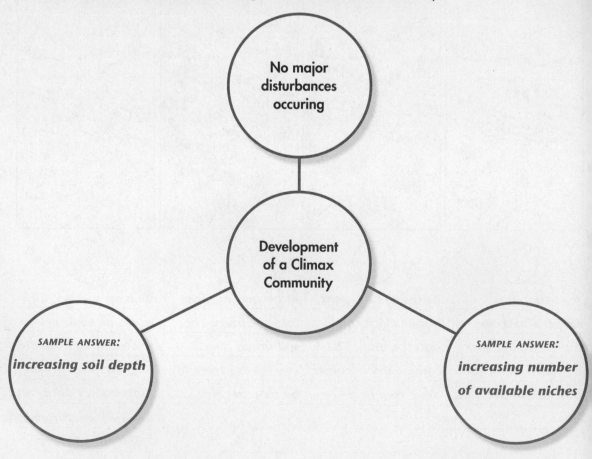

4.4 Biomes

Lesson Objectives

⊃ Describe and compare the characteristics of the major land biomes.

⊃ Identify the areas that are not classified into a major biome.

Lesson Summary

The Major Biomes A biome is a group of terrestrial regional climate communities that covers a large area and is characterized by soil type, climate, and plant and animal life.

- In tropical rain forests, the tops of tall trees form a covering called the **canopy**. Shorter trees and vines form another layer called the **understory**. It is hot and wet all year.

- Tropical dry forests are found in areas with alternating wet and dry seasons. The trees in these forests may be **deciduous**, meaning they shed their leaves during a particular season.

- In a tropical grassland, grassy areas are spotted with isolated trees.

- Deserts have less than 25 centimeters of precipitation annually.

- Temperate grasslands have warm summers, cold winters, and deep soil.

- Temperate woodlands and shrublands are large areas of grasses and wildflowers such as poppies interspersed with trees or shrubs.

- Temperate forests are made up of deciduous and evergreen coniferous trees. **Coniferous** trees produce seed-bearing cones and most have waxy needles. Temperate forests have soils rich in **humus**, which forms from decaying leaves and makes soil fertile.

- Northwestern coniferous forests have mild temperatures with cool, dry summers and abundant precipitation in fall, winter, and spring.

- Boreal forests, or **taiga**, are dense forests of coniferous evergreens.

- Tundra is characterized by **permafrost**, a layer of permanently frozen subsoil.

Other Land Areas Some areas, such as mountains and polar ice caps, do not fall neatly into the major biomes.

The Major Biomes

For Questions 1–4, complete each statement by writing the correct word or words.

1. The side of a mountain range that faces the wind often receives more _____rainfall_____ than the downwind side of the same range.

2. A(n) _____biome_____ is a group of terrestrial communities that covers a large area and is characterized by certain soil and _____climate_____ conditions and particular types of plants and animals.

3. Organisms within each biome can be characterized by _____adaptations_____ that enable them to live and reproduce successfully in the environment.

4. In a tropical rain forest, the layer formed by the leafy tops of tall trees is called the _____canopy_____ and the layer of shorter trees and vines is called the _____understory_____.

5. **THINK VISUALLY** In the box below, draw and label a diagram showing how a coastal mountain range can affect a region's climate.

> *Students' drawings should be similar to the figure in the textbook.*

Use the graph to answer Questions 6–9.

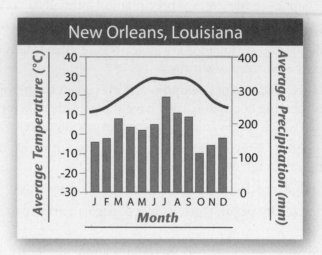

6. Complete the climate diagram by adding labels to the bottom and both sides of the graph to show what the variables are.

7. Describe what a climate diagram summarizes.

> *A climate diagram summarizes a region's climate, including temperature and*
>
> *precipitation.*

8. Explain what the line plot on a climate diagram shows.

> *The line plot shows changes in temperature through the months of a year.*

9. Explain what the vertical bars on a climate diagram show.

> *The vertical bars show the amount of precipitation each month of a year.*

0. Complete the table about some of Earth's major biomes.

Some Major Biomes		
Biome	**Climate and Soil**	**Plants and Animals**
Tropical dry forest	warm year-round with wet and dry seasons; rich soil	plants: tall, deciduous trees; succulents animals: undergo estivation or migration
Tropical rain forest	*hot and wet year round; nutrient poor soil*	*plants; broad leaved evergreen trees, vines; animals: many use camouflage to hide from predators; animals that live in the canopy have adaptations for climbing, jumping, and/or flight.*
Tundra	cold, dark winters and short, soggy summers; permafrost	plants: ground-hugging plants animals: birds and mammals that can tolerate the harsh conditions
Temperate grassland	*warm to hot summers, cold winters; fertile soil*	*plants: grasses and herbs; animals: predator and herbivore mammals, camouflage and burrowing are two common protective adaptations*
Desert	low precipitation with variable temperatures	plants: short growth cycles, cacti animals: adaptations to quickly lose body heat and regulate body temperature
Boreal forest	*long, cold winters; short, mild summers; moderate precipitation; acidic, nutrient-poor soils*	*plants: conifers; animals: most have small extremities and extra insulation, some migrate to warmer areas in winter*

Other Land Areas

11. What is the main cause for variation of abiotic and biotic conditions on a mountain?
elevation

12. Describe the conditions you would most likely find on a mountain in the Rocky Mountains as you moved from the base to the mountain's summit.
Most likely there is a grassland at the base of the mountain. As you go higher, you pass through pine woodland and then a forest of spruce and other conifers. You find thickets of deciduous trees growing along streambeds in protected valleys. Past the tree line, soils are thin. Only grasses, wildflowers, and stunted plants grow. Strong winds blow. A glacier may be found at the summit of the mountain.

13. Which producers can be found in the polar ice regions?
Produces in polar ice regions include some algae, mosses, and lichens.

14. Which animals can be found in the northern polar region?
Animals include polar bears, marine mammals, insects, and mites.

Apply the Big idea

15. How are the plants and animals found in a biome related to the biome's climate? Give at least two examples to support your answer.
SAMPLE ANSWER: *The plants and animals that live in a certain biome have adaptations that help them survive the climatic conditions that shape the biome. For example, animals living in the boreal forest have insulation in the form of blubber or downy feathers. These adaptations help them survive the cold temperatures during the long winters of the taiga. Cacti growing in deserts have waxy leaves and specialized tissue that helps them store large amounts of water. These adaptations help a cactus survive in a biome with very little precipitation.*

4.5 Aquatic Ecosystems

Lesson Objectives

- Discuss the factors that affect aquatic ecosystems.
- Identify the major categories of freshwater ecosystems.
- Describe the importance of estuaries.
- Describe and compare the distinct ocean zones that make up marine ecosystems.

Lesson Summary

Conditions Underwater Aquatic ecosystems are determined mainly by the depth, flow, temperature, and amount of dissolved nutrients of the water.

- The **photic zone** is the sunlit upper layer of water where photosynthesis can occur.
- The **aphotic zone** is the dark lower layer where photosynthesis cannot occur.
- The benthic zone is found on the bottoms of lakes, streams, and oceans. The organisms that live on the floor of a body of water are called **benthos**.

Freshwater Ecosystems Freshwater ecosystems include flowing-water ecosystems, standing-water ecosystems, and freshwater **wetlands**. **Plankton** are common. They form the base of many aquatic food webs.

Estuaries **Estuaries** are wetlands formed where rivers meet the sea. They contain a mixture of fresh and salt water. Most of the food produced in estuaries enters food webs as tiny pieces of organic matter, or detritus.

Marine Ecosystems Marine ecosystems are found in the ocean.

- The intertidal zone is the shallowest and closest to land. It is exposed to the rise and fall of tides each day.
- The coastal ocean is the relatively shallow border of water that surrounds the continents.
- The open ocean begins at the continental shelf and extends outward. The open ocean can be divided into the photic zone and the aphotic zone.

Conditions Underwater

1. What are the four main factors that affect aquatic ecosystems?
water depth, temperature, flow, and amount of dissolved nutrients

2. What does the depth of the water determine?
the amount of light that organisms can receive

3. What distinguishes the photic zone from the aphotic zone in an aquatic ecosystem?
Sunlight penetrates the photic zone but not the aphotic zone.

Freshwater Ecosystems

For Questions 4–10, complete each statement by writing the correct word or words.

4. The three main categories of freshwater ecosystems are __*rivers and streams*__, __*lakes and ponds*__, and __*freshwater wetlands*__.

5. Flowing-water ecosystems originate from underground water sources in __*mountains or hills*__.

6. Circulating water in lakes and ponds distributes __*heat*__, __*oxygen*__, and __*nutrients*__ throughout the system.

7. Plankton is a general term that includes both __*phytoplankton*__ and __*zooplankton*__.

8. An ecosystem in which water either covers the soil or is present at or near the surface of the soil is called a(n) __*wetland*__.

9. Freshwater wetlands purify water by __*filtering*__ pollutants.

10. The three types of freshwater wetlands are __*freshwater bogs*__, __*freshwater marshes*__, and __*freshwater swamps*__.

Estuaries

Write the letter of the correct answer on the line at the left.

__B__ 11. Estuaries form where
   A. a lake evaporates.
   B. a river meets the sea.
   C. a river becomes dammed.
   D. a wetland becomes filled in.

__C__ 12. The salinity of estuary water is
   A. equal to the salinity of river water.
   B. less than the salinity of river water.
   C. less than the salinity of ocean water.
   D. greater than the salinity of ocean water.

__C__ 13. Shallow estuaries allow
   A. freshwater wetlands to merge with the estuary.
   B. large marine mammals to hibernate in the estuary.
   C. sunlight to reach the benthos to power photosynthesis.
   D. salt to sink to the bottom of the estuary.

__B__ 14. Temperate estuaries characterized by salt-tolerant grasses above the low-tide line and seagrasses below water are called
   A. bogs.   C. mangrove swamps.
   B. salt marshes.   D. freshwater wetlands.

Marine Ecosystems

15. Complete the diagram by adding labels for each marine zone. Then shade in the aphotic zone.

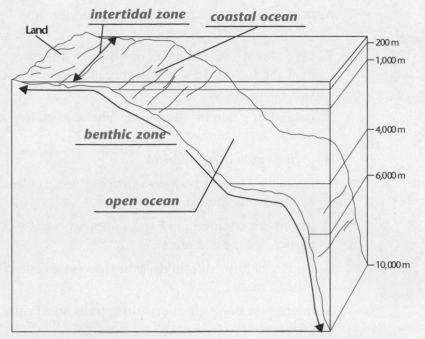

Students should shade in everything under the 200 m mark.

16. Complete the table about the type of organisms living in each ocean zone.

Marine Life by Ocean Zone	
Zone	**Life Forms**
Coastal	kelp forests, coral reefs
Intertidal	barnacles, seaweed, starfish
Open ocean	large marine mammals such as whales, chemosynthetic bacteria

Apply the Big idea

17. Which type of marine ecosystem do you think supports the least life? Explain your answer.

The aphotic open ocean zone most likely supports the least life because food webs

there must be based on organisms that fall from the photic zone above or on chemo-

synthetic organisms. This would limit the number of niches that could develop in the

aphotic open ocean zone.

Chapter Vocabulary Review

Match the term with its definition.

Term

_F_	**1.** weather
_C_	**2.** greenhouse effect
_B_	**3.** niche
_E_	**4.** predation
_A_	**5.** climate
_H_	**6.** herbivory
_G_	**7.** humus
_D_	**8.** permafrost

Definition

A. the average yearly condition of temperature and precipitation in a region

B. the full range of conditions in which an organism lives and the way in which the organism uses those conditions

C. natural situation in which atmospheric gases trap heat inside Earth's atmosphere

D. permanently frozen subsoil

E. interaction in which an organism captures and feeds on another organism

F. day-to-day condition of Earth's atmosphere at a particular time and place

G. a material formed from decaying leaves and other organic matter

H. interaction in which an organism feeds on a primary producer

Complete each statement by writing the correct word or words.

9. The three main types of symbiotic relationships in nature are ___mutualism___, ___commensalism___, and ___parasitism___.

10. The gradual change in living communities that follows a disturbance is called ___ecological succession___.

11. The first species to live in an area of primary succession are called ___pioneer species___.

12. The area where an organism lives is its ___habitat___.

13. The ability of organisms to survive and reproduce under a range of environmental circumstances is called ___tolerance___.

14. The ___taiga___ contains dense evergreen forests of coniferous trees.

15. The well-lit upper layer of ocean water is known as the ___photic zone___.

16. The tiny, free-floating, weakly swimming algae and animals that occur in both freshwater and saltwater environments are called ___plankton___.

17. Organisms that live on the ocean floor are referred to as ___benthos___.

CHAPTER MYSTERY
THE WOLF EFFECT

In March 1995, biologists with the Yellowstone Wolf Project helped to reintroduce the gray wolf into Yellowstone National Park. Gray wolves had been eliminated from the park almost 70 years before that.

21st Century Learning

Advantages and Disadvantages of Wolf Reintroduction

Newspapers, magazines, and media broadcasts contained editorials that argued either for or against the reintroduction of wolves in Yellowstone. People who were against reintroduction might have made arguments such as those in the paragraphs below.

World News Daily

Why We Shouldn't Allow Wolves Back in Yellowstone National Park

An Opinion From a Concerned Rancher

Crazy P Ranch has been in my family for three generations. I have worked alongside my parents and grandparents and heard many stories about my great-grandparents raising cattle here. Ranching is not an easy life. In fact, it's really hard. However, it is our livelihood.

Our Wyoming ranch overlooks the Absaroka Mountain Range, a place abundant with elk and other game that our family has hunted for years. Now we feel that our very livelihood will be endangered by the reintroduction of wolves.

Gray wolves are predators with incredible hunting skills. They hunt in packs to take down the weakest prey animals.

How can my 500 head of cattle survive attacks by these predators? The sick and young cattle are at their mercy, especially after a long winter. Not only are my cattle in danger, but so are the elk that my father, son, and I hunt each fall. We rely on the meat of the elk for food throughout the winter. We face an economic loss if our cattle herd is decimated. This rancher says no to wolves.

21st Century Themes Science and Civic Literacy

1. Explain this rancher's view on the reintroduction of wolves in Yellowstone National Park.

The rancher does not want wolves reintroduced because he is afraid the wolves will

kill his cattle and lower his income and because of the potential decrease in elk

populations due to wolf predation.

Continued on next page ▶

2. What time of year do you think ranchers are most concerned about their cattle? Why?

SAMPLE ANSWER: *I think ranchers are probably most concerned about wolves in late win-*
ter or early spring. The wolves might be hungry after a long winter and looking for
food in the spring, when offspring are typically born.

3. What specific evidence does the rancher give to support his argument that the ranch's 500 head of cattle are in danger?

Wolves are excellent hunters that prey on weak and young cattle. They hunt in
packs, which makes them efficient hunters.

4. In his arguments, the rancher focuses only on his family. In what way is this technique effective? Could his arguments benefit from additional information? If so, what kinds of information?

SAMPLE ANSWER: *The rancher's arguments personalize the issue and make the rancher's*
situation seem real to the reader. The rancher's arguments would be stronger if they
included specific data about cattle losses and economic hardships to ranches where
wolves are present.

5. What did you learn from the chapter in the textbook that would support the opinion that the reintroduction of wolves in 1995 was a good idea?

SAMPLE ANSWER: *Prior to the late 1920s, the Yellowstone ecosystem had a wolf popula-*
tion. Biologists were trying to restore the ecosystem and the biodiversity of animals
and plants within the park to how it once was.

6. Do you agree with the rancher's opinion in this editorial? Why or why not?

SAMPLE ANSWER: *I don't agree because I think that a national park should have as natural*
an ecosystem as possible. SAMPLE ANSWER: *I agree with his opinion because I think the gov-*
ernment should help protect people's property.

Arguments Pro and Con 21st Century Skills

The skills used in this activity include **information and media literacy, communication skills,** and **creativity and intellectual curiosity.**

Conduct independent research to find facts that support the reintroduction of the gray wolf in Yellowstone National Park. You might begin your search by visiting the Web sites of the National Park Service, the Fish and Wildlife Service, and private conservation groups. Then search for and read editorials that both support and oppose wolf reintroduction. Write an editorial from the perspective of someone in favor of the reintroduction of gray wolves to the park. As an alternative to writing an editorial, conduct a debate with your classmates on whether or not wolves should have been reintroduced to Yellowstone.

Evaluate students' editorials or debates based on the number and quality of facts or
data they use to support their argument, the logic and organization of the argument,
and the clarity with which they present their point of view.

5 Populations

 Interdependence in Nature

Q: What factors contribute to changes in populations?

WHAT I KNOW	WHAT I LEARNED
5.1 How do populations grow?	SAMPLE ANSWER: **Populations can increase or decrease in size.**	SAMPLE ANSWER: **Populations vary in their geographic range, density, distribution, growth rate, and age structure. Exponential or logistic growth patterns result from births, deaths, immigration, and emigration.**
5.2 What factors limit a population's growth?	SAMPLE ANSWER: **Predation, disease, and other factors slow or stop population growth.**	SAMPLE ANSWER: **Density-dependent factors that limit population growth include competition, predation, herbivory, parasitism, disease, and overcrowding. Density-independent factors include unusual weather and introduced species.**
5.3 How is the human population growing?	SAMPLE ANSWER: **The human population has been growing for thousands of years.**	SAMPLE ANSWER: **Some countries have higher growth rates than others because of differences in birthrates, death rates, and the age structure of their populations.**

5.1 How Populations Grow

Lesson Objectives

- List the characteristics used to describe a population.
- Identify factors that affect population growth.
- Describe exponential growth.
- Describe logistic growth.

Lesson Summary

Describing Populations Researchers study five important characteristics of a population:

▶ Geographic range is the area in which a population lives.

▶ **Population density** is the number of individuals per unit area.

▶ Population distribution is how individuals are spaced out in their range.

▶ Growth rate determines whether a population grows, shrinks, or stays the same size.

▶ **Age structure** is the number of males and females of each age in a population.

Population Growth Populations can grow, shrink, or stay the same size.

▶ Factors that increase population size include births and **immigration**, which is the movement of individuals into an area.

▶ Factors that decrease population size include deaths and **emigration**, which is the movement of individuals out of an area.

Exponential Growth When conditions are ideal, the larger a population gets, the faster it grows. When a population's numbers grow larger with each generation, **exponential growth** is occurring. Ideal conditions include unlimited resources and absence of predation and disease.

Logistic Growth Resources become less available as a population grows.

▶ **Logistic growth** occurs when population growth slows and then stops after a period of exponential growth has occurred.

▶ Population size stabilizes at the **carrying capacity**, the maximum number of individuals of a given species that an environment can support.

Describing Populations

For Questions 1–5, complete each statement by writing the correct word or words.

1. The __*geographic range*__ is the area in which a population lives.

2. Population density is the __*number*__ of individuals per unit area.

3. How the individuals are spaced in their range is a population's __*distribution*__.

4. Growth rate is how quickly a population __*increases or decreases*__ in size.

5. To find the __*age structure*__ of a population, count the number of males and females of each age.

Population Growth

For Questions 6–10, write True if the statement is true. If the statement is false, change the underlined word or words to make the statement true.

greater **6.** If the death rate is <u>less</u> than the birthrate, the population is likely to shrink.

True **7.** <u>Immigration</u> increases population size.

emigrate **8.** Young animals may <u>immigrate</u> from the place where they were born to establish new territories.

increase **9.** A high birthrate and immigration <u>decrease</u> population size.

True **10.** Populations grow if <u>more</u> individuals are born than die in a period of time.

11. **THINK VISUALLY** The dots in the box represent individuals in a population with a random pattern of distribution. Use arrows and dots to show what will happen to this population if emigration is greater than immigration. (Assume birthrate and death rate are equal.) On the lines below, explain your drawing.

Students should show more dots leaving (with arrows out) the square than dots (with arrows in) entering it.

SAMPLE ANSWER: **When emigration is greater than immigration, there are more dots leaving the population (arrows out) than entering it (arrows in). The result will be a decrease in population size.**

Exponential Growth

12. Describe the conditions in which exponential growth occurs.

Exponential growth occurs under ideal conditions with no limits on food, water, or space and no predation or disease.

13. Can exponential growth occur in a population of organisms that take a long time to reproduce? Why or why not?

Yes, it can. If population size grows larger and the growth rate increases with each generation, exponential growth occurs.

14. Complete the graph by drawing the characteristic shape of exponential population growth.

Exponential Growth of Bacterial Population

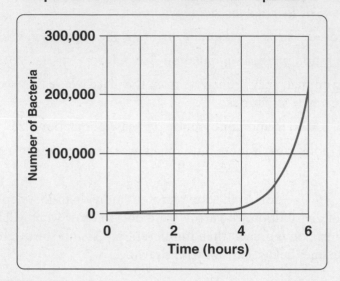

15. What letter is used to refer to the characteristic shape of an exponential growth curve?
    An exponential growth curve is shaped like the letter J.

Logistic Growth

16. Complete the graph by drawing the characteristic shape of logistic population growth.

Logistic Growth of a Population

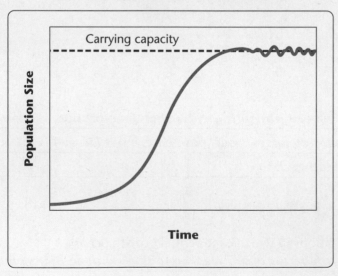

17. What letter is used to refer to the characteristic shape of the logistic growth curve?
    The logistic growth curve is shaped like an S.

18. When real-world populations of plants and animals are analyzed, why do they most often have the logistic growth curve?

Exponential growth cannot continue indefinitely. Resources become limited, which

slows birthrate and may increase death rate. Eventually, a population's growth slows

or stops and the population size becomes more or less stable.

19. What does the term carrying capacity refer to?

It refers to the largest number of individuals of a species (population) that can be sup-

ported by a particular environment.

20. Complete the table to name and explain three phases of logistic growth. Use the terms *growth rate, population size,* and *carrying capacity* in your explanations.

Phases of Logistic Growth		
Phase	**Phase name**	**Explanation**
1	**Exponential growth**	**Individuals reproduce rapidly and few die. Both the population size and the growth rate increase rapidly.**
2	**Growth slows down.**	**Population size increases slowly. The growth rate slows.**
3	**Growth stops.**	**The growth rate drops to zero, and the population size stabilizes at the carrying capacity.**

Apply the Big idea

21. What is an example of a limiting factor that humans use to control the carrying capacity of an environment for a particular type of organism? Explain your answer.

SAMPLE ANSWER: *Agriculture and gardening are ways humans control the carrying capac-*

ity of an area that includes farms or gardens. Adding fertilizer, for example, promotes

plant growth and increases the environment's carrying capacity for plants. Growing

only one kind of crop can leave some animal populations without a food source, and

the carrying capacity for those animals would decrease.

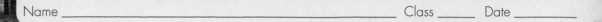

5.2 Limits to Growth

Lesson Objectives

🔑 Identify factors that determine carrying capacity.

🔑 Identify the limiting factors that depend on population density.

🔑 Identify the limiting factors that do not depend on population density.

Lesson Summary

Limiting Factors A **limiting factor** is a factor that controls the growth of a population.

▶ Some factors depend on the density of the population. Others do not.

▶ Acting separately or together, limiting factors determine an environment's carrying capacity.

▶ Limiting factors produce the pressures of natural selection.

Density-Dependent Limiting Factors

▶ **Density-dependent limiting factors** operate strongly when the number of individuals per unit area reaches a certain point.

▶ Examples include:
  • competition
  • predation and herbivory
  • parasitism and disease
  • stress from overcrowding

Density-Independent Limiting Factors Some limiting factors do not necessarily depend on population size.

▶ **Density-independent limiting factors** depend on population density, or the number of organisms per unit area.

▶ Examples include severe weather, natural disasters, and human activities.

▶ Some of these factors may have more severe effects when population density is high.

Limiting Factors

For Questions 1–6, write True if the statement is true. If the statement is false, change the underlined word to make the statement true.

carrying **1.** Limiting factors determine the <u>immigration</u> capacity of a population.

True **2.** A limiting factor controls the growth of a <u>population</u>.

logistic **3.** Limiting factors operate when growth is <u>exponential</u>.

True **4.** Populations grow too large in the <u>absence</u> of limiting factors.

True **5.** <u>Competition</u> is an example of a limiting factor.

True **6.** Population <u>size</u> can be limited by factors such as predation.

Density-Dependent Limiting Factors

7. What is a density-dependent limiting factor?

It is a limiting factor that depends on the number of organisms per unit area.

8. When do density-dependent factors operate most strongly?

They operate most strongly when a population is large and dense.

9. What are four density-dependent limiting factors?

Possible answers include: competition, predation, herbivory, parasitism, disease, and

stress from overcrowding

Use the graph to answer Questions 10–13.

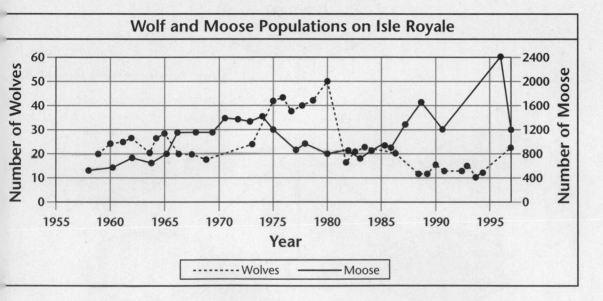

10. What happened to the number of wolves on Isle Royale between 1975 and 1985?

It dropped by about half, from about 40 to about 20.

11. What happened to the moose population when the number of wolves was low?

It grew large rapidly.

12. What is the relationship between the moose and the wolves on Isle Royale?

The wolf is the predator. The moose is the prey.

13. Is the number of moose on the island a density-dependent or density-independent limiting factor for the wolf? Explain your answer.

It is density-dependent because when the wolf population is small, there may be

enough moose for food; when the wolf population is large, food may be scarce for the

wolf if the moose population is small.

Density-Independent Limiting Factors

14. What term describes a limiting factor that affects all populations in similar ways, regardless of population size?

It is a density-independent limiting factor.

15. What is the usual response in the population size of many species to a density-independent limiting factor?

The population size decreases.

16. Complete the graphic organizer with examples of density-independent limiting factors.

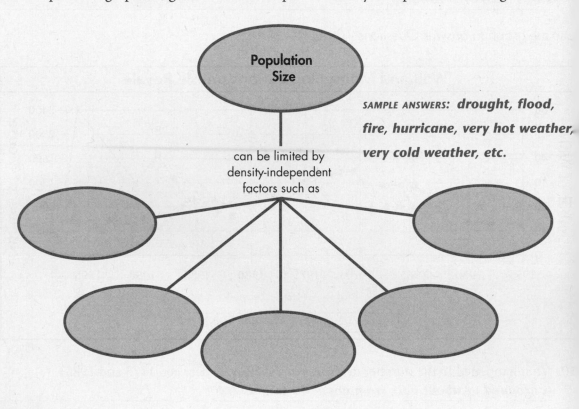

Population Size

can be limited by density-independent factors such as

SAMPLE ANSWERS: *drought, flood, fire, hurricane, very hot weather, very cold weather, etc.*

Apply the Big idea

17. A population continues at a stable size for many years. Suddenly, in a single season, the population size drops by half. Is the cause more likely to be density-dependent, density-independent, or both? Explain your answer.

It could be either or both. A density-independent factor such as extreme weather or a natural disaster could reduce numbers quickly. A density-dependent factor such as disease, parasitism, human activities, or a newly introduced predator or herbivore could also reduce numbers quickly.

5.3 Human Population Growth

Lesson Objectives

▭ Discuss the trend of human population growth.

▭ Explain why population growth rates differ in countries throughout the world.

Lesson Summary

Historical Overview The size of the human population has increased over time.

▶ For most of human existence, limiting factors such as the scarcity of food kept death rates high.

▶ As civilization advanced, agriculture, industry, improved nutrition, sanitation, and medicine reduced death rates. Birthrates stayed high in most places. This led to exponential growth.

▶ Today, the human population continues to grow exponentially, although the doubling time has slowed.

Patterns of Human Population Growth **Demography** is the scientific study of human populations. Demographers try to predict how human populations will change over time.

▶ Over the past century, population growth in developed countries slowed. As death rates dropped, birthrates dropped also. Demographers call this shift the **demographic transition**. Most people live in countries that have not undergone the demographic transition.

▶ An age-structure graph shows how many people of each gender are in each age group in a population. Demographers use such graphs to predict how a population will change. More people of reproductive age usually means faster growth.

▶ Many factors, including disease, will affect human population growth in the twenty-first century. Current data suggest the human population will grow more slowly over the next 50 years than it did for the last 50 years.

Historical Overview

For Questions 1–5, write True if the statement is true. If the statement is false, change the underlined word or words to make the statement true.

___*increased*___ 1. Over the last 1000 years, the size of the human population has <u>decreased</u>.

___*exponential*___ 2. Since the 1800s, human population growth has been <u>logistic</u>.

___*death rates*___ 3. The human population has increased because <u>birthrates</u> have dropped.

___*True*___ 4. The combination of low death rates and high <u>birthrates</u> led to exponential growth.

___*Thomas Malthus*___ 5. <u>Charles Darwin</u> suggested that human populations are regulated by war, famine, and disease.

6. Complete the table below to explain how each factor affected the size and growth rate of the human population over the last 10,000 years.

Factors That Affected Human Population Growth	
Cause	**Effect**
Agriculture	*Increased population size and growth rate*
Improved health care and medicine	*Increased population size and growth rate*
Improved sanitation	*Increased population size and growth rate*
Bubonic plague	*Decreased population size, but growth rate rose again soon after*
Industrial Revolution	*Increased population size and growth rate*

Patterns of Human Population Growth

7. **THINK VISUALLY** Complete the diagram below by adding the information for stages II and III of the demographic transition. Draw bars to represent the birthrate and the death rate and describe the stages on the lines provided. Stage I is done for you.

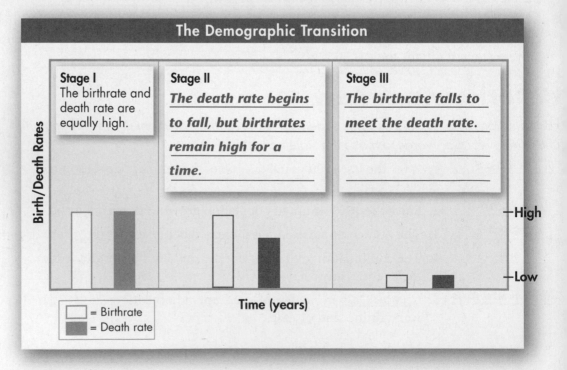

The Demographic Transition

Stage I The birthrate and death rate are equally high.

Stage II *The death rate begins to fall, but birthrates remain high for a time.*

Stage III *The birthrate falls to meet the death rate.*

Birth/Death Rates

—High

—Low

Time (years)

☐ = Birthrate
■ = Death rate

Use these age structure diagrams to answer Questions 8–11.

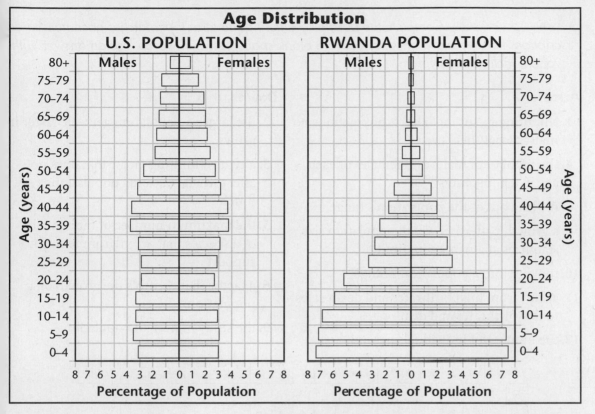

Age Distribution

U.S. POPULATION   RWANDA POPULATION

8. Which country has gone through the demographic transition? How do you know?
   The United States appears to have undergone the demographic transition because it has larger numbers of older people. The birthrate and death rate are both low.

9. Which country do you predict will experience a slow and steady growth rate in the near future? Why? *The United States will grow slowly because it has smaller numbers of young people of reproductive age.*

10. Which country is most likely to grow exponentially in the near future? Why?
    Rwanda will because it has large numbers of young people of reproductive age.

11. Suggest three factors that might slow population growth in Rwanda.
    SAMPLE ANSWER: *Three factors that might slow population growth in Rwanda are war, food shortages, and disease.*

Apply the Big idea

12. Explain why human population size is likely to increase in the twenty-first century, but not as rapidly as it did in the twentieth century.
    Some countries are still experiencing exponential growth, but the growth rate has slowed in a number of countries. All countries, however—even those undergoing the demographic transition—still have a higher birthrate than death rate.

Chapter Vocabulary Review

Crossword Puzzle *Complete the puzzle by entering the term that matches each numbered description. For two-word answers, leave a blank space between words. For an answer with a hyphen, include the hyphen.*

Across

1. a limiting factor that affects populations no matter what their size
4. the number of males and females of each age in a population
7. moving out of the population's range
8. a growth pattern in which population size stabilizes at a maximum limit
10. moving into a population's range
11. a shift from high birthrates and death rates to low birthrates and death rates
12. the number of individuals per unit area

Down

2. the larger a population gets, the faster it grows
3. a type of limiting factor that does not affect small, scattered populations very much
5. the maximum number of individuals of a species that an environment can support
6. a factor that controls the growth of a population
9. the study of human populations

1. DENSITY-INDEPENDENT
2. EXPONENTIAL
3. DENSITY DEPENDENT
4. AGE STRUCTURE
5. CARRYING CAPACITY
6. LIMITING FACTOR
7. EMIGRATION
8. LOGISTIC
9. DEMOGRAPH
10. IMMIGRATION
11. DEMOGRAPHIC TRANSITION
12. POPULATION DENSITY

CHAPTER MYSTERY

PLAGUE OF RABBITS

In the Chapter Mystery, you learned about the effects of the deliberate release of the European rabbit by an Australian farmer. With few predators and plentiful food, the rabbit population exploded. Animal populations rise and fall even in the healthiest ecosystems.

21st Century Learning

Deer, Deer, Everywhere

White-tailed deer were hunted almost to extinction a little over 100 years ago. Today, many regions of the United States are home to large populations of this species. This increase is the result of the disappearance of predators, the use of conservation practices, and the deer's ability to thrive in a variety of habitats.

Like all species, white-tailed deer have characteristics that set them apart from other species. Field guides describe the characteristics of organisms, enabling people to identify them. The following is a description that might appear in a field guide.

White-tailed deer, *Odocoileus virginianus*

SIZE: Size can vary. Weight varies from 50–300 lbs.

IDENTIFICATION: Color changes with the seasons. The upper body is reddish or yellowish in warmer months and gray in the winter. The underside and inside of the legs are white. The tail is long and bushy. It is brown with white along the edges of the tail. Male white-tail deer grow antlers, which are shed after the mating season.

HABITAT: Habitat will vary. It includes woodland areas, farmland, gardens, and pastures.

FOOD: Grasses, shrubs, tree leaves and buds, and other plants provide food.

PREDATORS: Primary predators are wolves and mountain lions, but the populations of these species have been eradicated in many areas of the United States.

BREEDING: Offspring are born in litters of 1 to 3 in the early spring. Fawns have white spots and are active within a few days of birth. Where resources are plentiful, populations may double every few years.

RANGE: Most of North America

Continued on next page ▶

21st Century Themes — Science and Health Literacy

Answer the following questions.

1. Based on the field guide excerpt, what animals prey on deer?

SAMPLE ANSWER: **Wolves and mountain lions are the deer's primary predators. According to the field guide, they no longer live in many areas where deer live.**

2. How might the habitat conditions in which deer thrive play a role in increasing their numbers?

SAMPLE ANSWER: **Deer can thrive in a variety of habitats, and this adaptability probably plays a role in increasing their numbers.**

3. How many offspring do white-tailed deer have each year? How might these numbers influence their population?

White-tailed deer have one to three fawns each year. In the absence of predators and the presence of plentiful food, deer populations can increase rapidly.

4. What do you think might happen if expanding human development led to a serious decrease in the amount of food available to white-tailed deer?

SAMPLE ANSWER: **I think there would be competition for the reduced amount of vegetation, and eventually the population would decrease.**

Controlling Deer Populations — 21st Century Learning

The skills used in this activity include **information and media literacy; critical thinking and systems thinking; problem identification, formulation, and solution;** and **self-direction.**

Work in a group to determine why white-tailed deer populations are increasing and to find out about the different techniques to manage these populations. Consult state and government Web sites, science articles, and newspaper articles. Present your findings in a report that describes the advantages and disadvantages of different methods of control. You might also want to present opposing viewpoints on the approach. Use maps, charts, and diagrams in your presentation.

Evaluate students' presentation based on the data and facts and their sources.

The maps, charts, and diagrams should support and extend the information in the oral report.

6 Humans in the Biosphere

Big idea **Interdependence in Nature**

Q: How have human activities shaped local and global ecology?

WHAT I KNOW	WHAT I LEARNED
6.1 How does human activity affect the environment?	*SAMPLE ANSWER:* **Humans do many things that change the environment.**	*SAMPLE ANSWER:* **Agriculture, development, and industry affect soil, water, and the atmosphere. Sustainable development provides for human needs while preserving resources.**
6.2 How can we use our natural resources wisely?	*SAMPLE ANSWER:* **Essential natural resources such as soil, fresh water, and clean air must be preserved and used wisely.**	*SAMPLE ANSWER:* **Soil erosion can be minimized through management of agriculture and forestry. Water should be conserved and protected from pollutants.**
6.3 Why is it important to protect and conserve biodiversity?	*SAMPLE ANSWER:* **Diverse forms of life inhabit planet Earth.**	*SAMPLE ANSWER:* **Biodiversity contributes to medicine, agriculture, and the provision of natural resources.**
6.4 How can we change our behaviors to help protect our planet?	*SAMPLE ANSWER:* **Humans should try to reduce their negative impacts on the environment.**	*SAMPLE ANSWER:* **We can recognize problems, research problems, and then use scientific understanding to change behavior.**

6.1 A Changing Landscape

Lesson Objectives

🔑 Describe human activities that can affect the biosphere.

🔑 Describe the relationship between resource use and sustainable development.

Lesson Summary

The Effect of Human Activity Humans and other organisms change the environment when they obtain food, eliminate wastes, and prepare places to live.

▶ Because Earth is like an island, life is limited to the resources that are here.

▶ Humans affect regional and global environments through three major activities:

• agriculture, particularly **monoculture**, which is the cultivation of a single crop

• development of cities and suburbs, including conversion of farmland and destruction of habitats for other organisms

• industrial growth, which consumes energy and emits pollutants

Sustainable Development In economic terms, ecosystems are providers of goods and services (natural resources).

▶ Healthy ecosystems produce or replace **renewable resources**.

▶ Humans must be careful about the use of **nonrenewable resources**, such as fossil fuels, which cannot be replaced.

▶ **Sustainable development** provides for human needs while preserving the ecosystems that provide renewable resources.

The Effect of Human Activity

1. What three human activities have transformed the biosphere?
agriculture, development, and industrial growth

2. What is monoculture?
Monoculture is the practice of clearing large areas of land to plant a single, highly productive crop, year after year.

3. List three resources used in agriculture.
soil, water, fossil fuels

4. How does urban and suburban development affect the environment and habitats?
Wastes need to be disposed of which can affect air, water, and soil. Development destroys or divides them into smaller fragments.

5. What source provides most of the energy for industrial production?
Most of the energy comes from fossil fuels.

6. Complete the table to show some consequences of human activities on global ecology.

Consequences of Some Human Activities		
Activity	**Positive Consequences**	**Negative Consequences**
Agriculture	*Efficient, high-yield food production*	*Consumption of fossil fuels and fertile soil; pollution of air and water*
Development	*Facilities for homes and businesses*	*Pollution from waste production; burning fossil fuels*
Industrial Growth	*Conveniences and luxuries of modern life*	*Waste production; burning fossil fuels; pollution of air, water, and soil*

Sustainable Development

7. Complete the Venn diagram to compare renewable and nonrenewable resources.

Renewable Resources

replaceable; Ex. fresh water, clean air, wood, etc.

Raw materials for building, manufacturing, fuels, and food

will be used up; Ex. fossil fuels, minerals, etc.

Nonrenewable Resources

8. How can development be sustainable?

Development that is sustainable preserves ecosystems that provide renewable resources, while it also provides for human needs.

Apply the Big idea

9. The human population (currently around 7 billion) may reach 9 billion by 2100. Most of those people will live in cities. Predict the impact of city growth on natural ecosystems and farmland. What will happen if sustainable development is not achieved?

SAMPLE ANSWER: *Increasing amounts of land will be needed to produce enough food. And increasing amounts of resources will be needed to transport goods to cities. Without sustainable development, air and water pollution will increase.*

6.2 Using Resources Wisely

Lesson Objectives

▱ Describe how human activities affect soil and land.

▱ Describe how human activities affect water resources.

▱ Describe how human activities affect air resources.

Lesson Summary

Soil Resources Soil is a renewable resource, but it must be managed properly.

▶ **Soil erosion** is the wearing away of surface soil by water and wind.

▶ In dry climates, farming and overgrazing change farmland into deserts, a process called **desertification**.

▶ **Deforestation** is loss of forests. Because healthy forests hold soil in place, deforestation increases erosion.

▶ Sustainable uses include leaving stems and roots of previous crops in place, crop rotation, contour plowing, terracing, selectively harvesting mature trees, and tree farms.

Freshwater Resources The amount of fresh water is limited, and some sources cannot be replaced.

▶ A **pollutant** is a harmful material that can enter the biosphere. Water pollutants come from industrial chemicals, residential sewage, and other sources.

▶ Many chemical pollutants become concentrated in organisms at higher trophic levels of the food chain through **biological magnification**.

▶ Sustainable uses include conservation, pollution control, and watershed protection.

Atmospheric Resources Clean air is important to human health and Earth's climate. Pollution reduces air quality.

▶ **Smog** is a mixture of chemicals formed from emissions from cars and industry.

▶ Burning fossil fuels releases compounds that join with water in air, forming **acid rain**.

▶ Greenhouse gases, such as carbon dioxide and methane, can cause global warming.

▶ Particulates are microscopic particles that cause health problems.

▶ One way of sustaining air quality is controlling automobile emissions.

Soil Resources

1. What is topsoil?
   Topsoil is the mineral- and nutrient-rich portion of soil.

2. How does topsoil form?
   Topsoil forms through the long-term interaction of the soil and the plants that grow

   in it.

3. What is soil erosion?

It is removal of soil by wind and water.

4. How does plowing land increase the rate of soil erosion?

It removes the roots of plants that hold soil in place.

5. What happens to farmland during desertification?

A combination of farming, overgrazing, drought, and climate change can turn farm-

land into a desert.

6. Are mature forests a renewable resource? Why or why not?

No. They will not grow back in a reasonable amount of time.

7. What happens to soil when rain forest is cut down?

It loses organic matter rapidly and becomes wasteland.

8. Complete the graphic organizer to give examples of sustainable uses of soil.

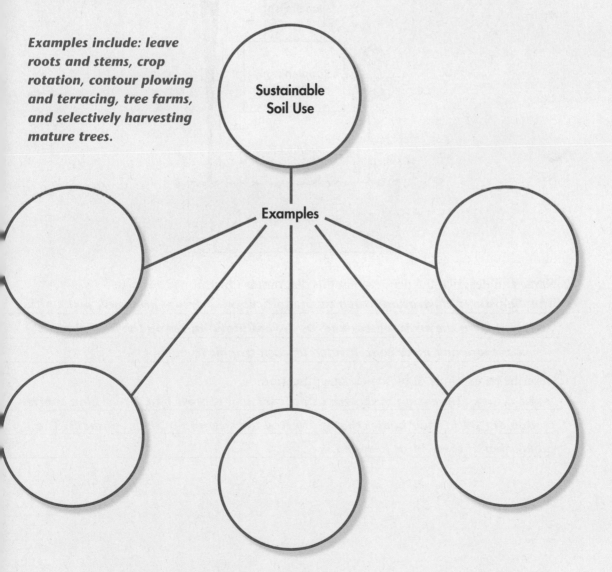

Examples include: leave roots and stems, crop rotation, contour plowing and terracing, tree farms, and selectively harvesting mature trees.

Sustainable Soil Use

Examples

Freshwater Resources

Use this diagram to answer Questions 9–11.

9. **THINK VISUALLY** The diagram shows the typical impact of a chemical pollutant in an aquatic ecosystem.

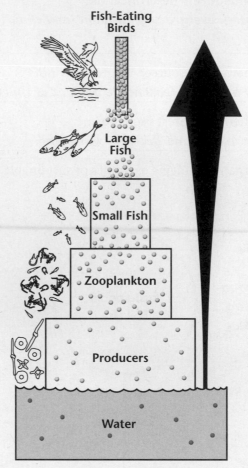

10. Name and describe the process that this diagram is illustrating.

    The diagram is illustrating biological magnification. Primary producers pick up the pollutant from the environment and, as the pollutant moves up the food chain, it becomes more and more concentrated at each trophic level.

11. Describe an example of biological magnification.

    SAMPLE ANSWER: *Fish-eating birds such as pelicans and ospreys had such a high concentration of DDT in their bodies that it affected the strength of their eggshells. The population of these birds dropped.*

12. What is a "dead zone," and what is its cause?

A dead zone is an area of freshwater or seawater that is oxygen-poor. Dead zones are

caused by excess amounts of nitrogen and phosphorus that is found in raw sewage.

These nutrients cause blooms of algae and bacteria that use up the oxygen.

13. Why is watershed management important to maintaining good water quality in a large river or lake?

A watershed is all the land whose groundwater and streams drain into a larger body

of water. Reducing pollutants in the watershed will help reduce pollution in the large

body of water.

Atmospheric Resources

For Questions 14–17, write the letter of the correct answer on the line at the left.

___B___ **14.** Which is the name for the mixture of chemicals that forms as a gray-brown haze in the atmosphere?

    A. dust   **C.** ozone

    B. smog   **D.** radiation

___C___ **15.** Which component of acid rain kills plants and harms soil?

    A. carbon dioxide and water   **C.** nitric and sulfuric acids

    B. CFCs and fossil fuels   **D.** ozone and particulates

___A___ **16.** Which is the name for the bits of ash and dust put into the air by certain kinds of diesel engines?

    A. particulates   **C.** ozone layer

    B. precipitation   **D.** greenhouse gases

___B___ **17.** Which is a pollutant of soil and water that is now dropping steadily due to laws that affected the automobile industry?

    A. carbon   **C.** nitrogen

    B. lead   **D.** ozone

Apply the Big idea

18. The citizens of Ecotown want to protect the quality of their soil, fresh water, and air. Suggest a plan for Ecotown that includes steps for achieving sustainable use of each of those three categories of resources.

Possible answers: Steps for soil include leaving stems and roots of crops in place, crop

rotation, contour plowing, terracing, selective harvesting of mature trees, and tree

farms. Steps for fresh water include conservation, pollution control, and watershed

protection. One step for air is controlling emissions from automobiles.

Name _____ Class _____ Date _____

6.3 Biodiversity

Lesson Objectives

- Define biodiversity and explain its value.
- Identify current threats to biodiversity.
- Describe how biodiversity can be preserved.

Lesson Summary

The Value of Biodiversity The sum of all the genetic diversity among all the organisms in the biosphere is called **biodiversity**. There are three general types of biodiversity:

- ▶ **Ecosystem diversity** is the variety of habitats, communities, and ecological processes in the biosphere.
- ▶ **Species diversity** is the number of different species in an area or in the biosphere.
- ▶ **Genetic diversity** is the total of all genetic information carried in living things.

Biodiversity benefits humans through its contributions to medicine and agriculture and through the provision of ecological goods and services.

Threats to Biodiversity Human activities threaten biodiversity.

- ▶ Development splits ecosystems into pieces, resulting in **habitat fragmentation**. The smaller the pieces of a habitat, the less likely that species in the habitat can survive.
- ▶ Other threats to biodiversity include hunting, introduced species, pollution, and climate change.

Conserving Biodiversity Conservation efforts are focused on three things:

- ▶ Protecting single species is the focus of groups such as the Association of Zoos and Aquariums (AZA), which oversees species survival plans (SSPs).
- ▶ Protecting habitats and ecosystems is the main thrust of global efforts. Biologists are particularly concerned about **ecological hot spots**, which are places where significant numbers of habitats and species are in immediate danger of extinction.
- ▶ Considering local interests is part of developing plans to replace harmful activities with ones that conserve environments and biodiversity.

The Value of Biodiversity

1. What is biodiversity?
   It is the total of all the genetically based variation in all organisms in the biosphere.

2. Why is biodiversity one of Earth's greatest natural resources?
   Species of many kinds provide us with foods, industrial products, and medicines.

   Diverse species play vital roles in the delivery of ecological goods and services.

3. Complete the table to define the types of biodiversity.

Diversity in the Biosphere	
Type of Diversity	**Definition**
Ecosystem diversity	*the variety of habitats, communities, and ecological processes in the biosphere*
Species diversity	*the number of different species in an area or in the biosphere*
Genetic diversity	*the total of all the genetic information carried in living things*

Threats to Biodiversity

For Questions 4–8, write True if the statement is true. If the statement is false, change the underlined word or words to make the statement true.

1000   4. The current rate of species loss is <u>10</u> times the typical rate of extinction.

smaller   5. The smaller a habitat "island," the <u>larger</u> the number of species that can live there.

True   6. Habitat fragmentation <u>increases</u> the impact of hunting on endangered species.

Introduced   7. <u>Endangered</u> species can become invasive and threaten biodiversity.

True   8. The increased concentration of carbon dioxide in air is making oceans <u>more acidic</u> and putting stress on coral reefs.

9. What are five ways that human activity reduces biodiversity?

Ways include altering habitats, hunting, introducing invasive species, releasing pollution into food webs, and contributing to climate change.

10. Identify three reasons why endangered species are hunted.

Answers may include: endangered species are hunted for food, hides or skins, medicines, or to sell them as pets.

11. How can introduced species lead to economic losses?

Introduced species can cause loss of natural food for range animals and loss of farm

crops, as well as loss of species in natural ecosystems (loss of ecological goods and

services).

12. How does climate change threaten biodiversity?

Many organisms have specific tolerance ranges to temperature. If conditions change

and the organism cannot move to a suitable habitat, it could face extinction.

Conserving Biodiversity

13. What is the main purpose of biodiversity conservation today?

The main purpose is to preserve whole ecosystems, not just individual endangered

species.

14. Why have ecologists identified ecological hot spots?

Ecological hot spots help focus attention and resources on areas where threats to bio-

diversity are the most immediate and the most extreme.

15. What are some of the challenges that conservationists face?

Protecting resources often requires people to change their habits or the way they earn

their living.

16. What are some strategies that encourage conservation? Provide an example of one of thes strategies.

Strategies include tax incentives (items like hybrid cars), ecotourism, and carbon

credits. Students' examples will vary.

> **Apply the Big idea**

17. Why is preserving entire ecosystems a better idea than protecting single species from extinction?

Preserving entire ecosystems maintains the genetic diversity of all the organisms in

that system and ensures that the ecosystem will continue to provide ecological goods

and services. Such benefits cannot be achieved by protecting species one at a time.

6.4 Meeting Ecological Challenges

Lesson Objectives

➥ Explain the concept of ecological footprint.

➥ Identify the role of ecology in a sustainable future.

Lesson Summary

Ecological Footprints The **ecological footprint** of an individual or a population is the amount of land and water needed to provide resources, absorb wastes, and render the wastes harmless.

Ecology in Action Three case studies illustrate the three steps of ecology in action: (1) recognize a change in the environment, (2) determine the cause of that change, and (3) change behavior to have a positive impact.

- **Case Study 1: Atmospheric Ozone** This gas blocks ultraviolet (UV) radiation.
  - Ozone gas blocks ultraviolet (UV) rediation.
  - The ozone layer is an area of relatively high concentration of ozone in the atmosphere, between 20 and 50 kilometers above Earth's surface. In the 1970s, a hole in the layer was observed.
  - Regulations reduced CFC use, and the hole may be slowly disappearing.
- **Case Study 2: North Atlantic Fisheries**
  - Commercial fish catches have declined in recent years.
  - The cause is overfishing.
  - Regulations closed some fishing grounds to allow fish stocks to replenish. In the mean time, **aquaculture**, or fish farming, also can provide food for people.
- **Case Study 3: Climate Change**
  - **Global warming**, the rise in the biosphere's average temperature, and climate change, a shift in Earth's overall weather patterns, has occurred.
  - Physical evidence includes rising sea levels due to melting ice. Biological evidence includes temperature-related behavior changes in organisms.
  - Using less fossil fuel will reduce greenhouse gases in the atmosphere.

Ecological Footprints

For Questions 1–2, refer to the Visual Analogy that shows examples of factors that contribute to a population's ecological footprint.

1. **VISUAL ANALOGY** Why do you think ecologists use the term *footprint* to describe the total resources a population uses and its wastes that must be absorbed?

SAMPLE ANSWER: *A footprint is a mark that an organism leaves behind. As a human population consumes resources and produces wastes, it leaves a mark on ecosystems.*

2. Explain this statement: The average American has an ecological footprint more than four times larger than the global average.

   The average American uses more than four times the amount of resources to live and

   process waste than the average global citizen uses.

Ecology in Action

3. List three factors that will affect the future of the biosphere.

   population growth, ecological footprints, and the development of technology

4. Complete the table to summarize how the basic principles of ecology can lead to positive impacts on the environment.

Examples of Ecology in Action		
Environmental Change	**Cause**	**Behavior Change Needed**
Hole in the ozone layer	*CFCs*	*Regulation of CFCs*
Declining numbers of fish in the oceans	*Overfishing*	*Regulation of fishing industry and aquaculture*
Global warming and climate change	*Increasing amounts of greenhouse gases*	*Reduction of emissions of greenhouse gases*

Case Study 1: Atmospheric Ozone

For Questions 5–7, complete each statement by writing the correct word or words.

5. The ozone layer is a high concentration of ozone at about _20–50 kilometers_ above Earth's surface.

6. The ozone layer is important to humans because it protects against exposure to ___UV radiation___ from the sun.

7. UV radiation causes _____cancer_____, damages eyes, and reduces resistance to disease.

Case Study 2: North Atlantic Fisheries

For Questions 8–10, complete each statement by writing the correct word or words.

8. Technologies that have led to large increases in the mass of ocean fish caught include large boats and high-tech __fish-locating__ equipment.

9. ___Overfishing___ caused the decline in fish catches since 1997.

10. An alternative to commercial fishing is __aquaculture__, which produces large amounts of food with minimal environmental damage if properly managed.

Case Study 3: Climate Change

Use the graph to answer Questions 11–12.

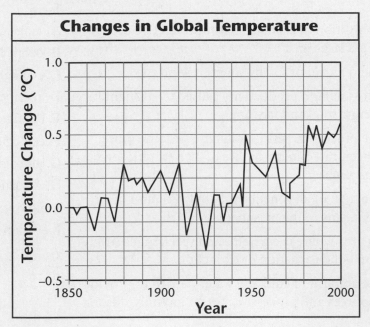

Changes in Global Temperature

Temperature Change (°C)

1.0 — 0.5 — 0.0 — −0.5

1850   1900   1950   2000

Year

1. How does the change in global temperature between 1850 and 2000 compare with the change that occurred between 1850 and 1880?

   The change between 1850 and 1880 was 0.3 degrees. The change between 1850 and

   2000 was close to 0.6 degrees. The change is nearly twice as large.

2. List three factors that may have contributed to the trend shown in the graph.

   SAMPLE ANSWER: *Factors include natural variation, burning fossil fuels, and cutting and*

   burning forests.

3. Suggest three possible effects of global warming on the future of the biosphere.

   Effects may include floods, droughts, and changes in local weather.

Apply the Big idea

14. Explain why populations with the largest ecological footprints change the biosphere the most.

   They use the most resources (land and water) to meet their needs, and more resources

   (land and water) are required to process their wastes. Land and freshwater resources

   are easy to pollute, but difficult to clean up. Other organisms also need these

   resources, which broadens the effect on the biosphere.

Chapter Vocabulary Review

For Questions 1–10, match the term with its definition.

Definition

_____D_____ 1. Cultivation of a single, highly productive crop over a large area

_____J_____ 2. The removal of soil by water or wind

_____H_____ 3. A loss in land productivity caused by drought, overgrazing, and farming

_____E_____ 4. The process in which pollutants become more concentrated in the bodies of high trophic level organisms

_____I_____ 5. The total of all genetically based variation in all organisms in the biosphere

_____F_____ 6. An area where ecosystems and species face severe threat of destruction or extinction

_____C_____ 7. The amount of land and water needed to provide resources and process wastes for an individual or a nation

_____B_____ 8. A part of the atmosphere that blocks UV rays of the sun from reaching Earth's surface

_____A_____ 9. The farming of fish and other aquatic organisms for food

_____G_____ 10. A rise in Earth's average temperature

Term

A. aquaculture

B. ozone layer

C. ecological footprint

D. monoculture

E. biological magnification

F. ecological hot spot

G. global warming

H. desertification

I. biodiversity

J. erosion

For Questions 11–17, complete each statement by writing in the correct word or words.

11. A resource that can be produced or replaced by a healthy ecosystem is a(n) _____renewable_____ resource.

12. Fossil fuels are examples of _____nonrenewable_____ resources.

13. _____Deforestation_____ can lead to severe soil erosion, especially on mountainsides.

14. Any harmful material that enters the biosphere is a(n) _____pollutant_____.

15. The mixture of chemicals that forms a gray-brown haze in the air of cities is _____smog_____.

16. The variety of habitats, communities, and ecological processes in the biosphere is _____ecosystem diversity_____

17. The number of different species in an area is _____species diversity_____.

CHAPTER
MYSTERY

EASTER ISLAND

21st Century Learning

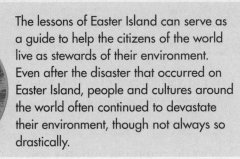

The lessons of Easter Island can serve as a guide to help the citizens of the world live as stewards of their environment. Even after the disaster that occurred on Easter Island, people and cultures around the world often continued to devastate their environment, though not always so drastically.

Creating a Butterfly Haven

Today, some people actively work to improve their environment to help wildlife. For example, butterflies and their larvae depend on vegetation for survival. When this vegetation is destroyed to develop suburban areas, butterflies are threatened. Some citizens have designed and planted gardens to attract butterflies and aid in their survival. Below is a brief guide that explains the steps necessary for creating a successful butterfly garden.

Getting Started on Your Own Community Butterfly Garden

STEP 1: Research the butterfly species that live in your area.

STEP 2: Based on your results from Step 1, research what plants these butterflies and their larvae are attracted to and use for survival. Plant species should vary and choices should be based on color, nectar, and bloom time. Remember that adult butterflies and their larvae may have different plant preferences.

STEP 3: Determine what other attractants would be appropriate for local butterflies.

STEP 4: Choose an ideal location based on your research.

STEP 5: Map out your location with a blueprint. This blueprint should include placement of vegetation and other landscaping projects.

STEP 6: Now build your garden! Plant vegetation for butterflies based on your blueprint.

Continued on next page ▶

21st Century Themes Science and Civic Literacy, Science and Economic Literacy

1. What variables should one study when developing a butterfly garden?

   Specific butterfly and larvae species in one's area, the different plants they depend

   on, and the nectar they prefer are some variables that should be considered.

2. Why do you think butterfly species may vary from one place to another?

   Species variation may depend on different climates, soil type, and other abiotic

   and biotic factors.

3. After choosing vegetation for a butterfly garden, are there other considerations that should be addressed regarding plant or shrub survival? What are they?

   SAMPLE ANSWER: *The care and maintenance of the plants should be considered. For*

   example, which plants need more sun or water than others?

4. Are there any steps that should be added to the list above?

   SAMPLE ANSWER: *One important step to add to the list above is to develop a plan to*

   care for and maintain the garden over time.

5. What might happen if you don't choose the location of the butterfly garden carefully?

   SAMPLE ANSWER: *Plants might not survive, and butterflies may not be attracted to the*

   garden. Instead, other insects or birds might utilize the garden.

21st Century Skills Collaborate on a Garden

The skills used in this activity include **communication skills; critical thinking and systems thinking; problem identification, formulation, and solution; interpersonal and collaborative skills; and accountability** and **adaptability.**

Work as a class to follow the steps above to design, implement, and build a community butterfly garden. Plan your work by assigning specific tasks to individual students or small groups. Start by researching other communities that have successfully accomplished this. Sources of information may include local garden clubs, Audubon societies, and conservation organizations. Make sure you seek permission from your school principal or local government officials. After completing the steps above, compile a list of materials you will need and determine the quantity of these materials you will need for the garden. Then comparison shop for the best prices. Based on your results, develop a budget. Think about how you can raise money to fund the garden. Present your findings to your school board as proposal. Once the proposal is accepted, begin fundraising and building your garden.

Evaluate students' projects based on the accuracy and sources of the information

gathered, the completeness of the plan, and the clarity and persuasiveness of the

written proposal.

7 Cell Structure and Function

Big Idea Cellular Basis of Life, Homeostasis

Q: How are cell structures adapted to their functions?

WHAT I KNOW	WHAT I LEARNED
7.1 Why is it important to study cells?	SAMPLE ANSWER: *Cells make up living things.*	SAMPLE ANSWER: *Cells are the basic units of structure and function in all living things. Cells work to maintain homeostasis. Specialized cells carry out particular functions, such as photosynthesis and energy conversion.*
7.2 How do cell structures enable a cell to carry out basic life processes?	SAMPLE ANSWER: *A cell is made up of cytoplasm that is surrounded by a cell membrane and carries out the basic life processes.*	SAMPLE ANSWER: *Every structure and organelle in a cell carries out certain processes, such as making or storing substances, that help the cell stay alive.*
7.3 How does a cell transport materials across the cell membrane?	SAMPLE ANSWER: *Materials must cross the cell membrane to enter or leave a cell.*	SAMPLE ANSWER: *A cell can transport materials across the membrane through passive transport, which does not require energy. A cell can move materials by active transport, which needs energy.*
7.4 How does a cell maintain homeostasis both within itself and as part of a multicellular organism?	SAMPLE ANSWER: *Cells are able to maintain homeostasis.*	SAMPLE ANSWER: *Cells, both by themselves and in multicellular organisms, maintain homeostasis by growing, responding to the environment, transforming energy, and reproducing.*

7.1 Life Is Cellular

Lesson Objectives

- State the cell theory.
- Describe how the different types of microscopes work.
- Distinguish between prokaryotes and eukaryotes.

Lesson Summary

The Discovery of the Cell The invention of the microscope in the 1600s enabled researchers to see cells for the first time.

▶ Robert Hooke named the empty chambers he observed in cork "cells."

▶ Anton van Leeuwenhoek was the first to observe living microorganisms.

▶ **Cells** are the basic units of life.

▶ Discoveries by German scientists Schleiden, Schwann, and Virchow led to the development of the **cell theory**, which states:

• All living things are made of cells.

• Cells are the basic units of structure and function in living things.

• New cells are produced from existing cells.

Exploring the Cell Scientists use light microscopes and electron microscopes to explore the structure of cells.

▶ Compound light microscopes have lenses that focus light. They magnify objects by up to 1000 times. Chemical stains and fluorescent dyes make cell structures easier to see.

▶ Electron microscopes use beams of electrons focused by magnetic fields. They offer much higher resolution than light microscopes. There are two main types of electron microscopes—transmission and scanning. Scientists use computers to add color to electron micrographs, which are photos of objects seen through a microscope.

Prokaryotes and Eukaryotes Cells come in an amazing variety of shapes and sizes, but all cells contain DNA. Also, all cells are surrounded by a thin flexible barrier called a **cell membrane**. There are two basic categories of cells based on whether they contain a nucleus. The **nucleus** (plural: nuclei) is a large membrane-enclosed structure that contains DNA.

▶ **Eukaryotes** are cells that enclose their DNA in nuclei.

▶ **Prokaryotes** are cells that do not enclose their DNA in nuclei.

The Discovery of the Cell

For Questions 1–6, complete each statement by writing the correct word or words.

1. The invention of the ___*microscope*___ made the discovery of cells possible.

2. Robert Hooke used the name ___*cells*___ to refer to the tiny empty chambers he saw when he observed magnified cork.

3. German botanist Matthias Schleiden concluded that <u>all plants</u> are made of cells.

4. German biologist Theodor Schwann concluded that <u>all animals</u> are made of cells.

5. Rudolph Virchow concluded that new cells are produced from <u>existing cells</u>.

6. The <u>cell theory</u> combines the conclusions made by Schleiden, Schwann, and Virchow.

Exploring the Cell

For Questions 7–9, write True if the statement is true. If the statement is false, change the underlined word or words to make the statement true.

<u>limited</u>   **7.** The size of the image formed by a light microscope is <u>unlimited</u> because light that passes through matter is diffracted.

__True__   **8.** Fluorescent dyes help scientists see the movement of <u>compounds and structures</u> in living cells.

<u>scanning</u>   **9.** <u>Transmission</u> electron microscopes form a 3-D image of the surface of a specimen.

10. **THINK VISUALLY** In the second row of the table, draw diagrams to show how a sample of three yeast cells would look in the types of micrographs indicated in the top row of the table. Then, in the third row, describe how each image would be formed.

A Comparison of Detail in Basic Types of Micrographs		
Light Micrograph (LM 500×)	**Transmission Electron Micrograph** (TEM 4375×)	**Scanning Electron Micrograph** (SEM 3750×)
See the textbook for what this drawing should look like.	*See the textbook for what this drawing should look like.*	*See the textbook for what this drawing should look like.*
A light microscope image is formed by *two lenses focusing light* _____ _____.	A transmission electron microscope image is formed by *beams of electrons* *passing through a thin* *sample* _____.	A scanning electron microscope image is formed by a *beam of electrons scanned* *over a specimen's surface* _____.

11. To study cells with a light microscope, different types of stains are usually available. Why is it generally more useful to stain eukaryotic cells than prokaryotic cells?

Specific stains can reveal certain compounds or structures within a cell. Eukaryotic

cells are more complex than prokaryotic cells and have more structures that can take

in the stains.

Prokaryotes and Eukaryotes

12. Complete the table about the two categories of cells.

Two Categories of Cells			
Category	**Definition**	**Size range**	**Examples**
Prokaryotic cells	*Cells that lack nuclei.*	*1–5 µm*	*bacteria*
Eukaryotic cells	*Cells that contain nuclei.*	*10–100 µm*	*cells of protists, fungi, plants, animals*

13. Which category of cells—prokaryotic or eukaryotic—is your body composed of?

eukaryotic cells

Apply the Big idea

14. Recall that in science, a theory is a well-tested explanation that unifies a broad range of observations and hypotheses and enables scientists to make accurate predictions about new situations. How does the cell theory demonstrate this definition of theory?

SAMPLE ANSWER: *The cell theory demonstrates the scientific definition of a theory in*

three ways. First, it has been tested extensively. Second, it summarizes the research

and observations of many different scientists who worked at different times. Third, it

allows researchers who observe evidence of cellular structure in unknown objects to

make predictions about the object, such as "it is a living thing" and "it can reproduce

itself."

7.2 Cell Structure

Lesson Objectives

⇒ Describe the structure and function of the cell nucleus.

⇒ Describe the role of vacuoles, lysosomes, and the cytoskeleton.

⇒ Identify the role of ribosomes, endoplasmic reticulum, and Golgi apparatus in making proteins.

⇒ Describe the function of the chloroplasts and mitochondria in the cell.

⇒ Describe the function of the cell membrane.

Lesson Summary

Cell Organization Eukaryotic cells contain a nucleus and many specialized structures.

▶ **Cytoplasm** is the portion of a cell outside the nucleus.

▶ **Organelles** are structures that have specialized functions in eukaryotic cells.

▶ The nucleus contains DNA and controls the activity of a cell.

Organelles That Store, Clean Up, and Support These structures include:

▶ **vacuoles:** membrane-enclosed saclike structures that store water, salts, and organic molecules

▶ **lysosomes:** small organelles filled with enzymes that break down large molecules and organelles that are no longer useful

▶ the **cytoskeleton:** a network of protein filaments; it helps the cell maintain its shape and is involved in movement

▶ **centrioles:** organelles made from tubulins; they help organize cell division in animal cells

Organelles That Build Proteins Three kinds of organelles work with the nucleus to make and distribute proteins:

▶ **ribosomes:** small particles of RNA and protein found throughout the cytoplasm in all cells; they produce proteins by following coded instructions from DNA

▶ the **endoplasmic reticulum (ER):** an internal membrane system where lipid components of the cell membrane are assembled, along with proteins and other materials

▶ the **Golgi apparatus:** an organelle that appears as a stack of flattened membranes; it modifies, sorts, and packages proteins and other materials from the ER for storage in the cell or release outside the cell

Organelles That Capture and Release Energy Two types of organelles act as power plants of the cells. Both types are surrounded by two membranes.

▶ **Chloroplasts** capture the energy from sunlight and convert it into food that contains chemical energy in a process called photosynthesis. Cells of plants and some other organisms contain chloroplasts, which contain chlorophyll.

▶ **Mitochondria** are found in nearly all eukaryotic cells; they convert the chemical energy stored in food to a usable form.

Cellular Boundaries All cells are surrounded by a cell membrane. Many cells also have a cell wall. Both cell membranes and cell walls separate cells from the environment and provide support.

▶ **Cell walls** support, shape, and protect the cell. Most prokaryotes and many eukaryotes have them. Animals do not have cell walls. Cell walls lie outside the cell membrane. Most cell walls allow materials to pass through them.

▶ A cell membrane consists of a **lipid bilayer**, a strong but flexible barrier between the cell and its surroundings. The cell membrane regulates what enters and leaves the cell and also protects and supports the cell. Most biological membranes are **selectively permeable**, allowing some substances, but not others, to pass across them.

Cell Organization

1. Describe the relationship between the cytoplasm and the nucleus of a cell.

   The nucleus of a cell is found in the cytoplasm, but is not part of the cytoplasm. The

   nucleus and cytoplasm work together to keep a cell alive.

   _____

2. What does the term *organelle* mean literally?

   little organ

For Questions 3–5, refer to the Visual Analogy comparing the cell with a factory.

3. **VISUAL ANALOGY** In the visual analogy of a cell as a factory, what two functions of the nucleus are represented? How are these functions illustrated?

   The nucleus acts as the office, or control center,

   as illustrated by the people at the desk. The

   nucleus is the source of messages, instructions,

   and blueprints, as illustrated by the two workers

   helping the chain (of RNA) leave the nucleus.

   _____

   _____

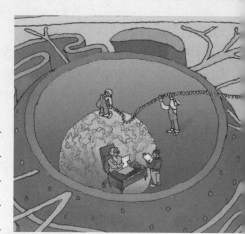

4. Which feature of the nucleus is *not* clearly shown by the visual analogy?

   SAMPLE ANSWER: *The chromatin is not shown.*

5. What is another possible analogy that could be compared with the structure and function of a cell? SAMPLE ANSWER: *The structure and function of an airport control tower could be*

   compared to the structure and function of a cell.

   _____

Organelles That Store, Clean Up, and Support

6. What are vacuoles?

Vacuoles are membrane-enclosed saclike structures that store materials such as water,

salts, proteins, and carbohydrates.

7. What are the two roles of the central vacuole in plant cells?

storage of materials and support of the cell

8. How are contractile vacuoles different from other types of vacuoles?

Contractile vacuoles pump excess water out of the cell, while other types of vacuoles

hold materials inside of cells.

9. In the diagrams of the animal cell and the plant cell, label the structures indicated by
the lines.

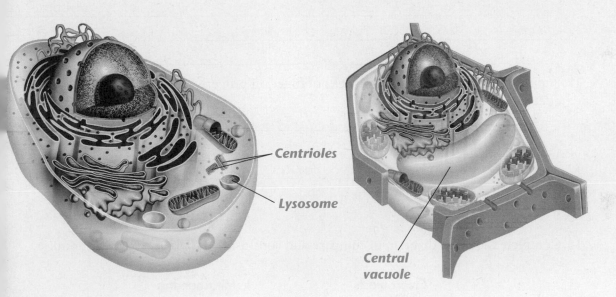

Centrioles

Lysosome

Central
vacuole

10. What is the role of lysosomes in the cell? Why is this a vital role?

Lysosomes break down large molecules and waste. Without them, clutter could accu-

mulate in the cell, which has been linked to serious human diseases.

11. Which structures of the cytoskeleton are found in animal cells but not in plant cells?

centrioles

12. What other structures of the cytoskeleton would show the same pattern of microtubules
as a flagellum?

cilia

Organelles That Build Proteins

13. What are ribosomes? What do they do?

Ribosomes are small particles of RNA and protein found throughout the cytoplasm.

They are involved in the synthesis of proteins.

14. In which organelle are the lipid components of the cell membrane assembled?

endoplasmic reticulum

15. What is the difference between rough ER and smooth ER?

Ribosomes are found on the surface of rough ER. Smooth ER has no ribosomes on its

surface.

16. Using the cell as a factory analogy, describe the role of the Golgi apparatus in cells.

The Golgi apparatus is like a customization shop in a factory. It puts the finishing

touches on proteins before they leave the factory.

17. Suppose a cell's Golgi apparatus does not function properly. How might this problem affect other cells?

SAMPLE ANSWER: If the cell manufactures proteins that are normally released to travel to

other cells, those cells would not receive the proteins. The loss of these proteins might

cause the "receiver" cells to function poorly.

Organelles That Capture and Release Energy

18. Complete the Venn diagram to compare and contrast chloroplasts and mitochondria.

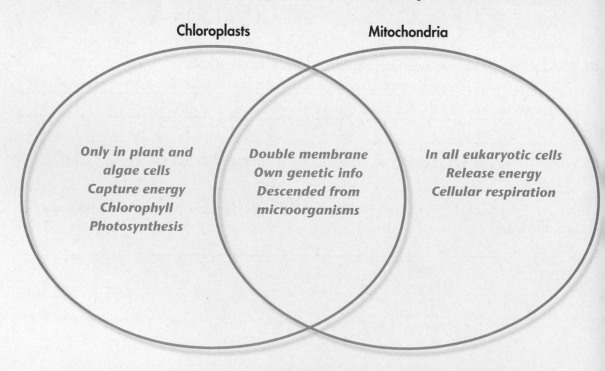

Chloroplasts | Mitochondria

Only in plant and algae cells
Capture energy
Chlorophyll
Photosynthesis

Double membrane
Own genetic info
Descended from microorganisms

In all eukaryotic cells
Release energy
Cellular respiration

For Questions 19–22, write True if the statement is true. If the statement is false, change the underlined word or words to make the statement true.

__True__   **19.** Chloroplasts are <u>never</u> found in animal cells.

__Like__   **20.** <u>Unlike</u> chloroplasts, mitochondria are surrounded by a double membrane.

__True__   **21.** Nearly all of the <u>mitochondria</u> in your cells were inherited from your mother.

__contain__   **22.** Both chloroplasts and mitochondria <u>lack</u> genetic information in the form of DNA.

Cellular Boundaries

For Questions 23–25, complete each statement by writing the correct word or words.

23. Most cell ____walls____ are porous to water and other materials but strong enough to support and protect cells.

24. Nearly all of the plant tissue called ____wood____ is made up of cell walls.

25. Besides supporting and protecting a cell, the cell membrane ____regulates____ what enters and leaves the cell.

26. Complete the diagram of a section of a cell membrane. Then, on the line below the diagram, write the name of the model that describes the cell membrane's structure.

Apply the Big idea

27. What is the function of vesicles in the synthesis of proteins and the release of those proteins outside the cell?

Vesicles transport newly synthesized proteins to the Golgi apparatus. After the Golgi

apparatus modifies the proteins, vesicles transport the modified proteins to the cell

membrane, where they are released.

_____

7.3 Cell Transport

Lesson Objectives

▭ Describe passive transport.

▭ Describe active transport.

Lesson Summary

Passive Transport The movement of materials across the cell membrane without using cellular energy is called passive transport.

▶ **Diffusion** is the process by which particles move from an area of high concentration to an area of lower concentration.

▶ **Facilitated diffusion** is the process by which molecules that cannot directly diffuse across the membrane pass through special protein channels.

▶ **Osmosis** is the facilitated diffusion of water through a selectively permeable membrane.

  • **Aquaporins** are water channel proteins that allow water to pass through cell membranes.

  • Two adjacent solutions are **isotonic** if they have the same concentrations of solute.

  • **Hypertonic** solutions have a higher concentration of solute compared to another solution.

  • **Hypotonic** solutions have a lower concentration of solute compared to another solution.

▶ **Osmotic pressure** is the force caused by the net movement of water by osmosis.

Active Transport The movement of materials against a concentration difference is called active transport. Active transport requires energy.

▶ Transport proteins that act like pumps use energy to move small molecules and ions across cell membranes.

▶ The bulk transport of large molecules and clumps of materials into and out of cells occurs by movements of the cell membrane, which require energy.

Passive Transport

For Questions 1–4, write the letter of the correct answer on the line at the left.

_____C_____ 1. Which of the following must be true for diffusion to occur?

    A. Molecules or particles must have different sizes.

    B. Special protein channels must always be available.

    C. There must be areas of different concentrations.

    D. Energy must be available.

_B_   **2.** Which term refers to the condition that exists when *no* net change in concentration results from diffusion?

     A. concentration   **C.** osmosis

     B. equilibrium   **D.** randomness

_D_   **3.** Air has a higher concentration of oxygen molecules than does the cytoplasm of your lung cells. Where in your lungs will there be a net increase of oxygen?

     A. in the air breathed in   **C.** outside of the lung cells

     B. in the air breathed out   **D.** inside of the lung cells

_C_   **4.** Which of the following statements tells how facilitated diffusion differs from simple diffusion?

     A. Particles move through cell membranes without the use of energy by cells.

     B. Particles tend to move from high concentration to lower concentration.

     C. Particles move within channel proteins that pass through cell membranes.

     D. Particles tend to move more slowly than they would be expected to move.

For Questions 5–7, match the situation with the result. Write the letter of the correct answer on the line at the left.

Situation

_C_   **5.** Cells are in an isotonic solution.

_A_   **6.** Cells are in a hypertonic solution.

_B_   **7.** Cells are in a hypotonic solution.

Result

A. The cells lose water.

B. The cells gain water.

C. The cells stay the same.

8. `THINK VISUALLY` In the table below, draw how each type of cell will look after being placed in a hypertonic solution.

Appearance of Cells in a Hypertonic Solution	
Animal Cells	**Plant Cells**
Students should draw a shrunken red blood cell similar to the one shown in the textbook.	*Students should draw a plant cell with shrunken cytoplasm and central vacuole similar to the one shown in the textbook.*

Active Transport

9. What is the function of active transport in moving small molecules and ions across cell membranes? Give an example.

Active transport enables cells to move some materials against a concentration gradient. For example, cells can concentrate substances such as sodium and potassium ions in particular locations. This would not happen by diffusion.

10. How does ATP enable transport proteins to move ions across a cell membrane?

Energy from ATP causes a transport protein to change shape, binding substances on one side of the membrane, and releasing them on the other.

11. What are the proteins used in active transport called? *protein pumps*

12. Complete the table to summarize the types of bulk transport.

Types of Bulk Transport	
Type	**Description**
Endocytosis	*The taking of materials into a cell by means of infoldings of the cell membrane*
Phagocytosis	*A type of endocytosis. An extension of cytoplasm surrounds a particle and packages it within a food vacuole.*
Exocytosis	*The release of large amounts of material from a cell*

Apply the Big idea

13. Most sports drinks are isotonic in relation to human body fluids. Explain why athletes should drink solutions that are isotonic to body fluids when they exercise rather than ones that are hypotonic to body fluids (contain a greater proportion of water in comparison to the fluids in and around human body cells).

SAMPLE ANSWER: *Athletes lose water and nutrients when they perspire. An isotonic solution restores both the water and the nutrients at levels healthy for the human body.*

Water alone or a hypotonic solution does not restore the nutrients. In addition, drinking a hypotonic solution might cause excessive water to enter the bloodstream.

7.4 Homeostasis and Cells

Lesson Objectives

⊃ Explain how unicellular organisms maintain homeostasis.

⊃ Explain how multicellular organisms maintain homeostasis.

Lesson Summary

The Cell as an Organism Sometimes a single cell is an organism. Single-celled organisms must be able to carry out all the functions necessary for life.

➤ Unicellular organisms maintain **homeostasis**, relatively constant internal conditions, by growing, responding to the environment, transforming energy, and reproducing.

➤ Unicellular organisms include both prokaryotes and eukaryotes.

➤ Unicellular organisms play many important roles in their environments.

Multicellular Life Cells of multicellular organisms are interdependent and specialized.

➤ The cells of multicellular organisms become specialized for particular tasks and communicate with one another to maintain homeostasis.

➤ Specialized cells in multicellular organisms are organized into groups.

• A **tissue** is a group of similar cells that performs a particular function.

• An **organ** is a group of tissues working together to perform an essential task.

• An **organ system** is a group of organs that work together to perform a specific function.

➤ The cells of multicellular organisms communicate with one another by means of chemical signals that are passed from one cell to another.

• Certain cells form connections, or cellular junctions, to neighboring cells. Some of these junctions hold cells together firmly.

• Other cells allow small molecules carrying chemical signals to pass directly from one cell to the next.

• To respond to a chemical signal, a cell must have a **receptor** to which the signaling molecule can bind.

The Cell as an Organism

For Questions 1–5, complete each statement by writing the correct word or words.

1. The term ____homeostasis____ refers to the relatively constant internal physical and chemical state of a living cell.

2. Unicellular prokaryotes, called ____bacteria____, are adapted to living in a remarkable number of different places.

3. Some unicellular eukaryotes, called ____algae____, contain chloroplasts.

4. Yeasts are unicellular ____fungi____, which are eukaryotes.

5. Other unicellular eukaryotes include ____protozoans____ and algae.

6. How do single-celled organisms maintain homeostasis?

They maintain homeostasis by growing, responding to their environment, transform-ing energy, and reproducing.

7. Why is maintaining homeostasis particularly important to single-celled organisms?

Because they consist of only one cell, loss of homeostasis by a single-celled organism would mean the immediate death of the organism. They do not have any other cells that can perform the activities of life for them.

Multicellular Life

8. How are the cells of a multicellular organism like a baseball team?

A multicellular organism has many different types of cells with different shapes that specialize in one of the functions that keep the organism alive. A baseball team has different players who each specialize in one of the jobs that must be done so the team can function.

9. How does a multicellular organism maintain homeostasis?

A multicellular organism maintains homeostasis by having specialized cells that must maintain their own homeostasis and cooperate with other cells. This requires the cells to communicate with one another. Each cell in a multicellular organism contributes to the overall homeostasis of the organism.

10. Complete the table by describing the functions of the specialized cells.

Examples of Specialized Cells		
Type of Cell	Name of Specialized Cell Part	Function of Specialized Cell Part
cells that line the upper air passages in humans	cilia	*sweep mucus, debris, and bacteria out of lungs*
pine pollen grains	wings	*enable pollen grains to float in the slightest breeze*

11. The Venn diagram below consists of four concentric circles. Complete the diagram to show the relationships among four levels of organization of life. Use the terms *cells, organ, organ system,* and *tissue.*

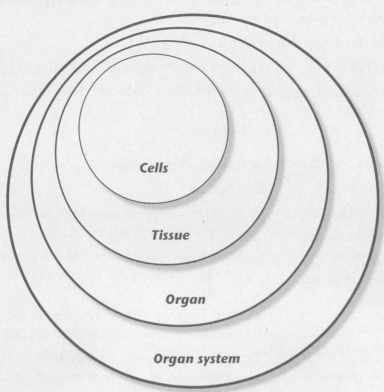

Cells

Tissue

Organ

Organ system

12. Starting with the outermost circle of the diagram, explain how each level is related to the next level within each circle.

Organ systems are made of one or more organs. Organs are made up of one or more

tissues. Tissues are made up of many cells with similar shapes and functions.

_____

13. What is the name of the areas that hold adjacent cells together and enable them to communicate?

Cellular junctions

_____

Apply the Big idea

14. On the Venn diagram above, where would you add a circle that represents the organism level of life? Where would you add a circle that represents another organ of the same organ system?

A circle that represents the organism level of life should be drawn outside of the

outermost circle for an organ system. A circle that represents another organ of the

same organ system would be drawn within the organ system circle but would be

separate from the series of circles that represent the organs already shown in the

Venn diagram.

Chapter Vocabulary Review

For Questions 1–4, write True if the statement is true. If the statement is false, change the underlined word or words to make the statement true.

membrane 1. All cells are surrounded by a cell <u>wall</u>.

lipid bilayer 2. The flexible nature of a cell membrane results from its <u>channel proteins</u>.

True 3. <u>Selectively permeable</u> membranes allow only certain materials to pass through them.

True 4. Centrioles are found in <u>animal</u> cells.

For Questions 5–11, match the organelle with its description.

Organelle	Description
F 5. Ribosomes	**A.** Convert energy from sunlight into chemical energy that is stored in food
D 6. Endoplasmic reticulum	
	B. Stack of membranes that modifies, sorts, and packages proteins and other materials for storage or release
B 7. Golgi apparatus	
G 8. Lysosomes	
E 9. Vacuoles	**C.** Convert chemical energy stored in food into a form that can be easily used by the cell
A 10. Chloroplasts	
C 11. Mitochondria	**D.** An internal membrane system where lipid components of cell membranes are made
	E. Saclike structures that store materials
	F. Small particles of RNA and protein on which proteins are assembled using instructions from DNA
	G. Filled with enzymes used to break down carbohydrates into smaller molecules

For Questions 12–15, complete each statement by writing the correct word or words.

12. Osmosis occurs through water channel proteins called **aquaporins**.

13. The force created by the net movement of water through a cell membrane is called **osmotic** pressure.

14. Red blood cells are able to maintain homeostasis because they are bathed in blood, which is **isotonic** to the fluid in the cells themselves.

15. To respond to a chemical signal, a cell must have a **receptor** to which the signaling molecule can bind.

CHAPTER MYSTERY

DEATH BY … WATER?

In the Chapter Mystery, you learned how the body's salt balance can be disrupted during periods of exertion, in this case a marathon. Running a marathon can disrupt other aspects of the body's homeostasis.

21st Century Learning

Preparing for, Completing, and Recovering From a Race

Marathon running poses some challenges to cellular homeostasis. Dehydration can occur due to sweating. Exercising muscles demand more oxygen and produce excess heat. But if participants take precautions, marathon running is generally a safe activity. The plan below explains some of the things that runners should do.

Six Weeks Before the Race
Do not try any new training techniques. Limit your strength training to exercises with minimal external resistance (that means no weights).

Three Weeks Before the Race
Reduce the length of long training runs by 25%.

Two Weeks Before the Race
Reduce the length of long training runs by another 25%.

The Week Before the Race
Stop all long training runs—just do light ones. Stop strength training. Do not try any unfamiliar foods, and that means ordinary meals as well as training foods. If you plan to use any new electrolyte drinks, nutrition bars, gel supplements, etc. during the race, start consuming them now. Get extra sleep every night.

The Day Before the Race
Stay off your feet. Take it easy. Eat lots of complex carbohydrates. Do not eat much fiber. Drink a lot of water. Do not drink any caffeine. Do not eat anything late at night.

The Day of the Race
Get up early. Eat a light breakfast. Drink a large glass of water two hours before the race. Do not drink again until after the race starts.

During the Race
Start slowly—you can pick up speed later in the race. Drink at every water station. Drink electrolyte drinks as well as water.

Within Two Hours of the End of the Race
Drink water or electrolyte drinks. Walk for 60 of the 120 minutes (not necessarily all at once, though). Eat something with carbohydrates and a little protein. Do not eat anything high in fat or sugar.

After That
Put ice on any sore muscles. Get lots of sleep. Do not run for the next week. Do not do any strength training for two weeks.

Continued on next page ▶

21st Century Themes Science and Health Literacy

1. When should a runner stop doing long training runs?

One week before the race

2. What should an athlete do after a marathon?

Put ice on sore muscles, get lots of sleep; avoid running and strength training

3. What should a runner do six weeks before a race? Why do you think that is advisable?

Avoid new training techniques and high-resistance techniques like weight training;

SAMPLE ANSWER: to prevent injuries

4. Should a runner eat nothing, a light, meal, or a heavy meal before the race? Why do you think this advice is given?

A light meal. SAMPLE ANSWER: You need to eat something in order to have the energy to

start the race, but eating too much could lead to an upset stomach while running.

5. What advice does the article give about eating the week before the race? Why might that advice be appropriate?

Do not eat any unfamiliar foods, but eat or drink any new supplements you plan to

use during the race. SAMPLE ANSWER: Unfamiliar foods might cause stomach problems or

allergies, so they should be avoided. The same is true for unfamiliar supplements, so

try them in advance to make sure they won't cause any problems during the race.

21st Century Skills Race for a Cause

The skills used in this activity include **problem identification, formulation, and solution; interpersonal and collaborative skills; accountability and adaptability;** and **social responsibility.**

Use library and Internet resources to research different ideas about what an athlete should do the week prior to a race, the day of the race, and the day after. Combine the tips you find with the ones presented here, and then write them up in the form of a calendar or schedule for prospective athletes.

Working with a group, choose a charity or non-profit organization in your community. Plan, organize, and stage a race to benefit that organization.

Have a sports physician and a gym teacher review your training calendar. Make any changes they suggest, and then mail a copy to each entrant.

Things you will need to do include determining the length of the race, planning the course, getting permits for the race, and finding sponsors. You will need to publicize the event twice—first to attract entrants, and later to attract spectators.

You will also need to check that entrants do not have any physical conditions that rule out their participation.

Evaluate students' schedules based on how each activity on the schedule will benefit a runner's health as he or she prepares for a long-distance race.

8 Photosynthesis

Cellular Basis of Life

Q: How do plants and other organisms capture energy from the sun?

WHAT I KNOW	WHAT I LEARNED
8.1 How do organisms store energy?	*SAMPLE ANSWER:* **Cells store energy in macromolecules.**	*SAMPLE ANSWER:* **Cells store energy mostly in the form of food molecules such as glucose. They briefly store small amounts of energy from food molecules in ATP molecules.**
8.2 What cellular structures and molecules are involved in photosynthesis?	*SAMPLE ANSWER:* **Chloroplasts are where photosynthesis occurs in eukaryotic cells.**	*SAMPLE ANSWER:* **Molecules of chlorophyll absorb light. Molecules of ATP and NADP⁺ are also involved in photosynthesis, which uses molecules of water and carbon dioxide to make carbohydrates.**
8.3 How do photosynthetic organisms convert the sun's energy into chemical energy?	*SAMPLE ANSWER:* **Photosynthetic organisms use the energy in sunlight to make sugars that store chemical energy.**	*SAMPLE ANSWER:* **Light-dependent reactions use light to produce high-energy electrons that are used to make energy carriers (ATP and NADPH). Light-independent reactions use the energy carriers to make food molecules.**

8.1 Energy and Life

Lesson Objectives

🔑 Describe the role of ATP in cellular activities.

🔑 Explain where plants get the energy they need to produce food.

Lesson Summary

Chemical Energy and ATP Energy is the ability to do work. Organisms need energy to stay alive.

▶ **Adenosine triphosphate (ATP)** is a chemical compound cells use to store and release energy.

  • An ATP molecule consists of adenine, the sugar ribose, and three phosphate groups.

  • Cells store energy by adding a phosphate group to adenosine diphosphate (ADP) molecules.

  • Cells release energy from ATP molecules by subtracting a phosphate group.

▶ Energy provided by ATP is used in active transport, to contract muscles, to make proteins, and in many other ways.

▶ Cells contain only a small amount of ATP at any one time. The regenerate it from ADP as they need it, using energy stored in food.

Heterotrophs and Autotrophs The energy to make ATP from ADP comes from food. Organisms get food in one of two ways.

▶ **Heterotrophs** get food by consuming (eating) other organisms.

▶ **Autotrophs** use the energy in sunlight to make their own food.

▶ **Photosynthesis** is the process that uses light energy to produce food molecules.

Chemical Energy and ATP

For Questions 1–6, complete each statement by writing the correct word or words.

1. _____Energy_____ is the ability to do work.

2. The main chemical compound cells use for energy is __adenosine triphosphate__ (ATP).

3. _____Ribose_____ is a 5-carbon sugar molecule that is part of an ATP molecule.

4. The __phosphate groups__ of ATP are the key to its ability to store and supply energy.

5. ATP releases energy when it _____breaks_____ bonds between its phosphate groups.

6. Most cells only store enough ATP for ___a few seconds___ of activity.

7. **THINK VISUALLY** Label each part of the diagram of an ATP molecule below.

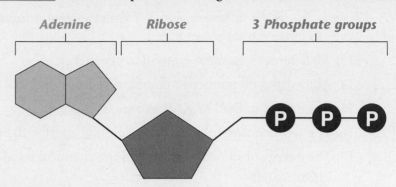

Adenine   Ribose   3 Phosphate groups

For Questions 8–10, refer to the Visual Analogy comparing ATP to a charged battery.

8. **VISUAL ANALOGY** In the visual analogy, what chemical is represented by the low battery?

ADP represents a low battery, which has *been discharged.*

9. What are two ways in which the diagram shows an increase in energy?

a brighter flashlight beam and a sunburst *background represent energy.*

10. Describe the concepts shown in the diagram.

When a phosphate group breaks off of an *ATP molecule, the remaining ADP molecule* *stores very little energy, like a discharged* *battery. When a phosphate group is added* *to ADP, the resulting ATP molecule stores a* *great deal more energy, like a recharged or* *new battery.*

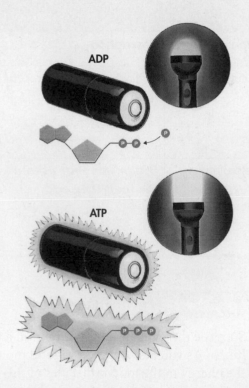

ADP

ATP

11. What are two ways in which cells use the energy temporarily stored in ATP?

SAMPLE ANSWER: *Active transport, cell movements, powering bioluminescence, making* *proteins and other macromolecules*

12. Energy is needed to add a third phosphate group to ADP to make ATP. What is a cell's source of this energy?

Food molecules such as sugars and starches provide energy for making ATP.

Heterotrophs and Autotrophs

For Questions 13–17, write True if the statement is true. If the statement is false, change the underlined word or words to make the statement true.

_____True_____	**13.**	All heterotrophs must <u>eat food</u> to get energy.
_____True_____	**14.**	<u>Autotrophs</u> do not need to eat food because they make food.
___the sun___	**15.**	The energy in food originally came from <u>ATP</u>.
putting together	**16.**	The term photosynthesis means "<u>pulling apart</u> with light" in Greek.
_____True_____	**17.**	The energy of sunlight is stored in the chemical bonds of <u>carbohydrates</u>.

18. Complete the table comparing two types of organisms.

Autotrophs and Heterotrophs		
Type	**Description**	**Examples**
Autotrophs	*Organisms that can make their own food*	*Grass, algae, some bacteria*
Heterotrophs	*Organisms that obtain energy from the food they eat*	*Cheetahs, hares, mushrooms*

Apply the Big idea

19. Suppose that you ate a hamburger on a wheat roll with lettuce, tomatoes, and onions for lunch. As you ate, you took in food molecules from plants and animals. Explain why all the energy in the food molecules of this hamburger could be traced back to the sun.

SAMPLE ANSWER: *The bread, lettuce, tomatoes, and onions in a hamburger all came from plants. The food molecules in those plants were made as a result of the process of photosynthesis, using the energy in sunlight. The hamburger meat came from a cow, which ate grass and other plants to obtain food. The cow made the molecules in the meat by using the energy in the food molecules from the plants, which originally came from the sun.*

8.2 Photosynthesis: An Overview

Lesson Objectives

▭ Explain the role of light and pigments in photosynthesis.

▭ Explain the role of electron carrier molecules in photosynthesis.

▭ State the overall equation for photosynthesis.

Lesson Summary

Chlorophyll and Chloroplasts In eukaryotes, photosynthesis occurs in organelles called chloroplasts. Chloroplasts house light-absorbing chemicals.

➤ Light is a form of energy. Sunlight is a mixture of all the different colors of visible light.

➤ Light-absorbing molecules called **pigments** capture the sun's energy.

➤ **Chlorophyll** is the principal pigment in photosynthetic organisms. Chlorophyll absorbs blue-violet and red light but reflects green light.

➤ Chloroplasts have a complex internal structure that includes:
  • **thylakoids:** saclike photosynthetic membranes that contain chlorophyll and other pigments and are arranged in stacks called grana.
  • **stroma:** the fluid portion outside of the thylakoids.

High-Energy Electrons The energy in light raises some of the electrons in chlorophyll to higher energy levels. These high-energy electrons are used in photosynthesis.

➤ Electron carriers are used to transport the electrons from chlorophyll to other molecules during photosynthesis.

➤ **NADP$^+$** is a compound that can accept and hold 2 high-energy electrons and 1 hydrogen ion. This process converts NADP$^+$ into NADPH.

An Overview of Photosynthesis Usually summarized by a simple chemical reaction, photosynthesis is a complex process that involves two interdependent sets of reactions.

➤ The **light-dependent reactions** require light, light-absorbing pigments, and water to form NADPH, ATP, and oxygen.

➤ The **light-independent reactions** do not use light energy. They use carbon dioxide from the atmosphere, NADPH, and ATP to make energy-rich carbon compounds.

Chlorophyll and Chloroplasts

For Questions 1–6, complete each statement by writing the correct word or words.

1. The ____wavelength____ of light determines its color.

2. Chemicals that absorb light are called ____pigments____.

3. Chlorophyll makes plants look green because it ____reflects____ green light.

4. Chloroplasts contain an abundance of saclike photosynthetic membranes called ____thylakoids____.

5. The ____stroma____ is the fluid portion of the chloroplast located outside the thylakoids.

6. The visible light absorbed by chlorophyll ____raises____ the energy level of the chlorophyll's electrons.

7. **THINK VISUALLY** Label the internal parts of the chloroplast below.

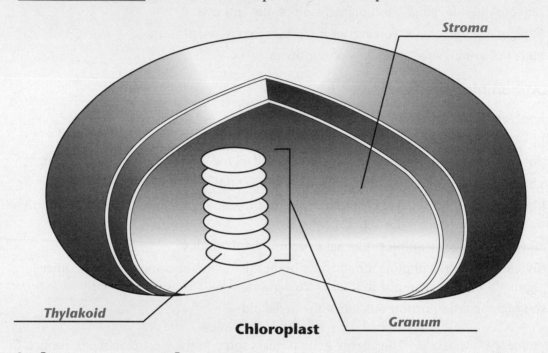

Stroma

Thylakoid

Chloroplast

Granum

High-Energy Electrons

For Questions 8–9, refer to the Visual Analogy comparing electron carriers to oven mitts.

8. **VISUAL ANALOGY** In the visual analogy of carrying electrons, what represents the high-energy electrons?

The hot potato represents two high-energy electrons.

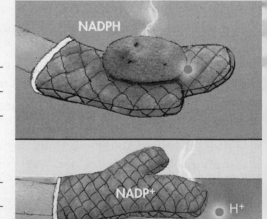

9. Write another analogy that describes the process of electron carriers.

SAMPLE ANSWER: *A laundry basket filled with warm laundry can also be compared to an electron carrier. In this analogy, the laundry basket represents the electron carrier and the warm laundry represents the high-energy electrons.*

10. Where do the high-energy electrons carried by NADPH come from?

The high-energy electrons come from chlorophyll molecules that have absorbed sunlight.

An Overview of Photosynthesis

For Questions 11–13, write the letter of the correct answer on the line at the left.

___B___ **11.** What are the reactants of the photosynthesis reaction?

    A. chlorophyll and light   **C.** carbohydrates and oxygen

    B. carbon dioxide and water   **D.** high-energy electrons and air

___C___ **12.** What are the products of the light-dependent reactions?

    A. chloroplasts and light   **C.** oxygen and ATP

    B. proteins and lipids   **D.** water and sugars

___A___ **13.** Where do the light-independent reactions occur?

    A. stroma   **C.** chlorophyll

    B. thylakoids   **D.** mitochondria

14. Complete the illustration by writing the reactants and products of the light-dependent and light-independent reactions. Also, fill in the energy source that excites the electrons.

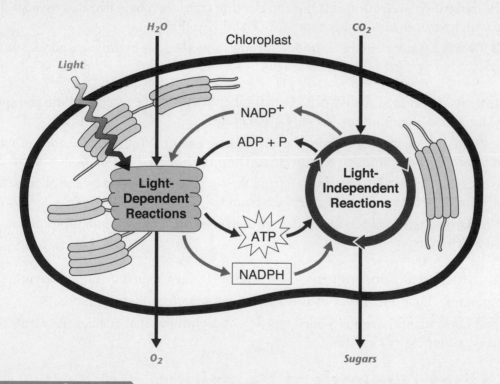

Apply the Big idea

15. Solar power uses cells or panels to absorb the sun's energy. That energy is then used to create electricity. How does this compare to the light dependent reactions of photosynthesis?

Solar power and photosynthesis both use energy from sunlight to create energy. The chloroplasts inside plant cells work like solar cells. The pigment chlorophyll in the chloroplasts absorbs the sun's energy. The light energy is transferred to the electrons of the chlorophyll. It raises the energy levels of the electrons. The high-energy electrons are picked up by carriers and used to power chemical reactions in the cell.

8.3 The Process of Photosynthesis

Lesson Objectives

🔑 Describe what happens during the light-dependent reactions.

🔑 Describe what happens during the light-independent reactions.

🔑 Identify factors that affect the rate at which photosynthesis occurs.

Lesson Summary

The Light-Dependent Reactions: Generating ATP and NADPH
Photosynthesis begins with these reactions, which occur in thylakoid membranes.

▶ **Photosystems** are clusters of proteins and chlorophyll in thylakoid membranes.

▶ High-energy electrons form when pigments in photosystem II absorb light. The electrons pass through **electron transport chains**, a series of electron carrier proteins.

  • The movement of electrons through an electron transport chain causes a thylakoid to fill up with hydrogen ions and generates ATP and NADPH.

  • **ATP synthase** is a membrane protein through which excess hydrogen ions escape a thylakoid in a process that makes ATP.

The Light-Independent Reactions: Producing Sugars
They occur in the stroma of thylakoids and are commonly called the **Calvin cycle**.

▶ Six carbon dioxide molecules from the atmosphere enter the Calvin cycle and combine with 5-carbon compounds already present. They produce twelve 3-carbon molecules.

▶ Two 3-carbon molecules are removed from the cycle. They are used by the plant to build sugars, lipids, amino acids, and other compounds.

▶ The remaining ten 3-carbon molecules are converted back to 5-carbon molecules and begin a new cycle.

Factors Affecting Photosynthesis
Many factors influence the rate of photosynthesis.

▶ Temperature, light intensity, and availability of water affect photosynthesis.

▶ C4 and CAM plants have a modified type of photosynthesis that enables the plants to conserve water in dry climates.

The Light-Dependent Reactions: Generating ATP and NADPH

For Questions 1–5, write True if the statement is true. If the statement is false, change the underlined word or words to make the statement true.

_____**True**_____ 1. Photosystems are clusters of chlorophyll and <u>proteins</u>.

**photosystem II** 2. The light-dependent reactions begin when <u>photosystem I</u> absorbs light.

_____**True**_____ 3. Electrons from <u>water</u> molecules replace the ones lost by photosystem II.

_____**NADPH**_____ 4. <u>ATP</u> is the product of photosystem I.

_____**energy**_____ 5. ATP and NADPH are two types of <u>protein</u> carriers.

6. How does ATP synthase produce ATP? *ATP synthase allows H⁺ ions to pass through the thylakoid membrane. As the ions pass through, ATP synthase rotates. The rotation creates the energy needed to bind ADP and a phosphate group together to produce ATP.*

7. When sunlight excites electrons in chlorophyll, how do the electrons change?
The electrons take on a great deal of energy, which causes them to move to a higher energy level.

8. Where do the light-dependent reactions take place? *The light-dependent reactions take place in the thylakoid membranes inside of chloroplasts.*

9. Complete the table by summarizing what happens in each phase of the light-dependent reactions of photosynthesis.

Light-Dependent Reactions	Summary
Photosystem II	*Photosystem II absorbs light and increases the electrons' energy level. The electrons are passed to the electron transport chain. Enzymes in the thylakoid break up water molecules into 2 electrons, 2 H⁺ ions, and 1 oxygen atom. The 2 electrons replace the high-energy electrons that have been lost to the electron transport chain.*
Electron Transport Chain	*Energy from the electrons is used by the proteins in the chain to pump H⁺ ions from the stroma into the thylakoid space. At the end of the electron transport chain, the electrons themselves pass to photosystem I.*
Photosystem I	*The electrons do not contain as much energy as they used to. Pigments use energy from light to reenergize the electrons. At the end of a short second electron transport chain, NADP⁺ molecules in the stroma pick up the high-energy electrons, along with H⁺ ions, at the outer surface of the thylakoid membrane, to become NADPH.*
Hydrogen Ion Movement and ATP Formation	*Hydrogen ions began to accumulate within the thylakoid space. The buildup of hydrogen ions makes the stroma negatively charged relative to the space within the thylakoids. This gradient, the difference in both charge and H⁺ ion concentration across the membrane, provides the energy to make ATP.*

The Light-Independent Reactions: Producing Sugars

10. What does the Calvin cycle use to produce high-energy sugars?

The Calvin cycle uses carbon dioxide molecules as well as ATP and NADPH from the light-dependent reactions to make sugars.

11. Why are the reactions of the Calvin cycle called light-independent reactions?

The reactions of the Calvin cycle use ATP and NADPH as energy sources. They do not directly require light.

12. What makes the Calvin cycle a cycle?

The compound with which CO_2 from the air combines is a product of the cycle, which enables the series of reactions to occur over and over.

13. Complete the diagram of the Calvin cycle by filling in the missing labels.

Calvin Cycle

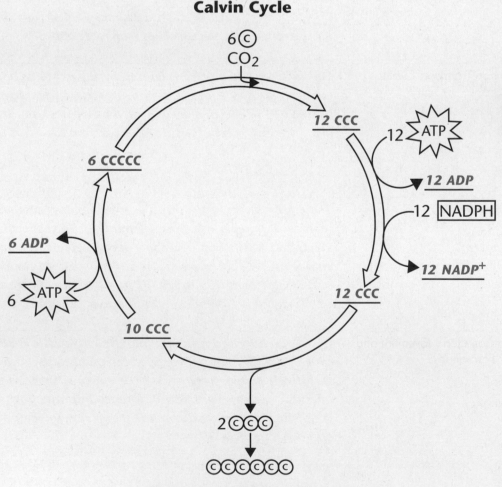

Sugars and other compounds

Factors Affecting Photosynthesis

14. What are three factors that affect the rate at which photosynthesis occurs?

Three factors that affect the rate of photosynthesis are temperature, light intensity,

and the availability of water.

15. Would a plant placed in an atmosphere of pure oxygen be able to conduct photosynthesis? Explain your answer.

SAMPLE ANSWER: *No. One of the materials that plants use in photosynthesis is carbon*

dioxide. None of this gas would be present in an atmosphere of pure oxygen. There-

fore, photosynthesis could not occur.

16. Complete the table about variations of photosynthesis.

Type	Description	Examples
C4 Photosynthesis	Occurs in plants that have a specialized chemical pathway that allows them to capture even very low levels of carbon dioxide and pass it to the Calvin cycle.	*corn, sugar cane, and sorghum*
CAM	*CAM plants only allow air into their leaves at night which minimizes water loses. Carbon dioxide is trapped in the leaves and it is released during the day, enabling carbohydrate production.*	pineapple trees, many desert cacti, and "ice plants"

Apply the Big idea

17. Photosynthesis plays an important role in supplying energy to living things. Considering what the products of photosynthesis are, what is another way in which photosynthesis is vital to life?

Photosynthesis is the way in which new organic macromolecules are added to the

living portion of the biosphere. All living things that are not photosynthetic rely on

photosynthesis as a source of the organic building blocks needed for growth. Photo-

synthesis also releases oxygen into the atmosphere. Without this oxygen we would not

be able to breathe.

Chapter Vocabulary Review

Crossword Puzzle *Complete the puzzle by entering the term that matches the description.*

Across

4. energy carrier cells use to transport high-energy electrons
6. cluster of pigments and proteins that absorbs light
7. a saclike photosynthetic membrane found in chloroplasts
8. energy carrier made as a result of photosystem II
9. process of using the sun's energy to make food
10. man who worked out the light-independent reactions

Down

1. liquid part of the inside of a chloroplast
2. chemical that absorbs light for photosynthesis
3. light-absorbing chemical
5. organism that makes its own food

			¹S		²C						³P
⁴N	⁵A	D	P⁺		T		H				I
	U		T		L						G
	T		⁶P	H	O	T	O	S	Y	S	T	E	M
	O		M		▓		R				E
	⁷T	H	Y	L	A	K	O	I	D		N
	R				P			⁸A	T	P
	O				H				
	⁹P	H	O	T	O	S	Y	N	T	H	E	S	I	S
	H				L				
			¹⁰C	A	L	V	I	N	

For Questions 11–16, complete each statement by writing the correct word or words.

11. The light-___*dependent*___ reactions occur in thylakoid membranes.

12. Carbon dioxide is used to make sugars in the light-___*independent*___ reactions.

13. The light-independent reactions are also called the ___*Calvin cycle*___.

14. ___*ATP synthase*___ spins to provide the energy for adding a phosphate group to ADP.

15. Electron ___*transport chains*___ move high-energy electrons between photosystems.

16. An animal that obtains food by eating other organisms is called a(n) ___*heterotroph*___.

CHAPTER MYSTERY

OUT OF THIN AIR?

In the Chapter Mystery, you read about a five-year-long experiment that Jan van Helmont performed in the middle of the seventeenth century. That experiment is a milestone in the history of science and is taught in high schools and colleges around the world.

21st Century Learning

Explore and Teach van Helmont's Experiment

But, van Helmont's experiment, as famous as it is, led him to the wrong conclusion. In the end, he did not know where the tree's mass came from. He guessed that it came from the water he'd added. It turns out he was wrong.

The problem was the way van Helmont set up his experiment. He set up his experiment to prove that the tree's extra mass came from the soil, and he did not consider other possible explanations of where the extra mass might come from. Therefore, the experiment, as carried out, could not prove where the tree's extra mass came from. In the 1600s, science and the scientific method were in their infancy. Now we know that an experiment should take all the variables into account and consider every possible outcome. An experiment should be done to find out what happens, or at least to find out if something happens, not to "prove" that the scientist's preconceived notion is correct.

Consider how you could modify van Helmont's procedures if you were to carry out the experiment today. Start with van Helmont's original hypothesis: A tree's mass comes from absorbing matter from the soil. What variable(s) would you need to control in this experiment?

SAMPLE ANSWER: *I would need to control all matter that could enter the tree, including air, water, and material in the soil.*

What procedure would you follow in your experiment?

SAMPLE ANSWER: *I would completely enclose the tree in a container so that I could measure the mass of everything that entered and exited the container. I would start by measuring the soil's mass, the tree's mass, the air's mass, and the mass of any water I added to the system. I would allow the tree to grow for a period of time, and then measure the mass of all the materials in the container again to see how their masses had changed.*

What materials and tools would you need for your experiment?

SAMPLE ANSWER: *a seedling; a large, airtight container; a scale; metered gas valves; soil; tubing*

Continued on next page ▶

21st Century Themes | Science Literacy

1. How does your experimental procedure make sure that nothing comes into contact with the tree without your being aware of it?

   SAMPLE ANSWER: *I would enclose the tree, soil, and all watering mechanisms inside an airtight dome.*

2. How would you account for the mass of the water that comes into contact with the tree during the five-year experiment?

   SAMPLE ANSWER: *I would measure the mass of the water before I introduced it into the dome.*

3. How would you account for the mass of the air that comes into contact with the tree over the five years?

   SAMPLE ANSWER: *I would have a metered valve at the air intake.*

4. How would you account for the gases that would be released by the tree over the five years?

   SAMPLE ANSWER: *I would have a metered valve at the air outtake.*

5. Are there any variables you would not be able to account for? If so, what are they?

   SAMPLE ANSWER: *There are no mass-related variables that are unaccounted for; the only other variable affecting the growth of the tree is sunshine. Energy from the sun is entering the system, but I don't know how to account for that.*

21st Century Skills | Communicating Results

The skills used in this activity include **communication skills; critical thinking and systems thinking; problem identification, formulation, and solution;** and **creativity** and **intellectual curiosity.**

How might you change your experiment to improve it? List any alterations you would make to ensure your results would be more valid. Then prepare a lesson plan that you could use to teach another student about van Helmont's experiment. The lesson plan should include an outline of what you would say, as well as any diagrams or pictures you would show to the student.

Ask your teacher to arrange for a time when you can meet with a middle-school student and teach him or her the lesson.

Students may suggest that they improve their experiment by more carefully controlling for the mass of materials entering and exiting the tree's enclosed container. Evaluate students' lesson plans based on the clarity, accuracy, and completeness of the written plan. Also make sure that the charts, diagrams, and pictures illustrate specific points made in the lesson and illuminate and expand these points.

9 Cellular Respiration and Fermentation

 Cellular Basis of Life

Q: How do organisms obtain energy?

WHAT I KNOW	WHAT I LEARNED
9.1 Why do most organisms undergo the process of cellular respiration?	SAMPLE ANSWER: *Cellular respiration occurs in mitochondria and supplies energy for life processes.*	SAMPLE ANSWER: *The process of cellular respiration takes place in stages. During cellular respiration, cells trap bits of chemical energy and use them to make ATP.*
9.2 How do cells release energy from food in the presence of oxygen?	SAMPLE ANSWER: *Oxygen enables much more energy to be released from food molecules.*	SAMPLE ANSWER: *Glycolysis does not require oxygen but the Krebs cycle and electron transport do require oxygen. Oxygen serves as the final electron acceptor of the electron transport chain, during which the majority of ATP is produced.*
9.3 How do cells release energy from food without oxygen?	SAMPLE ANSWER: *Cells use glycolysis to release energy without oxygen.*	SAMPLE ANSWER: *When oxygen is not present, glycolysis is followed by a pathway that continues the production of ATP. This pathway plus glycolysis is called fermentation. Fermentation releases energy from food molecules by producing ATP.*

9.1 Cellular Respiration: An Overview

Lesson Objectives

🔑 Explain where organisms get the energy they need for life processes.

🔑 Define cellular respiration.

🔑 Compare photosynthesis and cellular respiration.

Lesson Summary

Chemical Energy and Food Chemical energy is stored in food molecules.

▶ Energy is released when chemical bonds in food molecules are broken.

▶ Energy is measured in a unit called a **calorie**, the amount of energy needed to raise the temperature of 1 gram of water 1 degree Celsius.

▶ Fats store more energy per gram than do carbohydrates and proteins.

Overview of Cellular Respiration **Cellular respiration** is the process that releases energy from food in the presence of oxygen.

▶ Cellular respiration captures the energy from food in three main stages:
  • glycolysis
  • the Krebs cycle
  • the electron transport chain

▶ Glycolysis does not require oxygen. The Krebs cycle and electron transport chain both require oxygen.
  • **Aerobic** pathways are processes that require oxygen.
  • **Anaerobic** pathways are processes that occur without oxygen.

Comparing Photosynthesis and Cellular Respiration The energy in photosynthesis and cellular respiration flows in opposite directions. Their equations are the reverse of each other.

▶ Photosynthesis removes carbon dioxide from the atmosphere, and cellular respiration puts it back.

▶ Photosynthesis releases oxygen into the atmosphere, and cellular respiration uses oxygen to release energy from food.

Chemical Energy and Food

For Questions 1–4, complete each statement by writing the correct word or words.

1. A calorie is a unit of ____energy____.

2. The Calorie used on food labels is equal to ____1000____ calories.

3. A Calorie is also referred to as a ____kilocalorie____.

4. Cells use the energy stored in chemical bonds of foods to produce compounds that directly power the cell's activities, such as ____ATP____.

Overview of Cellular Respiration

For Questions 5–10, complete each statement by writing the correct word or words.

5. The equation that summarizes cellular respiration, using chemical formulas, is
   $6O_2 + C_6H_{12}O_6 \rightarrow 6CO_2 + 6H_2O + Energy$.

6. If cellular respiration took place in just one step, most of the ___energy___ would be lost
   in the form of light and ___heat___ .

7. Cellular respiration begins with a pathway called ___glycolysis___ , which takes place in the
   ___cytoplasm___ of the cell.

8. At the end of glycolysis, about ___90___ percent of the chemical energy is locked in
   the bonds of the ___pyruvic acid___ molecule.

9. Cellular respiration continues in the ___mitochondria___ of the cell with the ___Krebs cycle___
   and electron transport chain.

10. The pathways of cellular respiration that require oxygen are said to be ___aerobic___ .
    Pathways that do not require oxygen are said to be ___anaerobic___ .

11. **THINK VISUALLY** Complete the illustration by adding labels for the three main stages
    of cellular respiration.

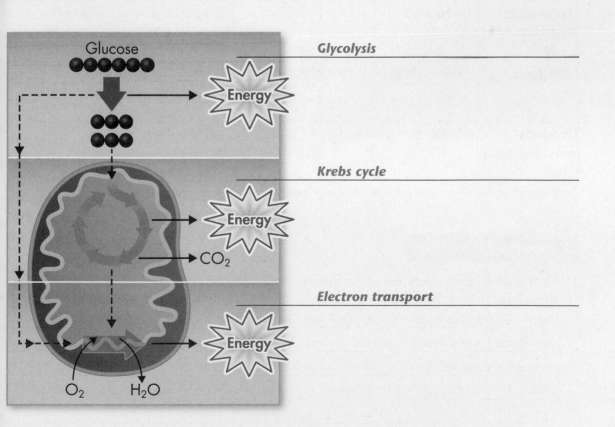

Comparing Photosynthesis and Cellular Respiration

For Questions 12–15, write True if the statement is true. If the statement is false, change the underlined word or words to make the statement true.

___opposite___ **12.** The energy flow in photosynthesis and cellular respiration occurs in the <u>same</u> direction.

___True___ **13.** Photosynthesis <u>deposits</u> energy in Earth's "savings account" for living organisms.

___oxygen___ **14.** Cellular respiration removes <u>carbon dioxide</u> from the air.

___cellular respiration___ **15.** <u>Photosynthesis</u> takes place in nearly all life.

16. Complete the table comparing photosynthesis and cellular respiration.

A Comparison of Photosynthesis and Cellular Respiration		
Aspect	**Photosynthesis**	**Cellular Respiration**
Function	energy capture	*energy release*
Location of reactions	chloroplasts	*cytoplasm and mitochondria*
Reactants	*carbon dioxide, water, and light*	*glucose and oxygen*
Products	*oxygen and glucose*	*carbon dioxide, water, and energy*

Apply the Big idea

17. How does an understanding of the process of cellular respiration support the theory that the cell is the basic functional unit of life?

SAMPLE ANSWER: *Cellular respiration is the fundamental process by which energy for life processes is obtained from food molecules. It occurs in both the cytoplasm and specialized structures of a cell—the mitochondria—instead of in a specialized tissue or organ of the body. It occurs in the same way in almost all cells.*

9.2 The Process of Cellular Respiration

Lesson Objectives

- Describe what happens during glycolysis.
- Describe what happens during the Krebs cycle.
- Explain how high-energy electrons are used by the electron transport chain.
- Identify how much ATP cellular respiration generates.

Lesson Summary

Glycolysis The word **glycolysis** literally means "sugar-breaking." The end result is 2 molecules of a 3-carbon molecule called pyruvic acid.

- 2 ATP molecules are used at the start of glycolysis to get the process started.
- High-energy electrons are passed to the electron carrier **NAD⁺**, forming two molecules of NADH.
- 4 ATP are synthesized during glycolysis for a net gain of 2 ATP.

The Krebs Cycle The second stage of cellular respiration is the **Krebs cycle**, which operates only when oxygen is available. The Krebs cycle is a series of energy-extracting reactions.

- Pyruvic acid produced by glycolysis enters mitochondria. In the innermost compartment of a mitochondrion, or the **matrix**, pyruvic acid molecules are broken down into carbon dioxide and acetyl-CoA molecules.
- Acetyl-CoA combines with a 4-carbon compound, producing a 6-carbon molecule—citric acid. Energy released by the breaking and rearranging of carbon bonds is captured in ATP, NADH, and FADH$_2$.
- The Krebs cycle produces four types of products:
  - high-energy electron carriers (NADH and FADH$_2$)
  - carbon dioxide
  - 2 ATP molecules (per glucose molecule)
  - the 4-carbon molecule needed to start the cycle again

Electron Transport and ATP Synthesis The electron transport chain uses the high-energy electrons from glycolysis and the Krebs cycle to convert ADP into ATP.

- The electron carriers produced during glycolysis and the Krebs cycle bring high-energy electrons to the electron transport chain. Oxygen is the final electron acceptor.
- The passing of electrons through the electron transport chain causes H⁺ ions to build up in the intermembrane space, making it positively charged relative to the matrix.
- The charge difference across the membrane forces H⁺ ions through channels in enzymes known as ATP synthases. As the ATP synthases spin, a phosphate group is added to ADP, generating ATP.

The Totals Together, glycolysis, the Krebs cycle, and the electron transport chain generate about 36 molecules of ATP per molecule of glucose.

Glycolysis

1. **THINK VISUALLY** Complete the diagram by writing on the lines provided the names and numbers of molecules used and produced during glycolysis.

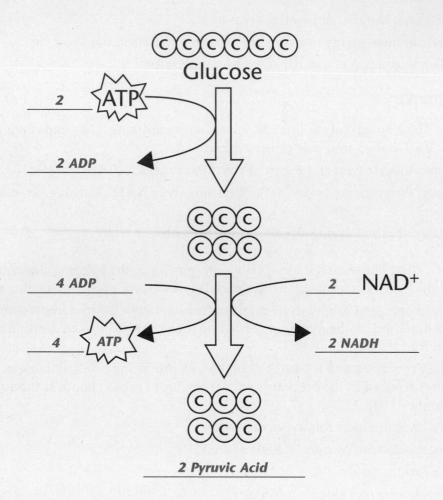

2. Why is it an investment for the cell to use two ATP at the beginning of glycolysis?

The end result of glycolysis is the production of four ATP. Using two ATP at the start

of glycolysis gives the cell a net gain of two ATP.

3. What are two advantages of glycolysis?

(1) Glycolysis occurs very quickly, which allows it to supply ATP if energy demand

suddenly increases. (2) Glycolysis can quickly supply energy to cells when oxygen is

not available.

The Krebs Cycle

For Questions 4–7, write True if the statement is true. If the statement is false, change the underlined word or words to make the statement true.

__mitochondria__ **4.** The pyruvic acid produced in glycolysis enters the <u>chloroplasts</u> if oxygen is present in a cell.

__acetic__ **5.** In the matrix, pyruvic acid is converted to <u>lactic</u> acid before the Krebs cycle begins.

__True__ **6.** The compound that joins with a 4-carbon molecule in the Krebs cycle is called <u>acetyl-CoA</u>.

__True__ **7.** <u>Carbon dioxide</u> is the only product of the Krebs cycle that is not re-used or used in other stages of cellular respiration.

8. Complete the flowchart to show which of the Krebs cycle's many products go on to the third stage of cellular respiration.

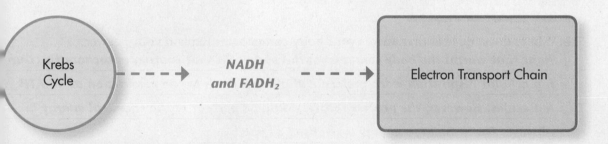

Krebs Cycle → NADH and FADH$_2$ → Electron Transport Chain

Electron Transport and ATP Synthesis

For Questions 9–14, complete each statement by writing the correct word or words.

9. In eukaryotes, the electron transport chain is composed of a series of electron carriers located in the __inner membrane__ of the mitochondrion.

10. In prokaryotes, the electron transport chain is in the __cell membrane__.

11. __Oxygen__ serves as the final electron acceptor of the electron transport chain.

12. __NADH__ and __FADH$_2$__ pass high-energy electrons to the electron transport chain.

13. The transfer of high-energy electrons down the electron transport chain causes __hydrogen ions__ to be transported across the mitochondrial membrane.

14. ATP synthases produce the force needed to add one __phosphate group__ to each ADP molecule by spinning when hydrogen ions flow through them.

The Totals

15. How many ATP molecules per glucose molecule does a cell gain from each of the three stages of cellular respiration?

A cell gains 2 ATP molecules per glucose molecule from glycolysis, 2 more ATP molecules from the Krebs cycle, and 32 ATP molecules from the electron transport chain.

16. Besides glucose, what other kinds of molecules can be used to produce ATP in cellular respiration?

lipids, proteins, and complex carbohydrates that can be broken down into glucose

17. Why is cellular respiration considered an efficient process?

The 36 ATP molecules generated represent about 36 percent of the total energy available. In fact, the cell is more efficient at using food than a typical automobile engine is at burning gasoline.

Apply the Big idea

18. Where does the heat that warms your body come from? Explain your answer.

Heat that warms the body comes from the body cells that contain mitochondria. During cellular respiration, each molecule of glucose leads to the production of 36 ATP molecules. However, the process recovers only 36 percent of the chemical energy in glucose. The remaining energy is released as heat.

9.3 Fermentation

Lesson Objectives

▢ Explain how organisms get energy in the absence of oxygen.

▢ Identify the pathways the body uses to release energy during exercise.

Lesson Summary

Fermentation **Fermentation** releases energy from food molecules by producing ATP without oxygen. Cells convert NADH to the electron carrier NAD⁺. This allows glycolysis to produce a steady stream of ATP. There are two forms of fermentation. Both start with the reactants pyruvic acid and NADH.

- alcoholic fermentation produces ethyl alcohol and carbon dioxide
  - occurs in yeast and a few other microorganisms
  - produces alcoholic beverages and causes bread dough to rise
- lactic acid fermentation produces lactic acid
  - occurs in most organisms, including humans
  - used to produce beverages such as buttermilk and foods such as cheese, yogurt, and pickles

Energy and Exercise The body uses different pathways to release energy.

- For short, quick bursts of energy, the body uses ATP already in muscles as well as ATP made by lactic acid fermentation.
- For exercise longer than about 90 seconds, cellular respiration is the only way to continue generating a supply of ATP.

Fermentation

For Questions 1–6, write True if the statement is true. If the statement is false, change the underlined word or words to make the statement true.

True	1.	<u>Glycolysis</u> provides the pyruvic acid molecules used in fermentation.
NAD⁺	2.	Fermentation allows glycolysis to continue by providing the <u>NADPH</u> needed to accept high-energy electrons.
anaerobic	3.	Fermentation is an <u>aerobic</u> process.
cytoplasm	4.	Fermentation occurs in the <u>mitochondria</u> of cells.
True	5.	<u>Alcoholic</u> fermentation gives off carbon dioxide and is used in making bread.
True	6.	Most organisms perform fermentation using a chemical reaction that converts pyruvic acid to <u>lactic acid</u>.

7. Compare and contrast fermentation and cellular respiration by completing the compare/contrast table. Write your answers in the empty table cells.

Aspect	Fermentation	Cellular Respiration
Function	produces ATP without oxygen	long-term, large production of ATP
Reactants	glucose, ATP pyruvic acid, NADH	glucose, ATP, pyruvic acid, NADH and FADH$_2$, oxygen
Products	NAD$^+$, ethyl alcohol and CO$_2$ in alcoholic fermentation or lactic acid in lactic acid fermentation, ATP	CO$_2$, H$_2$O, ATP

8. Compare and contrast alcoholic fermentation and lactic acid fermentation by completing the compare/contrast table. Write your answers in the empty table cells.

Type of Fermentation	Summary Equation	Use in Industry
Alcoholic	Pyruvic acid + NADH → Alcohol + CO$_2$ + NAD$^+$	used to produce alcoholic beverages, causes bread dough to rise
Lactic acid	Pyruvic acid + NADH → Lactic acid + NAD$^+$	used to produce cheese, yogurt, sour cream, pickles and other foods

9. What causes humans to become lactic acid fermenters?

Brief periods without oxygen will cause many of the cells of a human body to produce ATP by lactic acid fermentation.

Energy and Exercise

0. What are three main sources of ATP available for human muscle cells?

The three sources are ATP already in muscles, ATP made by lactic acid fermentation,

and ATP produced by cellular respiration.

_____

1. During a race, how do your muscle cells produce ATP after the store of ATP in muscles is used?

After the ATP in muscles is used, the muscles produce ATP by lactic acid fermentation.

_____

2. Why does a sprinter have an oxygen debt to repay after the race is over?

Lactic acid fermentation produces lactic acid as a byproduct. The only way to get rid

of the lactic acid is in a chemical pathway that requires extra oxygen.

_____

3. A runner needs more energy for a longer race. How does the body generate the necessary ATP?

Cellular respiration is the only way to continue generating a supply of ATP.

_____

4. Why are aerobic forms of exercise so beneficial for weight control?

The body stores energy in the form of glycogen. These stores of glycogen are usually

enough for 15–20 minutes of activity. After that, the body begins to break down

other stored molecules, including fats, for energy.

Apply the Big idea

5. Compare and contrast the role of fermentation and cellular respiration in the actual production of ATP. In your response, consider which process produces ATP and which process contributes to its production.

For every molecule of glucose, cellular respiration produces 36 ATP molecules, while

fermentation produces two ATP molecules. In fermentation, the two ATP molecules

are produced during glycolysis. Fermentation supplies glycolysis with NAD$^+$ to keep it

going. In cellular respiration, ATP is produced during glycolysis, the Krebs cycle, and

the electron transport chain.

Chapter Vocabulary Review

For Questions 1–7, match the term with its definition.

Term

F **1.** anaerobic

D **2.** glycolysis

C **3.** Krebs cycle

G **4.** calorie

A **5.** matrix

E **6.** aerobic

B **7.** fermentation

Definition

A. Innermost compartment of a mitochondrion

B. Process that forms either lactic acid or ethyl alcohol when no oxygen is present

C. Stage of cellular respiration that starts with pyruvic acid and produces carbon dioxide

D. Process in which glucose is broken down into two molecules of pyruvic acid

E. "In air"

F. "Without air"

G. Amount of energy needed to raise the temperature of 1 gram of water 1°C

For Questions 8–10, write the letter of the correct answer on the line at the left.

A **8.** Which is the process that releases energy by breaking down food molecules in the presence of oxygen?

    A. cellular respiration   **C.** glycolysis

    B. electron transport   **D.** photosynthesis

C **9.** Which is the electron carrier that accepts electrons during glycolysis?

    A. ADP   **C.** NAD^+

    B. ATP   **D.** $NADP^+$

C **10.** When comparing cellular respiration and photosynthesis, these two processes are best described as

    A. energy-releasing processes.   **C.** opposite processes.

    B. energy-storing processes.   **D.** similar processes.

11. Complete the illustration by adding the words "aerobic" or "anaerobic" on the lines provided.

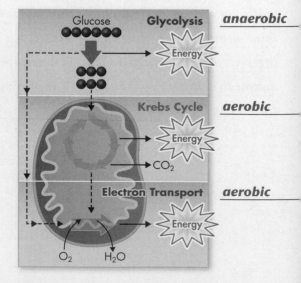

CHAPTER MYSTERY

DIVING WITHOUT A BREATH

In the Chapter Mystery, you read about the traits that allow a whale to stay underwater for 45 minutes. The human body doesn't have any of those traits, so while swimming, we must stay near the surface where we have access to oxygen.

21st Century Learning

Does Carbon Sink?

You have learned about the ways in which photosynthesis and cellular respiration are different. To put it simply, during respiration, animals and plants take in oxygen and release carbon dioxide and water; during photosynthesis, plants take in carbon dioxide and release oxygen.

As you may already know, many human-made machines burn fossil fuels, such as coal and oil that release large quantities of carbon dioxide into the air. People began building carbon-emitting machines in the mid-1700s when the Industrial Revolution began. More and more of them, including factories and cars, have been built ever since. As a result, much more carbon dioxide is being released into Earth's atmosphere than in the past. Carbon dioxide absorbs and retains heat near Earth's surface, and the additional carbon dioxide in the atmosphere contributes to global warming.

Scientists and governments around the world are trying to find ways to reduce and eventually reverse global warming. This article presents one possible method for reducing carbon dioxide emissions to the atmosphere.

We'll Try Everything—Including Making New Carbon Sinks

These days everyone is talking about reducing carbon dioxide emissions. Reducing carbon emissions is important. But we also could use a reliable way to dispose of the CO_2 we create. Nature does it every day, through carbon reservoirs, also known as carbon sinks. The word *sink* has many definitions, including "something that stores or disposes of something else."

In fact, Earth has two major types of carbon sinks: oceans and trees. The world's oceans absorb and store CO_2 from the air. All the world's plants take in carbon dioxide and release the oxygen we breathe. The catch is, these natural carbon sinks may not last. Studies indicate that oceans are reaching the limit of the carbon dioxide they can hold. And trees? Well, you've probably heard how quickly we're cutting down rain forests.

Perhaps people can make new carbon sinks. We've been pumping oil and natural gas out of the ground for more than 150 years. What if we could pump CO_2 back into the ground to take their place? We have the technology to convert old oil and gas wells into carbon dioxide storage units that can hold the CO_2 we pump into them. It would be expensive to retrofit existing power plants, or to build pipelines to carry the gas away. But if we can find underground storage areas near fossil-fuel burning power plants, then transport would not be an issue. Also, building new carbon-disposal plants near power plants would be a relatively inexpensive way to store carbon emissions near their source.

Continued on next page ▶

21st Century Themes Science and Global Awareness

1. What are two main natural carbon sinks?

The oceans and plants

2. What type of carbon sink does the author propose people use?

An underground storage facility from which fossil fuels were previously removed

3. Most power plants are not located near sites where fossil fuels are mined. How do you think this would affect the practicality of this proposal?

SAMPLE ANSWER: *I think it will make the proposal less attractive because it will make extensive transportation of carbon dioxide emissions necessary.*

4. According to the article, costs can be kept down if new plants are built "in the right places." What are the right places?

The right places are close to where carbon dioxide emissions are being created, such as power plants.

5. Do you think what the author proposes is a good long-term solution? Why or why not?

SAMPLE ANSWER: *I think it's not a good long-term solution because one day we'll run out of places on Earth to store the carbon dioxide, or because the gas may escape from its underground location.*

21st Century Skills Planning a Carbon Sink

The skills used in this activity include **communication skills, creativity and intellectual curiosity, interpersonal and collaborative skills, accountability and adaptability,** and **social responsibility.**

What types of carbon sinks or carbon dioxide storage can be used to dispose of CO_2 in your community? Find out who in your local government is in charge of the trees on city property. Interview that person to identify places where trees could be planted. Can all new trees be planted in one place or must they be scattered around town? Get an estimate for the number of trees that might be planted on all sites in your community. Try to obtain as many trees as you can, either by asking local nurseries to donate them or by holding fundraisers to get the money to buy them. Then assemble a group of volunteers to spend "Carbon Sink Day" planting the trees. Make sure you get the necessary permits and oversight from your community government before you start planting. You might also have to prepare a plan for taking care of the small trees as they grow.

Evaluate students' projects based on the questions they prepare for their interview and the quality of the notes they take at the interview, the thoroughness and "politeness" of their request for tree donations, the creativity and organization of the fundraisers they hold, and the manner in which they cooperate with community officials in the planting and maintenance of the trees they plant.

10 Cell Growth and Division

 Big Idea ▶ Growth, Development, and Reproduction

Q: How does a cell produce a new cell?

WHAT I KNOW	WHAT I LEARNED
10.1 Why do cells divide?	SAMPLE ANSWER: *Cells divide to produce more cells.*	SAMPLE ANSWER: *Cells divide because the DNA in a large cell cannot meet the cell's needs. Also, large cells have difficulty exchanging materials.*
10.2 How do cells divide?	SAMPLE ANSWER: *Cells divide by splitting into two cells.*	SAMPLE ANSWER: *Prokaryotic cells divide by binary fission. Eukaryotic cells divide by a process that includes mitosis, division of the nucleus, and cytokinesis, division of the cytoplasm.*
10.3 How does a cell control the process of cell division?	SAMPLE ANSWER: *Cell division is part of the cell cycle.*	SAMPLE ANSWER: *Proteins such as cyclins, internal regulators, and external regulators control the cell cycle and cell division.*
10.4 How does a single, undifferentiated cell lead to a complex multicellular organism?	SAMPLE ANSWER: *A single, undifferentiated cell divides and leads to many cells that become specialized.*	SAMPLE ANSWER: *Specialized cells come from undifferentiated cells called stem cells. Embryonic stem cells are pluripotent and can become more types of cells than can adult stem cells, which are multipotent.*

10.1 Cell Growth, Division, and Reproduction

Lesson Objectives

🔑 Explain the problems that growth causes for cells.

🔑 Compare asexual and sexual reproduction.

Lesson Summary

Limits to Cell Size There are two main reasons why cells divide:

▶ Information "overload": The larger a cell gets, the more demands it places on its DNA. Eventually, the cell's DNA cannot meet the cell's needs.

▶ Exchange of materials: Cells take in nutrients and eliminate wastes through the cell membrane.

  • The larger a cell's volume, the more materials it needs to function and the more waste it creates.

  • A cell's volume increases at a faster rate than its surface area. As a cell grows, its surface-area-to-volume ratio becomes too small.

  • The larger a cell gets, the harder it is for enough materials to move across its cell membrane.

▶ **Cell division** solves the information overload and materials exchange problems.

Cell Division and Reproduction Cell division is part of both types of reproduction:

▶ **Asexual reproduction**:

  • produces genetically identical organisms.

  • occurs in many single-celled organisms and in some multicellular organisms.

  • allows rapid reproduction of organisms in favorable environments.

▶ **Sexual Reproduction**:

  • produces organisms with genetic information from both parents.

  • occurs in most animals and plants and in many single-celled organisms.

  • increases genetic diversity, which aids species survival in changing environments.

Limits to Cell Size

For Questions 1–4, write True if the statement is true. If the statement is false, change the underlined word or words to make the statement true.

stays the same 1. As a cell's size increases, its amount of DNA <u>also increases</u>.

True 2. The amount of activity in a cell is related to its <u>volume</u>.

larger 3. The smaller the cell, the <u>smaller</u> its ratio of surface area to volume.

True 4. The <u>information crisis</u> in a cell is solved by the replication of the DNA before cell division.

5. **VISUAL ANALOGY** In the visual analogy of the growing town, what does the library represent? Identify two characteristics that make it a good choice for this analogy.

SAMPLE ANSWER: *The library represents the cell's DNA. It is a good choice because a library contains information and typically there is only one per small town.*

Cell Division and Reproduction

For Questions 6–8, complete each statement by writing the correct word or words.

6. ___Reproduction___ is the formation of new individuals.

7. For single-celled organisms, cell division is a form of ___asexual___ reproduction.

8. Most multicellular organisms reproduce by ___sexual___ reproduction.

9. Use the table to compare and contrast asexual and sexual reproduction.

Asexual and Sexual Reproduction	
Similarities	**Differences**
Both produce new organisms. Both involve the transfer of genetic material from parent to offspring.	*The offspring of asexual reproduction are genetically identical to their parents. The offspring of sexual reproduction have some genetic information from each parent. In asexual reproduction, cells separate to form a new individual. In sexual reproduction, two cells fuse.*

Apply the Big idea

10. Vascular tissue helps plants transport water against the force of gravity. Because of this, plants that lack vascular tissue do not grow very tall. How is this situation similar to the information you have learned in this lesson? Explain.

SAMPLE ANSWER: *Plants that lack vascular tissue cannot grow very tall because they cannot transport water very far. A cell cannot grow very large because if it did, it would be unable to transport needed materials into the cell and transport wastes out.*

10.2 The Process of Cell Division

Lesson Objectives

🔑 Describe the role of chromosomes in cell division.

🔑 Name the main events of the cell cycle.

🔑 Describe what happens during the four phases of mitosis.

🔑 Describe the process of cytokinesis.

Lesson Summary

Chromosomes Packages of DNA called **chromosomes** hold a cell's genetic information.

▶ Prokaryotic chromosomes consist of a single, circular strand of DNA.

▶ Eukaryotic chromosomes are highly organized structures.

   • The DNA winds around histone proteins, forming **chromatin**.

   • Chromosomes make the precise separation of DNA possible during cell division.

The Cell Cycle The **cell cycle** is the series of events in the growth and division of a cell.

▶ In the prokaryotic cell cycle, the cell grows, duplicates its DNA, and divides by pinching in the cell membrane.

▶ The eukaryotic cell cycle has four stages (the first three of which are referred to as **interphase**):

   • In the G_1 phase, the cell grows.

   • In the S phase, the cell replicates its DNA.

   • In the G_2 phase, the cell produces organelles and materials for division.

   • In the M phase, the cell divides in two stages—**mitosis**, the division of the nucleus, and **cytokinesis**, the division of the cytoplasm.

Mitosis The division of the nucleus, mitosis, occurs in four stages:

▶ **Prophase**: a cell's genetic material condenses, a spindle starts to form, and the nuclear envelope breaks down.

▶ **Metaphase**: the duplicated chromosomes line up and spindle fibers connect to the **centromeres**.

▶ **Anaphase**: sister **chromatids** separate and move toward the **centrioles**.

▶ **Telophase**: the chromosomes begin to unwind and a nuclear envelope reforms.

Cytokinesis Division of the cytoplasm differs in plant cells and animal cells.

▶ In animal cells, the cell membrane draws in and pinches off.

▶ In plant cells, a cell plate forms, followed by a new cell membrane, and finally a new cell wall forms.

Chromosomes

For Questions 1–5, complete each statement by writing the correct word or words.

1. Cells carry genetic information in packages of DNA called __chromosomes__.

2. Most __prokaryotes__ have only one circular strand of DNA.

3. In eukaryotic cells, the genetic structure consists of DNA and a tightly wound protein, which together form a substance called __chromatin__.

4. The beadlike structures formed by DNA wrapped around __histone__ molecules are called nucleosomes.

5. __Chromosomes__ make possible the precise separation of DNA during cell division.

The Cell Cycle

6. What is the name of the type of cell division that occurs in the prokaryotic cell cycle?
  Cell division in prokaryotes is called binary fission.

7. What happens during interphase?
  The cell grows, copies its DNA, and prepares for cell division.

8. Complete the cell cycle diagram by writing the correct name of a phase on each line.

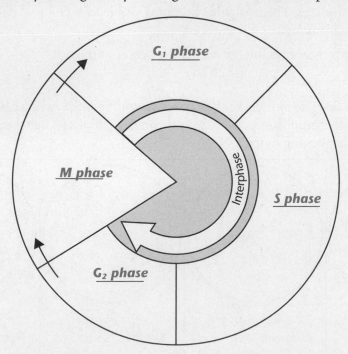

G₁ phase

M phase

Interphase

S phase

G₂ phase

9. In eukaryotic cells, what happens in the G₁ phase that differs from the G₂ phase?
  In the G₁ phase, the cell grows. In the G₂ phase, the cell gets ready for mitosis.

10. In eukaryotic cells, what are the two main stages of cell division?
  Mitosis and cytokinesis are the two main stages of cell division.

Mitosis

11. During prophase, when cell chromosomes become visible, what are the duplicated strands of DNA called? What is the name for the area in which these duplicated strands are joined?

Duplicated strands of chromosomal DNA are called chromatids, or sister chromatids,

and they are joined by a centromere.

12. What structures are spindle fibers attached to that help pull the paired chromosomes apart?

The spindle fibers are attached to centrioles that move toward the poles of the cell,

pulling the chromatids apart.

For Questions 13–16, match the description of the event with the phase of mitosis in which it occurs. Each phase may be used more than once.

Event

_____ D _____ **13.** The chromosomes separate and begin to move to opposite sides of the cell.

_____ B _____ **14.** The chromosomes become visible. The centrioles take up positions on opposite sides of the nucleus.

_____ A _____ **15.** A nuclear envelope re-forms around each cluster of chromosomes. The nucleolus becomes visible in each daughter nucleus.

_____ C _____ **16.** The chromosomes line up across the center of the cell.

Phase of Mitosis

A. Telophase

B. Prophase

C. Metaphase

D. Anaphase

17. THINK VISUALLY The four circles below represent the nucleus of a cell going through mitosis. Draw four chromosomes as they go through each phase. Label each phase and describe what is happening to the DNA.

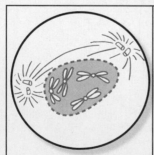

Prophase
DNA has been duplicated and condenses into chromosomes.

Metaphase
Chromosomes line up at center of cell, spindle fibers attach to centromeres.

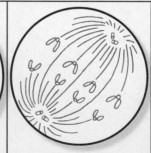

Anaphase
Spindles shorten, pulling separated chromatids to opposite ends of cell.

Telophase
New chromosomes at opposite poles as nucleus starts to re-form.

Cytokinesis

8. What is cytokinesis?

Cytokinesis is the final step of cell division. It completes the M phase of the cell cycle

by dividing the cytoplasm of the original cell between the two new cells.

9. Use the Venn diagram to compare and contrast cytokinesis in animal cells with cytokinesis in plant cells.

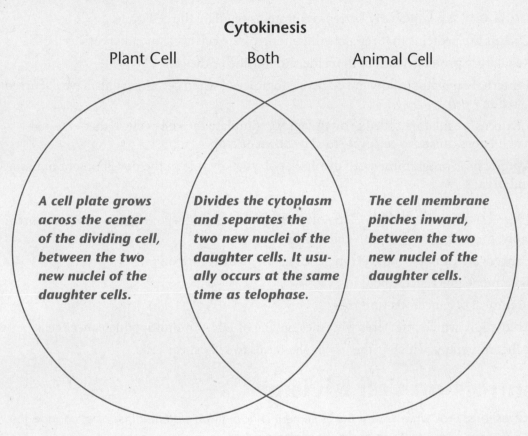

Cytokinesis

Plant Cell   Both   Animal Cell

A cell plate grows across the center of the dividing cell, between the two new nuclei of the daughter cells.

Divides the cytoplasm and separates the two new nuclei of the daughter cells. It usually occurs at the same time as telophase.

The cell membrane pinches inward, between the two new nuclei of the daughter cells.

Apply the Big idea

20. During certain stages of their life cycle, some cells repeatedly undergo mitosis but do not undergo cytokinesis. What would you expect to see if you looked at such cells, or a tissue made up of such cells, under a microscope? Explain your answer.

Under microscopic examination, a tissue whose cells complete all parts of the cell

cycle except cytokinesis would appear to be made up of a mass of cytoplasm with

many nuclei scattered in it.

10.3 Regulating the Cell Cycle

Lesson Objectives

Describe how the cell cycle is regulated.

Explain how cancer cells are different from other cells.

Lesson Summary

Controls on Cell Division Dozens of proteins regulate the cell cycle.

▶ **Cyclins** are proteins that regulate the timing of the cell cycle in eukaryotic cells.

▶ Regulatory proteins work both inside and outside of the cell.

- Internal regulators allow the cell cycle to proceed when certain events have occurred within a cell.

- External regulators called **growth factors** stimulate the cell cycle. Other external regulators cause the cell cycle to slow down or stop.

▶ **Apoptosis** is programmed cell death that plays a key role in the development of tissues and organs.

Cancer: Uncontrolled Cell Growth **Cancer** is a disorder in which cells divide uncontrollably, forming a mass of cells called a **tumor**.

▶ Cancers are caused by defects in genes that regulate cell growth.

▶ Treatments for cancer include:

- removal of cancerous tumors.

- radiation, which interferes with the copying of DNA in multiplying cancer cells.

- chemotherapy, which is the use of chemicals to kill cancer cells.

Controls on Cell Division

For Questions 1–6, write True if the statement is true. If the statement is false, change the underlined word or words to make the statement true.

___stop___ 1. Cells tend to <u>continue</u> dividing when they come into contact with other cells.

___slows down___ 2. Cell division <u>speeds up</u> when the healing process nears completion.

___cyclins___ 3. Proteins called <u>growth factors</u> regulate the timing of the cell cycle in eukaryotic cells.

___True___ 4. If chromosomes have not attached to spindle fibers during metaphase, an <u>internal</u> regulatory protein will prevent the cell from entering anaphase.

___speed up___ 5. Growth factors are external regulatory proteins that <u>slow down</u> the cell cycle.

___True___ 6. Once apoptosis is triggered, a cell proceeds to <u>self-destruct</u>.

7. Complete the cause-and-effect chart by giving an example of an effect caused by each type of regulatory protein.

Factors Affecting the Cell Cycle

Cause	Effect
Cyclins	SAMPLE ANSWER: **Tell a cell when to begin steps of the cell cycle (e.g., growth, DNA synthesis, mitosis, cytokinesis).**
Internal regulatory proteins	SAMPLE ANSWER: **Stop a cell from going to the next stage of the cell cycle if internal events have not occurred (e.g., prevent a cell from entering mitosis until chromosomes are replicated).**
External regulatory proteins	SAMPLE ANSWER: **Speed up the cell cycle (e.g., for embryonic growth and wound healing) or slow down the cell cycle (e.g., so that one body tissue's growth does not disrupt another's).**

Cancer: Uncontrolled Cell Growth

8. What is cancer?

Cancer is a disorder in which some of the body's own cells lose the ability to control growth.

9. What are the two basic types of tumors? Explain how they are different.

Tumors may be malignant or benign. A malignant tumor is cancerous and will invade and destroy healthy tissue around it or in other parts of the body. A benign tumor is noncancerous and does not spread into surrounding tissues or to other parts of the body.

10. Why can cancer be life threatening?

Rapidly dividing cancer cells take nutrients away from healthy tissues. This leads to a disruption of the proper functioning of body organs that causes illness and may lead to death.

11. What is the cause of cancer?

Defects in genes that regulate cell growth and division cause cancer.

12. How do radiation and chemotherapy affect cancer cells?

Radiation disrupts the cancer cell cycle by interfering with the copying of DNA.

Chemotherapy kills cancer cells.

13. Fill out the flowchart by completing each statement with the correct word or words.

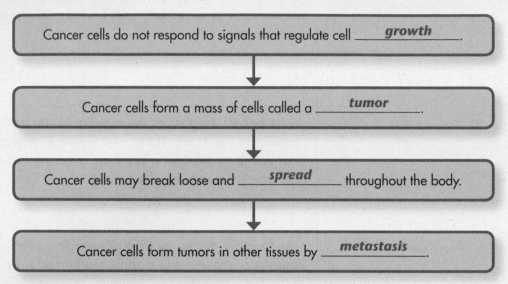

Cancer cells do not respond to signals that regulate cell ____*growth*____.

Cancer cells form a mass of cells called a ____*tumor*____.

Cancer cells may break loose and ____*spread*____ throughout the body.

Cancer cells form tumors in other tissues by ____*metastasis*____.

Apply the Big idea

14. Hair grows from hair follicles, pockets of continually dividing cells in the outer layer of the skin. New cells are added to the base of a hair shaft, inside each follicle. Use what you have learned in this lesson to explain why cancer patients often lose their hair when receiving chemotherapy and grow more hair after chemotherapy stops.

SAMPLE ANSWER: *The chemicals stop cell division in both cancer cells and healthy cells,*

such as the ones that produce hair. When no new cells are being added to the hair

shafts, the shafts break and the hairs fall out. When chemotherapy stops, cell division

in the hair follicles resumes and hair starts to grow again.

10.4 Cell Differentiation

Lesson Objectives

- Describe the process of differentiation.
- Define stem cells and explain their importance.
- Identify the possible benefits and issues relating to stem cell research.

Lesson Summary

From One Cell to Many Multicellular organisms produced via sexual reproduction begin life as a single cell.

- Early cell divisions lead to the formation of an **embryo**.
- Then, individual cells become specialized in both form and function through the process of **differentiation**.
- Once cells of a certain type, such as nerve cells or muscle cells, have formed, the cells cannot develop into a different type of cell.

Stem Cells and Development During an organism's development, some cells differentiate to become a wide variety of body cells.

- A fertilized egg and the first few cells in an embryo are able to form any kind of cell and tissue. Such a cell is termed **totipotent**.
- A **blastocyst** is an embryonic stage that consists of a hollow ball of cells. These cells are able to become any type of body cell. Such cells are termed **pluripotent**.
- Unspecialized cells that can develop into differentiated cells are called **stem cells**. Stem cells are found in embryos and in adults.
  - Embryonic stem cells are the pluripotent cells of an early embryo.
  - Adult stem cells are **multipotent**, which means they can produce many, but not all, types of differentiated cells.

Frontiers in Stem Cell Research Scientists want to learn about the signals that tell a cell to become either specialized or multipotent.

- Potential benefits of stem cell research include the repair or replacement of damaged cells and tissues.
- Research with human stem cells is controversial because it involves ethical issues of life and death.

From One Cell to Many

For Questions 1–4, complete each statement by writing the correct word or words.

1. Humans, pets, and petunias all pass through an early stage of development called a(n) ____*embryo*____.

2. Cells become ____*specialized*____ through the process of differentiation.

3. Scientists have mapped the outcome of every ____*cell division*____ that leads to differentiation in the development of the microscopic worm *C. elegans.*

4. Most cells in the adult body are no longer capable of ____*differentiation*____.

Stem Cells and Development

For Questions 5–7, write the letter of the correct answer on the line at the left.

___C___ 5. Which is an example of a totipotent cell?

    A. blastocyst

    B. bone cell

    C. fertilized egg

    D. lymphocyte

___D___ 6. Cells that are pluripotent are unable to develop into the tissue that

    A. forms the skin.

    B. lines the digestive tract.

    C. produces blood cells.

    D. surrounds an embryo.

___A___ 7. Adult stem cells are best described as

    A. multipotent.

    B. pluripotent.

    C. totipotent.

    D. unable to differentiate.

8. Complete the concept map by identifying some of the types of cells that embryonic stem cells give rise to. Then explain how stem cells are like the stem of a plant.

Many different types of cells can come from stem cells, like the branches emerging

from a stem.

_____

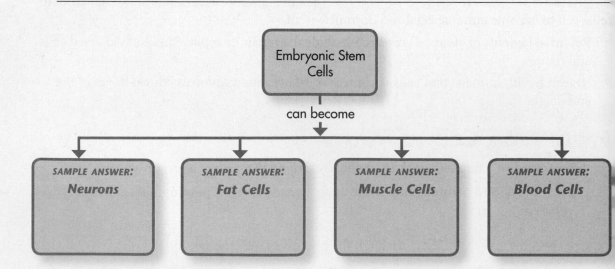

Frontiers in Stem Cell Research

For Questions 9–11, write the letter of the correct answer on the line at the left.

___A___ 9. Which is not a new, potential benefit of stem cell research?

    A. growing new skin cells to repair a cut

    B. replacing heart cells damaged by heart attacks

    C. repairing breaks between nerve cells in spinal injuries

    D. preventing suffering and death caused by cellular damage

___D___ 10. What is the main reason that embryonic stem cell research is considered ethically controversial?

    A. Embryos contain totipotent cells.

    B. Embryos are the result of sexual reproduction.

    C. Embryos from many different organisms must be used.

    D. Embryos are destroyed in the process.

___B___ 11. What is one new technology that could make stem cell research less controversial?

    A. implanting skin cells instead of stem cells in damaged tissue

    B. developing the ability to switch on the genes that make an adult cell pluripotent

    C. replacing stem cells with cancer cells

    D. using the Internet to get more people to accept stem cell research

Apply the Big idea

12. Many plants such as orchids are grown by a technique called tissue culture. Small pieces of plant tissue from a leaf, stem, or root of a mature plant are placed in a medium that contains the proper nutrients. The cells first form a mass of undifferentiated cells, from which tiny roots, stems, and leaves eventually grow. How do the plant cells placed in a medium for tissue culture change in terms of their degree of specialization? What types of animal cells are most similar to the undifferentiated plant cells in a tissue culture? Explain your answer.

SAMPLE ANSWER: *The plant cells first placed in a medium for tissue culture are differentiated cells. The cells produce undifferentiated cells that are pluripotent, or able to develop into all the specialized cell types and structures of the plant. The embryonic stem cells of an animal are the most similar to the plant cells that first develop in a tissue culture because they can develop into all the different cell types and structures of a specific animal.*

Chapter Vocabulary Review

1. Describe how the following terms are related to one another.

asexual reproduction, sexual reproduction: *Both produce a new organism: asexual reproduction involves one parent—offspring have same DNA; sexual reproduction involves two parents—offspring have a mix of DNA.*

chromosome, centrioles: *centrioles are structures in animal cells that organize spindle fibers so duplicated chromosomes can be separated during mitosis*

centromere, chromatid: *a centromere is an area on chromosomes where spindle fibers attach and pull apart sister chromatids during mitosis*

binary fission, mitosis: *Binary fission is the process by which duplicated DNA in prokaryotes is separated between two new cells/organisms. Mitosis is similar in that it involves the separation of duplicated DNA between dividing cells in eukaryotes; unlike binary fission, mitosis is not typically a form of reproduction.*

For Questions 2–9, match the event with the phase of the cell cycle in which it takes place. A phase may be used more than once.

Event   **Phase of the Cell Cycle**

_F_ **2.** A nuclear envelope forms around chromosomes.   **A.** anaphase

_C_ **3.** The cell grows and replicates DNA.   **B.** cytokinesis

_E_ **4.** A spindle forms.   **C.** interphase

_D_ **5.** Chromosomes line up across the center of the cell.   **D.** metaphase

_E_ **6.** The genetic material condenses and chromosomes   **E.** prophase
       become visible.
                                                                                        F. telophase
_A_ **7.** Chromosomes move to opposite sides of the cell.

_B_ **8.** The cytoplasm divides.

_A_ **9.** Sister chromatids separate.

For Questions 10–13, complete each statement by writing the correct word or words.

10. ___*Cyclins*___ and growth factors are examples of regulatory proteins that control the cell cycle.

11. ___*Apoptosis*___ is the controlled series of steps that lead to cell death.

12. The first few cells that form a(n) ___*embryo*___ are said to be ___*totipotent*___ because they can become any type of cell.

13. The hollow ball of cells that forms in early embryonic development is called the ___*blastocyst*___.

CHAPTER MYSTERY

PET SHOP ACCIDENT

21st Century Learning

In the Chapter Mystery, you learned that stem cells make it possible for salamanders to regrow limbs. Developments in stem cell research tend to produce excitement in the media, particularly when the research might lead to a remedy for human health problems.

Stem Cells in the Media

When you read an article about stem cells, as with any scientific topic, you need to consider the source and whether the reporter is giving an accurate account of the facts. You should also try to determine whether the article shows bias. Bias is a preference for a particular point of view, and it may involve distorting facts or slanting information so that it seems to support the preferred point of view.

Read the following two articles. Determine to what degree each article uses facts to back up its conclusions. Also look for evidence of bias or distorted facts.

World News Daily

Stem Cells Improve Memory in Brain-Damaged Mice

FROM THE SCIENCE DESK—A research team at Watson University today announced that stem cells can improve the memory of mice with brain injuries. The researchers were interested in how an injection of stem cells might affect mice that had injuries in the area of the brain involved in memory.

Working with 100 mice, the scientists injected 50 of the mice with stem cells known to give rise to mouse nerve cells. The other 50 mice did not receive any treatment. After three months, the scientists tested the memory of both groups of mice by seeing whether they recognized objects. The group that did not receive the stem cells remembered the objects about 40 percent of the time. In contrast, the group that received the stem cells remembered the objects about 70 percent of the time.

The scientists hope that their research will one day lead to a treatment for human diseases and conditions, such as Alzheimer's disease, in which people suffer significant memory loss. "We are very excited by our results," said Diane Brandon, the leader of the research team. "But we are not ready to try this treatment with humans."

LOOKING AHEAD

A Weekly Guide for People in the Know

Alzheimer's Disease— Is a CURE for Memory Loss Just Around the Corner?

Don't look now, but those mice that you hate to see scurry across the kitchen floor might just provide a cure for the thousands of people afflicted with Alzheimer's Disease. Scientists at Watson University are reporting that stem cells injected into brain-damaged mice can cure memory loss. The researchers suspected that the stem cells would give rise to new mouse nerve cells. Indeed, the mice that received the stem cells were found to have greatly improved memories. "We are very excited by our results," said Diane Brandon, the leader of the research team. The scientists are confident that, since stem cells can treat memory loss in mice, stem cells can also be used to cure Alzheimer's disease in humans.

Continued on next page ▶

21st Century Themes · Science and Health Literacy

1. Which article provides the reader with the most facts that describe the procedure of the research team and the result of the experiment? Give examples.

   The first article provided more facts. It explained that the researchers tested two groups of mice, injecting only one group with the stem cells. Also, it detailed how the mice were tested for their ability to remember things. Finally, for both groups, it gave the percentages of the times that mice remembered objects.

2. Carefully look at the words that each article uses to describe the results of the research. According to the first article, how did the injected stem cells affect memory loss in mice?

   The stem cells improved the memory of the mice.

   According to the second article, how did the injected stem cells affect memory loss in mice?

   The stem cells cured the memory loss.

3. Compare the titles of both articles. Which of the two titles more accurately describes the results of the research? Explain your answer.

   The title of the first article is more accurate, because the scientists did not discover a cure for human Alzheimer's disease, but they did see improvement from the stem cells.

4. Both articles use quotations from one of the scientists. Compare the use of quotations in the two articles. Which of the two articles omits something important that the scientist said? How does this omission affect the reader's impression of the implication of this research for humans? *The second article omits the quotation that says that the scientists are not ready to test the procedure on humans. This omission implies that the researchers are on the verge of discovering a cure for Alzheimer's disease.*

5. Which of the two articles do you trust more? Which would attract more attention? Explain your answers. *Students will probably choose the first article as being the more trustworthy, because it provides specific numbers and does not distort the results. However, they may choose the second article as attracting more attention given the claim it makes in its title.*

21st Century Skills · Comparing Articles

The skills used in this activity include **information and media literacy** and **critical thinking and systems thinking.**

Use Internet or library resources to find two articles that evaluate the treatments for a specific type of cancer, such as leukemia or prostate cancer. Compare the articles by answering the following questions: How easy is the article to understand? Are opinions supported by facts? Is there evidence of bias? Does the article omit important information? On the basis of your analysis, write an essay comparing the effectiveness of the two articles.

Evaluate students' essays based on the quality of their resources, the effectiveness of their writing, and their attention to the content of the two articles.

11 Introduction to Genetics

Big idea ▶ **Information and Heredity**

Q: How does biological information pass from one generation to another?

WHAT I KNOW	WHAT I LEARNED
11.1 How does an organism pass its characteristics on to its offspring?	SAMPLE ANSWER: *Offspring inherit their physical characteristics from their parents.*	SAMPLE ANSWER: *Alleles (forms of genes) segregate during gamete formation. Recessive alleles exhibit a trait only when a dominant allele is not present.*
11.2 How can you predict the outcome of a genetic cross?	SAMPLE ANSWER: *Outcomes of inheritance are not certain, but the odds can be determined.*	SAMPLE ANSWER: *Alleles for different traits separate independently during gamete formation. A Punnett square can be used to predict which alleles will combine in offspring.*
11.3 How can interactions between alleles, genes, and the environment affect an organism's traits?	SAMPLE ANSWER: *Some traits do not show simple Mendelian patterns of inheritance.*	SAMPLE ANSWER: *Many genes have multiples alleles. Many traits are produced by the interaction of several genes. The environment affects gene expression.*
11.4 How does a cell divide to create cells with exactly half of the original cell's genetic information?	SAMPLE ANSWER: *Segregation and independent assortment occur during gamete formation.*	SAMPLE ANSWER: *Meiosis is the process that cuts chromosome numbers in half as gametes form. Meiosis occurs in several phases.*

11.1 The Work of Gregor Mendel

Lesson Objectives

🔑 Describe Mendel's studies and conclusions about inheritance.

🔑 Describe what happens during segregation.

Lesson Summary

The Experiments of Gregor Mendel The delivery of characteristics from parents to offspring is heredity. The scientific study of heredity is **genetics**. Gregor Mendel founded modern genetics with his experiments on a convenient model system, pea plants:

▶ **Fertilization** is the process in which reproductive cells (egg from the female and sperm from the male) join to produce a new cell.

▶ A **trait** is a specific characteristic, such as (in peas) seed color or plant height.

▶ Mendel prevented self-pollination in the peas. He controlled fertilization so he could study how traits passed from one generation to the next.

▶ He created **hybrids**, which are crosses between true-breeding parents (the P generation) with different traits.

   • These hybrids were the F_1 (first filial) generation.

   • They each showed the characteristic of only one parent.

▶ Mendel found that traits are controlled by factors that pass from parent to offspring. Those factors are **genes**. The different forms of a gene are **alleles**.

▶ Mendel's **principle of dominance** states that some alleles are dominant and others are recessive. The recessive allele is exhibited only when the dominant allele is not present.

Segregation Mendel allowed members of the F_1 generation to self-pollinate. The trait controlled by the recessive allele appeared in the next generation (F_2) in about one-fourth of the offspring—even when it did not appear in the F_1 generation.

▶ Separation of alleles is **segregation**.

▶ When **gametes** (sex cells) form, alleles segregate so that each gamete carries only one allele for each gene.

▶ The F_2 generation gets a new combination of alleles: one from each parent.

The Experiments of Gregor Mendel

Match the term with its definition.

Term		Definition
C	1. genes	A. Specific characteristics that vary among individuals
B	2. hybrids	B. The offspring of true-breeding parents with different traits
A	3. traits	C. Factors that determine traits
E	4. alleles	D. Sex cells, egg or sperm
D	5. gametes	E. The different forms of a gene

6. Why are peas a good model system for studying heredity?

They are small, easy to grow, and they produce large numbers of offspring.

7. How did Mendel cross-pollinate flowers?

He removed the male parts from one flower and dusted their pollen (containing

sperm) onto the female parts of another flower.

8. What is the difference between a gene and an allele?

A gene is a factor that passes from parent to offspring and determines a trait. An

allele is one form of a gene.

9. State the principle of dominance.

Some alleles are dominant and some are recessive. An organism with one dominant

allele for a trait will exhibit that form of the trait.

The table shows some crosses between true-breeding parents that carry pairs of dominant alleles (such as SS) or pairs of recessive alleles (such as ss). Complete the table to show the combination of alleles in the offspring. Then use it to answer Questions 10–11.

Dominant and Recessive Forms of Pea Plant Traits			
Trait	Parent Plants (P Generation)		Offspring (F₁ Generation)
Seed Color	Yellow YY	Green yy	Yellow Yy
Seed Coat Color	White gg	Gray GG	Gray Gg
Pod Shape	Constricted ss	Smooth SS	Smooth Ss
Pod Color	Green CC	Yellow cc	Green Cc

10. What is the dominant shape of a pea pod? How do you know?

The dominant shape of a pea pod is smooth. You know because the smooth trait

shows up in the F₁. That's why its allele is a capital letter.

11. What symbol represents the recessive allele for pod color?

The symbol for the recessive allele for pod color is c (lower-case).

Segregation

12. What is segregation? What is the result of segregation?

Segregation is the separation of alleles during formation of gametes. The result is

that each gamete carries only one allele for each gene.

13. THINK VISUALLY The capital letter *G* represents the allele in peas that causes the dominant trait, gray seed coat. The lower-case letter *g* represents the recessive allele that causes the recessive trait, white seed coat.

In the circles, show the alleles in the gametes of the parent generation. Show how the alleles recombine in the F₁ plants.

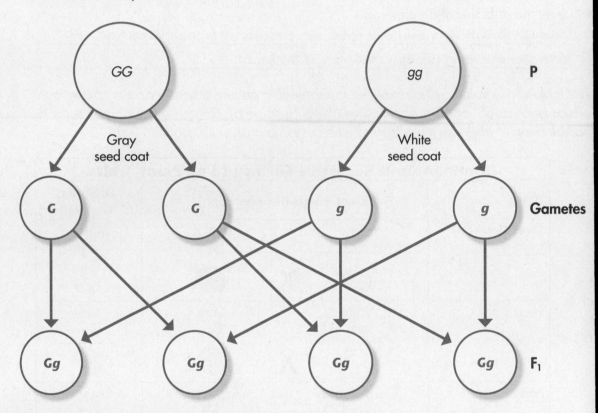

Apply the Big idea

14. A black cat and a white cat have four black kittens in the F_1 generation. In the F_2 generation, there are three black kittens and one white kitten. Explain how the F_2 generation proves that genetic information passes unchanged from one generation to the next, even when a specific trait is not exhibited.

The trait produced by a pair of recessive alleles (white fur) was not exhibited in the

individuals of the F₁ generation, but it reappeared in one fourth of the F₂ offspring.

That proves the genetic information was never lost, even though it was not expressed.

11.2 Applying Mendel's Principles

Lesson Objectives

▢ Explain how geneticists use the principles of probability to make Punnett squares.

▢ Explain the principle of independent assortment.

▢ Explain how Mendel's principles apply to all organisms.

Lesson Summary

Probability and Punnett Squares **Probability** is the likelihood that a particular event will occur. Probability predicts the recombination of alleles:

➤ Of an allele pair, the probability of each allele in a gamete is ½, or 50 percent.

➤ When F_1 hybrid individuals are crossed, the probability of
  - two recessive alleles is ¼.
  - two dominant alleles is ¼.
  - one dominant allele and one recessive allele is ½ (¼ + ¼).

➤ Organisms that have two identical alleles for a gene are **homozygous** for that trait. If they have different alleles for the same gene, they are **heterozygous** for that trait.

➤ Physical traits are an organism's **phenotype**. Its **genotype** is its genetic makeup.

➤ A **Punnett square** is a mathematical tool that helps predict combinations in genetic crosses.

Independent Assortment The principle of **independent assortment** states that genes for different traits segregate independently during the formation of gametes. In two-factor crosses, the phenotypes of the F_2 offspring occur in a 9:3:3:1 ratio: 9 with with both traits dominant, 3 with the first trait dominant and the second trait recessive, 3 with the first trait recessive and the second trait dominant, and 1 with both traits recessive.

A Summary of Mendel's Principles

▶ Genes are passed on from parents and determine traits.

▶ Where two or more alleles for a gene exist, some may be dominant and others recessive.

▶ In sexually reproducing organisms, offspring receive a copy of each gene from each parent. The alleles segregate when forming gametes.

▶ Alleles for different genes usually segregate independently.

Probability and Punnett Squares

1. What is probability? *Probability is the likelihood that a certain event will occur.*

_____

2. In a parent pea plant with the allele pair *Gg*, what is the probability that one gamete will contain the *G* allele? *½, or 50 percent*

_____

3. Complete the graphic organizer to define the characteristics of homozygous and heterozygous genotypes and phenotypes.

	Homozygous	Heterozygous
Genotype	*Both alleles are the same.*	*The alleles are different.*
Phenotype	*The phenotype depends on whether both alleles are dominant or recessive. The corresponding phenotype will be expressed.*	*The phenotype will be that produced by the dominant allele.*

4. The dominant allele for smooth pod shape in peas is S. The recessive allele for constricted pod shape is s. In the Punnett square, show the result of crossing two heterozygous parents (Ss). Write the genotype and the phenotype of each type of offspring in the space provided.

	S	s
S	Genotype: _**SS**_ Phenotype: _**Smooth**_	Genotype: _**Ss**_ Phenotype: _**Smooth**_
s	Genotype: _**Ss**_ Phenotype: _**Smooth**_	Genotype: _**ss**_ Phenotype: _**Constricted**_

For Questions 5–9, refer to the Punnett square above.

5. What is the probability of a heterozygous offspring? Explain your answer.
   The probability of a heterozygous offspring Ss is ½ (¼ + ¼).

6. What is the probability of a homozygous offspring? Explain.
   It is ½ (¼ SS + ¼ ss).

7. What is the probability of a homozygous recessive offspring?
   It is ¼ (ss).

8. What is the probability of a smooth phenotype?
   It is ¾ (¼ SS + ½ Ss).

9. What is the probability of a homozygous recessive individual (ss) producing a gamete with a dominant allele (S)? Explain.
   The probability is zero because this individual did not inherit a dominant allele.

Independent Assortment

10. State the principle of independent assortment below.

Genes for different traits segregate independently during the formation of gametes.

11. Using the principle of independent assortment, complete the Punnett square to show the results of an F$_1$ cross between two individuals heterozygous for both pod color (C = green and c = yellow) and pod shape (S = smooth and s + constricted). The gametes and some of the genotypes of the F$_2$ offspring are given.

	CS	**cS**	**Cs**	**cs**
CS	CCSS	CcSS	CCSs	CcSs
cS	CcSS	ccSS	CcSs	ccSs
Cs	CCSs	CcSs	CCss	Ccss
cs	CcSs	ccSs	Ccss	ccss

For Questions 12–15, refer to the Punnett square above.

12. Which genotype belongs to an offspring that is homozygous recessive for both traits? What is the probability of that genotype?

That genotype is ccss. Its probability is 1/16.

13. What is the phenotype of an individual heterozygous for both traits?

The phenotype is green pod color and smooth pod shape.

14. What is the probability of an F$_2$ offspring having the green pod color and smooth pod shape? Explain. (Note: Remember that more than one genotype can produce this phenotype.)

The probability is 9/16 (the combined probability of CCSS, CCSs, CcSS, and CcSs).

15. The Punnett square predicts a 9:3:3:1 ratio for phenotypes. Explain what that ratio means.

It means that the probability of an offspring that exhibits both dominant traits (green pod color and smooth pod shape) is 9/16. The probability of one dominant and one recessive (either green pod color and constricted pod shape or yellow pod color and smooth pod shape) is 3/16 each. The probability of both recessive traits showing in the phenotype (yellow, constricted pod) is 1/16.

Summary of Mendel's Principles

For Questions 16–20, complete each statement by writing the correct word or words.

16. The units that determine the inheritance of biological characteristics are ____*genes*____.

17. A form of a gene is a(n) ____*allele*____.

18. If two or more forms of a gene exist, some may be dominant and others may be ____*recessive*____.

19. The offspring of most sexually reproducing organisms have two copies of each gene. One came from each ____*parent*____.

20. Alleles from different genes usually ____*segregate*____ independently from each other when gametes form.

For Questions 21–25, match the term with its description.

E	**21.** Determine traits	**A.** parents
B	**22.** Can be two of these in one gene	**B.** alleles
C	**23.** Allele that is expressed	**C.** dominant
A	**24.** Where genes come from	**D.** segregate
D	**25.** What genes do during gamete formation	**E.** genes

26. Explain the importance of Thomas Hunt Morgan's experiments with fruit flies. Why was his work an important addition to Mendel's research?

He experimented with fruit flies instead of plants. He was the first to discover that

Mendel's principles apply to organisms other than plants.

Apply the Big idea

27. Four sisters begin attending your school. One has brown hair and brown eyes. Another has brown hair and blue eyes. The third also has blue eyes, but blond hair. The fourth has blond hair, too, but she has brown eyes. Explain how the principle of independent segregation accounts for these sisters having four different phenotypes for two traits.

If their parents are heterozygous for both traits, the genes and alleles segregate

independently, resulting in all possible phenotype combinations: dominant-dominant,

dominant-recessive, recessive-dominant, and recessive-recessive.

_____

Name _____ Class _____ Date _____

11.3 Other Patterns of Inheritance

Lesson Objectives

- Describe the other patterns of inheritance.
- Explain the relationship between genes and the environment.

Lesson Summary

Beyond Dominant and Recessive Alleles Some alleles are neither dominant nor recessive:

▶ In cases of **incomplete dominance**, neither allele is completely dominant over the other. The phenotype is a blend of the two homozygous phenotypes.

▶ In cases of **codominance**, both alleles in the heterozygous genotype are expressed in the phenotype.

▶ Genes with **multiple alleles** have more than two forms of the same gene. There may be more than one dominant form and several different phenotypes.

▶ **Polygenic traits** are controlled by the interaction of two or more genes and exhibit a wide range of phenotypes.

Genes and the Environment The phenotype of an organism results only partly from its genotype. Environmental conditions can affect how genes are expressed.

Beyond Dominant and Recessive Alleles

1. Complete the graphic organizer to summarize exceptions to Mendel's principles.

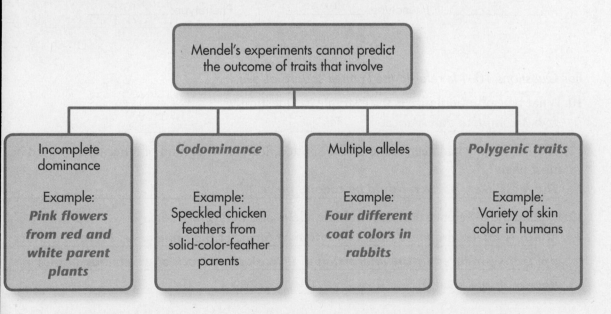

For Questions 2–8, write True if the statement is true. If the statement is false, change the underlined word to make the statement true.

_____neither_____ 2. When offspring show a blend of the parents' traits, <u>one</u> allele is dominant over the other.

_____incomplete_____ 3. In <u>complete</u> dominance, the heterozygous phenotype lies somewhere between the two homozygous phenotypes.

_____True_____ 4. A heterozygous individual that exhibits the traits of both parents is an example of <u>codominance</u>.

_____multiple_____ 5. Many genes exist in several forms and are said to have <u>codominant</u> alleles.

_____True_____ 6. While multiple alleles may exist in a population, an individual usually carries only two alleles for each <u>gene</u>.

_____polygenic_____ 7. Traits produced by two or more genes are <u>codominant</u>.

_____True_____ 8. Polygenic traits often show a wide range of <u>phenotypes</u>.

9. A plant breeder produced a purple flower by crossing a red parent with a blue parent. Use *RR* as the genotype for the red parent and *BB* for the blue parent. Complete the Punnett square to show the resulting genotypes and phenotypes of the offspring.

	Gamete allele: ___R___	**Gamete allele:** ___R___
Gamete allele: ___B___	Genotype: ___RB___ Phenotype: ___Purple___	Genotype: ___RB___ Phenotype: ___Purple___
Gamete allele: ___B___	Genotype: ___RB___ Phenotype: ___Purple___	Genotype: ___RB___ Phenotype: ___Purple___

For Questions 10–11, refer to the Punnett square above.

10. What type of inheritance is the example in Question 9?

It is incomplete dominance.

11. If the offspring had been red and blue spotted flowers, what kind of inheritance would be most likely?

The most likely pattern would be codominance.

12. Explain the difference between multiple alleles and polygenic traits.

Multiple alleles are more than two different forms of the same gene. Polygenic traits are traits produced by the interaction of several genes (each of which may or may not have multiple alleles).

Genes and the Environment

For Questions 13–16, complete each statement by writing in the correct word or words.

13. An organism's ___*phenotype*___ results from its genotype and its environment.

14. Some ___*genes*___ produce variable traits depending on environmental conditions.

15. Western white butterflies vary in their wing color because their ___*environment*___ varies depending on when they hatch.

16. ___*Temperature*___ is an environmental variable that affects wing color in western white butterflies.

For each of the following examples, write G if the trait is determined by genotype, and E if it is determined by environment.

17. ____*E*____ Turtles whose eggs hatch at higher temperatures tend to be female.

18. ____*G*____ A blue-eyed girl is born to two blue-eyed parents.

19. ____*E*____ Bees in a colony are assigned different jobs. As they develop, workers begin to look dramatically different.

20. ____*E*____ A pair of twins is separated at birth. They grow up in different countries and speak different languages.

21. ____*G*____ A litter of puppies is born. They are all gray except one, which is brown.

22. ____*E*____ Tall pea plant seeds are planted in different locations around a yard. They produce plants of different heights.

23. ____*G*____ A kitten is born with six toes.

24. ____*E*____ A rabbit is born weak with hunger.

Apply the Big idea

25. A dog gave birth to four puppies. The father has brown eyes, and the mother has green eyes. Two puppies have brown eyes. One has green eyes. One puppy has blue eyes. What does this tell you about how the cellular information for eye color is passed on? Explain.

In Mendelian genetics, these puppies would all have brown eyes. However, they have

a wide variety of eye colors, including blue, which is not expressed in the parents. This

tells me that eye color in this breed is not a matter of simple dominance. Eye color

must be either a polygenic trait or its genes must have multiple alleles, or both.

11.4 Meiosis

Lesson Objectives

- Contrast the number of chromosomes in body cells and in gametes.
- Summarize the events of meiosis.
- Contrast meiosis and mitosis.
- Describe how alleles from different genes can be inherited together.

Lesson Summary

Chromosome Number **Homologous** chromosomes are pairs of chromosomes that correspond in body cells. One chromosome from each pair comes from each parent.

▶ A cell that contains both sets of homologous chromosomes has a **diploid** number of chromosomes (meaning "two sets").

▶ **Haploid** cells contain only one set of chromosomes. Gametes are haploid.

Phases of Meiosis **Meiosis** is the process that separates homologous pairs of chromosomes in a diploid cell, forming a haploid gamete. The phases are as follows:

▶ Meiosis I, which is preceded by a replication of chromosomes. Its stages are
  - Prophase I: Each replicated chromosome pairs with its corresponding homologous chromosome forming a **tetrad**. During tetrad formation, alleles can be exchanged between chromatids, a process called **crossing-over**.
  - Metaphase I: Paired homologous chromosomes line up across the center of the cell.
  - Anaphase I: Spindle fibers pull each homologous pair toward opposite ends of the cell.
  - Telophase I: A nuclear membrane forms around each cluster of chromosomes. Cytokinesis then occurs, resulting in two new cells. The resulting daughter cells contain chromosome sets that are different from each other and the parent cell.

▶ Meiosis II: Chromosomes do not replicate.
  - Prophase II: Chromosomes, each consisting of two chromatids, become visible.
  - Metaphase II, Anaphase II, Telophase II, and Cytokinesis: These phases are similar to meiosis I. Four haploid cells form. They are the gametes. During fertilization, two gametes unite forming a **zygote**.

Comparing Meiosis and Mitosis

▶ Mitosis is one cell division that results in two genetically identical diploid cells.

▶ Meiosis is two cell divisions that result in four genetically different haploid cells.

Gene Linkage and Gene Maps

▶ Alleles tend to be inherited together if they are located on the same chromosome.

▶ Chromosomes, not genes, segregate independently.

▶ The farther apart genes are on a chromosome, the more likely is cross over.

▶ Information on linkage and the frequency of crossing-over lets geneticists construct maps of the locations of genes on chromosomes.

Chromosome Number

For Questions 1–8, write True if the statement is true. If the statement is false, change the underlined word to make the statement true.

True 1. The offspring of two parents obtains a single copy of every <u>gene</u> from each parent.

True 2. A <u>gamete</u> must contain one complete set of genes.

chromosomes 3. Genes are located at specific positions on <u>spindles</u>.

homologous 4. A pair of corresponding chromosomes is <u>homozygous</u>.

parent 5. One member of each homologous chromosome pair comes from each <u>gene</u>.

diploid 6. A cell that contains both sets of homologous chromosomes is <u>haploid</u>.

True 7. The gametes of sexually reproducing organisms are <u>haploid</u>.

12 8. If an organism's haploid number is 6, its diploid number is <u>3</u>.

Phases of Meiosis

On the lines provided, identify the stage of meiosis I or meiosis II in which the event described occurs.

Prophase I 9. Each replicated chromosome pairs with its corresponding homologous chromosome.

Prophase I 10. Crossing-over occurs between tetrads.

Metaphase I 11. Paired homologous chromosomes line up across the center of the cell.

Anaphase I 12. Spindle fibers pull each homologous chromosome pair toward an opposite end of the cell.

Telophase I 13. A nuclear membrane forms around each cluster of chromosomes and cytokinesis follows, forming two new cells.

Prophase II 14. Chromosomes consist of two chromatids, but they do not pair to form tetrads.

Telophase II 15. A nuclear membrane forms around each cluster of chromosomes and cytokinesis follows, forming four new cells.

16. **THINK VISUALLY** Draw two homologous pairs of chromosomes (in different colors if you have them) in these diagrams to illustrate what happens during these three phases of meiosis.

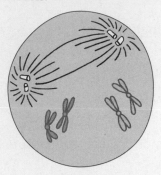

Prophase I

Metaphase I

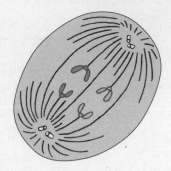

Anaphase II

17. Identify which phase of meiosis is shown in the diagrams below.

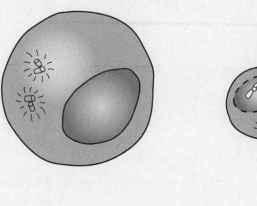

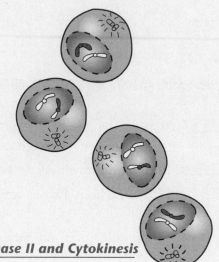

    ___Interphase I___   **Telophase II and Cytokinesis**

Use this diagram to answer Questions 18–20.

18. What does the diagram show?

    It shows crossing-over of genes between a pair

    of homologous chromosomes.

19. During what phase of meiosis does this process occur?

    It occurs during prophase I of meiosis.

20. What is the result of this process?

    The result is a new combination of alleles.

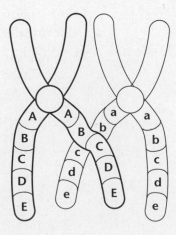

Comparing Meiosis and Mitosis

21. Complete the table to compare meiosis and mitosis.

	Mitosis	Meiosis
Form of reproduction	*Asexual*	*First stage in sexual*
Number of daughter cells	*2*	*4*
Change in chromosome number	*No change; stays diploid*	*Cut in half to haploid*
Number of cell divisions	*1*	*2*
Difference in alleles between parent cell and daughter cells	*None*	*Each of the four daughter cells is genetically different from the parent.*

For Questions 22–27, complete each statement by writing the correct word or words.

22. A diploid cell that enters mitosis with 16 chromosomes will divide to produce _____2_____ daughter cells. Each of these daughter cells will have _____16_____ chromosomes.

23. If the diploid number of chromosomes for an organism is 16, each daughter cell after mitosis will contain _____16_____ chromosomes.

24. A diploid cell that enters meiosis with 16 chromosomes will pass through _____2_____ cell divisions, producing _____4_____ daughter cells, each with _____8_____ chromosomes.

25. Gametes have a _____haploid_____ number of chromosomes.

26. If an organism's haploid number is 5, its diploid number is _____10_____.

27. While a haploid number of chromosomes may be even or odd, a diploid number is always _____even_____.

Gene Linkage and Gene Maps

28. What did Thomas Hunt Morgan discover that seemed to violate Mendel's principles?

Some genes appeared to be linked; they seemed to violate the principle of indepen-

dent assortment.

29. How did Morgan explain his finding?

Linked genes were inherited together because they were close to each other on the

same chromosome.

30. How did Alfred Sturtevant use gene linkage to create gene maps?

He reasoned that alleles that frequently cross over must be farther apart than those

that hardly ever cross over.

Use this diagram to answer Questions 31–34.

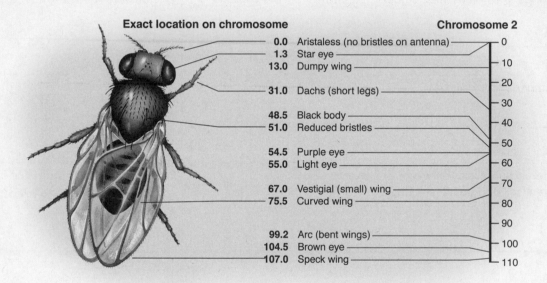

31. What does the diagram show?

It shows a gene map.

32. How was the information in this diagram gathered?

It was gathered from studies of the frequency of crossing-over.

33. Which pairs of characteristics are more likely to cross over: curved wing and dumpy wing; or curved wing and vestigial (small) wing? Why?

Curved wing and dumpy wing are more likely to cross over because they are farther

apart on the chromosome.

34. Which pair of genes shown is least likely to cross over? How do you know?

Purple eye and light eye are least likely to cross over because they are only 0.5 units

apart. The distance between all the other adjacent genes is greater.

Use this diagram to answer Questions 35–38.

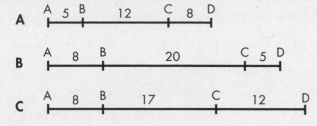

35. In which gene map is the probability of crossing-over between A and D greatest?

_____C_____

36. In which gene map is the probability of crossing-over between A and D the least?

_____D_____

37. In which map are genes C and D most closely linked? _____B_____

38. In map D, which genes are least likely to cross over? _____C and B_____

Apply the Big idea

39. Some housecats have orange fur with darker orange stripes. The traits of these *tabby* cats are usually seen in male cats. *Tortoiseshell* cats have patches of many different colors. "Torties," as they are called, are almost always female. What does this tell you about the way cellular information about color and sex are passed on in cats?

It tells me that the genes for color and sex are linked. The genes for these two traits

must be located on the same chromosome.

_____

_____

Chapter Vocabulary Review

Crossword Puzzle *Complete the puzzle by entering the term that matches each numbered description.*

Across

1. a specific characteristic
4. physical traits
6. the separation of alleles during formation of sex cells
9. containing two identical alleles for a trait
11. the likelihood of an event occurring
12. scientific study of heredity
13. the union of male and female sex cells

Down

2. one form of a gene
3. the offspring of a cross between parents with different, true-breeding traits
4. word that describes a trait controlled by two or more genes
5. containing two different alleles for a trait
7. genetic makeup
8. a phenotype in which both alleles are expressed
10. reproductive cell, egg or sperm

¹T	R	²A	I	T

Crossword solution grid:

- 1 Across: TRAIT
- 2 Down: ALLELE
- 3 Down: HYBRID
- 4 Across: PHENOTYPE
- 4 Down: POLYGENIC
- 5 Down: HETEROZYGOUS
- 6 Across: SEGREGATION
- 7 Down: GENOTYPE
- 8 Down: CODOMINANCE
- 9 Across: HOMOZYGOUS
- 10 Down: GAMETE
- 11 Across: PROBABILITY
- 12 Across: GENETICS
- 13 Across: FERTILIZATION

CHAPTER MYSTERY

GREEN PARAKEETS

In the Chapter Mystery, you read about a brood of parakeets that gave the owners results they didn't expect. Do you think Gregor Mendel ever got results he didn't expect?

21st Century Learning

Can Results Be Too Good?

As odd as it sounds, if you perform a lot of experiments, you should expect to get results you don't expect. Random chance will cause some of the experiments to have different outcomes from the rest of the experiments. Scientists have a mathematical formula to express an experiment's deviation, or how much the actual results varied from the expected results. If an experiment has a deviation of 0, that means the results were exactly as was expected. If it has a deviation of 2 or –2, that means the results were quite different from what was expected. A negative deviation indicates that the actual observations were smaller than average. A positive deviation indicates that the actual observations were larger than average.

The table below was created for the number and type of experiments Mendel performed. Each number in the second column represents the number of experiments we would expect Mendel to have had with the deviation in the first column. For example, we would expect Mendel to have had 13 experiments in which the deviation was between 0 and 0.5, and two experiments with deviations between –2.0 and –2.5. Each number in the third column represents the actual number of experiments with the deviation in the first column. For example, Mendel recorded 16 experiments in which the deviation was between 0 and 0.5.

An Analysis of Mendel's Data		
Deviation	**Expected Number of Experiments with This Deviation**	**Actual Number of Experiments with This Deviation**
–2 to –2.5	2	0
–1.5 to –2	3	0
–1 to –1.5	6	4
–0.5 to –1	10	12
–0 to –0.5	13	14
0 to 0.5	13	16
0.5 to 1	10	20
1 to 1.5	6	2
1.5 to 2	3	1
2 to 2.5	2	0

Continued on next page ▶

21st Century Themes Science Literacy

1. How many experiments with deviations between 1.5 and 2.0 would you expect Mendel to have had? How many did he have? *3; 1*

2. Look at the deviations between –1.0 and 1.0. Did Mendel have more or fewer experiments with deviations in this range than expected? *More*

3. Look at the deviations beyond –1.0 and 1.0. Did Mendel have more or fewer experiments with deviations in this range than expected? *Fewer*

4. Do you think scientists ever throw out results that were quite different from expected? Why might a scientist be tempted to do this? *SAMPLE ANSWER:* **A scientist might do this to make his or her hypothesis appear to be more valid than it really was.**

5. Mendel worked with an assistant, a gardener, and two other monks, all of whom helped count and record the results, and none of whom were scientists. These nonscientists spent years counting tens of thousands of peas. It wouldn't take them long to figure out what the usual results were. How might one or more of Mendel's helpers have caused the low number of high-deviation results?

   SAMPLE ANSWER: **Mendel's helpers may not have reported results that were very different from the results they were usually getting.**

6. Do you think that what you described in your answer to Question 4 is excusable? Is what you described in Question 5 excusable? Why or why not? **Students' answers should be based on logical premises and indicate respect for scientific methodology.**

7. Would your answer to Question 6 be changed if you were considering a case in which a scientist altered data collected while testing a new medicine? Explain your answer. **Students' answers should indicate that they understand the greater ethical implications of altering data in an experiment that affects people's lives, such as testing a new medicine or the strength of a new bridge design.**

21st Century Skills A Gardening Play

The skills used in this activity include **creativity and intellectual curiosity, self-direction,** and **accountability and adaptability.**

You described what one or more of Mendel's helpers might have done to skew the results of the experiments and how you felt about those actions. Now it's time to get creative. Write a one-act play about Mendel's gardener and what he may or may not have done. The gardener may be the main character, or one or more main characters may affect what the gardener does. The play may be a comedy, a drama, or a tragedy.

When the play is finished, assign each of the roles to one of your classmates and have a play reading, either in class or after school. **Evaluate students' plays based on how well the script addresses the topic of tampering with the results of a scientific experiment.**

12 DNA

Big idea ▶ Information and Heredity, Cellular Basis of Life

Q: What is the structure of DNA, and how does it function in genetic inheritance?

WHAT I KNOW	WHAT I LEARNED
12.1 How did scientists determine that DNA is responsible for storing, copying, and transmitting genetic information?	SAMPLE ANSWER: **Scientists studied chromosomes, which include genes, the factors that carry genetic information from parents to offspring.**	SAMPLE ANSWER: **From experiments with bacteria and viruses, scientists discovered that genes are made of DNA, which stores, copies, and transmits genetic information in a cell.**
12.2 How was the basic structure of DNA discovered?	SAMPLE ANSWER: **DNA carries genetic information in its structure, but for a long time, no one knew how.**	SAMPLE ANSWER: **In the 1950s, evidence disclosed the structure of DNA, leading to the double-helix model of Watson and Crick. The model explains how DNA strands are held together.**
12.3 How do cells copy their DNA?	SAMPLE ANSWER: **DNA copies itself during mitosis and meiosis.**	SAMPLE ANSWER: **An enzyme splits the two strands of DNA apart. Each strand serves as a template for the replication of another identical molecule of DNA.**

12.1 Identifying the Substance of Genes

Lesson Objectives

- Summarize the process of bacterial transformation.
- Describe the role of bacteriophages in identifying genetic material.
- Identify the role of DNA in heredity.

Lesson Summary

Bacterial Transformation In 1928, Frederick Griffith found that some chemical factor from heat-killed bacteria of one strain could change the inherited characteristics of another strain.

▶ He called the process **transformation** because one type of bacteria (a harmless form) had been changed permanently into another (a disease-carrying form).

▶ Because the ability to cause disease was inherited by the offspring of the transformed bacteria, he concluded that the transforming factor had to be a gene.

In 1944, Oswald Avery tested the transforming ability of many substances. Only DNA caused transformation. By observing bacterial transformation, Avery and other scientists discovered that the nucleic acid DNA stores and transmits genetic information from one generation of bacteria to the next.

Bacterial Viruses A **bacteriophage** is a kind of virus that infects bacteria. When a bacteriophage enters a bacterium, it attaches to the surface of the bacterial cell and injects its genetic material into it.

▶ In 1952, Alfred Hershey and Martha Chase used radioactive tracers to label proteins and DNA in bacteriophages.

▶ Only the DNA from the bacteriophage showed up in the infected bacterial cell.

▶ Hershey and Chase concluded that the genetic material of the bacteriophage was DNA.

▶ Their work confirmed Avery's results, convincing many scientists that DNA was the genetic material found in genes—not just in viruses and bacteria, but in all living cells.

The Role of DNA The DNA that makes up genes must be capable of storing, copying, and transmitting the genetic information in a cell.

Bacterial Transformation

1. What happened when Griffith injected mice with the pneumonia-causing strain of bacteria that had been heat-killed?

The mice stayed healthy.

2. What happened when Griffith injected mice with a mixture of heat-killed, pneumonia-causing bacteria and live bacteria of the harmless type?

The mice got pneumonia and many died.

3. What was the purpose of Oswald Avery's experiments?

Avery wanted to find out which molecule in the heat-killed bacteria was the most

important for transformation.

4. What experiments did Avery do?

He used enzymes that destroyed various molecules from the heat-killed bacteria,

including lipids, proteins, carbohydrates, and RNA. Transformation still occurred, but

when he used enzymes that broke down DNA, transformation did not occur.

5. What did Avery conclude?

He concluded that DNA transmits genetic information.

Bacterial Viruses

6. Fill in the blanks to summarize the experiments of Hershey and Chase. (Note: The circles represent radioactive labels.)

_____DNA_____ with
radioactive label

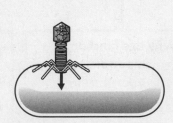

Bacteriophage infects bacterium

Radioactivity inside bacterium

_____Protein_____ with
radioactive label

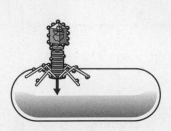

Phage infects bacterium

No radioactivity inside bacterium

7. What did Hershey and Chase conclude? Why?

They concluded that the genetic material must be DNA because the phage injected

only DNA, not protein, into the bacterium.

8. How did Hershey and Chase confirm Avery's results?

Avery said that DNA transmits genetic information from one generation to the next.

Hershey and Chase concluded that the genetic material of the bacteriophage was DNA

and not protein, confirming what Avery said.

The Role of DNA

9. Complete this graphic organizer to summarize the assumptions that guided research on DNA in the middle of the twentieth century. Use an oak tree to give an example of each function.

DNA must perform three functions:

Function: *Storing information*	Function: Copying information	Function: *Transmitting information*

Why this function is important: *The DNA that makes up genes controls development and characteristics of different kinds of organisms.*	**Why this function is important:** *Genetic information must be copied accurately with every cell division.*	**Why this function is important:** *Genetic information must pass from one generation to the next.*

Example: *The instructions that cause a single cell to develop into an oak tree must be written into the DNA of the organism.*	**Example:** *After mitosis, each daughter oak-tree cell has the same genes and chromosomes as the parent cell.*	**Example:** *The gametes of the oak tree carry information from parents to offspring, so the offspring develops as an oak tree.*

VISUAL ANALOGY

10. DNA is like a book titled *How to Be a Cell*. Explain why that title is appropriate for each of DNA's three functions.

a. *Storing information:* **How to Be a Cell** *contains all the information needed to direct the cell's activities, from growth to energy use.*

b. *Copying information: Multiple copies of* **How to Be a Cell** *can be "printed" every time a cell divides, so each daughter cell "knows" what to do.*

c. *Transmitting information: Copies of* **How to Be a Cell** *can be passed from parents to offspring, so the offspring have the instructions needed to function.*

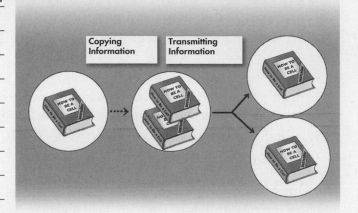

Apply the Big idea

11. By 1952, many scientists were convinced that genes are made of DNA, but they did not yet know how DNA worked. Why was it important to determine the structure of DNA to understand how DNA stored, copied, and transmitted information?

The structure of the molecule had to provide a way for instructions on "how to be a cell" to be coded and stored. DNA had to have something in its molecular structure that allowed it to copy itself with each cell division and pass from one cell to another during mitosis and meiosis.

12. Why was the fact of transformation so important to the study of DNA's role? What did transformation demonstrate?

Transformation showed that what a cell becomes is determined by DNA. If DNA in a cell was changed, then the cell itself changed. It demonstrated that DNA controlled the fate of a cell.

12.2 The Structure of DNA

Lesson Objectives

🗝 Identify the chemical components of DNA.

🗝 Discuss the experiments leading to the identification of DNA as the molecule that carries the genetic code.

🗝 Describe the steps leading to the development of the double-helix model of DNA.

Lesson Summary

The Components of DNA DNA is a nucleic acid made up of nucleotides joined into long strands or chains by covalent bonds. Nucleotides may be joined in any order.

▶ A DNA nucleotide is a unit made of a nitrogenous base, a 5-carbon sugar called deoxyribose, and a phosphate group.

▶ DNA has four kinds of nitrogenous bases: adenine, guanine, cytosine, and thymine.

Solving the Structure of DNA

▶ Erwin Chargaff showed that the percentages of adenine and thymine are almost always equal in DNA. The percentages of guanine and cytosine are also almost equal.

▶ Rosalind Franklin's X-ray diffraction studies revealed the double-helix structure of DNA.

▶ James Watson and Francis Crick built a model that explained the structure of DNA.

The Double-Helix Model The double-helix model explains Chargaff's rule of base pairing and how the two strands of DNA are held together. The model showed the following:

▶ The two strands in the double helix run in opposite directions, with the nitrogenous bases in the center.

▶ Each strand carries a sequence of nucleotides, arranged almost like the letters in a fourletter alphabet for recording genetic information.

▶ Hydrogen bonds hold the strands together. The bonds are easily broken allowing DNA strands to separate.

▶ Hydrogen bonds form only between certain base pairs–adenine with thymine, and cytosine with guanine. This is called **base pairing**.

The Components of DNA

For Questions 1–5, complete each statement by writing in the correct word or words.

1. The building blocks of DNA are ___nucleotides___.

2. Nucleotides in DNA are made of three basic components: a sugar called ___deoxyribose___, a ___phosphate___, and a nitrogenous ___base___.

3. DNA contains four kinds of nitrogenous bases: ___adenine___, ___thymine___, ___guanine___, and ___cytosine___.

4. In DNA, ___nucleotides___ can be joined in any order.

5. The nucleotides in DNA are joined by ___covalent___ bonds.

Solving the Structure of DNA

6. Complete the table to describe each scientist's contribution to solving the structure of DNA.

Scientist	Contribution
Erwin Chargaff	*Showed that percentages of adenine and thymine are equal in the DNA of a species, as are the percentages of guanine and cytosine.*
Rosalind Franklin	*Took X-ray diffraction pictures that revealed the double-helix structure of DNA.*
James Watson and Francis Crick	*Built a model of the DNA molecule that explained both the structure and the properties of DNA.*

7. Complete the table by estimating the percentages of each based on Chargaff's rules.

DNA sample	Percent of adenine	Percent of thymine	Percent of guanine	Percent of cytosine
1	31.5	*31.5*	*18.5*	*18.5*
2	*30*	30	20	*20*
3	*33*	*33*	*17*	17

The Double-Helix Model

For Questions 8–13, on the lines provided, label the parts of the DNA molecule that correspond to the numbers in the diagram.

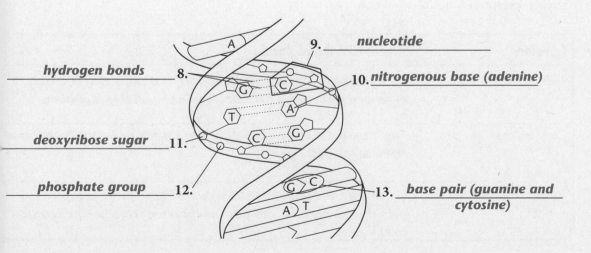

9. ___nucleotide___

____hydrogen bonds____ 8.

10. __nitrogenous base (adenine)__

____deoxyribose sugar____ 11.

____phosphate group____ 12.

13. ___base pair (guanine and cytosine)___

14. **THINK VISUALLY** The drawing below shows half of a DNA molecule. Fill in the appropriate letters for the other half. Explain why you drew your sketch the way you did.

C	G
A	T
G	C
G	C
C	G
C	G
T	A
A	T
C	G

Key
A = Adenine
C = Cytosine
G = Guanine
T = Thymine

The bases link with hydrogen bonds in pairs across the "rungs" of the ladder: A with T and G with C.

Apply the Big idea

15. Complete this table to show how the structure of the DNA molecule allows it to perform each essential function.

Function	Structure of the Molecule
Store information	*Each strand of the double helix carries a sequence of bases, arranged something like letters in a four-letter alphabet.*
Copy information	*The base pairs can be copied when hydrogen bonds break and the strands pull apart.*
Transmit information	*When DNA is copied, the sequence of base pairs is copied, so genetic information can pass unchanged from one generation to the next.*

12.3 DNA Replication

Lesson Objectives

➥ Summarize the events of DNA replication.

➥ Compare DNA replication in prokaryotes with that of eukaryotes.

Lesson Summary

Copying the Code Each strand of the double helix has all the information needed to reconstruct the other half by the mechanism of base pairing. Because each strand can be used to make the other strand, the strands are said to be complementary. DNA copies itself through the process of **replication**:

- The two strands of the double helix unzip, forming replication forks.

- New bases are added, following the rules of base pairing (A with T and G with C).

- Each new DNA molecule has one original strand and one new strand.

- **DNA polymerase** is an enzyme that joins individual nucleotides to produce a new strand of DNA.

- During replication, DNA may be lost from the tips of chromosomes, which are called **telomeres**.

Replication in Living Cells The cells of most prokaryotes have a single, circular DNA molecule in the cytoplasm. Eukaryotic cells have much more DNA. Nearly all of it is contained in chromosomes, which are in the nucleus.

- Replication in most prokaryotic cells starts from a single point and proceeds in two directions until the entire chromosome is copied.

- In eukaryotic cells, replication may begin at dozens or even hundreds of places on the DNA molecule, proceeding in both directions until each chromosome is completely copied.

Copying the Code

1. Why are the strands of a DNA molecule said to be complementary?

   Because each strand can be used to make the other strand.

2. What is the first step in eukaryotic DNA replication?

   The strands of the double helix separate, or unzip.

3. If the base sequence on a separated DNA strand is CGTAGG, what will the base sequence on its complementary strand be?

   The complementary strand will be GCATCC.

4. What enzyme joins individual nucleotides to produce the new strand of DNA?

   DNA polymerase

5. What enzyme makes it less likely that DNA will be lost from telomeres during replication

telomerase

6. How does this enzyme work?

It adds short, repeated DNA sequences to telomeres.

7. What is a replication fork?

A replication fork is a point in a DNA molecule where the two strands separate during

replication.

8. Does DNA replication take place in the same direction along both strands of the DNA molecule that is being replicated? Explain your answer. (Hint: Look at the illustration of DNA replication in your textbook.)

No. DNA replication proceeds in opposite directions between replication forks.

9. **THINK VISUALLY** Make a sketch of the double helix of DNA. Show how it unzips for replication and how complementary strands are built. Label the nitrogenous bases, replication fork, DNA polymerase, the original strand, and the new strand.

Students' sketches should resemble the top part of the figure in the textbook. Labels should include nitrogenous bases, replication fork, DNA polymerase, original strand, and new strand. Students should label some pairs of A-T and G-C along the new strand.

Replication in Living Cells

0. Complete the table to compare and contrast DNA replication in prokaryotes and eukaryotes.

	Prokaryotes	Eukaryotes
Location of DNA	*Singular, circular molecule in the cytoplasm*	*Packaged in chromosomes in the nucleus*
Amount of DNA	*Less than eukaryotes*	*Up to 1000 times more than prokaryotes*
Starting Point(s) for Replication	*Single*	*Dozens or hundreds*

1. Is DNA replication always a foolproof process? Explain your answer.

No. Although many proteins check the DNA for damage or errors, damaged regions can still be replicated. This may result in gene alterations and serious complications for the organism.

Apply the Big idea

2. Why is the pairing of bases during replication essential for the transmission of inherited traits from parent to offspring?

The match is (nearly always) perfect between A and T and G and C, so that the code is copied correctly every time. Offspring get the same sequence of bases their parents had.

Chapter Vocabulary Review

For Questions 1–6, match the term with its definition.

Definition

_C_ 1. In DNA, the fit between thymine and adenine and the fit between cytosine and guanine.

_E_ 2. An enzyme that joins individual nucleotides to produce a new strand of DNA

_A_ 3. The process that can change a harmless bacterial strain into a disease-causing strain

_F_ 4. The tip of a chromosome

_D_ 5. The process that copies a DNA molecule

_B_ 6. A kind of virus that infects bacteria

Term

A. transformation

B. bacteriophage

C. base pairing

D. replication

E. DNA polymerase

F. telomere

For Questions 7–15, complete each statement by writing in the correct word or words.

7. Each time a chromosome is replicated, some DNA may be lost from the tip of the chromosome, or ____telomere____.

8. Griffith's experiments showed that some chemical compound in cells must be responsible for bacterial ____transformation____.

9. Hershey and Chase studied a ____bacteriophage____ that was composed of a DNA core and a protein coat.

10. The center of the DNA strand exhibits ____base pairing____.

11. The enzyme that "proofreads" each new DNA strand so that each molecule is a near-perfect copy of the original is ____DNA polymerase____.

12. In eukaryotic cells, ____replication____ can begin at dozens or even hundreds of places on the DNA molecule.

13. The double-helix model explains Chargaff's rule of ____base pairing____.

14. The DNA molecule separates into two strands during ____replication____.

15. The principal enzyme involved in DNA replication is ____DNA polymerase____.

CHAPTER MYSTERY

UV LIGHT

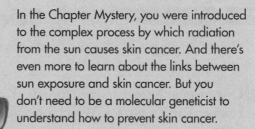

In the Chapter Mystery, you were introduced to the complex process by which radiation from the sun causes skin cancer. And there's even more to learn about the links between sun exposure and skin cancer. But you don't need to be a molecular geneticist to understand how to prevent skin cancer.

21st Century Learning

The Sun and Your Skin

Even people who don't understand how radiation from the sun causes skin cancer know they should protect themselves. Even so, only 40 percent of Americans consistently use sunscreen when they're in the sun. And 20 percent of American adults actually sunbathe—that is, they deliberately expose their skin to solar radiation. This poster presents information everyone should know.

What is ultraviolet radiation?
► Ultraviolet (UV) rays are an invisible form of radiation.
  • They make up a part of sunlight.
► There are three types of UV rays.
  • ultraviolet A (UVA), ultraviolet B (UVB), and ultraviolet C (UVC)

What are the results of exposure to ultraviolet radiation?
► various types of skin cancer
► various eye conditions, including cataracts
► premature aging
► dry, sagging, and wrinkled skin
► yellowing of the skin

How does UV radiation cause skin cancer?
► Phase 1
  • UV radiation interferes with the mechanism by which cells repair damage.
  • These abnormal cells are more vulnerable to injury.
► Phase 2
  • Normal cells that are overexposed to UV radiation die.
  • Abnormal cells that are overexposed to UV radiation do not die.
  • Genetic damage accumulates.

How can you protect yourself from UV radiation?
► Seek shade, especially from 10:00 A.M. to 4:00 P.M. when UV rays are strongest.
► Cover exposed skin with clothing.
► Wear a hat with a wide brim that shades your face, head, ears, and neck.
► Wear sunglasses.
  • Wraparounds are best.
  • They should block as close to 100 percent of both UVA and UVB rays as possible.
► Use sunscreen.
  • Use one with a sun protective factor (SPF) of 15 or higher.
  • Use one that blocks both UVA and UVB radiation.
  • Reapply it every two hours, as well as right after you swim or sweat.

These sunscreen ingredients block UVA radiation.
► benzophenone
► oxybenzone
► sulisobenzone
► titanium dioxide
► zinc oxide
► butyl methoxydibenzoylmethane, also called avobenzone, also called Parsol 1789

These sunscreen ingredients block UVB radiation.
► Cinnamates, including octyl methoxycinnamate and cinoxate
► Salicylates, including homomenthyl salicylate, octyl salicylate, and triethanolamine salicylate
► Octocrylene
► Ensulizole, or PBSA

Some risk factors make you more likely to contract skin cancer.
► lighter natural skin, eye, or hair color
► family or personal history of skin cancer
► exposure to the sun
► history of sunburns early in life
► skin that burns, freckles, or reddens easily
► certain types of moles
► a large number of moles

Skin cancer is an undeclared epidemic.
► It's the most common of all the types of cancer.
► It's roughly as common as all other cancers combined.
► This year a million Americans will develop skin cancer.

It's time to explode some myths.
► UV radiation causes damage whether you get it from the sun or from a tanning bed.
► Damage done now will not become evident for many years.
► More frequent sun exposure at an early age results in a higher risk of skin damage; 80 percent of a person's lifetime sun exposure is acquired before age 18.
► There is no such thing as a healthy tan.

Continued on next page ►

21st Century Themes Science and Health Literacy

1. How many types of ultraviolet radiation are there? What are they?

three; UVA, UVB, and UVC

2. One form of ultraviolet radiation is absorbed by the ozone in the atmosphere and never reaches Earth's surface. Which one do you think that is? Why?

UVC; it's never mentioned on the poster, while UVA and UVB are.

3. When is the sun's UV radiation strongest?

from 10:00 in the morning to 4:00 in the afternoon

4. Your friend says she's going sunbathing. She says, "I've been in the sun all summer. I've tanned, but I haven't burned. My skin is still soft and it isn't dry at all. I have nothing to worry about." Is she right or wrong? Why?

She is wrong. The fact that her skin seems fine now is irrelevant because damage done now will not become evident for many years. Besides, more frequent sun exposure now results in a higher risk of skin damage later. There is no such thing as a safe tan.

5. Do you think that skin cancer can be inherited? Why or why not?

SAMPLE ANSWER: No. Skin cancer is caused by damage to the DNA in adult skin cells, which would not be passed along to any offspring. However, a tendency toward skin cancer might be inherited.

21st Century Skills Warning Signs of Skin Cancer

The skills used in this activity include **creativity and intellectual curiosity, information and media literacy,** and **social responsibility**.

The poster on the previous page was intended to educate people about how UV radiation in sunlight damages skin cells and show them how they can avoid exposure to UV. For some people, though, these warnings come too late. Use Internet and library resources to research the warning signs of skin cancer and what a person who detects one or more of these warning signs should do.

Compile this information into a booklet that could be distributed in doctors' offices and drugstores.

Students' booklets may be illustrated or text-only. Evaluate booklets based on the accuracy of the information, whether it is presented in an easy-to-read and easy-to-understand format, and creativity.

13 RNA and Protein Synthesis

Information and Heredity

Q: How does information flow from DNA to RNA to direct the synthesis of proteins?

WHAT I KNOW	WHAT I LEARNED
13.1 What is RNA?	SAMPLE ANSWER: **RNA is a nucleic acid that carries coded genetic information.**	SAMPLE ANSWER: **RNA contains the sugar ribose and the nitrogenous base uracil instead of thymine. It is usually a single strand. mRNA molecules are made using DNA as a template.**
13.2 How do cells make proteins?	SAMPLE ANSWER: **The bases in DNA—A, T, G, and C—form a four-letter "alphabet" that writes the "words" of the genetic code.**	SAMPLE ANSWER: **The genetic code is read in mRNA codons, which are sequences of three bases that correspond to a single amino acid. Ribosomes use the sequence of codons to assemble amino acids into polypeptides.**
13.3 What happens when a cell's DNA changes?	SAMPLE ANSWER: **When DNA changes, mistakes can be made. The organism may look or function differently.**	SAMPLE ANSWER: **Mutations are heritable changes in genetic information. They can involve only one DNA nucleotide or the whole chromosome. Mutations may or may not affect gene function.**
13.4 How do cells regulate gene expression?	SAMPLE ANSWER: **Cell proteins regulate gene expression.**	SAMPLE ANSWER: **DNA-binding proteins regulate genes by controlling transcription in prokaryotes. In eukaryotes, transcription factors control gene expression by binding DNA sequences in the regulatory regions.**

13.1 RNA

Lesson Objectives

- Contrast RNA and DNA.
- Explain the process of transcription.

Lesson Summary

The Role of RNA RNA (ribonucleic acid) is a nucleic acid like DNA. It consists of a long chain of nucleotides. The RNA base sequence directs the production of proteins. Ultimately, cell proteins result in phenotypic traits. The main differences between RNA and DNA are:

▶ The sugar in RNA is ribose instead of deoxyribose.

▶ RNA is generally single-stranded and not double-stranded like DNA.

▶ RNA contains uracil in place of thymine.

RNA can be thought of as a disposable copy of a segment of DNA. Most RNA molecules are involved in protein synthesis. The three main types of RNA are:

▶ **Messenger RNA** (mRNA) carries copies of instructions for polypeptide synthesis from the nucleus to ribosomes in the cytoplasm.

▶ **Ribosomal RNA** (rRNA) forms an important part of both subunits of the ribosomes, the cell structures where proteins are assembled.

▶ **Transfer RNA** (tRNA) carries amino acids to the ribosome and matches them to the coded mRNA message.

RNA Synthesis Most of the work of making RNA takes place during transcription. In **transcription**, segments of DNA serve as templates to produce complementary RNA molecules. In prokaryotes, RNA synthesis and protein synthesis takes place in the cytoplasm. In eukaryotes, RNA is produced in the cell's nucleus and then moves to the cytoplasm to play a role in the production of protein. The following focuses on transcription in eukaryotic cells.

▶ The enzyme **RNA polymerase** binds to DNA during transcription and separates the DNA strands. It then uses one strand of DNA as a template from which to assemble nucleotides into a complementary strand of RNA.

▶ RNA polymerase binds only to **promoters**, regions of DNA that have specific base sequences. Promoters are signals to the DNA molecule that show RNA polymerase exactly where to begin making RNA. Similar signals cause transcription to stop when a new RNA molecule is completed.

▶ RNA may be "edited" before it is used. Portions that are cut out and discarded are called **introns**. The remaining pieces, known as **exons**, are then spliced back together to form the final mRNA.

The Role of RNA

1. Complete the table to contrast the structures of DNA and RNA.

	Sugar	Number of Strands	Bases
DNA	*deoxyribose*	*2*	*A, T, G, and C*
RNA	*ribose*	*usually 1*	*A, G, and C, but no T; contains U (uracil) instead*

2. On the lines provided, identify each kind of RNA.

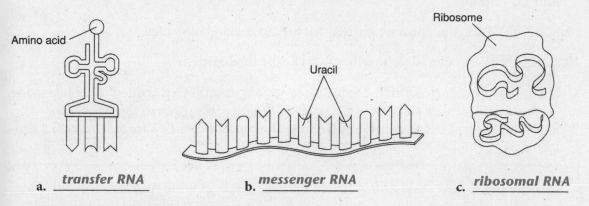

a. *transfer RNA*

b. *messenger RNA*

c. *ribosomal RNA*

3. **VISUAL ANALOGY** The master plan of a building shows how to build and place important parts of the building, such as walls, pipes, and electrical outlets. On the building site, workers use copies of the master plan called blueprints to show them what to do. The master plan is kept in the office. Explain how mRNA works like a blueprint in constructing proteins.

The master plan is the DNA molecule. The cell uses this molecule to prepare mRNA

"blueprints." The mRNA carries the instructions for protein synthesis from the nucleus

to the ribosomes in the cytoplasm, where the proteins are built.

RNA Synthesis

For Questions 4–10, complete each statement by writing the correct word or words.

4. The process of using DNA to produce complementary RNA molecules is called ___*transcription*___.

5. The sequence of ___*bases*___ in mRNA complements the sequence in the DNA template.

6. In eukaryotes, RNA is formed in the ___*nucleus*___ and then travels to the ___*cytoplasm*___.

7. The enzyme ___*RNA polymerase*___ binds to DNA during transcription.

8. RNA polymerase binds to regions of DNA called ___*promoters*___, which are "start" signals for transcription.

9. ___*Introns*___ are portions of RNA that are cut out and discarded.

10. ___*Exons*___ are spliced together to make the final mRNA.

11. **THINK VISUALLY** Sketch the sequence in which pre-mRNA is "edited" after it is made on the DNA template and before it is ready to function as mRNA in the cytoplasm. Show the original DNA, the pre-mRNA, and the final mRNA. Be sure to label exons and introns.

> *Drawing should show a DNA strand with introns and exons labeled. The introns and exons are contained in the pre-mRNA strand, but introns are removed and exons spliced together to form the mRNA. Drawing should resemble the figure in the textbook.*

Apply the Big idea

12. Use the analogy of the master plan and blueprints used by builders to identify what represents messenger RNA, where the "ribosome" is, and who performs the same kind of job as transfer RNA.

Explain your reasoning.

The blueprints represent messenger RNA because they carry instructions for the building from the office (the "nucleus") to the outside ("cytoplasm"). The "ribosome" is the job site where the building is being constructed. In the cell, proteins are "built" on the ribosome. The people at the job site are like transfer RNA because they carry the building materials, such as bricks and blocks ("amino acids") and match their placement to the instructions in the blueprint.

13.2 Ribosomes and Protein Synthesis

Lesson Objectives

⊐ Identify the genetic code and explain how it is read.

⊐ Summarize the process of translation.

⊐ Describe the "central dogma" of molecular biology.

Lesson Summary

The Genetic Code A specific sequence of bases in DNA carries the directions for forming a **polypeptide**, a chain of amino acids. The types and order of amino acids in a polypeptide determine the properties of the protein. The sequence of bases in mRNA is the **genetic code**. The four bases, A, C, G, and U, act as "letters."

➤ The code is read three "letters" at a time, so that each "word" is three bases long and corresponds to a single amino acid. Each three-letter "word" in mRNA is known as a **codon**.

➤ Some codons serve as "start" and "stop" signals for protein synthesis.

Translation Ribosomes use the sequence of codons in mRNA to assemble amino acids into polypeptide chains. The process of decoding of an mRNA message into a protein is **translation**.

➤ Messenger RNA is transcribed in the nucleus and then enters the cytoplasm.

➤ On the ribosome, translation begins at the start codon. Each codon attracts an **anticodon**, the complementary sequence of bases on tRNA.

➤ Each tRNA carries one kind of amino acid. The match between the codon and anticodon ensures that the correct amino acid is added to the growing chain.

➤ The amino acids bond together, each in turn. The ribosome moves along the mRNA, exposing codons that attract still more tRNAs with their attached amino acids.

➤ The process concludes when a "stop code" is reached. The newly formed polypeptide and the mRNA molecule are released from the ribosome.

The Molecular Basis of Heredity Molecular biology seeks to explain living organisms by studying them at the molecular level, using molecules like DNA and RNA.

➤ The central dogma of molecular biology is that information is transferred from DNA to RNA to protein.

➤ **Gene expression** is the way in which DNA, RNA, and proteins are involved in putting genetic information into action in living cells.

➤ The genetic code is generally the same in all organisms.

The Genetic Code

Use the diagram to answer Questions 1–7.

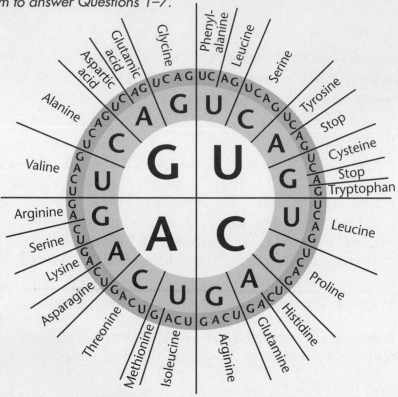

1. What are the words along the outside of the circle?
   They are the names of amino acids.

2. What can you find by reading this diagram from the inside out?
   the mRNA codons for amino acids

3. For which amino acid is AAA a codon?
   AAA is a codon for lysine.

4. What is the codon for tryptophan?
   The codon for tryptophan is UGG.

5. For which amino acid is GGA a codon?
   GGA is a codon for glycine.

6. What is a codon for alanine?
   A codon for alanine is GCC.

7. What are three other codons for alanine?
   GCG, GCA, GCU

Translation

Use the diagram to answer Questions 8–10.

8. What is the anticodon for leucine? __GAC__

9. What is the codon for leucine? __CUG__

10. List the amino acids in the order they would appear in the polypeptide coded for by this mRNA.

    __methionine, phenylalanine, lysine, leucine__

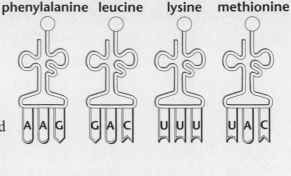

phenylalanine leucine lysine methionine

mRNA

11. What is the difference between transcription and translation?

    RNA is produced from DNA templates during transcription. In translation, that RNA

    is read to form polypeptide chains. In a eukaryotic cell, transcription goes on in the

    nucleus and translation is carried out by ribosomes.

12. Complete the table to describe the steps in protein synthesis.

Step	Description
Beginning of translation	*Translation begins when a ribosome attaches to an mRNA molecule at a "start" codon. Transfer RNA molecules carry amino acids to the mRNA, where the anticodon matches the codon and ensures the placement of the correct amino acid.*
Assembly of polypeptide	*Amino acids join one at a time onto the growing chain, and a tRNA floats away after it releases its amino acid. The ribosome moves along the mRNA, binding a new tRNA molecule and the amino acid it carries.*
Completing the polypeptide	*The process continues until a "stop" codon is reached, the polypeptide is complete, and the mRNA is released from the ribosome.*

13. Describe the role of rRNA during translation.

    rRNA molecules make up part of a ribosome. These molecules help hold ribosomal

    proteins in place and help locate the beginning of the mRNA message. They may even

    carry out the chemical reaction that joins amino acids together.

The Molecular Basis of Heredity

For Questions 14–18, write the letter of the correct answer on the line at the left.

__A__ 14. The instructions for assembling proteins are contained in the
- **A.** genes.
- **B.** ribosomes.
- **C.** exons.
- **D.** introns.

__D__ 15. The central dogma of molecular biology is that information is transferred from
- **A.** RNA to protein to DNA.
- **B.** DNA to protein to RNA.
- **C.** protein to DNA to RNA.
- **D.** DNA to RNA to protein.

__B__ 16. An exception to the central dogma is
- **A.** the infection of a virus by a bacteriophage.
- **B.** the ability of some viruses to transfer information from RNA to DNA.
- **C.** the expression of different genes during different stages of development.
- **D.** the translation of the codon into the anticodon of tRNA.

__C__ 17. The way in which DNA, RNA, and proteins are all involved in putting genetic information into action in living cells is called
- **A.** translation.
- **B.** transcription.
- **C.** gene expression.
- **D.** viral transfer.

__D__ 18. All organisms are mostly the same in
- **A.** the proteins they make on their ribosomes.
- **B.** how their proteins catalyze chemical reactions.
- **C.** the size of their genes.
- **D.** the molecular biology of their genes.

Apply the Big idea

19. Whether the organism is a pea plant or a human being, the information in the DNA of the cell's nucleus directs synthesis of proteins in the cytoplasm. Why, then, are pea plants and human beings so different?

They contain different DNA, which directs the synthesis of different proteins. Those proteins form different structures and functions, making pea plant cells very different from human cells.

13.3 Mutations

Lesson Objectives

Define mutations and describe the different types of mutations.

Describe the effects mutations can have on genes.

Lesson Summary

Types of Mutations **Mutations** are heritable changes in genetic information. There are two categories of mutations: gene mutations and chromosomal mutations.

► Gene mutations produce changes in a single gene. **Point mutations** involve only one or a few nucleotides. Substitutions, insertions, and deletions are all types of point mutations.

- In a substitution, one base is changed to a different base, which may affect only a single amino acid and have no effect at all.

- In insertions and deletions, one base is inserted or removed from the DNA sequence. Insertions and deletions are called **frameshift mutations** because they shift the "reading frame" of the genetic message. Frameshift mutations can change every amino acid that follows the point of mutation and can have dramatic effects on the organism.

► Chromosomal mutations produce changes in the number or structure of chromosomes. They include deletions, duplications, inversions, and translocations.

- Deletion involves the loss of all or part of a chromosome.
- Duplication produces an extra copy of all or part of a chromosome.
- Inversion reverses the direction of parts of a chromosome.
- Translocation occurs when part of one chromosome breaks off and attaches to another.

Effects of Mutations Genetic material can be altered by natural events or by artificial means. Errors can be made during replication. Environmental conditions may increase the rate of mutation. **Mutagens** are chemical or physical agents in the environment that cause mutations.

The effects of mutations on genes vary widely:

► Some mutations have little or no effect.

► Some mutations produce beneficial variations. One example is **polyploidy** in plants, in which an organism has extra sets of chromosomes. Polyploid plants are often larger and stronger than diploid plants. Mutations can also produce proteins with new or altered functions that can be useful to organisms in different or changing environments.

► Some mutations negatively disrupt gene function or dramatically change protein structure. Genetic disorders such as sickle cell disease can result.

Types of Mutations

For Questions 1–8, match the term with its definition.

Definition

B **1.** The change of one base to another in a DNA sequence

C **2.** A change in one or a few nucleotides that occur at a single point in the DNA sequence

F **3.** Part of one chromosome breaks off and attaches to another

A **4.** A heritable change in genetic information

H **5.** A mutation that produces an extra copy of all or part of a chromosome

G **6.** A chromosomal mutation that reverses the direction of parts of a chromosome

D **7.** A kind of mutation that can change every amino acid that follows the point of mutation

E **8.** The addition of a base to the DNA sequence

Term

A. mutation

B. substitution

C. point mutation

D. frameshift mutation

E. insertion

F. translocation

G. inversion

H. duplication

9. Complete the table to describe the processes and outcomes of the different types of gene (point) mutations.

Type	Description	Outcome
Substitution	*One base is changed to a different base.*	*usually affects no more than a single amino acid, and sometimes has no effect at all*
Insertion	*An extra base is inserted into the DNA sequence.*	*The effects can be dramatic. The groupings of bases shift in every codon that follows the mutation.*
Deletion	*A base is removed from the DNA sequence.*	*The effects can be dramatic. The groupings of bases shift in every codon that follows the mutation.*

10. Deletion can happen as a gene mutation or as a chromosomal mutation. What is the difference?

In a gene mutation, a deletion happens when a base is removed from the DNA sequence. In a chromosomal mutation, deletion involves the loss of all or part of a chromosome.

Effects of Mutations

For Questions 11–18, write the letter of the correct answer on the line at the left.

____D____ 11. The cellular machinery that replicates DNA inserts an incorrect base

A. most of the time.

B. about half the time.

C. roughly once in every million bases.

D. roughly once in every 10 million bases.

____B____ 12. Small changes in genes

A. disappear quickly.

B. gradually accumulate over time.

C. prevent the next generation from developing.

D. do not affect future generations.

____D____ 13. A possible mutagen is

A. an anticodon.

B. translocation.

C. hemoglobin.

D. ultraviolet light.

____A____ 14. What happens when cells cannot repair the damage caused by a mutagen?

A. The DNA base sequence changes permanently.

B. The DNA base sequence is not affected.

C. The organism is not affected.

D. The organism is affected temporarily.

____B____ 15. Which of the following most accurately summarizes the effects of mutations on living things?

A. Most mutations are harmful, but some have little effect.

B. Many mutations have little or no effect, but some can be harmful or beneficial.

C. Most mutations are beneficial and a few are harmful.

D. About half of mutations are beneficial and half are harmful.

____C____ 16. Mutations are important to the evolution of a species because they

A. happen over the long period of time that evolution requires.

B. cut out and replace damaged or useless genes.

C. are a source of genetic variability.

D. accelerate the transcription rate of DNA.

____A____ 17. Cancer is the product of a mutation that

A. causes the uncontrolled growth of cells.

B. changes the structure of hemoglobin in the blood.

C. brings about stunted growth and severe pain.

D. causes a translocation in a pair of chromosomes.

_____B_____ **18.** Polyploidy is the condition in which

    A. a piece of a chromosome breaks off and reattaches to another chromosome.

    B. an organism has an extra set of chromosomes.

    C. a mutagen speeds the mutation rate.

    D. an insect develops a resistance to a pesticide.

19. In the space below, draw an example of a normal blood cell and an example of a sickle cell

> *Students' drawings should look like those in the textbook.*

Apply the Big idea

20. A gene that codes for one of the polypeptide chains of the blood protein hemoglobin lies on chromosome 11 in humans. A substitution mutation in that gene causes the amino acid valine to be incorporated into hemoglobin in a place where glutamic acid would normally lie. The result is sickle cell disease. Explain how a change in a single base in DNA can bring about such a serious disorder.

A single DNA base-pair change in a gene can create an incorrect codon in the mRNA molecule made from this DNA. When the incorrect codon is "read" on the ribosome, the wrong amino acid (in this case valine rather than glutamic acid) is placed into the polypeptide. With the wrong amino acid sequence, the protein does not form or function properly.

13.4 Gene Regulation and Expression

Lesson Objectives

▭ Describe gene regulation in prokaryotes.

▭ Explain how most eukaryotic genes are regulated.

▭ Relate gene regulation to development in multicellular organisms.

Lesson Summary

Prokaryotic Gene Regulation Prokaryotes do not need to transcribe all of their genes at the same time. They can conserve energy and resources by regulating their activities, producing only those genes necessary for the cell to function. In prokaryotes, DNA-binding proteins regulate genes by controlling transcription. An **operon** is a group of genes that are regulated together. An example is the *lac* operon in the bacterium *E. coli*:

► This group of three genes must be turned on together before the bacterium can use lactose as food.

► When lactose is not present, the DNA-binding protein called *lac* repressor binds to a region called the **operator**, which switches the *lac* operon off.

► When lactose binds to the repressor, it causes the repressor to fall off the operator, turning the operon on.

Eukaryotic Gene Regulation Transcription factors are DNA-binding proteins. They control the expression of genes in eukaryotes by binding DNA sequences in the regulatory regions. Gene promoters have multiple binding sites for transcription factors, each of which can influence transcription.

► Complex gene regulation in eukaryotes makes cell specialization possible.

► The process by which microRNA (miRNA) molecules stop mRNA molecules from passing on their protein-making instructions is **RNA interference (RNAi)**.

► RNAi technology holds the promise of allowing scientists to turn off the expression of genes from viruses and cancer cells, and it may provide new ways to treat and perhaps even cure diseases.

Genetic Control of Development Regulating gene expression is especially important in shaping the way a multicellular organism develops. Gene regulation helps cells undergo **differentiation**, becoming specialized in structure and function. Master control genes are like switches that trigger particular patterns of development and differentiation in cells and tissues.

► **Homeotic genes** are master control genes that regulate organs that develop in specific parts of the body.

► **Homeobox genes** share a similar 130-base DNA sequence called homeobox. They code for transcription factors that activate other genes that are important in cell development and differentiation in certain regions of the body.

► **Hox genes** are a group of homeobox genes that tell the cells of the body how to differentiate as the body grows.

Environmental factors can also affect gene expression.

Prokaryotic Gene Regulation

1. How do prokaryotes conserve energy?

Prokaryotes regulate their activities, producing only those genes necessary for the cell to function.

2. How do DNA-binding proteins in prokaryotes regulate genes?

They control transcription. Some of these regulatory proteins help switch genes on, while others turn genes off.

3. What is an operon?

It is a group of genes that are regulated together.

4. What is in the *lac* operon in *E. coli*?

three genes

5. What is the function of the genes in the *lac* operon of *E. coli*?

They allow **E. coli** *to use lactose for food when it is present.*

6. What turns the *lac* operon off?

A repressor protein turns the operon off.

7. How does a repressor protein turn off the *lac* operon?

It binds to the operating region, blocking RNA polymerase from transcribing the **lac** *genes.*

8. How does lactose turn on the *lac* operon?

It attaches to the repressor, which causes the repressor to fall off the operator. Transcription can take place.

9. Complete the table to describe the role of each regulatory region or molecule in the operation of the *lac* operon.

Regulatory Region or Molecule	What It Does
Repressor protein	*Binds to the operator, preventing transcription of the* **lac** *genes*
Operator	*Binding site for the repressor protein*
RNA polymerase	*When the repressor is not present, this enzyme carries out the transcription of* **lac** *genes.*
Lactose	*Causes the repressor to drop off the operator so transcription of the* **lac** *genes can begin*

Eukaryotic Gene Regulation

10. In what two ways is gene regulation in eukaryotes different from gene regulation in prokaryotes?

a. *Most eukaryotic genes are controlled individually.*

b. *Eukaryotic cells have more complex regulatory sequences than those of the* **lac** *repressor system.*

11. What is a TATA box? What does a TATA box do?

It is a short region of DNA that contains a sequence of T and A base pairs. The protein that binds to this site helps position RNA polymerase.

12. What are transcription factors and what do they do?

They are DNA-binding proteins that bind to DNA sequences in the regulatory regions of genes and help control gene expression.

13. Explain how gene regulation makes cell specialization possible.

It allows particular genes to be expressed in some kinds of cells but not others.

14. What is microRNA and how is it related to mRNA?

Small RNA molecules are called microRNA. They attach to certain mRNA molecules and stop them from passing on their protein-making instructions.

15. Explain how the process of RNA interference works.

Certain small RNA molecules fold into loops. The Dicer enzyme cuts them into microRNA (miRNA). The strands then separate. An miRNA piece attaches to a cluster of proteins to form a silencing complex. The silencing complex binds to and destroys an mRNA molecule that contains a base sequence complementary to the miRNA. In this way, it blocks gene expression.

Genetic Control of Development

For Questions 16–23, write the letter of the correct answer on the line at the left.

___C___ 16. As an embryo develops, different sets of genes are regulated by

 A. mRNA and *lac* repressors.   C. transcription factors and repressors.

 B. operons and operators.   D. promoters and operators.

___C___ 17. The process through which cells become specialized in structure and function is

 A. transcription.   C. differentiation.

 B. gene expression.   D. RNA interference.

___B___ 18. Homeotic genes are

 A. regulator genes that bind to operons in prokaryotes.

 B. master control genes that regulate organs that develop in specific parts of the body.

 C. parts of the silencing complex that regulates gene action through RNA interference.

 D. base sequences complementary to sequences in microRNA.

___A___ 19. What role do homeobox genes play in cell differentiation?

 A. They code for transcription factors that activate other genes important in cell development and differentiation.

 B. They block certain gene expression.

 C. They cut double-stranded loops into microRNA.

 D. They attach to a cluster of proteins to form a silencing complex, which binds to and destroys certain RNA.

___D___ 20. In flies, the group of homeobox genes that determines the identities of each segment of a fly's body is the group known as

 A. silencing complexes.   C. operators.

 B. promoters.   D. Hox genes.

___D___ 21. Clusters of Hox genes are found in

 A. flies only.   C. plants only.

 B. flies and frogs only.   D. nearly all animals.

___B___ 22. The "switches" that trigger particular patterns of development and differentiation in cells and tissues are

 A. mRNA molecules.   C. silencing complexes.

 B. master control genes.   D. Dicer enzymes.

___A___ 23. Metamorphosis is

 A. a series of transformations from one life stage to another.

 B. the master switch that triggers development and differentiation.

 C. the product of interactions among homeotic genes.

 D. the process by which genetic information is passed from one generation to the next.

24. Environmental factors can influence gene expression. Fill in the table below to show how organisms respond to conditions in their environment.

	Environmental Factor Influencing Gene Expression	How the Organism Responds
E. coli with limited food supply	nutrient availability	*The lac operon is switched on when lactose is the only food source.*
A tadpole in a drying pond	*lack of water*	*The tadpole may speed up its metamorphosis.*

Apply the Big idea

25. Many research studies have shown that different species may possess some of the exact same genes but show vastly different traits. How can that happen?

The difference arises not from the genes themselves but from how they are regulated

and expressed. For example, a gene may be turned on at a different time in one

species than in another. Perhaps environmental factors have an effect, too.

_____

_____

Chapter Vocabulary Review

For Questions 1–7, write True if the statement is true. If the statement is false, change the underlined word or words to make the statement true.

_____RNA_____ 1. <u>DNA</u> contains the sugar ribose.

_____True_____ 2. <u>Messenger RNA</u> carries copies of the instructions for making proteins from DNA to other parts of the cell.

_____Transfer RNA_____ 3. <u>RNA polymerase</u> transfers amino acids to ribosomes.

_____True_____ 4. The process of <u>transcription</u> produces a complementary strand of RNA on a DNA template.

_____True_____ 5. The enzyme that assembles a complementary strand of RNA on a DNA template is <u>RNA polymerase</u>.

_____promoter_____ 6. The region of DNA where the production of an RNA strand begins is called the <u>intron</u>.

_____True_____ 7. <u>Exons</u> are spliced together in forming messenger RNA.

For Questions 8–16, match the term with its definition.

Definition

___B___ 8. The sequence of bases that serves as the "language" of life

___E___ 9. A sequence of three bases on a tRNA molecule that is complementary to a sequence of bases on an mRNA molecule

___F___ 10. How genetic information is put into action in a living cell

___I___ 11. Having extra sets of chromosomes

___D___ 12. The decoding of an mRNA message into a protein

___G___ 13. A heritable change in genetic information

___A___ 14. A chain of amino acids

___C___ 15. The three consecutive bases that specify a single amino acid to be added to the polypeptide chain

___H___ 16. A chemical or physical agent that causes a change in a gene

Term

A. polypeptide

B. genetic code

C. codon

D. translation

E. anticodon

F. gene expression

G. mutation

H. mutagen

I. polyploidy

For Questions 17–19, complete each statement by writing the correct word or words.

17. A group of genes that are regulated together is called a(n) _____operon_____.

18. A region of DNA where a repressor can bind is a(n) _____operator_____.

19. Master control genes, called _____homeotic_____ genes, regulate organs that develop in specific parts of the body.

CHAPTER MYSTERY
MOUSE-EYED FLY

In the Chapter Mystery, you learned about a fly that was genetically manipulated to grow eyes in different places on its body. Scientists continue to develop techniques to modify a variety of other animals. But should they?

21st Century Learning

Should Genetic Experiments Be Performed on Animals?

Some people think that the type of research that produced the mouse-eyed fly is perfectly acceptable. Others think that it's a terrible thing to do even to a fly. In the biological sciences, animal testing has always been controversial, and it probably always will be.

Perspectives on Animal Genetic Experiments

Animal rights groups have come a long way in recent years. More people are responding to the issues brought up by animal rights groups. For example, animal testing of cosmetics has been banned in a number of countries, and in the United States many companies have voluntarily stopped testing on animals. So what's the next frontier for animal rights activists? According to Edward Avellone of Animal Rights Now!, it's genetic experimentation. "What purpose is there in creating a mouse with six legs or a sheep with one eye in the middle of its forehead?" asks Avellone. "Scientists are just playing around with a new technology. They're creating horribly deformed animals for no real reason."

Some people disagree with this point of view. Says Ann Wilber of Scientists for the Ethical Treatment of Animals, "We're responsible professionals, not monsters." Wilber explains that the one-eyed sheep was the unintended result of an attempt to understand how the eye developed and how it works. "We've also developed a sheep whose milk contains a protein that might cure emphysema. There are reasons for what we do."

But to Avellone, the point is not simply the motivation behind the experimentation. It's also the process of the experiment. "Only 10 percent of the animals they breed have the gene they want to study. The remaining 90 percent [of the animals] are simply killed." Wilber admits that this situation is "sad, but true." Still, she says, "We're working every day to improve our techniques and therefore our success rate." Even if the success rate never tops 10 percent, she asks, "Isn't that a small price to pay for a cure for cancer, or multiple sclerosis, or Parkinson's disease?"

Continued on next page ▶

21st Century Themes Science and Civic Literacy

1. Edward Avellone makes several arguments against animal testing in genetics experiments. Why does he think the *process* of animal genetic experimentation is flawed?

He says that only 10 percent of animals scientists breed have the gene they want to study.

He says the remaining 90 percent of the animals are killed because they are not useful.

2. Avellone argues that genetic experiments are unnecessary. What claim does he make about scientists' motivations for doing such experiments?

He says that scientists are performing experiments with no real scientific purpose,

and that they are "playing with new technology."

3. What is Ann Wilber's main argument in favor of genetic testing on animals?

It could lead to cures for serious human diseases.

4. Which of her arguments could be summed up as, "It's a necessary evil"?

Killing 90 percent of the animals they breed is a small price to pay to cure diseases.

5. Do you agree with Avellone, with Wilber, or with neither of them? Why?

Accept any answers that are clearly argued, logical, and based on evidence, either

from the article or from other reliable sources.

21st Century Skills Evaluating an Issue

The skills used in this activity include **creativity and intellectual curiosity, communication skills, interpersonal and collaborative skills, information and media literacy,** and **social responsibility.**

The issue of experimenting on animals, especially genetic experimentation, is complex; you can't construct an informed opinion after reading just one article. Working with a group, use library and Internet resources to collect opinions on both sides of the issue. Work through the material thoroughly and then make up your mind about how you feel about the issue.

If everyone in the group agrees, create a multimedia presentation for your class in which you present your point of view. If the members of your group disagree, stage a debate in front of the class, with the same number of students arguing each side of the issue.

Evaluate students' presentations based on the thoroughness of their research, the inclusion of sources from both sides of the issue, and the quality of the sources they used; also, consider the cogency of the arguments they make to support their point of view.

14 Human Heredity

Information and Heredity

Q: How can we use genetics to study human inheritance?

WHAT I KNOW	WHAT I LEARNED
14.1 How does studying the human genome help us to draw conclusions about the inheritance of traits?	*SAMPLE ANSWER:* **Humans inherit their traits from their parents. They have genes made of DNA just as other organisms do.**	*SAMPLE ANSWER:* **Inheritance in humans may follow a simple dominance pattern, or it may involve codominance of multiple alleles. Some traits are sex-linked. Pedigrees reveal patterns of inheritance.**
14.2 What causes some human genetic disorders?	*SAMPLE ANSWER:* **Mutations can cause changes in genes that lead to human disorders. Mutations can occur in single genes or in entire chromosomes.**	*SAMPLE ANSWER:* **A mutation in human DNA may change a protein by altering an amino acid sequence. That change can affect an individual's phenotype. So can nondisjunction, which may lead to a chromosomal disorder.**
14.3 How do we study the human genome and what have we learned so far?	*SAMPLE ANSWER:* **Humans have many genes on their 46 chromosomes.**	*SAMPLE ANSWER:* **Tools that can isolate, separate, and replicate DNA allow researchers to read the base sequences in human DNA. That technology has made possible the Human Genome Project, which has identified the base pairs in all human genes.**

14.1 Human Chromosomes

Lesson Objectives

- Identify the types of human chromosomes in a karotype.
- Describe the patterns of the inheritance of human traits.
- Explain how pedigrees are used to study human traits.

Lesson Summary

Karyotypes A **genome** is the full set of all the genetic information that an organism carries in its DNA. Chromosomes are bundles of DNA and protein found in the nucleus of a eukaryotic cell. A **karyotype** is a picture that shows the complete diploid set of human chromosomes, grouped in pairs and arranged in order of decreasing size. A typical human diploid cell contains 46 chromosomes, or 23 pairs:

▶ Two of the 46 are the **sex chromosomes** that determine an individual's sex: XX = female and XY = male. The X chromosome carries nearly 10 times the number of genes as the Y chromosome.

▶ The other 44 are **autosomes**, or autosomal chromosomes.

Transmission of Human Traits Human genes follow the same Mendelian patterns of inheritance as the genes of other organisms:

▶ Many human traits follow a pattern of simple dominance.

▶ The alleles for many human genes display codominant inheritance.

▶ Many human genes, including the genes for blood group, have multiple alleles.

▶ A gene located on a sex chromosome is a **sex-linked gene**. The genes on sex chromosomes show a sex-linked pattern of inheritance, since females have two copies of many genes (located on X chromosomes) while males have just one.

▶ In females, most of the genes in one of the X chromosomes are inactivated in each cell.

Human Pedigrees A chart used to analyze the pattern of inheritance that shows the relationships in a family is a **pedigree**. Pedigrees can be used to determine the nature of genes and alleles associated with inherited human traits.

Karyotypes

1. **THINK VISUALLY** Make a sketch of a human karyotype. Number the chromosome pairs. Label autosomes and sex chromosomes.

   Sketch should resemble the illustration in the textbook. It should show 22 pairs of autosomes, arranged in order from largest to smallest. It should show an additional pair, labeled sex chromosomes. The pair of sex chromosomes may show two X chromosomes or one X and one Y.

For Questions 2–8, write the letter of the correct answer on the line at the left.

__B__ 2. The complete set of genetic information an organism carries in its DNA is its
   A. karyotype.
   B. genome.
   C. chromosomes.
   D. autosomes.

__A__ 3. From what is a karyotype made?
   A. A photograph of cells in mitosis
   B. A series of X-ray diffraction images
   C. A preparation of gametes on a microscope slide
   D. A Punnett square

__B__ 4. How many chromosomes are in a normal human karyotype?
   A. 23
   B. 46
   C. 44
   D. 2 (either XX or XY)

__D__ 5. Which of the following genetic abbreviations denotes a male human?
   A. 23, XX
   B. 23, XY
   C. 46, XX
   D. 46, XY

__D__ 6. Why is the ratio of male to female births roughly 50:50?
   A. All egg cells carry an X chromosome.
   B. Half of all egg cells carry a Y chromosome.
   C. All sperm cells carry an X chromosome.
   D. Half of all sperm cells carry a Y chromosome.

__C__ 7. How are the X and Y chromosomes different?
   A. Only one is an autosome.
   B. The X is smaller than the Y.
   C. The Y carries fewer genes than the X.
   D. Only females have a Y.

__A__ 8. All human cells carry
   A. at least one X chromosome.
   B. at least one Y chromosome.
   C. a pair of X chromosomes.
   D. one X and one Y chromosome.

Transmission of Human Traits

9. Complete the graphic organizer to list, describe, and give examples of three types of inheritance patterns in humans:

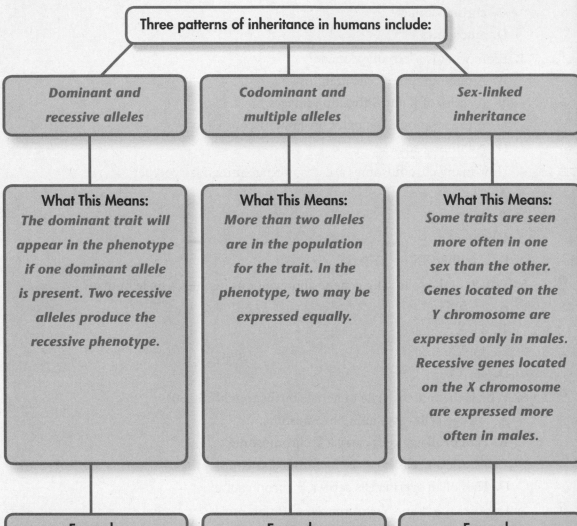

Three patterns of inheritance in humans include:

Dominant and recessive alleles

Codominant and multiple alleles

Sex-linked inheritance

What This Means:
The dominant trait will appear in the phenotype if one dominant allele is present. Two recessive alleles produce the recessive phenotype.

What This Means:
More than two alleles are in the population for the trait. In the phenotype, two may be expressed equally.

What This Means:
Some traits are seen more often in one sex than the other. Genes located on the Y chromosome are expressed only in males. Recessive genes located on the X chromosome are expressed more often in males.

Example:
Red hair results from a pair of recessive alleles. One dominant allele is enough to produce the Rh+ blood type.

Example:
Three alleles for ABO blood type are present in the population. Both alleles in the gene pair are expressed.

Example:
The genes for color vision are all located on the X chromosome. Color-blindness is a recessive allele. It is is more common in men because they inherit only one allele for color vision.

10. Colorblindness is a sex-linked trait. Let C represent an allele for normal color vision. Let c represent an allele for colorblindness. The genotype for a male with normal color vision is $X^C Y$. The genotype for a female heterozygous for normal color vision is $X^C X^c$.

Complete the Punnett square to show the genotypes and phenotypes of their possible offspring.

	Male Gamete: X^c	**Male Gamete:** Y
Female Gamete: X^C	Genotype: $X^C X^c$ Phenotype: *Female with normal color vision (homozygous)*	Genotype: $X^C Y$ Phenotype: *Male with normal color vision*
Female Gamete: X^c	Genotype: $X^c X^c$ Phenotype: *Female with normal color vision (heterozygous)*	Genotype: $X^c Y$ Phenotype: *Male with colorblindness*

11. Use your Punnett square to explain why a female with one c allele has normal color vision but a male with one c allele is colorblind.

The female also inherited the dominant C allele, so her color vision is normal. The male has no matching allele on his Y chromosome, so the recessive gene is expressed.

12. How does the cell "adjust" to the extra X chromosome in female cells?

In female cells, most of the genes on one X chromosome are switched off.

13. What is a Barr body?

It is a dense region in the nucleus that is formed by the switched-off genes on an X chromosome.

14. Why don't males have Barr bodies?

Males don't have Barr bodies because they have only one X chromosome and it remains active.

15. Is a cat with three colors of spots more likely to be male or female?

The gene that controls a cat's coat color is located on the X chromosome. The multi-colored cat is probably a female because different X chromosomes are switched off in different cells, allowing different colors of spots to show up in the phenotype.

Human Pedigrees

For Questions 16–21, match the labels to the parts of the pedigree chart shown below. Some of the labels may be used more than once.

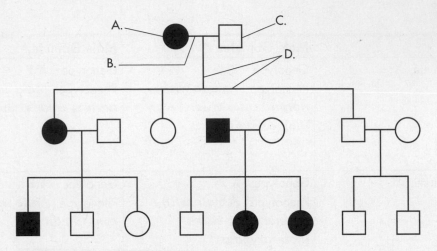

_____**A**_____ **16.** A person who expresses the trait

_____**C**_____ **17.** A male

_____**C**_____ **18.** A person who does not express the trait

_____**B**_____ **19.** A marriage

_____**A**_____ **20.** A female

_____**D**_____ **21.** A connection between parents and offspring

Apply the Big idea

22. Dimples in the cheeks are inherited as a dominant trait on an autosome. Using the proper form and symbols, draw a pedigree chart, beginning with a heterozygous, dimpled father (*Dd*), and a nondimpled mother (*dd*). Show four children of the expected types: boys, girls, dimples, and no dimples. Label your pedigree with phenotypes and genotypes.

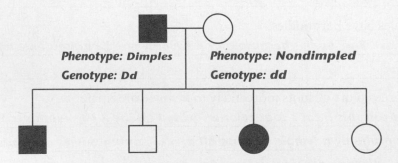

Note: Boys and girls can be in any order, as long as half are male and half are female. Half of them should be dimpled (Dd), and half should not be dimpled (Nondimpled dd). The gender associated with dimples or no dimples is not important; it can be both boys, both girls, or a boy and a girl.

14.2 Human Genetic Disorders

Lesson Objectives

Explain how small changes in DNA cause genetic disorders.

Summarize the problems caused by nondisjunction.

Lesson Summary

From Molecule to Phenotype There is a molecular reason for genetic disorders. A change in DNA can alter an amino acid sequence, which can change a protein and therefore, the phenotype. Some common inherited disorders result from a change in DNA. They include:

▶ sickle cell disease, in which a defective polypeptide makes hemoglobin in the blood less soluble;

▶ cystic fibrosis, in which a deletion of three bases in a gene causes cell membranes to lose their ability to transport chloride ions;

▶ Huntington's disease, in which a single codon for a certain amino acid repeats more than 40 times, causing mental deterioration and uncontrolled movements.

Some alleles that cause disease in the homozygote can provide an advantage in the heterozygote. The geographic associations between sickle cell disease and malaria and between cystic fibrosis and typhoid demonstrate how the heterozygous state reduces the risk of infection.

Chromosomal Disorders Sometimes, during meiosis, homologous chromosomes fail to separate. This **nondisjunction** (not coming apart) can create a gamete with an abnormal number of chromosomes, leading to offspring with missing or extra chromosomes. Examples include:

▶ Down syndrome, most often a result of three copies of chromosome 21;

▶ Turner's syndrome, a female with a single X chromosome;

▶ Klinefelter's syndrome, a male with an extra X chromosome.

From Molecule to Phenotype

1. The boxes below each show a step to explain how genetic disorders have a molecular basis. Number them so that the steps are in the correct order.

A change in phenotype results. __3__	A gene's DNA sequence changes. __1__	The amino acid sequence that alters a protein changes. __2__

For Questions 2–7, write the letter of the correct answer on the line at the left.

___D___ 2. How many human genetic disorders are known?

    A. three

    B. about 20

    C. about 100

    D. thousands

___B___ 3. The inherited disease in which hemoglobin molecules clump into long fibers, changing the shape of blood cells is

    A. cystic fibrosis.

    B. sickle cell disease.

    C. Huntington's disease.

    D. Klinefelter's syndrome.

___C___ 4. What happens to the CFTR gene in individuals who have cystic fibrosis?

    A. The entire gene is deleted.

    B. The entire gene is duplicated.

    C. Three bases are deleted, causing one amino acid to be missing.

    D. Three bases are duplicated, causing one amino acid show up about 40 times.

___C___ 5. Why are individuals who are heterozygous for the cystic fibrosis allele unaffected by the disease?

    A. They have an extra copy of the allele on their X chromosome.

    B. Cystic fibrosis only occurs in males, so females are unaffected.

    C. They make enough of a particular protein to allow their cells to work properly.

    D. Their cells can transport chloride ions through diffusion channels.

___B___ 6. How might the allele that causes a disease stay in the population if it is fatal to those who have the disease?

    A. It is present only in heterozygotes.

    B. It makes the heterozygote resistant to a fatal disease.

    C. It disappears but is continuously replaced by mutations.

    D. It occurs only in certain geographic areas.

___A___ 7. What advantage do individuals with one sickle cell allele have?

    A. a stronger resistance to malaria

    B. immunity to typhoid fever

    C. more rigid red blood cells

    D. no advantage

Chromosomal Disorders

8. Complete this graphic organizer to explain the process and outcomes of nondisjunction.

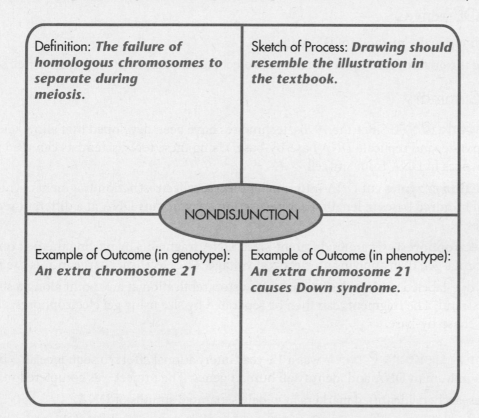

Definition: *The failure of homologous chromosomes to separate during meiosis.*

Sketch of Process: *Drawing should resemble the illustration in the textbook.*

NONDISJUNCTION

Example of Outcome (in genotype): *An extra chromosome 21*

Example of Outcome (in phenotype): *An extra chromosome 21 causes Down syndrome.*

9. What is trisomy?

Trisomy is a result of nondisjunction, in which an individual has three copies of a chromosome instead of two.

10. What happens when a male has XXY sex chromosomes?

The male will have Klinefelter's syndrome, which will most likely prevent him from reproducing.

Apply the Big idea

11. Most of the genetic disorders you have learned about are the result of a change in DNA sequence, as with cystic fibrosis, or the presence of an extra chromosome, as with Down syndrome. The exception is Turner's syndrome. Women with Turner's syndrome have only 45 chromosomes. They are missing an X chromosome. This disorder is the *only* case in which a person can survive with one less chromosome. What does this tell you about how genetic information is inherited in humans?

Much of our genetic information must be carried on the X chromosome. A person cannot survive without at least one X chromosome.

_____

14.3 Studying the Human Genome

Lesson Objectives

▸ Summarize the methods of DNA analysis.

▸ State the goals of the Human Genome Project and explain what we have learned so far.

Lesson Summary

Manipulating DNA Since the 1970s, techniques have been developed that allow scientists to cut, separate, and replicate DNA base-by-base. Using these tools, scientists can read the base sequences in DNA from any cell.

▸ **Restriction enzymes** cut DNA into smaller pieces, called restriction fragments, which are several hundred bases in length. Each restriction enzyme cuts DNA at a different sequence of bases.

▸ **Gel electrophoresis** separates different-sized DNA fragments by placing them at one end of a porous gel, then applying an electrical voltage. The electrical charge moves the DNA.

▸ Using dye-labeled nucleotides, scientists can stop replication at any point along a single DNA strand. The fragments can then be separated by size using gel electrophoresis and "read," base-by-base.

The Human Genome Project was a 13-year international effort to sequence all 3 billion base pairs in human DNA and identify all human genes. The project was completed in 2003.

▸ The researchers identified markers in widely separated strands of DNA.

▸ They used "shotgun sequencing," which uses a computer to match DNA base sequences.

▸ To identify genes, they found promoters, exons, and other sites on the DNA molecule.

▸ To locate and identify as many haplotypes (collections of linked single-base differences) in the human population as possible, the International HapMap Project began in 2002.

▸ The Human Genome Project identified genes associated with many diseases and disorders. From the project came the new science of **bioinformatics**, the creation and use of databases and other computing tools to manage data. Bioinformatics launched **genomics**, the study of whole genomes.

▸ The human genome project pinpointed genes and associated particular sequences in those genes with numerous diseases and disorders. It also found that the DNA of all humans matches base-for-base at most sites, but can vary at 3 million sites.

▸ The 1000 Genomes Project, launched in 2008, will catalogue the variation among 1000 people.

Manipulating DNA

For Questions 1–4, write True if the statement is true. If the statement is false, change the underlined word to make the statement true.

_____True_____ 1. Bacteria produce restriction enzymes that cut the <u>DNA</u> molecule into smaller pieces.

nucleotides 2. Restriction fragments are always cut at a particular sequence of <u>proteins</u>.

_____True_____ 3. The technique that separates differently sized DNA fragments is <u>gel electrophoresis</u>.

polymerase 4. The enzyme that copies DNA is DNA <u>restrictase</u>.

5. Complete the graphic organizer to summarize the steps used to determine the sequences of bases in DNA.

Purpose	Tool or Technique Used	Outcome
Cutting DNA	**Restriction enzymes**	**Large molecule of DNA is cut into smaller fragments.**
Separating DNA	**Gel electrophoresis**	**Smaller DNA fragments move faster on the gel, so fragments are separated according to size.**
Reading DNA	**Dye-labeled nucleotides and gel electrophoresis**	**Labeled nucleotides stop the synthesis of a new strand at different lengths. Gel electrophoresis then separates them so they can be read.**

For Questions 6–10, complete each statement by writing in the correct word or words.

6. By using tools that cut, separate, and then replicate DNA, scientists can now read the _____base_____ sequence in DNA from any cell.

7. Restriction enzymes cut pieces of DNA sometimes called restriction __fragments__.

8. Each restriction enzyme cuts DNA at a different sequence of __nucleotides__.

9. The smaller the DNA, the _____faster_____ and farther it moves during gel electrophoresis.

10. After chemically dyed bases have been incorporated into a DNA strand, the order of colored _____bands_____ on the gel reveals the exact sequence of bases in DNA.

The Human Genome Project

For Questions 11–16, write the letter of the correct answer on the line at the left.

___A___ **11.** What technology made the Human Genome Project possible?

   A. DNA sequencing

   B. RNA replication

   C. protein synthesis

   D. enzyme activation

___C___ **12.** What were the "markers" that the researchers of the Human Genome Project used?

   A. restriction enzymes

   B. gel electrophoresis

   C. base sequences

   D. restriction fragments

___B___ **13.** What does "shotgun sequencing" do?

   A. separate fragments using gel electrophoresis

   B. find overlapping areas of DNA fragments

   C. cut DNA into millions of "puzzle pieces"

   D. bind colored dyes to base sequences

___D___ **14.** What are SNPs?

   A. points where a restriction enzyme cuts a DNA molecule

   B. missing sequence of base pairs in a restriction fragment

   C. proteins formed by a mutated gene

   D. differences in a base between two individuals

___C___ **15.** Bioinformatics would not have been possible without

   A. microscopes.

   B. genes.

   C. computers.

   D. genomics.

___A___ **16.** In humans, single-base differences

   A. occur at about 3 million sites.

   B. occur rarely in the sex chromosomes.

   C. seldom occur in normal DNA.

   D. cannot be identified from DNA analysis.

17. What were the goals of the Human Genome Project?

The main goals were to sequence the base pairs of DNA and identify all human genes.

Other goals included sequencing genomes of model organisms, developing technology

for research, exploring gene functions, studying variation in humans, and training

future scientists.

18. **THINK VISUALLY** The field of bioinformatics combines both life sciences and modern technology. Fill in the Venn diagram to show how.

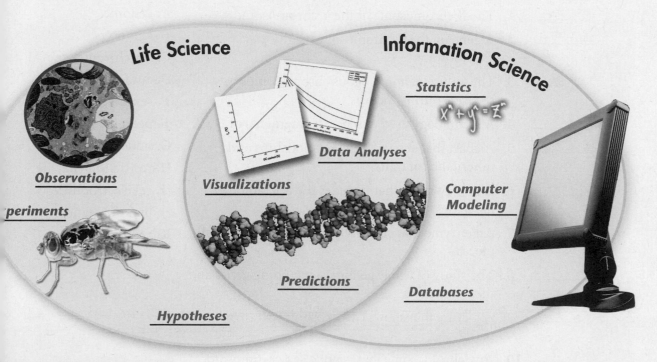

Apply the Big idea

19. The Icelandic people have always placed high importance on knowing about their ancestors. In fact, 80% of all the Icelandic people who have ever lived can be added to a family tree. Medical records are just as detailed. The population is quite isolated, so the gene pool is considered to be homogeneous. Why would these conditions make the genome of the Icelandic population ideal for studying rare inherited disorders associated with gene sequencing errors?

The homogeneous population makes the task of finding DNA sequences easier.

Unusual base pairs, such as those associated with disorders, would stand out. Since

people are aware of their family's medical histories, scientists would be able to test

descendants with no signs of the disorder to see just how it is inherited between

generations.

Chapter Vocabulary Review

For Questions 1–11, match the term with its definition.

Definition

Term

___C___ 1. The X chromosome or the Y chromosome

___E___ 2. A gene on the X chromosome or the Y chromosome

___G___ 3. The failure of homologous chromosomes to separate during meiosis

___I___ 4. A technology used to separate fragments of DNA

___F___ 5. A chart that shows family relationships and inheritance of traits

___J___ 6. A field of study that includes the operation of databases

___H___ 7. An enzyme that cuts a DNA molecule into small pieces

___K___ 8. The study of whole genomes, including genes and their functions

___B___ 9. A picture that shows chromosomes arranged in pairs

___D___ 10. Any chromosome that is not a sex chromosome

___A___ 11. The full set of genetic information in an organism's DNA

A. genome
B. karyotype
C. sex chromosome
D. autosome
E. sex-linked gene
F. pedigree
G. nondisjunction
H. restriction enzyme
I. gel electrophoresis
J. bioinformatics
K. genomics

For Questions 12–19, complete each statement by writing in the correct word or words.

12. A circle represents a female in a(n) ____pedigree____.

13. The protein that cuts DNA into pieces is a restriction ____enzyme____.

14. An inherited disorder that appears more often in males than females is probably caused by a ____sex-linked gene____.

15. The 23 pairs of human chromosomes are arranged from largest to smallest in a ____karyotype____.

16. Humans have 22 pairs of ____autosomes____.

17. The cause of Down syndrome is ____nondisjunction____ during meiosis.

18. Humans have 3 billion base pairs in their ____genome____.

19. The new field of ____bioinformatics____ resulted from the Human Genome Project.

CHAPTER MYSTERY

THE CROOKED CELL

In the Chapter Mystery, you learned how genetic testing can help identify risk for an inheritable disease, such as sickle-cell anemia. Geneticists have made great strides in recent years to develop many more DNA-based genetic tests.

21st Century Learning

Genetic Testing: A Personal Choice

Today, more than 1000 genetic tests are available to determine whether patients carry genes associated with diseases from breast cancer to the degenerative neurological disorder known as Huntington's disease. But the genetic tests pose a difficult dilemma for many people at risk for genetic disease.

The choice is especially difficult for those conditions, such as Huntington's disease, for which there are no treatments or cures. Recent polls have found that a significant majority of people say they would want to undergo genetic testing for a treatable disease. But respondents remain almost evenly split on whether they would undertake testing for an untreatable condition. Many people are concerned that testing positive for an untreatable genetic disease could lead to employment discrimination, denial of medical insurance, or other types of discrimination. The National Institutes of Health has issued the following information to help people make their decisions.

How Do I Decide Whether to Be Tested?

● ●

People have many different reasons for being tested or not being tested. For many, it is important to know whether a disease can be prevented if a gene alteration causing a disease is found. For example, those who have inherited forms of breast or colon cancer have options such as screening or early treatment. Pharmacogenetic testing can find the best medicine or dose of a medicine for a certain person. (Pharmacogenetic testing involves the analysis of a person's genetic makeup in order to prescribe the most effective medications for that person.)

But in some cases, there is no treatment or cure available. There are no preventive steps or cures for Huntington's disease, for example. Some people simply do not want to know that they will develop a serious illness for which there is no treatment or cure. Others, however, feel that knowing the test results might help them make decisions such as career choices, family planning, or insurance coverage.

To help make such decisions, people can seek advice from a genetic counselor. Genetic counselors help individuals and families think about the scientific, emotional, and ethical factors that affect their decision whether or not to test. But the difficult decision is still up to the individual or family.

Continued on next page ▶

21st Century Themes **Science and Health Literacy**

1. What is a genetic test?

A genetic test examines a patient's DNA to determine whether that patient carries

a gene associated with a given disease.

2. How many genetic tests are currently available?

more than 1000

3. According to the National Institutes of Health, why would someone want to undergo a genetic test?

to find out whether a disease can be prevented, to begin early treatment, to find

the best medicine or dose of a medicine, to make more appropriate decisions

4. What major factor, according to polls, affects the way people feel about a particular genetic test?

People would want to undergo genetic testing for a treatable disease, but are almost

evenly split on whether they would undertake genetic testing for an untreatable condition.

5. Do you think anti-discrimination laws should be put in place to protect people who test positive for an untreatable condition like Huntington's disease? Why or why not?

Students may express different viewpoints, which should be supported by logical

rationales.

21st Century Skills **An Individual's Case**

The skills used in this activity include **information and media literacy; communication skills;** and **problem identification, formulation, and solution.**

Use Internet or library resources to research the case of neuropsychologist Nancy Wexler. Twenty years ago, Wexler identified the gene that causes Huntington's disease. She was spurred on in her research because Huntington's disease runs in her family. Wexler spent much of her career working to develop a genetic test for Huntington's disease. But when the test finally became available, she decided that she would rather not know whether she carried the gene because no treatment exists for the disease.

Organize into groups to present your findings in a panel discussion about genetic testing.

Here are some questions you might consider:

▶ What are the arguments that someone should consider about the decision to undergo genetic testing?

▶ Should a genetic test even be offered for an untreatable condition like Huntington's? If so, why?

Evaluate the students' performance in the panel discussion based on the reasons

why people want to be tested, as well as scientific, emotional, and ethical factors

that affect the testing decision.

15 Genetic Engineering

 Big idea ▸ **Science as a Way of Knowing**

Q: How and why do scientists manipulate DNA in living cells?

WHAT I KNOW	WHAT I LEARNED
15.1 How do humans take advantage of naturally occurring variation among organisms?	SAMPLE ANSWER: **People use organisms with specific traits for certain functions. For example, some plants provide food.**	SAMPLE ANSWER: **Selective breeding takes advantage of natural genetic variation and passes wanted traits to the next generation.**
15.2 How do scientists study and work with specific genes?	SAMPLE ANSWER: **Scientists have methods for working with DNA.**	SAMPLE ANSWER: **Scientists have developed ways to isolate and copy genes, and then recombine DNA to change the genetic composition of organisms.**
15.3 How do humans use genetic engineering?	SAMPLE ANSWER: **Scientists can recombine the DNA of organisms to change their inherited traits.**	SAMPLE ANSWER: **Genetic engineering can lead to better, less expensive, and more nutritious food. DNA technology is leading to advances in medicine and forensic science.**
15.4 What are some of the ethical issues raised by genetic engineering?	SAMPLE ANSWER: **The ability to modify DNA raises some difficult ethical questions.**	SAMPLE ANSWER: **In deciding how to develop genetic engineering safely and responsibly, society must answer ethical questions about profits, privacy, safety, and regulation.**

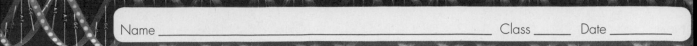

15.1 Selective Breeding

Lesson Objectives

- Explain the purpose of selective breeding.
- Explain how people increase genetic variation.

Lesson Summary

Selective Breeding Through **selective breeding**, humans choose organisms with wanted characteristics to produce the next generation.

▶ This takes advantage of natural variation among organisms and passes wanted traits to offspring.

▶ The numerous breeds of dogs and varieties of crop plants and domestic animals are examples of selective breeding.

Hybridization crosses dissimilar individuals to bring together the best of both parents in the offspring. **Inbreeding** is the continued breeding of individuals with selected characteristics. It ensures that wanted traits are preserved, but can also result in defects being passed on.

Increasing Variation Mutations are the source of biological diversity. Breeders introduce mutations into populations to increase genetic variation. **Biotechnology** is the application of a technological process, invention, or method to living organisms. Selective breeding is one example of biotechnology.

▶ Radiation and chemicals can increase the mutation rate. Diverse bacterial strains have been bred from mutated lines.

▶ Drugs can prevent the separation of chromosomes during mitosis, leading to polyploidy in plants. Such plants may be larger or stronger than their diploid relatives.

Selective Breeding

For Questions 1–5, write True if the statement is true. If the statement is false, change the underlined word or words to make the statement true.

True	1. <u>Selective breeding</u> works because of the natural genetic variation in a population.
dissimilar	2. Hybridization crosses <u>similar</u> individuals to bring together the best of both.
hybrids	3. The individuals produced by crossing dissimilar parents are <u>purebreeds</u>.
inbreeding	4. The continued crossing of individuals with similar characteristics is <u>hybridization</u>.
True	5. Inbreeding <u>increases</u> the risk of genetic defects.

6. Complete the table describing the types of selective breeding.

Selective Breeding		
Type	**Description**	**Examples**
Hybridization	Crossing dissimilar individuals to bring together the best of both organisms	*Disease-resistant Burbank potato*
Inbreeding	The continued breeding of individuals with similar characteristics	*Elberta peaches*

Increasing Variation

7. Complete this concept map about biotechnology.

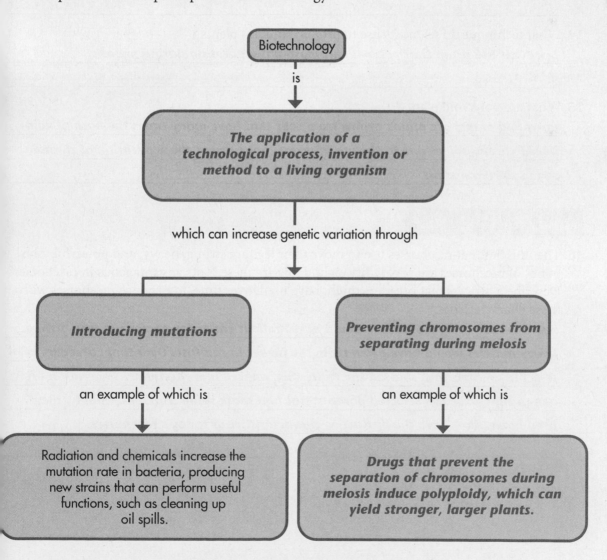

For Questions 8–11, match the example with the probable method used to introduce the mutation. Each answer can be used more than once.

_____**A**_____ 8. Bacteria that clean up radioactive substances   **A.** radiation or chemicals

_____**B**_____ 9. Larger, stronger banana trees   **B.** polyploidy

_____**A**_____ 10. Bacteria that clean up metal pollution

_____**B**_____ 11. Watermelons that grow faster and larger

12. Is it easy for breeders to produce mutants with desirable mutations? Explain.

No, many mutations are harmful, and it requires luck and perseverance to pro-

duce a few mutants with desirable characteristics that are not found in the original

population.

13. Why are radiation and chemicals useful techniques for producing mutant bacteria?

The small size of bacteria enables millions of organisms to be treated at the same

time, thus increasing the chances of producing a useful mutant.

14. What technique do scientists use to produce mutant plants?

Scientists use drugs that prevent chromosomal separation during meiosis.

15. What are polyploid plants?

Polyploid plants are plants grown from cells that have many times the normal num-

ber of chromosomes due to the use of drugs that prevent the separation of chromo-

somes during meiosis.

Apply the Big idea

16. The muscles that racehorses use to move their legs are strong, heavy, and powerful. The bones of racehorses are very lightweight. How are these traits advantageous in racehorses? Describe a process that breeders might have used, over time, to produce racehorses with these characteristics.

SAMPLE ANSWER: A light skeleton would have made it easier for horses run fast. Strong,

heavy muscles would have given them the power to run fast. Over time, breeders

selected animals that showed the traits they wanted in a racehorse. Generation after

generation, breeders selected parents that had those same traits. Eventually, they

bred horses that have the distinctive characteristics of today's racehorses.

15.2 Recombinant DNA

Lesson Objectives

▧ Explain how scientists manipulate DNA.

▧ Describe the importance of recombinant DNA.

▧ Define transgenic and describe the usefulness of some transgenic organisms to humans.

Lesson Summary

Copying DNA Genetic engineers can transfer a gene from one organism to another to achieve a goal, but first, individual genes must be identified and separated from DNA. The original method (used by Douglas Prasher) involved several steps:

- Determine the amino acid sequence in a protein.
- Predict the mRNA code for that sequence.
- Use a complementary base sequence to attract the predicted mRNA.
- Find the DNA fragment that binds to the mRNA.

Once scientists find a gene, they can use a technique called the **polymerase chain reaction** to make many copies.

- Heat separates the DNA into two strands.
- As the DNA cools, primers are added to opposite ends of the strands.
- DNA polymerase adds nucleotides between the primers, producing two complementary strands. The process can be repeated as many times as needed.

Changing DNA **Recombinant DNA** molecules contain DNA from two different sources. Recombinant-DNA technology can change the genetic composition of living organisms.

- **Plasmids** are circular DNA molecules found in bacteria and yeasts; they are widely used by scientists studying recombinant DNA, because DNA joined to a plasmid can be replicated.
- A **genetic marker** is a gene that is used to differentiate a cell that carries a recombinant plasmid from those that do not.

Transgenic Organisms **Transgenic** organisms contain genes from other species. They result from the insertion of recombinant DNA into the genome of the host organism. A **clone** is a member of a population of genetically identical cells.

Copying DNA

For Questions 1–5, complete each statement by writing in the correct word or words.

1. Genetic engineers can transfer _____*genes*_____ from one organism to another.

2. As a first step toward finding a gene, Douglas Prasher studied the _____*amino acid*_____ sequence of part of a protein.

3. Prasher next found the _____*mRNA*_____ base sequence that coded for the protein.

4. Using the technique of *gel electrophoresis*, Prasher matched the mRNA to a DNA fragment that contained the gene for GFP.

5. Southern blot analysis uses ____*radioactive*____ probes to bind to fragments with complementary base sequences.

6. **THINK VISUALLY** Make a sketch to show the steps in the polymerase chain reaction (PCR) method of copying genes. Label each part of your sketch.

> *See the textbook illustration of polymerase chain reaction for what the students' sketches should look like. The sketches should show the four steps in the procedure.*

Changing DNA

For Questions 7–10, write the letter of the correct answer on the line at the left.

___B___ 7. Why is DNA ligase so important in recombinant DNA technology?

    A. It causes DNA to make multiple copies of itself.

    B. It joins two DNA fragments together.

    C. It shapes bacterial DNA into a circular plasmid.

    D. It cuts DNA into restriction fragments.

___D___ 8. A recombinant plasmid can be used to

    A. prevent nondisjunction at meiosis.

    B. double the number of chromosomes in a plant cell.

    C. cut DNA into restriction fragments.

    D. transform a bacterium.

__C__ 9. What do genetic engineers use to create the "sticky ends" needed to splice two fragments of DNA together?

    A. an amino acid sequence

    B. DNA ligase

    C. restriction enzymes

    D. mRNA

__B__ 10. Why must a genetically engineered plasmid contain a genetic marker?

    A. to prevent the construction of an artificial chromosome

    B. to separate cells that contain recombinant DNA from those that do not

    C. to produce multiple copies of the recombined plasmid after heat treatment

    D. to break apart the circular plasmid and introduce another DNA fragment

11. Give a reason why a plasmid is useful for DNA transfer.

It has a DNA sequence that helps promote plasmid replication, helping to ensure that the foreign DNA will be replicated.

Transgenic Organisms

12. Complete the flowchart about how a transgenic plant is produced, using *Agrobacterium* as an example.

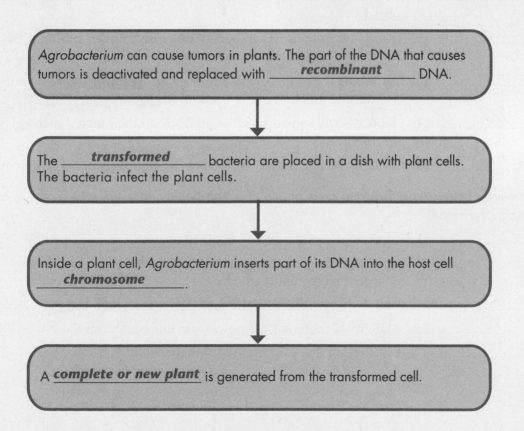

Agrobacterium can cause tumors in plants. The part of the DNA that causes tumors is deactivated and replaced with ___**recombinant**___ DNA.

↓

The ___**transformed**___ bacteria are placed in a dish with plant cells. The bacteria infect the plant cells.

↓

Inside a plant cell, *Agrobacterium* inserts part of its DNA into the host cell ___**chromosome**___.

↓

A ___**complete or new plant**___ is generated from the transformed cell.

13. What is a transgenic organism?

It is an organism that contains genes from other species.

14. What can happen when DNA is injected into the nucleus of an animal's egg cell?

Enzymes that are normally responsible for repair and recombination may help insert the foreign DNA into the chromosomes of the injected cell.

15. How is a DNA molecule constructed so that it will eliminate a particular gene?

The DNA molecule is constructed with two ends that will sometimes recombine with specific sequences in the host chromosome. The host gene between the two sequences may then be lost or replaced with a new gene.

16. What is a clone?

It is a member of a population of genetically identical cells produced from a single cell.

17. What kinds of mammals have been cloned in recent years?

Sheep, cows, pigs, mice, and cats have been cloned.

For Questions 18–22, write True if the statement is true. If the statement is false, change the underlined word to make the statement true.

transgenic **18.** An organism that contains one or more genes from another species is <u>inbred</u>.

True **19.** Transgenic organisms can be made by inserting recombinant DNA into the <u>genome</u> of the host organism.

gene **20.** Examining the properties of a transgenic organism allows scientists to discover the function of the transferred <u>chromosome</u>.

True **21.** Plant cells will sometimes take up DNA on their own if their <u>cell walls</u> are absent.

True **22.** Carefully designed DNA molecules can achieve gene <u>replacement</u>.

On the lines below, write T next to an example of a transgenic organism, and C next to an example of a clone.

T **23.** A goat that produces spider's silk in its milk

T **24.** A plant that is grown from a cell into which *Agrobacterium* has incorporated recombinant DNA

C **25.** A lamb that is born with the same DNA as a donor cell

C **26.** A colony of bacteria that grows from one bacterium

T **27.** A bacterium that can produce human insulin

8. **THINK VISUALLY** Complete the sentences in the diagram below to show the steps in cloning a sheep.

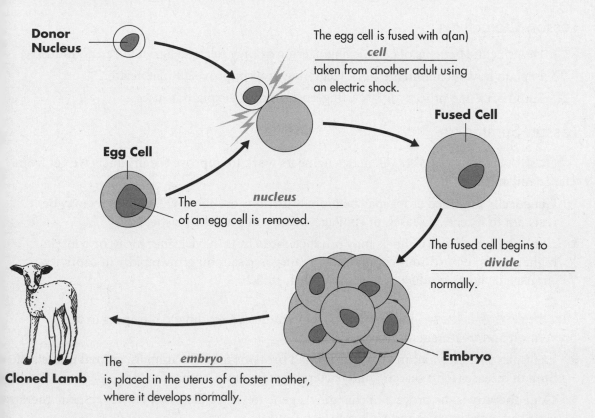

Donor Nucleus

The egg cell is fused with a(an) _____*cell*_____ taken from another adult using an electric shock.

Egg Cell

Fused Cell

The _____*nucleus*_____ of an egg cell is removed.

The fused cell begins to _____*divide*_____ normally.

Embryo

The _____*embryo*_____ is placed in the uterus of a foster mother, where it develops normally.

Cloned Lamb

Apply the Big idea

9. The most successful heart transplants occur when proteins in the donor heart closely match those of the recipient's original heart. If the proteins don't match, the recipient's immune system may reject the transplanted organ. Scientists would like to develop a strain of transgenic pigs that could provide donor hearts for humans. How might such an animal be developed? How might cloning help provide hearts for human recipients?

SAMPLE ANSWER: *Recombinant DNA techniques could be used to splice human genes into the genes of a fertilized egg from a pig. Those genes would direct the developing pig embryo to make a heart similar to a human heart. If the proteins in the pig's heart matched the proteins in a patient's original heart closely enough, the pig's heart would not be rejected by the human recipient's immune system. Once such an animal was developed, many hundreds of hearts might be "farmed" by cloning the transgenic pig.*

15.3 Applications of Genetic Engineering

Lesson Objectives

🔑 Describe the benefits of genetic engineering as they relate to agriculture and industry.

🔑 Explain how recombinant DNA technology can improve human health.

🔑 Summarize the process of DNA fingerprinting and explain its uses.

Lesson Summary

Agriculture and Industry Genetic engineers work to improve the products we get from plants and animals.

▶ Genetically modified crops may be more nutritious or higher yielding. They may be resistant to insects, diseases, or spoilage. Some can produce plastics.

▶ Genetically modified animals may produce more milk, have leaner meat, or contain higher levels of nutritious compounds. Transgenic salmon grow rapidly in captivity. Transgenic goats produce spider silk in their milk.

Health and Medicine Recombinant DNA studies are leading to advances in the prevention and treatment of disease.

▶ Examples include vitamin-rich rice, human proteins made in animals, animal models of human disease (for research), and bacteria that produce human insulin.

▶ **Gene therapy** is the process of changing a gene to treat a disorder. However, gene therapy is still an experimental and high-risk technique.

▶ Genetic testing can identify hundreds of inherited disorders.

Not all genes are active in every cell. **DNA microarray** technology lets scientists study thousands of genes at once to determine their activity level.

Personal Identification **DNA fingerprinting** analyzes sections of DNA that may have little or no function but that vary from one individual to another.

▶ DNA fingerprinting is used in **forensics**—the scientific study of crime-scene evidence—to identify criminals. It is also used to identify the biological father when paternity is in question.

▶ Common ancestry can sometimes be determined using mitochondrial DNA (mtDNA) and Y-chromosome analysis.

Agriculture and Industry

1. Give two examples of how genetically modified organisms lead to more environmentally friendly agricultural practices.

a. _SAMPLE ANSWER: **Some GM crops do not need pesticides.**_

b. _SAMPLE ANSWER: **Some GM pigs have leaner meat.**_

2. Name two other benefits that may be gained from genetically engineering food crops.

a. SAMPLE ANSWER: **Less expensive food**

b. SAMPLE ANSWER: **Crops resistant to insects, disease, or spoilage.**

3. Give two examples of how DNA modification has increased the importance of transgenic animals to our food supply.

a. SAMPLE ANSWER: **Recombinant-DNA techniques increase milk production in cows.**

b. SAMPLE ANSWER: **Transgenic salmon grow faster than wild salmon.**

Health and Medicine

For Questions 4–6, write True if the statement is true. If the statement is false, change the underlined word or words to make the statement true.

bacteria — **4.** Human growth hormone is now widely available because it is mass produced by recombinant <u>viruses</u>.

gene therapy — **5.** In <u>DNA fingerprinting</u>, an absent or faulty gene is replaced by a normal, working gene.

True — **6.** Prospective parents can find out if they carry the alleles for a genetic disease through genetic <u>testing</u>.

7. Complete the flowchart to show the steps required to analyze gene activity using a microarray.

1. Preparing the cDNA Probe
A. *mRNA samples are isolated from two different types of cells or issues.*

B. *Enzymes are used to prepare complementary DNA molecules (cDNA). Constrasting fluorescent labels are attached to both groups.*

2. Preparing Microarray
A. *DNA fragments corresponding to different genes are bound to wells in a microarray plate.*

B. *Single strands of DNA are attached to wells in the plate.*

3. Combining the Probe and Microarray Samples
Labeled cDNA molecules bind to complementary sequences on the plate.

Personal Identification

8. Complete the flowchart about how DNA fingerprints are made.

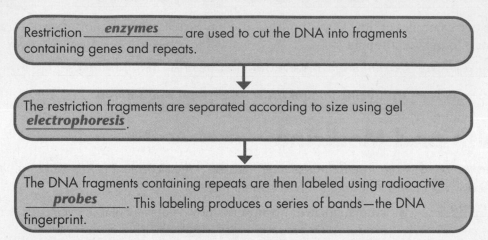

Restriction ____enzymes____ are used to cut the DNA into fragments containing genes and repeats.

↓

The restriction fragments are separated according to size using gel _electrophoresis_.

↓

The DNA fragments containing repeats are then labeled using radioactive ____probes____. This labeling produces a series of bands—the DNA fingerprint.

9. Study the DNA fingerprint below. Which two samples may be from a set of identical twins? How do you know?

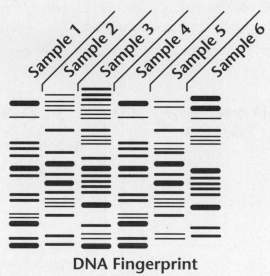

DNA Fingerprint

Samples 1 and 4 may be from identical twins because they are exactly the same.

Apply the Big idea ▶

10. In 2001, scientists reported the successful use of gene therapy to treat three dogs that had been born blind. The animals' blindness was the result of a mutated gene. Explain the steps that the scientists probably would have used to restore sight to the dogs.

The scientists engineered a harmless virus to carry the normal gene. They injected the

viruses into the dogs' eyes. The viruses inserted the normal gene into the cells of the

eye. The normal gene replaced the mutated gene, and vision was restored.

15.4 Ethics and Impacts of Biotechnology

Lesson Objectives

- Describe some of the issues that relate to biotechnology.
- Identify some of the pros and cons of genetically modified food.
- Describe some of the ethical issues relating to biotechnology.

Lesson Summary

Profits and Privacy Most of the research in genetic engineering is done by private companies.

- They patent their findings and inventions to protect their investment and make a profit.
- The patents block other scientists from pursuing certain lines of research.
- In 2007, the Genetic Information Nondiscrimination Act was signed into law in the United States. It prohibits discrimination based on genetic information.

Safety of Transgenics There is controversy about the safety of GM foods.

- Proponents of genetically modified foods argue that GM crops are better, safer, and higher yielding than conventional crops. GM crops require less land and energy to grow, and insecticides need not be applied to insect-resistant strains. Careful studies have provided no support for concerns about the safety of GM crops.
- Opponents argue that the safety of GM crops has been neither adequately tested for long-term use, nor regulated. Patents on GM seeds may force small farmers out of business. The resistance of GM plants to insects may harm beneficial insect species. Resistance to herbicides may result in the overuse of toxic chemicals.
- Some states have introduced legislation to require that GM foods be labeled.

Ethics of the New Biology Few argue that gene therapy for curing disease is ethically wrong, but many ask the question of how far genetic modification should go.

- Is it right to try to engineer children to have certain characteristics?
- Should human cloning be allowed?

Profits and Privacy

1. Should you be able to keep your genetic information confidential? State two answers: one giving a reason for a "yes" answer, and the other giving a reason for a "no" answer.

Yes *SAMPLE ANSWER:* **My genetic information is private and personal.**

_____

_____

No *SAMPLE ANSWER:* **Doctors who might treat me for disease or scientists would find it useful.**

_____

_____

2. Explain what the Genetics Information Nondiscrimination Act is, and give an example of how it might protect people.

The act states that people cannot be discriminated based on genetic information. For

example, a person cannot be denied health insurance because they carry alleles for an

inherited disease.

Safety of Transgenics

3. Complete the table to summarize the pros and cons of genetically modified foods. List at least four items in each column.

Pros	Cons
SAMPLE ANSWER: • *May be safer than other crops.* • *Higher yields reduce amount of land and energy needed for agriculture.* • *Insect-resistant GM plants require no insecticides, so fewer chemical residues enter the environment.* • *GM foods have proven their safety over more than ten years.*	SAMPLE ANSWER: • *GM crops have not been tested or regulated for safety.* • *Patents on GM seeds may force small farmers out of business, especially in the developing world.* • *Insect-resistant GM plants may threaten beneficial insects.* • *Herbicide resistance may lead to overuse of herbicides.*

For Questions 4–8, write True if the statement is true. If the statement is false, change the underlined word or words to make the statement true.

___*True*___ 4. Most GM plants are grown in the <u>United States</u>.

___*fewer*___ 5. Growing GM crops requires <u>more</u> energy resources than growing traditional crops.

___*has not been*___ 6. With all the questions raised about GM agriculture, the wider use of biotechnology <u>has been</u> blocked.

___*do not require*___ 7. Federal laws in the U. S. <u>require</u> that GM foods be labeled as such.

___*are not required*___ 8. GM foods are <u>required</u> to undergo safety testing before they enter the U. S. market.

9. Some proponents of GM agriculture argue that GM crops are safer than others. Explain what they mean.

   GM crops may not have been sprayed with pesticides. They may have added nutrients,

   such as the provitamin-A in golden rice.

10. Some critics of GM agriculture fear that GM plants' resistance to herbicides could result in the overuse of toxic chemicals. Explain why this may happen.

    Because the plants are resistant to the chemicals in herbicides, farmers do not have to

    worry about overusing the herbicides. They may use more than normal to be sure to

    kill all weeds.

Ethics of the New Biology

11. It is easy to move genes from one species to another. Is it right to do this? Explain your position.

    The affirmative argument states that genetic engineering has many useful applications,

    such as better-yielding food crops or animal models for research on disease. The

    negative argument states that humans may lack sufficient knowledge or wisdom to

    alter life forms safely or that such alteration is ethically wrong.

Apply the Big idea

12. Recent developments have resulted in the ability to clone cats. Many people argue that cloning offers pet owners comfort in a time of need. Others argue that there are many homeless pets at shelters in need of homes, and that adopting one of these animals is a better solution for owners who have lost a pet. Do you think that the cloning of pets is acceptable? Explain why or why not.

    Reasons for saying cloning pets is acceptable may include that the owner's comfort

    is worth the price and it could be a cutting edge new business that creates new jobs;

    Reasons for saying cloning pets is not acceptable may include ethical objections to

    genetic modifications of living things or concerns about the misuse of genetic infor-

    mation and technology, as well as concern for the homeless animals already living.

Chapter Vocabulary Review

For Questions 1–8, complete each statement by writing in the correct word or words.

1. ___*Selective breeding*___ consists of allowing only those organisms with particular characteristics to produce the next generation.

2. In the process called ___*hybridization*___, dissimilar organisms are crossed in order to obtain bigger or stronger offspring.

3. When organisms that are genetically similar are crossed over and over to produce the next generation, the process is called ___*inbreeding*___.

4. ___*Biotechnology*___ is the application of a technological process, invention, or method to living organisms.

5. The technology that makes copies of DNA is called ___*polymerase chain reaction*___.

6. The DNA that results from the transfer of DNA from one organism into another is ___*recombinant DNA*___.

7. The small, circular DNA molecule in a bacterial cell is a(n) ___*plasmid*___.

8. A gene that allows scientists to distinguish a cell that carries recombinant DNA from one that does not is a(n) ___*genetic marker*___.

For Questions 9–15, match the term with its definition.

Definition

___B___ 9. One of a population of genetically identical cells produced from a single cell

___E___ 10. A technique that allows the identification of individuals using differences in their DNA

___D___ 11. A technique that allows scientists to study thousands of genes at once

___A___ 12. Containing genes from another species

___C___ 13. Treating a disease by changing a gene

___F___ 14. The scientific study of evidence from a crime scene

___G___ 15. A gene that scientists use to find transformed bacteria

Term

A. transgenic

B. clone

C. gene therapy

D. DNA microarray

E. DNA fingerprinting

F. forensics

G. genetic marker

Write the letter of the correct answer on the line at the left.

___D___ 16. Hybridization and inbreeding are both types of
    A. gene therapy.   C. transgenics.
    B. forensics.   D. selective breeding.

___B___ 17. Because of their replication process, plasmids are excellent carriers of
    A. genetic markers.   C. clones.
    B. recombinant DNA.   D. transgenics.

CHAPTER MYSTERY

A CASE OF MISTAKEN IDENTITY

In the Chapter Mystery, as in tens of thousands of real-life cases, police used DNA fingerprinting to avoid arresting the wrong suspect. However, DNA fingerprinting is a very new technology.

21st Century Learning

DNA Forensics: The Innocence Project

Many people in prison today were convicted of a crime before DNA fingerprinting was widely available. Should DNA forensic evidence be used to reopen such cases? At least one national legal group believes prisoners should have access to DNA testing. The Innocence Project has led the effort in the United States to use DNA forensic evidence to exonerate (or free from blame) and release wrongly convicted prisoners. They also work to improve evidence preservation techniques, to investigate possible wrongful executions based on DNA evidence, and to re-open cases based on today's more sensitive and modern methods of testing DNA evidence.

The group still faces obstacles in its battle to gain acceptance for its methods. For instance, the laws in six states still will not allow newly discovered DNA evidence to be introduced after a trial. But the power of this technology has already worked in many states. In some cases where doubts about a conviction remain, or where prisoners have steadfastly maintained that they have been wrongly convicted, scientists and lawyers from the Innocence Project have worked together to subject the cases' physical evidence to DNA forensic analysis. In more than 200 cases so far the DNA analysis has proved that innocent people have been mistakenly convicted and forced to spend many years in jail.

Learn more about the DNA exonerations by reading the fact sheet below, adapted from information provided by the Innocence Project.

THE INNOCENCE PROJECT:

Facts on Post-Conviction DNA Exonerations as of 2008

- Number of post-conviction DNA exonerations in the United States: 223
- The year the first DNA exoneration took place: 1989
- Number of states in which exonerations have been won: 32
- Number of exonerees who served time on death row before being freed: 17
- Average length of time served by exonerees: 12 years
- Total number of years served by exonerees: approximately 2754
- The average age of exonerees at the time of their wrongful convictions: 26
- Cases in which the true suspects and/or perpetrators have been identified: 88

Continued on next page ▶

21st Century Themes · Science and Civic Literacy

1. What is the mission of the Innocence Project?

To use DNA forensic evidence to exonerate and release wrongly convicted and jailed

prisoners in the United States

2. By 2008, how many times had DNA evidence been used successfully to exonerate prisoners in the United States? *At least 223 times*

3. In what portion of the cases of people exonerated by the Innocence Project have the true suspects and/or perpetrators been identified? *Roughly one third (88 out of 223)*

4. Considering the Innocence Project's statistics, do you think prisoners jailed before DNA testing was widely available should be given access to the technology? Why or why not?

Accept viewpoints that are supported by logical arguments.

5. Do you think DNA evidence could be used to unintentionally convict an innocent person of a crime? Explain your answer.

Accept viewpoints that are supported by logical arguments.

21st Century Skills · Letter to a Lawmaker

The skills used in this activity include **problem identification, formulation, and solution; critical thinking and systems thinking;** and **information and media literacy.**

Search newspapers' Web sites to read about cases in which the Innocence Project or DNA evidence has helped exonerate people. Then, find out about your own state's position on prisoner access to DNA testing by contacting your state legislature or doing research online. Use the information you find to take the part of a citizen activist.

If your state allows access, then find out about a case in your state in which DNA testing was used after a conviction. Write a letter to a newspaper expressing your opinion on the outcome of the case. If the case is pending, you can discuss in your letter what you think should happen.

If your state does not allow post-conviction access, express your opinion in a letter to a state lawmaker. Explain how DNA fingerprinting works and what position you think the lawmaker should take regarding legislation allowing prisoners access to DNA testing.

Evaluate the students' letters based on the inclusion of correct facts about DNA testing and the information provided about the work of the Innocence Project. Students may take a position for or against prisoner access to DNA testing, but should defend either position with facts.

16 Darwin's Theory of Evolution

 Big idea **Evolution**
Q: What is natural selection?

WHAT I KNOW	WHAT I LEARNED

16.1 What patterns of biodiversity did Darwin observe aboard the *Beagle*?

SAMPLE ANSWER: **On each island that Darwin visited, he saw different species of plants and animals.**

SAMPLE ANSWER: **Darwin noticed that different, yet similar, species inhabited separated, but similar, habitats around the globe. Also, different, yet related, species often occupied different habitats within a local area.**

16.2 How did other scientists' work help Darwin develop his theory of natural selection?

SAMPLE ANSWER: **Other scientists did research on how organisms inherited different traits.**

SAMPLE ANSWER: **Hutton and Lyell concluded that Earth is extremely old. Lamarck suggested that species are not fixed. Malthus reasoned larger populations would deplete resources.**

16.3 What is Darwin's theory of evolution by natural selection?

SAMPLE ANSWER: **Organisms that are best adapted to their environment survive longer and have more offspring.**

SAMPLE ANSWER: **Natural selection is the process by which organisms with variations most suited to their local environment survive and leave more offspring. Over time, beneficial traits accumulate in a population.**

16.4 What are the main lines of scientific evidence that support Darwin's theory of evolution by natural selection?

SAMPLE ANSWER: **Fossils show how organisms have changed over time.**

SAMPLE ANSWER: **Biogeography, fossils, homologous structures, similarities in embryological development, the universal genetic code, homologous molecules, and field studies provide evidence of evolution.**

16.1 Darwin's Voyage of Discovery

Lesson Objectives

- State Charles Darwin's contribution to science.
- Describe the three patterns of biodiversity noted by Darwin.

Lesson Summary

Darwin's Epic Journey Darwin developed a scientific theory to explain how **evolution**, or change over time, occurs in living things. Darwin's theory explains how modern organisms have evolved over long periods of time through descent from common ancestors.

Observations Aboard the *Beagle* During his five-year trip on the *Beagle*, Darwin made many observations and collected a great deal of evidence.

▶ He noticed that many different, yet ecologically similar, animal and plant species occupied different, yet ecologically similar, habitats around the globe.

▶ On the Galápagos Islands, Darwin noticed that the traits of many organisms—such as the shell shapes of tortoises—varied from island to island. He noticed that different, yet related, animal and plant species occupied different habitats within a local area.

▶ Darwin collected **fossils**, the preserved remains of ancient organisms. He noticed that some fossils of extinct species resembled living species.

Darwin's findings led him to think that species are not fixed and that they could change by some natural process.

Darwin's Epic Journey

1. **THINK VISUALLY** On the map below, (1) find and label the Galápagos Islands (2) circle the names of three large land masses Darwin did not visit on his voyage.

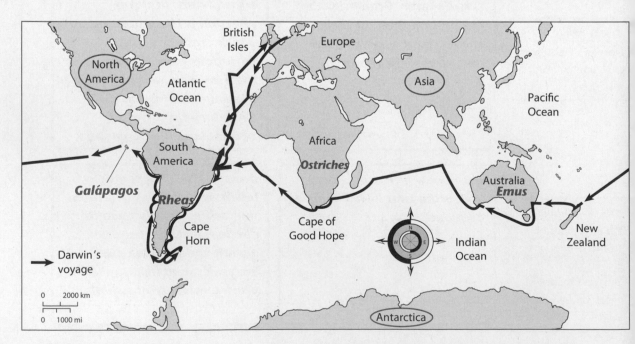

For Questions 2–4, complete each statement by writing the correct word or words. Refer to the map on the previous page as needed.

2. Darwin spent most of his time exploring the continent of __South America__; he did not visit __North America__, __Asia__, or __Antarctica__.

3. During Darwin's time, geologists were suggesting that Earth was __ancient and changed over time__.

4. Darwin's work offers insight into the living world by showing organisms are constantly __changing or evolving__.

Observations Aboard the *Beagle*

Use the drawings of the tortoises to answer Questions 5 and 6.

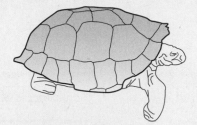
Isabela Island tortoise

Hood Island tortoise

5. What important information about the Galápagos Islands tortoises did Darwin learn?
   Darwin learned that the shell shape of a tortoise could be used to identify the island it inhabited.

6. Given its body structure, which tortoise above would require a habitat where food is easy to reach?
   Because the Isabela Island tortoise has a short neck that restricts the movement of its head, it would require a habitat where food is easy to reach.

Use the map on the previous page to answer Questions 7 and 8.

7. On the map, place the labels Rheas, Emus, and Ostriches on the continents where they are found. Why were the similarities among rheas, ostriches, and emus surprising to Darwin?
   It was surprising because these different birds lived so far away from each other.

8. Why might Darwin come to think that the finches of the Galápagos Islands might be related to the finches of South America, despite how different the birds were in appearance?
   The islands are very close to the coast of South America and so the birds may have migrated from there.

9. Darwin observed that the birds he would eventually discover were finches had differently shaped beaks. What might this suggest about the eating habits of the birds? Explain.
   Because birds use their beaks to eat or capture food, differently shaped beaks might mean that the birds lived on different diets.

10. What did the similarities between fossil animals and modern animals, like the glyptodont and armadillo, suggest to Darwin?

The similarities suggested to Darwin that the modern species may be related to the

extinct fossil species.

11. Complete the graphic organizer by listing three ways that species vary. For each pattern of biodiversity, list an example that Darwin observed.

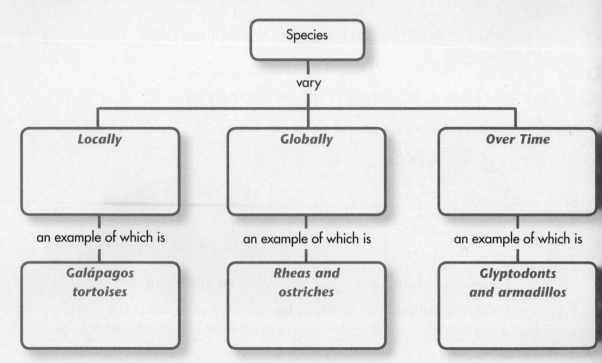

Species

vary

| Locally | Globally | Over Time |

an example of which is | an example of which is | an example of which is

| Galápagos tortoises | Rheas and ostriches | Glyptodonts and armadillos |

Apply the Big idea

12. When Darwin returned to England, he learned that the small brown birds he observed on the Galápagos Islands were all finches. They resembled South American finches. What hypothesis does this observation support?

The birds are descended from South American ancestors that traveled to the

Galápagos Islands. The species have changed over time as they adapted to particular

niches on each island.

16.2 Ideas That Shaped Darwin's Thinking

Lesson Objectives

- Identify the conclusions drawn by Hutton and Lyell about Earth's history.
- Describe Lamarck's hypothesis of evolution.
- Describe Malthus's view of population growth.
- Explain the role of inherited variation in artificial selection.

Lesson Summary

An Ancient, Changing Earth In Darwin's day, most Europeans believed that Earth and all its life forms were only a few thousand years old and had not changed very much in that time. Several scientists who lived around the same time as Darwin began to challenge these ideas. These scientists had an important influence on the development of Darwin's theory of evolution.

- Geologists James Hutton and Charles Lyell argued that Earth is many millions of years old.
- They also argued that the processes changing Earth today, like volcanism and erosion, are the same ones that changed Earth in the past.

Knowing that Earth could change over time helped Darwin realize that species might change as well. Knowing that Earth was very old convinced Darwin that there had been enough time for life to evolve.

Lamarck's Evolutionary Hypothesis Jean-Baptiste Lamarck was one of the first scientists to propose hypotheses about how evolution occurred.

- To explain evolution, Lamarck hypothesized that all organisms have an inborn drive to become more complex and perfect. According to Lamarck, an organism could gain or lose traits during its lifetime by using or not using certain organs.
- Lamarck also hypothesized that acquired characteristics could be passed on to an organism's offspring leading to evolution of the species.

Scientists now know that most of Lamarck's ideas about evolution are incorrect. However, he correctly suggested that life is not fixed and was the first to offer a natural and scientific explanation for evolution. Further, he recognized that an organism's traits are linked to its environment.

Population Growth Thomas Malthus thought that if the human population continued to grow unchecked, it would run out of living space and food. Darwin realized that this was true of all organisms, not just humans.

Artificial Selection Plant and animal breeders in Darwin's time used a process now known as artificial selection to improve their crops and livestock. In **artificial selection**, nature provides the variations, and humans select those they find desirable. Darwin experimented with artificial selection. The results from his experiments indicated natural variation was very important because it provided the raw material for evolution.

An Ancient, Changing Earth

1. In what two ways did an understanding of geology influence Darwin?

Knowing that Earth could change over time helped Darwin believe that life might change as well. Knowing that Earth was very old assured Darwin that there had been enough time for life to change.

For Questions 2–5, write True if the statement is true. If the statement is false, change the underlined word or words to make the statement true.

_____**older**_____ **2.** Hutton realized that Earth was much <u>younger</u> than previously believed.

_____**slowly**_____ **3.** Lyell thought most geological processes operated extremely <u>quickly</u>.

_____**the same as**_____ **4.** The processes that changed Earth in the past are <u>different from</u> the processes that operate in the present.

_____**True**_____ **5.** <u>Lyell's</u> work explained how large geological features could be built up or torn down over long periods of time.

Lamarck's Evolutionary Hypotheses

6. How did Lamarck propose that species change over time?

Lamarck proposed that by selective use or nonuse of organs, organisms acquired or lost certain traits during their lifetime. These traits could then be passed on to their offspring. Over time, this process led to change in a species.

_____

Use the diagram to answer Questions 7–8.

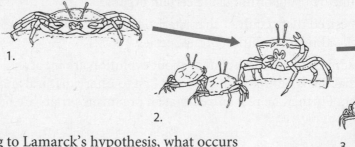

1.

2.

3.

7. According to Lamarck's hypothesis, what occurs between steps 2 and 3 in the diagram above to make the crab's claw grow larger?

The crab selectively uses its left claw more. This increased use causes the claw to grow in size.

_____

8. Which step in the diagram above shows the inheritance of acquired traits as proposed by Lamarck?

Step 3 shows the inheritance of acquired traits by the young.

9. How did Lamarck pave the way for the work of later biologists?

Lamarck was one of the first to develop scientific hypotheses about evolution and to realize that organisms change over time.

10. Which of Lamarck's ideas turned out to be true? Which turned out to be false?

Lamarck's ideas that evolution occurs and that an organism's traits are linked to its environment are true. Lamarck's idea that acquired characteristics can be inherited is false. Also, Lamarck's idea that species have an inborn drive to become more complex and perfect is false.

11. How would Lamarck have explained the length of a giraffe's neck?

A giraffe could have acquired a long neck because it began to stretch its neck upward to reach higher and higher on trees looking for leaves to eat. As the giraffe stretched toward leaves on higher branches, its neck would grow a little longer. Giraffes could then pass on their long neck to their offspring who could further lengthen their necks during their lifetimes.

Population Growth

For Questions 12–14, write the letter of the correct answer on the line at the left.

A **12.** Which observation caused Thomas Malthus to form his theory about population growth?

    A. Human birth rate was higher than the death rate.

    B. War caused the death of thousands of people.

    C. Famines were common in England in the 1800s.

    D. The offspring of most species survived into adulthood.

D **13.** Which of the following is an idea attributed to Malthus?

    A. As a population decreases in size, warfare and famine become more common.

    B. As a population increases in size, the percentage of offspring that survive also increases.

    C. If the human population grew unchecked, its rate of evolution would increase geometrically.

    D. If the human population grew unchecked, there wouldn't be enough living space and food for everyone.

C **14.** Malthus's ideas led Darwin to conclude that

    A. Earth is much older than previously thought.

    B. the size of the human population can grow indefinitely.

    C. many more organisms are born than will survive and reproduce.

    D. organisms are able to evolve through a process known as artificial selection.

Artificial Selection

15. How do humans affect artificial selection? What role does nature play?

Darwin stated that nature provides the variation among organisms, and humans

select and breed for the variations they find useful or appealing.

16. What is another name for artificial selection?

selective breeding

17. Describe how you could use artificial selection to breed pigeons with large beaks.

Find pigeons that naturally have larger than normal beaks. Mate these pigeons.

Repeat this process over several generations until you achieve the desired beak size.

Apply the Big idea

18. Complete the table about scientists who contributed to the development of the theory of evolution.

Scientists Who Contributed to Darwin's Theory of Evolution	
Scientist	**Contribution to Darwin's Theory**
James Hutton	*Hutton argued that Earth is many millions of years old. Knowing that Earth was very old convinced Darwin that there had been enough time for life to evolve.*
Charles Lyell	*Lyell argued that the processes that changed Earth in the past were the same as the processes that are still changing Earth in the present. Knowing that Earth could change over time helped Darwin realize that life might change as well.*
Jean-Baptiste Lamarck	*Lamarck was one of the first scientists to recognize that evolution has occurred and that organisms change to live more successfully in their environment. His general ideas about evolution and adaptation influenced Darwin.*
Thomas Malthus	*Malthus thought that if the human population continued to grow unchecked, it would run out of living space and food. Darwin realized that this was true of all organisms, not just humans.*

16.3 Darwin Presents His Case

Lesson Objectives

Describe the conditions under which natural selection occurs.

Explain the principle of common descent.

Lesson Summary

Evolution by Natural Selection Darwin published *On the Origin of Species* in 1859. In the book, Darwin describes and provides evidence for his explanation of how evolution occurs. He called this process **natural selection** because of its similarities to artificial selection. Darwin's theory of evolution by natural selection can be summed up as follows:

► More offspring are produced than can survive to reproduce. There is competition for limited resources, or a struggle for existence.

► Individuals exhibit variation in their traits and some of these differences can be passed on to their offspring.

► Inherited traits that increase an organism's ability to survive and reproduce are called **adaptations**.

► Differences among adaptations affect an individual's **fitness**—the ability to survive and reproduce in a specific environment.

► Only the fittest organisms live to reproduce and pass on their adaptive traits to offspring. This is known as the survival of the fittest.

From generation to generation, populations continue to evolve as they become better adapted, or as their environment changes.

Common Descent Darwin argued that all species are descended, with modification, from common ancestors. Through descent with modification, all organisms—living and extinct— are linked on a single tree of life.

Evolution by Natural Selection

1. What does the phrase *struggle for existence* mean?

   It means that members of a population compete regularly to obtain food, living space, and other necessities of life.

2. Why is camouflage considered an adaptation?

   Camouflage is a heritable trait that can help an organism avoid predation and thereby increases the chances of its survival.

3. How does an animal's level of fitness relate to its chances of survival and reproduction?

   The higher an animal's level of fitness in its particular environment, the better its chances for survival and reproduction.

For Questions 4–6, write True if the statement is true. If the statement is false, change the underlined word or words to make the statement true.

_____inherited_____ **4.** Natural selection acts on <u>acquired</u> traits.

_____True_____ **5.** Any inherited characteristic that increases an organism's chance of survival is considered <u>an adaptation</u>.

_____fitness_____ **6.** <u>Natural selection</u> is the ability of an individual to survive and reproduce in its specific environment.

7. Below is a partially completed flowchart that models how natural selection drives evolution. The missing steps are listed below, out of order, and lettered A–D. Write the letter of the missing step in a blank box in the flowchart.

A. Adaptations are passed on to the next generation.

B. The accumulation of adaptations may lead to the evolution of a new species.

C. These offspring have few or no offspring of their own.

D. Some offspring inherit traits that increase fitness (adaptations).

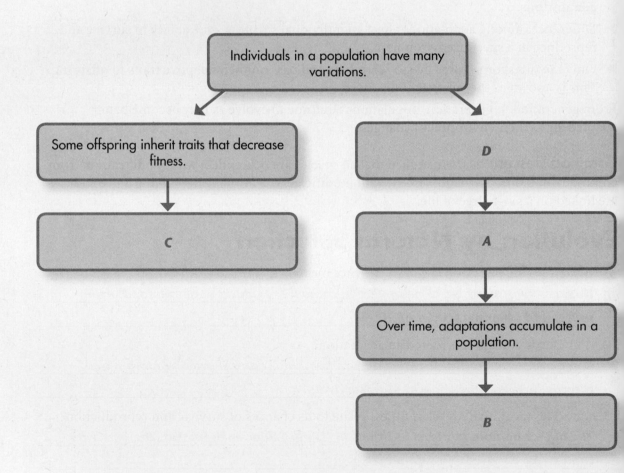

Common Descent

For Questions 8–13, complete each statement by writing the correct word or words.

8. Natural selection depends on the ability of organisms to ___reproduce___, which means to leave descendants.

9. Every organism alive today ___descended___ from ancestors who survived and reproduced.

10. Over many generations, adaptation could cause successful species to ___evolve___ into new species.

11. Common descent suggests that all species, living and extinct, are ___related___.

12. The principle that living species descend, with changes, from other species over time is referred to as ___descent with modification___.

13. The ___fossil record___ provides physical evidence of descent with modification over long periods of time.

Apply the Big idea

14. In the three boxes on the left, draw an example of natural selection that might occur in a population of frogs. Then, on the lines at right, describe each stage.

The Struggle for Existence

SAMPLE ANSWER: *A population of frogs has a large number of offspring. Only a small fraction of these offspring will survive.*

Variation and Adaption/Survival of the Fittest

SAMPLE ANSWER: *In this population of frogs, heritable variation includes short tongues and long tongues. Long tongues are an adaptation: The frogs with long tongues are able to catch more flies than frogs with short tongues. Long-tongued frogs eat more and so survive and reproduce more often than short-tongued frogs do.*

Natural Selection

SAMPLE ANSWER: *Long-tongued frogs become more common than short-tongued frogs in this population over time because (1) more frogs are born than can survive, (2) individuals vary in tongue-length and tongue-length is a heritable trait, and (3) long-tongued individuals have higher fitness in this particular environment.*

16.4 Evidence of Evolution

Lesson Objectives

🔑 Explain how geologic distribution of species relates to their evolutionary history.

🔑 Explain how fossils and the fossil record document the descent of modern species from ancient ancestors.

🔑 Describe what homologous structures and embryology suggest about the process of evolutionary change.

🔑 Explain how molecular evidence can be used to trace the process of evolution.

🔑 Explain the results of the Grants' investigation of adaptation in Galápagos finches.

Lesson Summary

Biogeography Biogeography is the study of where organisms live now and where they and their ancestors lived in the past. Two biogeographical patterns are significant to Darwin's theory:

▶ The first is a pattern in which closely related species differentiate in slightly different climates. The Galápagos tortoises and finches follow this pattern.

▶ The second is a pattern in which very distantly related species develop similarities in similar environments. The rheas, ostriches, and emus fall into this pattern.

The Age of Earth and Fossils

▶ Radioactive dating techniques have confirmed that Earth is ancient—approximately 4.5 billion years old.

▶ Recent fossil finds document intermediate stages in the evolution of many groups including whales, birds, and mammals.

Comparing Anatomy and Embryology

▶ **Homologous structures** are shared by related species and have been inherited from a common ancestor. Similarities and differences among homologous structures help determine how recently two groups shared a common ancestor.

• Body parts that share a common function, but neither structure nor common ancestry, are called **analogous structures**. Analogous structures do not provide any evidence for evolutionary descent.

• Homologous structures that are greatly reduced in size or have little to no function are called **vestigial structures**.

• Many homologous structures develop in the same order and in similar patterns during the embryonic, or pre-birth, stages of related groups. These similarities provide further evidence that the animals share common ancestors.

Genetics and Molecular Biology At the molecular level, the universal genetic code and homologous molecules such as genes and proteins provide evidence of common descent.

Testing Natural Selection Scientists have designed experiments to test natural selection. Observations of Galápagos finches confirm that competition and environmental change drive natural selection.

Biogeography

For Questions 1–3, complete each statement by writing the correct word or words.

1. Biogeographers study where organisms live now and where they and their
   ___**ancestors**___ lived in the past.

2. When individuals from a mainland bird population immigrate to various islands, natural
   selection may result in ___**closely related**___, but different, island species.

3. Distantly related organisms may be similar if they live in ___**similar environments**___.

4. What explains the distribution of finch species on the Galápagos Islands?
   The finch species had descended with modification from a common mainland
   ancestor.

5. What explains the existence of similar but unrelated species?
   Such species evolved features in common because they were exposed to similar pres-
   sures of natural selection.

The Age of Earth and Fossils

6. **THINK VISUALLY** The illustrations below show organisms whose fossils make up part
   of the fossil record. The organisms are in order from oldest to most recent. In the boxes,
   draw an animal that might have been an intermediate form between the shown organisms.

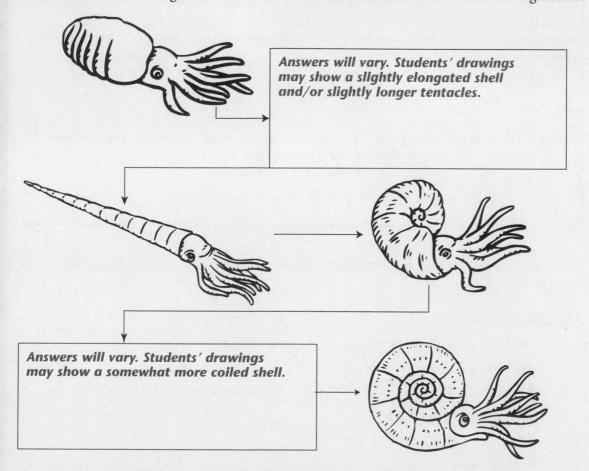

Answers will vary. Students' drawings may show a slightly elongated shell and/or slightly longer tentacles.

Answers will vary. Students' drawings may show a somewhat more coiled shell.

Use the illustrations of the marine organisms on the previous page to answer Questions 7–8.

7. Describe a situation in which organism 3 might have had an advantage over organism 2?

SAMPLE ANSWER: *Having a more compact body may have made it easier for the organism*

to escape predators.

8. How might these fossils provide evidence for evolution?

They show similarities to one another, but they also show changes that have occurred

over time.

Comparing Anatomy and Embryology

9. Complete the table about types of anatomical structures.

Types of Anatomical Structures		
Structure Type	**Description**	**Example**
Homologous structure	Structures that are shared by related species and that have been inherited from a common ancestor	*Mammalian leg and amphibian leg*
Analogous structure	Body parts that share common function, but not structure	*Wing of a bee and wing of a bird*
Vestigial structure	Body parts in animals that are so reduced in size that they are just vestiges, or traces, of homologous structures in other species	*Hipbones in dolphins*

For Questions 10–14, match the structure with the correct type. A structure type may be used more than once.

Anatomical Structure

__A__ 10. bat wing and mouse arm

__A__ 11. reptile foot and bird foot

__B__ 12. dolphin fin and fish tail

__C__ 13. eyes on a blind cave fish

__B__ 14. snake tongue and dog nose

Structure Type

A. homologous structure

B. analogous structure

C. vestigial structure

Use the illustrated homologous structures to answer Questions 15–17.

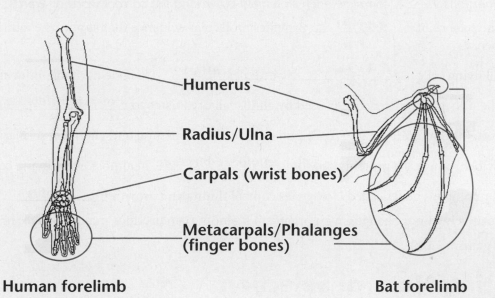

Humerus

Radius/Ulna

Carpals (wrist bones)

**Metacarpals/Phalanges
(finger bones)**

Human forelimb　　　　　　　**Bat forelimb**

15. How are the forelimbs similar?

The forelimbs have the same kinds of bones in approximately the same positions.

16. How are the forelimbs different?

SAMPLE ANSWER: *The bat's "finger bones" are elongated and form the structure of a wing, while the human phalanges are shorter and form the structure for fingers.*

17. How are homologous structures such as forelimbs evidence for common descent?

The bones are noticeably similar in structure and arrangement. It is, therefore, reasonable to assume that they are descended from a common ancestral form.

18. How does the pattern of embryological development provide further evidence that organisms have descended from a common ancestor?

The early developmental stages of many vertebrates look very similar. Therefore, it is reasonable to assume that vertebrates are descended from a common ancestor.

Genetics and Molecular Biology

For Questions 19–25, complete each statement by writing the correct word or words.

19. The science of **genetics** provides molecular evidence that supports evolutionary theory.

20. All living cells use **DNA** and **RNA** to code heritable information.

21. The universal genetic code is used by almost all organisms to **direct protein synthesis**.

22. Proteins that are **homologous** share extensive structural and chemical similarities.

23. Cytochrome c is a protein used for **cellular respiration** in almost every living cell.

24. Homologous genes called Hox genes control timing and growth in **embryos**.

25. Relatively minor changes in an organism's genome can produce major changes in an organism's **structure**.

Testing Natural Selection

Write the letter of the correct answer on the line at the left.

A 26. Which of the following hypotheses did the Grants test?
A. Differences in beak size and shape produce differences in fitness.
B. For beak size and shape to evolve, the birds must leave the islands.
C. For beak size and shape to evolve, the climate must change radically.
D. Differences in beak size and shape are not determined by genetic mutations.

C 27. The data that the Grants collected proved that there is
A. no link between the environment and the shape of finch feet.
B. no link between the environment and the shape of finch beaks.
C. great variation of heritable traits among Galápagos finches.
D. very little variation of heritable traits among Galápagos finches.

A 28. The Grants conducted their experiment to test which of the following processes?
A. Natural selection
B. Genetic mutation
C. Artificial selection
D. Sexual reproduction

29. **VISUAL ANALOGY** The art shows how finch beaks are similar to certain kinds of hand tools. Suppose a finch fed on insects that burrowed into small holes on tree trunks. What type of tool do you think this finch's beak would resemble? Explain your answer.

Tree Finches

Platyspiza

Certhidea

Ground Finches

Pinaroloxias

Geospiza

SAMPLE ANSWER: *The finch's beak might resemble a very thin probe that can reach into a small hole and skewer or grasp the insect.*

Apply the Big idea

30. Complete the concept map.

```
              ┌─────────────┐
              │ Evidence for │
              │  Evolution   │
              └─────────────┘
                  includes
    ┌──────────┬──────────┬──────────┬──────────┬──────────┐
```

| the geographic distribution of living species | the fossil record | similarities in anatomical structures and embryological development | the universal genetic code and homologous proteins and genes | experiments that verify natural selection occurs in nature |

Chapter Vocabulary Review

Match the term with its definition.

Term

<u> A </u> **1.** evolution

<u> C </u> **2.** fossil

<u> G </u> **3.** fitness

<u> B </u> **4.** adaptation

<u> D </u> **5.** natural selection

<u> F </u> **6.** homologous structures

<u> E </u> **7.** vestigial structures

Definition

A. Change over time

B. Inherited characteristic that increases an organism's chance of survival

C. Preserved remains of an ancient organism

D. The process by which organisms with variations most suited to their environment survive and leave more offspring than others

E. Small structures with little or no function

F. Structures that develop from the same embryonic tissues but have different mature forms

G. Ability of an individual to survive and reproduce in a specific environment

For Questions 8–10, write a definition for the vocabulary term.

8. biogeography

the study of where organisms live now and where they and their ancestors lived in the

past

9. artificial selection

the use of selective breeding to produce organisms with certain desirable traits

10. analogous structures

body parts that share common function, but not structure

11. Does the illustration below show analogous or homologous structures? Explain.

Turtle   Alligator   Bird   Mammals

Homologous structures. These limbs evolved from the front limbs of a common ances-

tor. If these animals had different origins, they would probably not share so many

common structures.

CHAPTER MYSTERY

SUCH VARIED HONEYCREEPERS

"The Chapter Mystery explained how the 'i'iwi and other Hawaiian honeycreeper species evolved adaptations suited to their specific habitats. What happens when species face a loss of their habitats due to urbanization or environmental degradation?

21st Century Learning

Habitat Loss and Endangered Species

Scientists report that in the United States, habitat loss is the most widespread cause of species endangerment, affecting approximately 85 percent of imperiled species according to a recent estimate. Designed to combat the problem, the U.S. Endangered Species Act of 1973 is a federal law that protects threatened and endangered species. When a species is listed as endangered, the government enforces more stringent protections on the species' remaining habitats, especially when those habitats are on federal lands. In addition, the Act allows the government to purchase land containing important habitats and forbids the capture, killing, or sale of an endangered species. In addition, people who violate the Act can be prosecuted.

Unfortunately, threats to many species continue. Experts believe that fewer than half the species native to the United States—especially insect, plant, and fungi species—have yet been discovered and catalogued. Therefore, it is impossible to know whether these species are endangered. Another problem, other scientists emphasize, is that the regulations protecting endangered species are not effective enough and are based on an underestimation of the problem. One recent expert analysis suggests that, even within the pool of known species, the number now threatened with extinction may actually be as much as ten times greater than the number currently protected under the U.S. Endangered Species Act.

The table below, adapted from data compiled by the nonprofit scientific group NatureServe, assesses the current situation for vertebrate species in the United States.

Vertebrate Species Data in the U.S.			
Group: Imperiled U.S. Vertebrates	Total Number of Known Species	Number of Species Imperiled or Extinct/ Possibly Extinct	Percentage of Species Imperiled or Extinct/ Possibly Extinct
Mammals	421	29	7
Birds	783	75	10
Reptiles	295	28	9
Amphibians	258	66	26
Freshwater Fishes	798	179	22
Vertebrate Totals	2555	377	15

Continued on next page ▶

21st Century Themes — Science and Global Awareness

1. What is believed to be the most widespread cause of species endangerment?

   Habitat loss is the most widespread cause.

2. According to the table, which group of vertebrates in the United States includes the largest number of imperiled or extinct species?

   Freshwater fish species, with 179 varieties imperiled or extinct

3. According to the table, which group of vertebrates appears to be most endangered overall? How can you tell? Why do you think this group is most imperiled?

   Amphibians are the most endangered group because they have the highest percentage of species imperiled or extinct of any of the vertebrate groups. Students may be able to draw a connection between the imperilment of amphibian species and the vulnerability of their wetland ecosystems.

4. What is the U.S. Endangered Species Act?

   Enacted in 1973, the U.S. Endangered Species Act is a law that designates threatened and endangered species and offers federal protection to the listed species' habitats.

5. Some experts think that a significant number of species native to the United States have yet to be discovered. Some experts think that the U.S. Endangered Species Act underestimates the number of endangered species. How does the first problem lead to the second?

   The U.S. Endangered Species Act cannot protect species that have yet to be identified. Meanwhile, habitat destruction and possible extinction of species continue.

21st Century Skills — Species Presentation

The skills used in this activity include **information and media literacy; critical thinking and systems thinking;** and **problem identification, formulation, and solution.**

Visit the Web site of the U.S. Fish and Wildlife Service to learn more about the agency's efforts to protect endangered species in the United States. Choose one endangered species and investigate the threats it faces. Present the information to the class, including whether you believe the species deserves protection under the Act and, if so, why.

Your presentation can be in the form of a video about the species or an illustrated guide.

Evaluate students' presentations by their inclusion of the description of the species and the threats it faces, its habitat range, what is being done to protect the species, and their opinion. Evaluation should also depend on the appropriate use of available media.

17 Evolution of Populations

Evolution

Q: How can populations evolve to form new species?

WHAT I KNOW	WHAT I LEARNED
17.1 How do genes make evolution possible?	*SAMPLE ANSWER:* **There are different variations of the same gene.**	*SAMPLE ANSWER:* **Evolution occurs when the allele frequency in the gene pool of a population changes over time.**
17.2 What makes a population's gene pool change?	*SAMPLE ANSWER:* **Over time useful traits (and the genes that control them) accumulate in a population.**	*SAMPLE ANSWER:* **Genetic changes can affect the number and types of possible phenotypes organisms in a population can have. These changes provide the variation that populations need to evolve.**
17.3 How do new species form?	*SAMPLE ANSWER:* **The genome of a species changes enough that it becomes a new species.**	*SAMPLE ANSWER:* **Speciation sometimes occurs when populations become reproductively isolated.**
17.4 What can genes tell us about an organism's evolutionary history?	*SAMPLE ANSWER:* **Some species' genomes are very similar. These species are closely related. The opposite is true for species with very different genomes.**	*SAMPLE ANSWER:* **A molecular clock uses mutation rates in DNA to estimate the time that two species have been evolving independently.**

17.1 Genes and Variation

Lesson Objectives

- Define evolution in genetic terms.
- Identify the main sources of genetic variation in a population.
- State what determines the number of phenotypes for a trait.

Lesson Summary

Genetics Joins Evolutionary Theory Darwin's original ideas can now be understood in genetic terms.

▶ Researchers discovered that traits are controlled by genes and that many genes have at least two forms, or alleles. The combination of different alleles is an individual's genotype. Natural selection acts on phenotype, not genotype.

▶ Genetic variation and evolution are studied in populations. Members of a population share a common group of genes, called a **gene pool**.

▶ **Allele frequency** is the number of times an allele occurs in a gene pool compared with the number of times other alleles for the same gene occur. In genetic terms, evolution is any change in the allele frequency in a population.

Sources of Genetic Variation The three main sources of genetic variation are mutations, genetic recombination during sexual reproduction, and lateral gene transfer.

▶ A mutation is any change in a sequence of DNA.

▶ Most heritable differences are due to genetic recombination during sexual reproduction. This occurs during meiosis when each chromosome in a pair moves independently. Genetic recombination also occurs during crossing-over in meiosis.

▶ Lateral gene transfer is the passing of genes from one organism to another organism that is not its offspring.

Single-Gene and Polygenic Traits The number of different phenotypes for a given trait depends on how many genes control the trait.

▶ A **single-gene trait** is controlled by one gene. An example in snails is the presence or absence of dark bands on their shells.

▶ A **polygenic trait** is controlled by two or more genes, and each gene often has two or more alleles. An example of a human polygenic trait is height.

Genetics Joins Evolutionary Theory

For Questions 1–4, complete each statement by writing the correct word or words.

1. Natural selection works on an organism's ___*phenotype*___ rather than its ___*genotype*___.

2. A(n) ___*gene pool*___ consists of all the genes, including the alleles for each gene, that are present in a population.

3. A gene pool typically contains different ____alleles____ for each heritable trait.

4. The number of times that an allele occurs in a gene pool compared with the number of times other alleles for the same gene occur is called the ____allele frequency____ of the population.

Use the circle graph of a sample mouse population to answer Questions 5–8.

5. **THINK VISUALLY** In the diagram below, use circles to represent the alleles within each segment of the population. Draw the *B* alleles as solid circles and the *b* alleles as outline circles. The total number of individuals in this population is ____25____; the total number of alleles is ____50____.

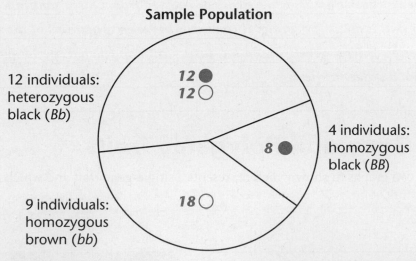

Sample Population

12 individuals: heterozygous black (*Bb*)

4 individuals: homozygous black (*BB*)

9 individuals: homozygous brown (*bb*)

6. How many alleles for black fur are in the sample population and what percentage of allele frequency does that represent?
20 B alleles, 40 percent

7. How many alleles for brown fur are in the sample population and what percentage of allele frequency does that represent?
30 b alleles, 60 percent

8. Describe how a geneticist might be able to tell that this population is evolving.
The frequency of alleles will change.

9. Can you determine whether an allele is dominant or recessive on the basis of the ratio of phenotypes in the population? Explain your answer.
No, because the phenotypic ratio depends on the allele frequencies of the dominant
and recessive alleles, and the frequency of alleles has nothing to do with whether the
allele is dominant or recessive.

Sources of Genetic Variation

10. What are mutations? When do they affect evolution?
A mutation is any change in the genetic material of a cell. Mutations only affect
evolution when they occur in germ line cells that produce eggs or sperm and if they
produce a change in phenotype that affects fitness.

11. How does sexual reproduction affect a population's genetic variation?

   Genetic recombination during sexual reproduction can produce many different pheno-

   types through the production of new and unique genetic combinations.

   _____

12. Identify two ways in which genes can be recombined during meiosis.

   by independent assortment of chromosomes and by gene swapping during meiosis

   _____

13. What is lateral gene transfer? How does it affect variation?

   Lateral gene transfer occurs when genes are passed from one organism to another

   organism that is not its offspring. It can occur between organisms of the same or dif-

   ferent species. Lateral gene transfer increases variation when a species picks up new

   genes from a different species.

   _____

Single Gene and Polygenic Traits

14. Label the two graphs to show which represents a single-gene trait and which represents a polygenic trait.

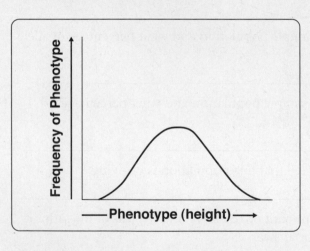

Polygenic Trait
_____

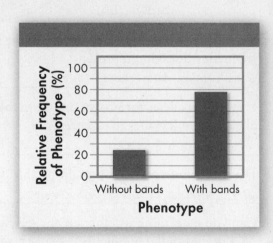

Single-Gene Trait
_____

For Questions 15–19, write True if the statement is true. If the statement is false, change the underlined word or words to make the statement true.

____*True*_____ 15. The number of <u>phenotypes</u> produced for a given trait depends on how many genes control the trait.

___*polygenic*___ 16. Height in humans is an example of a <u>single-gene</u> trait.

alleles **17.** Each gene of a polygenic trait often has two or more <u>phenotypes</u>.

True **18.** A single polygenic trait often has many possible <u>genotypes</u>.

True **19.** A symmetrical bell-shaped graph is typical of <u>polygenic</u> traits.

20. Use the Venn diagram to compare and contrast single-gene traits and polygenic traits.

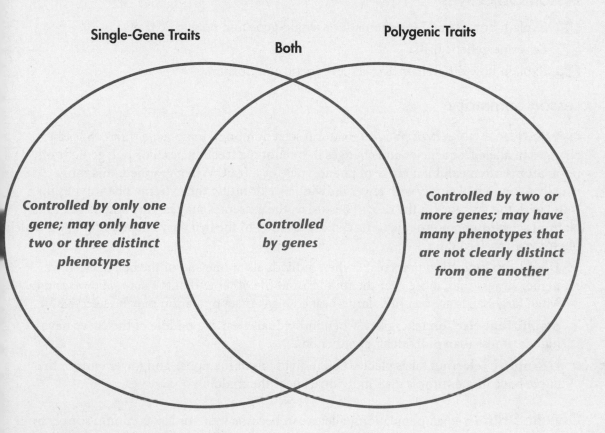

Single-Gene Traits

Both

Polygenic Traits

Controlled by only one gene; may only have two or three distinct phenotypes

Controlled by genes

Controlled by two or more genes; may have many phenotypes that are not clearly distinct from one another

Apply the Big idea

21. Why is genetic variation important to the process of evolution?

Genetic variation is the raw material of evolution, which can lead to different

members of a population having different levels of fitness in a certain environment.

The variation allows species to adapt to changes in their environment. Without such

variation, the population would not evolve.

_____

_____

_____

17.2 Evolution as Genetic Change in Populations

Lesson Objectives

- Explain how natural selection affects single-gene and polygenic traits.
- Describe genetic drift.
- Explain how different factors affect genetic equilibrium.

Lesson Summary

How Natural Selection Works Natural selection on a single-gene trait can lead to changes in allele frequencies and changes in phenotype frequencies. For polygenic traits, populations often exhibit a range of phenotypes for a trait. When graphed, this range usually forms a bell curve, with fewer individuals exhibiting the extreme phenotypes than those with the average (in the case of beak size, the extremes may be tiny and large beaks). Natural selection on polygenic traits can cause shifts to the bell curve depending upon which phenotype is selected for.

- **Directional selection** takes place when individuals at one end of the bell curve have higher fitness than those near the middle or at the other end of the curve. For example, when large seeds are plentiful, large-beaked birds in a population may be selected for.

- **Stabilizing selection** takes place when individuals near the middle of the curve have higher fitness than individuals at either end.

- **Disruptive selection** takes place when individuals at the upper and lower ends of the curve have higher fitness than individuals near the middle.

Genetic Drift In small populations, alleles can become more or less common simply by chance. This kind of change in allele frequency is called **genetic drift**.

- The **bottleneck effect** is a change in allele frequency following a dramatic reduction in the size of a population.

- The **founder effect** is a change in allele frequency that may occur when a few individuals from a population migrate to and colonize a new habitat.

Evolution Versus Genetic Equilibrium If allele frequencies in a population do not change, the population is in **genetic equilibrium**. Evolution is not taking place.

- The **Hardy-Weinberg Principle** states that allele frequencies in a population should remain constant unless one or more factors cause those frequencies to change. These factors include: non-random mating, small population size, immigration or emigration, mutations, and natural selection.

- Populations are rarely in genetic equilibrium. Most of the time, evolution is occurring. For example, many species exhibit non-random mating patterns. **Sexual selection**, or the process in which an individual chooses its mate based on heritable traits (such as size or strength), is a common practice for many organisms.

How Natural Selection Works

1. If a trait made an organism less likely to survive and reproduce, what would happen to the allele for that trait? *Fewer copies of the allele would pass to future generations and the allele could even disappear from the gene pool completely.*

2. If a trait had no effect on an organism's fitness, what would likely happen to the allele for that trait? *The allele would not be under pressure from natural selection, and its frequency would probably stay about the same.*

Use the table showing the evolution of a population of mice to answer Questions 3–5.

Initial Population	Generation 10	Generation 20	Generation 30
90%	80%	70%	40%
10%	20%	30%	60%

3. Is the trait for fur color a single-gene trait or a polygenic trait? Explain your answer.
The fur color is controlled by a single gene. There are only two phenotypes for this trait, gray or black fur.

4. Describe how the relative frequency of fur color alleles is changing in this population and propose one explanation for this change.
The lighter fur color allele is decreasing in frequency and the darker fur color allele is increasing in frequency. Darker mice may be harder for predators to see, so they are more likely to survive and reproduce.

5. Suppose a mutation causes a white fur phenotype to emerge in the population. What might happen to the mouse population after 40 generations?
SAMPLE ANSWER: *If individuals with the new phenotype are more fit than the gray or black mice, the white allele may increase in frequency in the population. Black mice will likely continue to be more common than the other phenotypes.*

6. What effect does stabilizing selection have on variation in a population?

Stabilizing selection would generally reduce the variation in a population.

_____

For Questions 7–9, match the type of selection with the correct situation.

Type of Selection

___B___ 7. Directional

___C___ 8. Stabilizing

___A___ 9. Disruptive

Situation

A. Individuals at the upper and lower ends of the curve have higher fitness than individuals near the middle.

B. Individuals at one end of the curve have higher fitness than individuals in the middle or at the other end.

C. Individuals near the center of the curve have higher fitness than individuals at either end.

10. **THINK VISUALLY** Draw the missing line in the graph on the right to show how disruptive selection affects beak size.

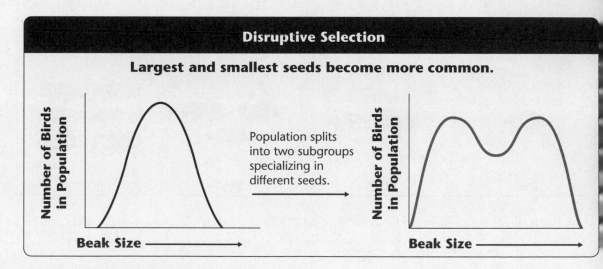

Disruptive Selection

Largest and smallest seeds become more common.

Number of Birds in Population | Beak Size →

Population splits into two subgroups specializing in different seeds.

Number of Birds in Population | Beak Size →

Genetic Drift

For Questions 11–13, complete each statement by writing the correct word or words.

11. In small populations, random changes in *allele frequencies* is called genetic drift.

12. A situation in which allele frequencies change as a result of the migration of a small subgroup of a population is known as the _____*founder effect*_____.

13. The _____*bottleneck effect*_____ is a change in allele frequency following a dramatic reduction in the size of a population.

14. Complete the concept map.

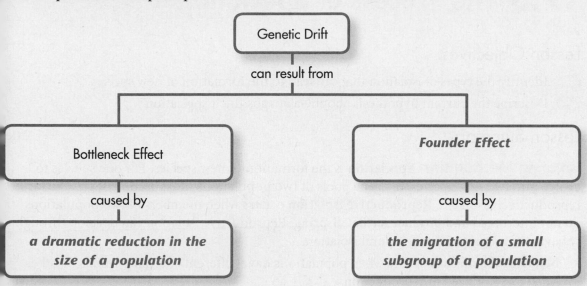

Evolution Versus Genetic Equilibrium

15. What does the Hardy-Weinberg principle state? _Allele frequencies in a population_
should remain constant unless one or more factors cause them to change.

16. What is genetic equilibrium? _the situation in which allele frequencies remain constant_
_____

17. List the five conditions that can disturb genetic equilibrium and cause evolution to occur.
non-random mating, small population size, immigration or emigration, mutations,
and natural selection

18. Explain how sexual selection results in non-random mating.
When an individual practices sexual selection, or choosing a mate based on heritable
characteristics such as size and strength, this individual's mate choice is not random.

Apply the Big idea

19. Suppose a population of insects live in a sandy habitat. Some of the insects have tan bodies and some have green bodies. Over time, the habitat changes to a grass-filled meadow. Use the ideas of natural selection to explain how and why the insect population might change.
In the original sandy habitat, tan insects may have been camouflaged from
predators, making them more successful than green insects. When the habitat
changes to a green, grassy meadow, individuals with green bodies may become
more successful at hiding from predators. The green-bodied insects may survive and
produce more offspring than the tan-bodied insects. Over time the frequency of the
green-bodied allele would probably increase.
_____

17.3 The Process of Speciation

Lesson Objectives

- Identify the types of isolation that can lead to the formation of new species.
- Describe the current hypothesis about Galápagos finch speciation.

Lesson Summary

Isolating Mechanisms **Speciation** is the formation of new species. For one species to evolve into two new species, the gene pools of two populations must become separated, or reproductively isolated. **Reproductive isolation** occurs when members of two populations do not interbreed and produce fertile offspring. Reproductive isolation can develop through behavioral, geographic, or temporal isolation.

▶ **Behavioral isolation** occurs when populations have different courtship rituals or other behaviors involved in reproduction.

▶ **Geographic isolation** occurs when populations are separated by geographic barriers, such as mountains or rivers.

▶ **Temporal isolation** occurs when populations reproduce at different times.

Speciation in Darwin's Finches Peter and Rosemary Grant's work supports the hypothesis that speciation in the Galápagos finches was, and still continues to be, a result of the founder effect and natural selection.

▶ Speciation in Galápagos finches may have occurred in a sequence of events that involved the founding of a new population, geographic isolation, changes in the gene pool, behavioral isolation, and ecological competition.

▶ For example, a few finches may have flown from mainland South America to one of the islands. There, they survived and reproduced. Some birds may have crossed to a second island, and the two populations became geographically isolated. Seed sizes on the second island could have favored birds with larger beaks, so the population on the second island evolved into a population with larger beaks. Eventually, these large-beaked birds became reproductively isolated and evolved into a new species.

Isolating Mechanisms

1. What is speciation?

It is the formation of new species.

2. What does it mean for two species to be reproductively isolated from each other?

Members of the two species do not interbreed and produce fertile offspring.

3. What must happen in order for a new species to evolve?

Populations must be reproductively isolated from one another.

4. List three ways that reproductive isolation occurs.

behavioral isolation, geographic isolation, temporal isolation

5. When does behavioral isolation occur?

It occurs when populations have differences in courtship rituals or other types of

behaviors that prevent them from interbreeding.

6. When does geographic isolation occur?

It occurs when populations are separated by geographic barriers such as rivers,

mountains, or bodies of water.

7. What is an example of temporal isolation?

SAMPLE ANSWER: *Each of three similar species of orchid in the same rain forest releases*

pollen on different days.

8. Suppose a seamount forms from an underwater volcano. Birds on the mainland colonize the island. How might this lead to speciation?

Answers may vary. The birds on the island may become reproductively isolated from

mainland birds through geographic isolation. As a result, the gene pool of the birds

that colonized the island would remain isolated, and the birds may evolve to become

a new species as they adapt to their island habitat.

Speciation in Darwin's Finches

For Questions 9–13, complete each statement by writing the correct word or words.

9. Peter and Rosemary Grant spent years on the Galápagos Islands studying changes in _____*finch*_____ populations.

10. Many finch characteristics appear in bell-shaped distributions typical of _____*polygenic*_____ traits.

11. The ancestors of the Galápagos Island finches originally came from the continent of _____*South America*_____.

12. The populations of finches on separate islands are _____*geographically*_____ isolated from one another by large stretches of open water.

13. Big-beaked finches that prefer to mate with other big-beaked finches are _____*behaviorally*_____ isolated from small-beaked finches living on the same island.

14. Write a paragraph that summarizes how speciation likely occurred in the Galápagos finches. Use the following terms in your response: *geographic isolation, gene pools, behavioral isolation,* and *competition.*

Many years ago, a few finches from South America arrived on a Galápagos island. These finches were geographically isolated from the original South American population. They survived and reproduced. Over time, some finches from the first island may have migrated to a new island, becoming a new geographically-isolated population. Differing conditions on the two islands, such as varied food sources, may have caused the populations to evolve in separate ways. So, the allele frequencies in each population's gene pool would have also changed in different ways. Over time, migration, geographic isolation, and natural selection may have occurred multiple times on different Galápagos islands. Additionally, populations on different islands may have evolved separate breeding behaviors causing them to become behaviorally isolated. Competition among individuals and responses to a changing environment could have created further selective pressures on these isolated populations. In the end, the combination of all these processes likely resulted in the evolution of the 13 finch species currently found in the Galápagos.

Apply the Big idea

15. Explain why reproductive isolation must occur for separate populations of the same species to evolve into different species.

Reproductive isolation must occur so that the gene pools are isolated. When the gene pools are isolated, changes that occur in one gene pool will not be carried over to the other gene pool. Thus, over time, accumulated gene pool changes can produce a new species.

17.4 Molecular Evolution

Lesson Objectives

Explain how molecular clocks are used.

Explain how new genes evolve.

Describe how Hox genes may be involved in evolutionary change.

Lesson Summary

Timing Lineage Splits: Molecular Clocks A molecular clock uses mutation rates in DNA to estimate the length of time that two species have been evolving independently.

▶ Molecular clock models assume that neutral mutations, which do not affect phenotype, accumulate in the DNA of different species at about the same rate.

▶ Two species evolving independently from each other will accumulate different neutral mutations through time. The more differences between the DNA, the more time has passed since the two species shared an ancestor.

Gene Duplication New genes evolve through the duplication, and then modification, of existing genes.

▶ Organisms may carry multiple copies of the same gene. The extra copies of a gene may undergo mutations.

▶ The mutated gene may have a new function that is different from the original gene. In this way, new genes evolve.

▶ Multiple copies of a duplicated gene can turn into a gene family.

Developmental Genes and Body Plans Researchers study the relationship between evolution and embryological development.

▶ Some genes, called Hox genes, control the forms of animals' bodies.

▶ Small changes in Hox genes during embryological development can produce major changes in adult organisms.

▶ Some scientists think that changes in Hox genes may contribute to major evolutionary changes.

Timing Lineage Splits: Molecular Clocks

1. What is a molecular clock?

It is a model that uses DNA comparisons to estimate the length of time that two

species have been evolving independently.

2. Why are only neutral mutations useful for molecular clocks?

Neutral mutations accumulate in the DNA of different species at about the same rate

because they are unaffected by natural selection.

3. Why are there many molecular clocks in a genome instead of just one?

Some genes accumulate mutations faster than others.

_____

Use the diagram of an ancestral species to answer Questions 4–5. Each picture in the diagram represents a gene. Each shaded portion of a gene represents a mutation.

4. Which species is most closely related to Species B? Explain your answer.

Species C; Species B and Species C

have two mutations in common.

Species B and Species A have no

mutations in common. This shows

that Species B and C are more closely

related than Species B and A.

5. How can you tell that Species C is probably not a descendant of the organism with Gene 2?

Species C and the species with Gene

2 do not share any mutations.

_____

_____

_____

_____

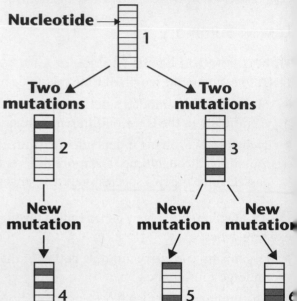

A gene in an ancestral species

Gene Duplication

For Questions 6–7, write the letter of the correct answer on the line at the left.

___D___ 6. Multiple copies of a duplicated gene can turn into a group of related genes called

    A. globins.

    B. duplicates.

    C. a Hox gene.

    D. a gene family.

___A___ 7. A chromosome may get several copies of the same gene during the process of

    A. crossing-over.

    B. gene mutation.

    C. gene expression.

    D. artificial selection.

8. Complete the flowchart to show how a new gene can evolve from a duplicated gene.

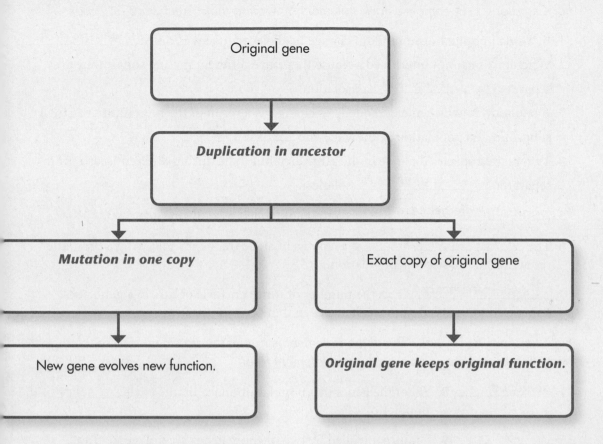

Original gene

↓

Duplication in ancestor

Mutation in one copy   Exact copy of original gene

↓   ↓

New gene evolves new function.   **Original gene keeps original function.**

Developmental Genes and Body Plans

9. What genetic factors might be responsible for a change in an organism's body plan?

A change in Hox gene activity during embryonic development can change an organism's body plan.

Apply the Big idea

0. How can Hox genes help reveal how evolution occurred?

Homologous Hox genes establish body plans in species that have not shared a common ancestor in hundreds of millions of years. In addition, major evolutionary changes may be based on Hox genes. A change in one Hox gene can result in major body changes in an animal. Scientists may be able to trace Hox gene changes to determine when and why certain species of organisms developed.

Chapter Vocabulary Review

For Questions 1–8, complete each statement by writing the correct word or words.

1. In a small population, a random change in allele frequency is called __genetic drift__.

2. When birds cannot interbreed because they have different mating songs, they are separated by __behavioral__ isolation.

3. A situation in which allele frequencies change as a result of the migration of a small subgroup of a population is known as the __founder effect__.

4. Two related species that live in the same area but mate during different seasons are separated by __temporal__ isolation.

5. A(n) __single-gene trait__ is a trait controlled by only one gene.

6. The __bottleneck effect__ is a change in allele frequency following a dramatic reduction in the size of a population.

7. __Allele frequency__ is the number of times an allele occurs in a gene pool, compared to the total number of alleles in that pool for the same gene.

For Questions 8–16, write True if the statement is true. If the statement is false, change the underlined word or words to make the statement true.

__gene pool__   8. All of the genes in a population make up the <u>allele frequency</u> of the population.

__True__   9. Traits controlled by two or more genes are <u>polygenic traits</u>.

__True__   10. <u>Reproductive isolation</u> occurs when members of two populations do not interbreed and produce fertile offspring.

__geographic__   11. The separation of two populations by barriers such as rivers or mountains results in <u>temporal</u> isolation.

__True__   12. The <u>Hardy-Weinberg</u> principle states that allele frequencies in a population should remain constant unless one or more factors cause those frequencies to change.

__Speciation__   13. <u>Genetic drift</u> is the formation of new species.

__Genetic equilibrium__   14. The <u>founder effect</u> occurs when the allele frequencies in a population remain constant.

__stabilizing__   15. For polygenic traits, when individuals near the center of the bell curve have higher fitness than individuals at either end, <u>disruptive</u> selection takes place.

__True__   16. When researchers use a <u>molecular clock</u>, they compare stretches of DNA to mark the passage of evolutionary time.

CHAPTER
MYSTERY
EPIDEMIC

The Chapter Mystery focused on the emergence of the deadly strain of influenza that led to the cataclysmic flu epidemic of 1918. Today, teams of scientists, doctors, and other health specialists are working hard to prevent contagious diseases from spreading out of control.

21st Century Learning

Preventing the Next Epidemic

The Global Outbreak Alert and Response Network, called "GOARN," is a vital and little-known group that serves as an international early warning system to prevent and contain disease outbreaks. It is based at the World Health Organization headquarters in Geneva, Switzerland. The World Health Organization is part of the United Nations system.

Read the following case study to learn more about GOARN's work fighting a disease outbreak known as SARS.

How GOARN Helped Prevent a SARS Epidemic

In late 2002, an outbreak of an unusual and deadly type of pneumonia occurred in southern China. After additional cases appeared early in 2003 in Vietnam and Hong Kong, doctors named the mysterious ailment "severe acute respiratory syndrome," or SARS. It appeared to be spreading fast and no drug seemed effective against it. SARS killed many of the people it infected. Within months, cases of SARS had begun to occur in more than a dozen countries around the world.

From the start, the Global Outbreak Alert and Response Network (GOARN) quickly swung into action. GOARN staff mobilized partners in many countries to support scores of professionals in the field working to fight SARS. They lent support for tracking the disease and controlling its spread. While GOARN staff worked to coordinate quarantine efforts and take blood samples from infected patients, they also mobilized scientists in GOARN's network of laboratories. These laboratories, located in nine different countries, studied the blood samples to try to identify the underlying cause for SARS.

GOARN set up a secure Web site so that its worldwide network of researchers could keep in contact as they worked around the clock. The communications system was so well designed that scientists could display patient samples and electron microscope images in real time to colleagues continents away. Details of each lab's analysis and testing of samples were immediately posted online so researchers elsewhere could instantly act upon relevant information. Scientists at all these laboratories participated in daily teleconferences to discuss progress and obstacles. With the extraordinary global collaboration, scientists in GOARN's global network were able to identify the previously unknown mutant virus responsible for SARS *in less than two weeks.*

GOARN's network of scientists succeeded in identifying the culprit and containing the spread of SARS in record time. But researchers say that a virulent strain of flu could spread even faster than SARS. So, night and day, the GOARN staff remains on alert, carefully monitoring outbreaks of disease wherever they occur around the world.

Continued on next page ▶

21st Century Themes Science and Global Awareness

1. What steps did GOARN take to fight SARS in the field?

GOARN staff worked to coordinate quarantine efforts and take blood samples from infected patients. They lent support for tracking the disease and controlling its spread.

2. What steps did GOARN take to identify the underlying cause of SARS?

GOARN mobilized scientists in its network of laboratories. It set up a special Web site to allow these researchers to share information about their work and collaborate around the clock.

3. Was the worldwide collaboration between the laboratories successful in identifying the virus responsible for SARS? If so, what were the key factors that led to its success?

The GOARN network was remarkably successful, finding the virus in just two weeks. The key was that laboratories around the world all shared their work and results. The combined effort allowed them to quickly build on one anothers' research.

4. How do you think GOARN could improve their response time to an emerging disease?

SAMPLE ANSWER: They could recruit several doctors from every major population center around the world and have the doctors flag any suspicious cases they see.

5. Today, emerging viruses can spread faster than ever before. What factors do you think contribute to this fast pace of transmission?

SAMPLE ANSWER: Today, much of the world's population live in densely packed urban areas, making transmission from one person to another very easy. In addition, modern transportation, such as airplanes, lets people in one part of the world reach another part of the world in just a few hours.

21st Century Skills Media Review

The skills used in this activity include **information and media literacy, critical thinking and systems thinking,** and **self-direction.**

A number of books and movies are based on the potential for, or the occurrence of, a disease outbreak. Two examples are Richard Preston's 1995 nonfiction thriller *The Hot Zone: A Terrifying True Story* and the 1995 Hollywood feature film "Outbreak." At the library or other local resource, find a book or a movie that dramatizes the threat of a disease epidemic. Also, find out more about how GOARN helps to fight epidemics. You may want to start by visiting the World Health Organization's Web site.

After getting permission from your teacher, write a review discussing the work and how its treatment of the subject compares with what you have learned about GOARN's real-life monitoring and prevention activities. Evaluate the students' performance based on their analysis of the accuracy of the film or book. They should discuss several ways the film or book compares with what they learned about GOARN's activities.

18 Classification

 Big idea **Unity and Diversity of Life**

Q: What is the goal of biologists who classify living things?

WHAT I KNOW	**WHAT I LEARNED**
18.1 Why do scientists classify organisms?	SAMPLE ANSWER: *Scientists classify organisms so that they will know all the kinds of life that are found on Earth.*	SAMPLE ANSWER: *Scientists classify organisms in order to study and understand their diversity.*
18.2 How do evolutionary relationships affect the way scientists classify organisms?	SAMPLE ANSWER: *Organisms are classified by their evolutionary relationships.*	SAMPLE ANSWER: *The goal of systematics is to group species into larger categories that have biological meaning.*
18.3 What are the major groups within which all organisms are currently classified?	SAMPLE ANSWER: *Organisms are classified into kingdoms, phyla, classes, orders, and so on.*	SAMPLE ANSWER: *The six-kingdom system of classification includes the kingdoms Eubacteria, Archaebacteria, "Protista," Fungi, Plantae, and Animalia.*

18.1 Finding Order in Diversity

Lesson Objectives

🔑 Describe the goals of binomial nomenclature and systematics.

🔑 Identify the taxa in the classification system devised by Linnaeus.

Lesson Summary

Assigning Scientific Names To study Earth's great diversity of organisms, biologists must give each organism a name. Biologists also must organize living things into groups in a logical way. Therefore, biologists need a classification system. The science of naming and grouping organisms is called **systematics**.

In the 1730s, Carolus Linnaeus developed a naming system, called **binomial nomenclature**. In binomial nomenclature, each species is assigned a two-part scientific name:

▶ The first part of the name refers to the **genus**, or a group of similar species.

▶ The second part of the name is unique to each species.

Linnaean Classification System Linnaeus's system of classification has seven different levels. From smallest to largest, the levels are species, genus, family, order, class, phylum, and kingdom. Each of the ranking levels is called a **taxon**.

▶ Just as a genus is a group of similar species, a **family** is a group of similar genera.

▶ An **order** is a group of similar families.

▶ A **class** is a group of similar orders.

▶ A **phylum** is a group of similar classes.

▶ A **kingdom** is a group of similar phyla.

Assigning Scientific Names

1. Complete the graphic organizer.

```
          ┌─────────────────────┐
          │  A useful scientific │
          │  name must have two  │
          │   characteristics:   │
          └─────────────────────┘
            │                 │
 ┌──────────────────────┐  ┌──────────────────────────┐
 │ Each name must refer │  │ Everyone must use the    │
 │ to only one species. │  │ same name.               │
 └──────────────────────┘  └──────────────────────────┘
```

For Questions 2–3, write the letter of the correct answer on the line at the left.

__C__ 2. What is the science of naming and grouping organisms called?

      A. genetics

      B. speciation

      C. systematics

      D. linnaeanology

__B__ 3. Modern systematists try to group organisms based on

      A. size.

      B. evolutionary relationships.

      C. ecological niche.

      D. physical appearance.

4. Why is it confusing to refer to organisms by common names?

Common names vary among languages and even among regions within a single

country. Also, different species may share a single common name.

5. What is binomial nomenclature?

the two-word naming system developed by Linnaeus

6. What genus does the grizzly bear, *Ursus arctos*, belong to?

*The genus is **Ursus**.*

7. What is the correct way to write scientific names in the binomial nomenclature system?

The genus starts with a capital letter and the species is lowercased. Both words

are written in italics.

Linnaean Classification System

For Questions 8–10, complete each statement by writing the correct word or words.

8. The goal of systematics is to organize living things into groups, called _____*taxa*_____, that have biological meaning.

9. The largest taxonomic category in the Linnaean system of classification is the _____*kingdom*_____, while the smallest is the _____*species*_____.

10. Similar classes are grouped into a(n) _____*phylum*_____, and similar orders are grouped into a(n) _____*class*_____.

11. THINK VISUALLY Fill in the name of each missing taxonomic category in the chart below.

KINGDOM
Animalia

Phylum
Chordata

Class
Mammalia

Order
Carnivora

Family
Ursidae

Genus
Ursus

SPECIES
Ursus arctos

Apply the Big idea

12. How does Linnaeus's system of classification help establish the unity of life?

The system classifies organisms based on overall similarities and differences to one
another. Organisms in the same genus share many similarities. Organisms in the
same kingdom may have many differences, but they still have common traits with one
another.

_____

_____

_____

_____

18.2 Modern Evolutionary Classification

Lesson Objectives

☞ Explain the difference between evolutionary classification and Linnaean classification.

☞ Describe how to make and interpret a cladogram.

☞ Explain the use of DNA sequences in classification.

Lesson Summary

Evolutionary Classification The study of evolutionary relationships among organisms is called **phylogeny**. Classification based on evolutionary relationships is called phylogenetic systematics, or evolutionary classification.

► Evolutionary classification places organisms into higher taxa whose members are more closely related to one another than they are to members of any other group. The larger the taxon, the further back in time all of its members shared a common ancestor.

► In this system, organisms are placed into groups called clades. A **clade** is a group of species that includes a single common ancestor and all descendants of that ancestor. A clade must be a monophyletic group. A **monophyletic group** must include all species that are descended from a common ancestor, and cannot include any species that are not descended from that common ancestor.

Cladograms A **cladogram** is a diagram that shows how species and higher taxa are related to each other. A cladogram shows how evolutionary lines, or lineages, branched off from common ancestors.

► In a cladogram, the place where the ancestral lineage splits is called a fork, or a node. Nodes represent the point where new lineages last shared a common ancestor.

► The bottom of the diagram, or the root, represents the ancestor shared by all of the organisms on the cladogram.

► Cladistic analysis relies on specific shared traits, or characters. A **derived character** is a trait that arose in the most recent common ancestor of a particular lineage and was passed to all of its descendants.

DNA in Classification All organisms have DNA. Because DNA is so similar across all forms of life, this molecule can be compared in different species. In general, the more derived genetic characters two species share, the more recently the species shared a common ancestor and the more closely related they are.

Evolutionary Classification

1. How did Darwin's theory of evolution change the way biologists thought about classification categories?

   Biologists now group organisms into categories that represent lines of evolutionary

   descent, not just physical similarities.

2. Describe the goal of phylogenetic systematics (evolutionary classification).

The goal of phylogenetic systematics is to group organisms together based on their

evolutionary history, not just their similarities and differences.

3. Which group of organisms would have the most recent common ancestor: the members of a clade corresponding to a genus or the members of a clade corresponding to an order? Explain your answer.

Members of a clade corresponding to a genus would have a more recent common

ancestor than members of a clade corresponding to an order. A genus is a smaller

taxon than an order. The larger a taxon is, the futher back in time its members

shared a common ancestor. This is true all the way up to the largest taxa.

4. Use the Venn diagram to compare and contrast the definitions of the Linnaean class Reptilia and the clade Reptilia.

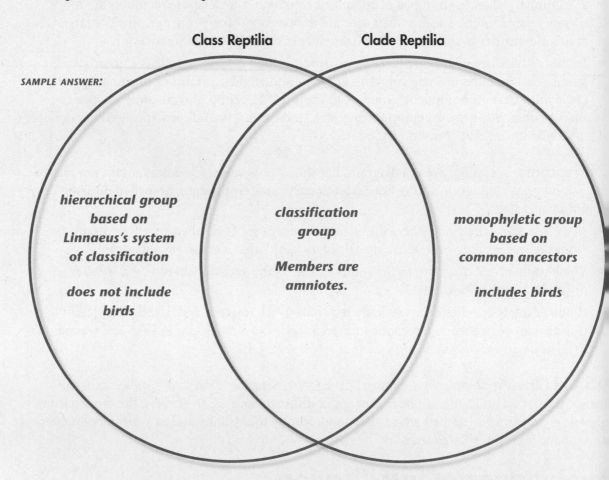

Class Reptilia   **Clade Reptilia**

SAMPLE ANSWER:

hierarchical group based on Linnaeus's system of classification

does not include birds

classification group

Members are amniotes.

monophyletic group based on common ancestors

includes birds

For Questions 5–7, complete each statement by writing the correct word or words.

5. All species descended from a(n) __common ancestor__ are part of a monophyletic group.

6. __Phylogeny__ is the study of how living and extinct organisms are related to one another.

7. A clade includes a common ancestor and all its descendants, living or __extinct__.

Cladograms

For Questions 8–10, complete each statement by writing the correct word or words.

8. A diagram that shows the evolutionary relationships among a group of organisms is called a(n) _cladogram_.

9. The place where the ancestral lineage splits on a cladogram is called a fork, or a(n) _node_.

10. Characteristics shared by members of a clade and only by members of that clade are called _derived characters_.

11. **THINK VISUALLY** Examine the cladogram below:

• Shade in the two organisms that belong to a clade that does not include the third organism. Cross-hatch the organism that does not belong to the clade.

• Circle the point on the cladogram that shows the most recent common ancestor of the crab and the barnacle.

• Mark an X on the point on the cladogram that shows the most recent common ancestor of mollusks and crustaceans.

• Underline the characteristic that all three organisms have in common.

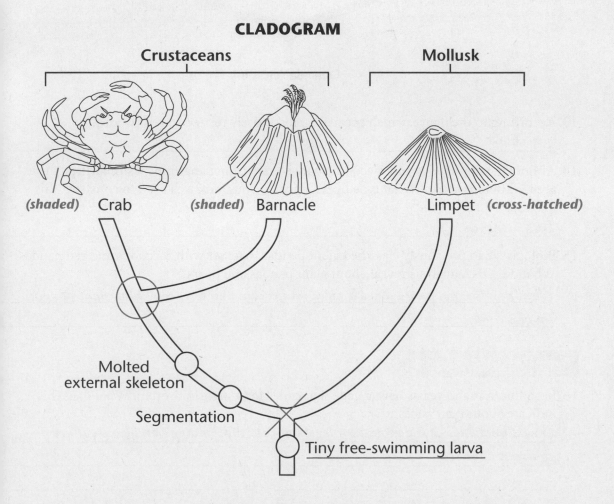

CLADOGRAM

Crustaceans   Mollusk

(shaded) Crab   (shaded) Barnacle   Limpet (cross-hatched)

Molted
external skeleton

Segmentation

Tiny free-swimming larva

DNA in Classification

12. Why can genes be considered derived characters?

Genes are passed on from generation to generation. Organisms share a number of

genes. Because all genes mutate over time, shared genes contain differences that can

be used as derived characters.

Use the figure below to answer Questions 13–15.

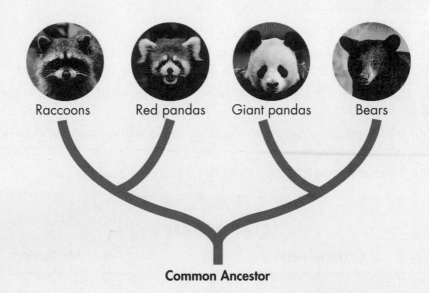

Raccoons   Red pandas   Giant pandas   Bears

Common Ancestor

13. According to the figure, which species is most closely related to red pandas?

raccoons

14. Although giant pandas and raccoons share some distinct anatomical similarities, they are in different clades. What type of evidence do you think was used to construct this diagram?

DNA evidence

15. Biologists had previously classified giant pandas together with raccoons and red pandas. What did DNA analysis reveal about giant pandas and bears?

Giant pandas and bears share a more recent common ancestor than giant pandas

and raccoons.

> ### Apply the Big idea

16. Both humans and yeasts have a gene that codes for a myosin protein. What does this indicate about their ancestry?

Their similarities at the molecular level indicate that humans and yeasts share a

common ancestry.

18.3 Building the Tree of Life

Lesson Objectives

☐ Name the six kingdoms of life as they are currently identified.

☐ Explain what the tree of life represents.

Lesson Summary

Changing Ideas About Kingdoms As biologists learned more about the natural world, they realized that Linnaeus's two kingdoms, Animalia and Plantae, did not represent all life.

▶ Researchers found that microorganisms were very different from plants and animals. They were placed in their own kingdom, called Protista.

▶ Then, yeast, molds, and mushrooms were separated from plants and placed in their own kingdom, called Fungi.

▶ Because bacteria lack nuclei, mitochondria, and chloroplasts, they were separated from Protista and placed in another new kingdom, called Monera.

▶ In the 1990s, kingdom Monera was divided into two kingdoms: Eubacteria and Archaebacteria. The six-kingdom system of classification includes the kingdoms Eubacteria, Archaebacteria, Protista, Fungi, Plantae, and Animalia.

▶ Genetic analysis revealed that two prokaryotic groups are even more different from each other, and from Eukaryotes, than previously thought. This discovery lead to the creation of a new taxon, called the domain. The **domain** is a larger, more inclusive category than a kingdom. The three domain system consists of: Bacteria, Archaea, and Eukarya.

▶ Domain Bacteria corresponds to the kingdom Eubacteria. Domain Archaea corresponds to the kingdom Archaebacteria. Domain Eukarya corresponds tokingdoms Fungi, Plantae, Animalia, and "Protista."

▶ Quotations are used for the old kingdom Protista to signify that it is not a valid clade.

The Tree of All Life The tree of life shows current hypotheses regarding evolutionary relationships among taxa within the three domains of life.

▶ The domain **Bacteria** includes unicellular organisms without a nucleus. They have cell walls containing a substance called peptidoglycan.

▶ The domain **Archaea** also includes unicellular organisms without a nucleus. These organisms have cell walls that do not contain peptidoglycan.

▶ The domain **Eukarya** includes the four remaining kingdoms: "Protista," Fungi, Plantae, and Animalia. All members of the domain Eukarya have cells with a nucleus.

• Most members of the kingdom "Protista," are unicellular organisms. Some Protista are photosynthetic; others are heterotrophs.

• Most members of the kingdom Fungi are multicellular, and all members of this kingdom are heterotrophs with cell walls containing chitin.

• All members of the kingdom Plantae are multicellular and photosynthetic. Most plants cannot move about, and their cells have cell walls.

• All members of the kingdom Animalia are multicellular heterotrophs. Most animals can move about, and their cells lack cell walls.

Changing Ideas About Kingdoms

1. What fundamental traits did Linnaeus use to separate plants from animals?

   Animals were mobile organisms that used food for energy. Plants were green

   organisms that did not move and got their energy from the sun.

2. What types of organisms were first placed in the kingdom Protista?

   At first, all microorganisms were placed in the kingdom Protista.

3. What types of organisms were placed into the kingdom Fungi?

   mushrooms, yeast, and molds

4. Why did scientists place bacteria in their own kingdom, the Monera?

   Bacteria lack the nuclei, mitochondria, and chloroplasts found in other forms of life.

5. What two kingdoms was kingdom Monera separated into?

   Eubacteria and Archaebacteria

6. Complete the concept map.

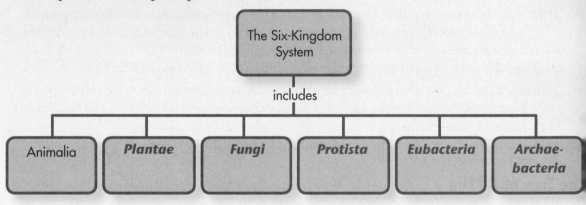

7. What is a domain?

   A domain is a larger, more inclusive category than a kingdom.

8. What did genomic analysis reveal about the two prokaryotic groups?

   They were more different from each other and from eukaryotes than previously

   thought.

The Tree of All Life

9. Complete the chart below.

Classification of Living Things		
Domain	**Kingdom**	**Examples**
Bacteria	Eubacteria	*Salmonella typhimurium*
Archaea	*Archaebacteria*	*Sulfolobus archaea*
Eukarya	"Protista"	**Ciliates, brown algae**
	Fungi	mushrooms, yeasts
	Plantae	**Mosses, ferns, cone-bearing plants, flowering plants**
	Animalia	Sponges, worms, insects, fishes, mammals

Match the kingdom with the description that applies to members of that kingdom.

Kingdom

_C_ **10.** "Protista"

_A_ **11.** Fungi

_D_ **12.** Plantae

_B_ **13.** Animalia

Description

A. They feed on dead or decaying organic matter.

B. They have no cell walls and they move about.

C. They are a "catchall" group of eukaryotes.

D. They include mosses and ferns.

Apply the Big idea

14. What characteristics led camels to be classified in the same domain, kingdom, phylum, and class as dogs?

Camels and dogs are members of the Eukarya domain because their cells have nuclei. They are members of the kingdom Animalia because they are multicellular heterotrophs that move from place to place. Camels and dogs are both members of the phylum chordata because they both share important body plan features including a nerve cord. Finally, they are both members of the same class, Mammalia, because they are warmblooded, have body hair, and produce milk for their young.

Chapter Vocabulary Review

Match the term with its definition.

Term

Definition

_H_ 1. phylogeny

_B_ 2. Bacteria

_E_ 3. order

_C_ 4. phylum

_F_ 5. clade

_D_ 6. class

_A_ 7. Eukarya

_G_ 8. domain

A. The domain containing all organisms that have a nucleus

B. The domain containing organisms that are prokaryotic and unicellular

C. A group of classes

D. A group of orders

E. A group of families

F. A group of species that includes a single common ancestor and all descendents of that ancestor

G. A larger, more inclusive category than a kingdom

H. The study of how living and extinct organisms are related to one another

For Questions 9–18, complete each statement by writing the correct word or words.

9. Members of the domain _____**Archaea**_____ live in some of the most extreme environments on Earth.

10. A(n) _**derived character**_ is a trait that arose in the most recent common ancestor of a particular lineage, and was passed along to its descendants.

11. Multicellular organisms that move about are placed in the _____**kingdom**_____ Animalia.

12. Under Linnaeus' classification system, similar genera were placed into a larger category called a(n) _____**family**_____.

13. Families, Orders, Classes, and Phyla are all _____**taxa**_____.

14. The science of naming and grouping organisms is called _____**systematics**_____.

15. A(n) _____**cladogram**_____ shows relative degrees of relatedness among lineages.

16. The name *Ursus arctos* is an example of the two-part scientific name given in the _____**binomial nomenclature**_____ system.

17. A(n) _____**genus**_____ is a group of similar species.

18. A clade is made up of a(n) _**monophyletic group**_.

CHAPTER
MYSTERY

GRIN AND BEAR IT

As you learned from solving the mystery, the question of what defines a species is sometimes hard to answer. The distinction is not just important to scientists. It can also have legal ramifications.

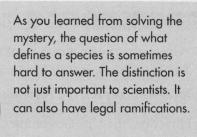

21st Century Learning

Legal Protection for a Threatened Species

WASHINGTON, D.C.—On May 14, 2008, the Secretary of the Interior Dirk Kempthorne announced that he would accept the recommendation of U.S. Fish and Wildlife Service to list the polar bear as a threatened species under the Endangered Species Act (ESA). Section 3 of the 1973 Endangered Species Act defines an endangered species as any species "which is in danger of extinction throughout all or a significant portion of its range." The opening paragraph of the rule is shown below.

AGENCY: Fish and Wildlife Service, Interior

ACTION: Final rule

SUMMARY: We, the U.S. Fish and Wildlife Service (Service), determine threatened status for the polar bear *(Ursus maritimus)* under the Endangered Species Act of 1973, as amended (Act) (16 U.S.C. 1531 et seq.). Polar bears evolved to utilize the Arctic sea ice niche and are distributed throughout most ice-covered seas of the Northern Hemisphere.

   We find, based upon the best available scientific and commercial information, that polar bear habitat—principally sea ice—is declining throughout the species' range, that this decline is expected to continue for the foreseeable future, and that this loss threatens the species throughout all of its range. Therefore, we find that the polar bear is likely to become an endangered species within the foreseeable future throughout all of its range.

Continued on next page ▶

21st Century Themes Science and Civic Literacy

1. Who wrote the document and who ruled on its findings?

The U.S. Fish and Wildlife Service made the recommendation. The Secretary of the Interior accepted the recommendation.

2. How does the U.S. Government define an endangered species?

An endangered species is any species "which is in danger of extinction throughout all or a significant portion of its range."

3. In making its ruling, the U.S. Government considered not only scientific information but also commercial information. What do you think this means?

SAMPLE ANSWER: **When deciding whether an animal should be protected, the government also considers the impact this would have on commercial interests in the area.**

4. What is the reason for listing the polar as a threatened species?

SAMPLE ANSWER: **Because sea ice is melting, polar bears are losing their habitat.**

5. The Government lists the polar bear as a threatened species, not an endangered one. What is the threat facing a species that is listed as threatened?

The threat facing threatened species is that the species will become endangered in the foreseeable future.

21st Century Skills Update: Status of Polar Bears

The skills used in this activity include **information and media literacy, communication skills,** and **critical thinking and systems thinking.**

Working with a small group, report back to the class on what has happened to the status of the polar bear since the U.S. Government made its initial ruling in May 2008. Find out if the status of the polar bear has changed and comment on whether the Government was right to make the ruling when it did.

Present your findings to the class using a digital slide show.

Evaluate students' work for completeness, accuracy, and reliability of sources.

Students' points of view on the status of polar bears should be logically argued and supported with facts.

19 History of Life

 Evolution

Q: How do fossils help biologists understand the history of life on Earth?

WHAT I KNOW	WHAT I LEARNED
19.1 How do scientists use fossils to study Earth's history?	SAMPLE ANSWER: **Fossils give clues about how organisms have changed.**	SAMPLE ANSWER: **From the fossil record, paleontologists learn about the structure of ancient organisms, their environment, and the way they lived.**
19.2 What are some patterns in which evolution has occurred?	SAMPLE ANSWER: **Organisms have grown in complexity over time.**	SAMPLE ANSWER: **Evidence shows that evolution has often proceeded at different rates for different organisms at different times over the long history of life on Earth. Patterns of macroevolution include speciation, extinction, adaptive radiation, convergent evolution, and coevolution.**
19.3 What happened during Earth's early history?	SAMPLE ANSWER: **Earth's features, such as its ocean and atmosphere, formed during its early history.**	SAMPLE ANSWER: **Early Earth had little or no oxygen in its atmosphere. Around 2.2 billion years ago, photosynthetic organisms evolved and began producing oxygen. Early multicellular organisms underwent adaptive radiations that led to great diversity.**

19.1 The Fossil Record

Lesson Objectives

🔑 Explain what information fossils can reveal about ancient life.

🔑 Differentiate between relative dating and radiometric dating.

🔑 Identify the divisions of the geologic time scale.

🔑 Describe how environmental processes and living things have shaped life on Earth.

Lesson Summary

Fossils and Ancient Life Fossils are preserved remains or traces of ancient life.

▶ Fossils are the most important source of information about extinct species. An **extinct** species is one that has died out.

▶ Most fossils are preserved in sedimentary rock. Sediments build up over time, and bury the remains and traces of dead organisms.

▶ Scientists who study fossils are called **paleontologists**.

Dating Earth's History Relative dating and radiometric dating are used to determine the age of fossils.

▶ **Relative dating** establishes the relative age of fossils. Fossils from deeper rock layers are assumed to be older than fossils from rock layers closer to the surface. **Index fossils** represent species that lived for a short period of time but over a wide geographic range. Index fossils can help determine the relative ages of rock layers and their fossils.

▶ **Radiometric dating** determines a fossil's approximate age in years by finding the proportion of radioactive to nonreactive isotopes in a sample. Radioactive isotopes in fossils and rock layers decay, or break down, at a steady rate, called a half-life. A **half-life** is the length of time needed for half of the radioactive atoms in a sample to decay. A fossil's age is calculated from the half-life and the amount of remaining radioactive atoms the fossil contains.

Geologic Time Scale The **geologic time scale** is a time line of Earth's history based on relative and absolute dating.

▶ The scale begins with the Precambrian.

▶ Geologic time is divided into four eons: the Hadean, Archean, Proterozoic, and Phanerozoic. The Phanerozoic eon is divided into three **eras**: the Paleozoic, Mesozoic, and Cenozoic.

▶ Each era is further divided into smaller lengths of time, called **periods**.

Life on a Changing Planet Climactic, geological, astronomical, and biological processes have affected the history of life on Earth.

▶ Earth's climate has changed often in the course of its history. Small temperature shifts can bring about heat waves and ice ages which have great effects on living things. **Plate tectonics** is a theory that Earth's outermost layer is divided into plates that move. The movement, called continental drift, has transformed life on Earth through the formation of mountain ranges, supercontinents, and other geologic features.

▶ The impact of objects from space has affected the global climate.

Fossils and Ancient Life

For Questions 1–3, complete each statement by writing the correct word or words.

1. Species that died out are said to be ___*extinct*___.

2. Most fossils are found in layers of ___*sedimentary*___ rock.

3. Scientists who study fossils are called ___*paleontologists*___.

4. What is the fossil record?

   It is the total collection of fossils on Earth, plus the information about past life

   inferred from fossils.

5. What information does the fossil record provide?

   It provides evidence about the history of life on Earth including how organisms have

   changed over time. It tells about the structures of ancient organisms, their environ-

   ment, and the way they lived.

6. Fill in the flowchart to explain how fossils are formed.

   Water carries small rock particles to lakes and seas.

   Dead organisms are buried by layers of sediment, which forms new rock.

   The preserved fossil remains may later be discovered and studied.

Dating Earth's History

7. What is an index fossil? What do index fossils reveal about other material found with them?

   Index fossils are distinctive fossils used to establish and compare the ages of rock

   layers and the fossils they contain. Useful index fossils existed for a relatively short

   period of time and were distributed over a wide area. Anything found in a rock layer

   near an index fossil is assumed to have existed at approximately the same time.

8. Fossil A is found in a layer of rock above a layer containing Fossil B. Which fossil is probably older? Explain your answer. *Fossil B is older. Newer layers of rock lie usually above older layers.*

9. List the two techniques paleontologists use to determine the age of fossils.

   relative dating, radiometric dating

10. What is a half-life? _It is the length of time required for half of the radioactive atoms in_
a sample to decay.

11. How do scientists calculate the age of a sample using radiometric dating?
They measure the amount of remaining radioactive isotopes it contains. The smaller
the amount is, the older the sample is.

For Questions 12–13, write the letter of the correct answer on the line at the left.

___A___ **12.** A species that is easily recognizable, existed for a relatively short period of time, and covered a wide geographic area may be used as a(n)

    A. index fossil.   **C.** microfossil.

    B. fossil record.   **D.** macrofossil.

___C___ **13.** The same index fossil is found in rock layers A and B that are separated by several miles. What can you infer about the relationship between the rock layers?

    A. Layer A is older than B.

    B. The sediments in layer B were deposited before those in layer A.

    C. Layers A and B are probably about the same age.

    D. Layer B probably contains more radioactive isotopes than layer A.

Geologic Time Scale

14. Fill in the missing eras and periods in the geologic time scale below.

Time (millions of years ago)	Period	Era
1.8–present	Quaternary	*Cenozoic*
23–1.8	*Neogene*	
65.5–23	Paleogene	
146–65.5	*Cretaceous*	*Mesozoic*
200–146	Jurassic	
251–200	*Triassic*	
299–251	Permian	Paleozoic
359–299	*Carboniferous*	
416–359	Devonian	
444–416	*Silurian*	
488–444	Ordovician	
542–488	*Cambrian*	
4600–542	Precambrian Time	

For Questions 15–16, refer to the Visual Analogy of life as a clock.

_____C_____ 15. **VISUAL ANALOGY** Which of the following appeared on Earth most recently?

  A. chordates

  B. tetrapods

  C. dinosaurs

  D. single-celled algae

_____A_____ 16. Dinosaurs appeared before

  A. mammals.

  B. photosynthesis.

  C. chordates.

  D. land plants.

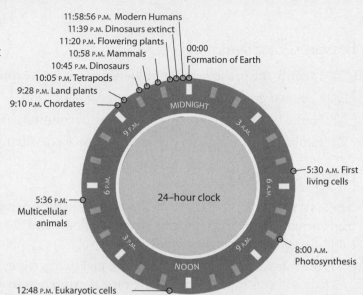

Processes Affecting Life's History

17. How might an asteroid impact change Earth's climate?

When the asteroid strikes Earth, It would throw up a great deal of debris into the atmosphere. The debris would block much of the sun's light, thus causing global temperatures to fall and decreasing the amount of plant life that could survive on Earth.

18. Explain the theory of plate tectonics and tell how it has affected the distribution of fossils and organisms. *According to the plate tectonics theory, Earth's outermost layer is divided into huge plates that have moved in the past and continue to move. The movement of the plates is called continental drift. Continental drift affected the distribution of fossils and living organisms. As the continents drifted apart, they carried organisms with them.*

Apply the Big idea

19. What are some aspects of a species' evolution that can't be studied using fossil evidence? Why don't fossils provide information about these characteristics?

SAMPLE ANSWER: **Fossils can't usually provide information about the soft tissues of an organism because soft tissues rarely become fossilized. Also, fossils rarely provide information about interactions among organisms and thus tell us little about animal behavior.**

19.2 Patterns and Processes of Evolution

Lesson Objectives

🔑 Identify the processes that influence survival or extinction of a species or clade.

🔑 Contrast gradualism and punctuated equilibrium.

🔑 Name two important patterns in macroevolution.

🔑 Explain the evolutionary characteristics of coevolving organisms.

Lesson Summary

Speciation and Extinction Macroevolutionary patterns are grand transformations in anatomy, phylogeny, ecology, and behavior that usually take place in clades larger than a single species.

▶ If the rate of speciation in a clade is equal to or greater than the rate of extinction, the clade will continue to exist. If the rate of extinction in a clade is greater than the rate of speciation, the entire clade will eventually become extinct.

▶ Background extinction is extinction caused by the slow process of natural selection. Mass extinctions affect huge numbers of species over a relatively short time.

Rate of Evolution Evidence shows that evolution has occurred at different rates for different organisms at different times.

▶ The idea that evolution occurs slowly and gradually is called gradualism.

▶ In punctuated equilibrium, long periods of little or no change are interrupted by short periods of rapid change.

Adaptive Radiation and Convergent Evolution Adaptive radiation is the process in which a single species evolves into diverse species that live in different ways. Convergent evolution is the process in which unrelated species come to look alike because they have evolved similar adaptations in response to similar environments.

Coevolution Coevolution is the process by which two species evolve in response to changes in each other over time. For example, plants evolved poisons that protected them from insects. In response, insects evolved ways of protecting themselves from the poisons.

Speciation and Extinction

For Questions 1–4, write True if the statement is true. If the statement is false, change the underlined word or words to make the statement true.

macroevolutionary patterns	1.	Large-scale evolutionary changes that usually take place over long periods of time are referred to as <u>speciation</u>.
mass extinction	2.	Many species disappear rapidly during a <u>background extinction</u>.
True	3.	The <u>rate of speciation</u> in a clade must be equal to or greater than the rate of extinction in order for a clade to survive.
True	4.	Immediately after a mass extinction, <u>biodiversity</u> is dramatically reduced.

5. What are possible causes of mass extinction?

Some possible causes of mass extinction include a huge asteroid striking Earth, many

large volcanoes erupting, continents changing position, and sea levels changing.

6. What effects have mass extinctions had on the history of life?

The disappearance of so many species leaves behind empty niches in an ecosystem.

New species often evolve to fill these niches.

Rate of Evolution

7. Horseshoe crabs have changed little in structure from the time they first showed up in the fossil record. Which pattern of evolution do horseshoe crabs likely follow—gradualism or punctuated equilibirum? Explain your answer.

Horsehoe crabs follow a punctuated equilibrium pattern. In punctuated equilibirum,

there are long periods of little or no change interrupted by rapid change. If horseshoe

crabs were following a gradualism pattern, you'd expect them to be changing slowly

and constantly.

8. Why does rapid evolution occur more often in small populations?

Because genetic changes can spread more easily in small populations. This happens in

both genetic drift and genetic bottlenecks.

9. Use the Venn diagram below to compare punctuated equilibrium with gradualism.

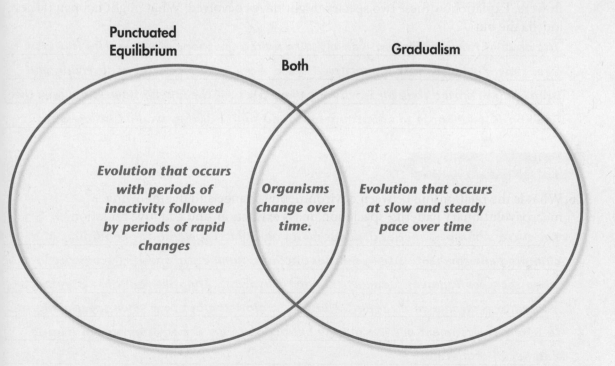

Punctuated Equilibrium — Both — Gradualism

Evolution that occurs with periods of inactivity followed by periods of rapid changes

Organisms change over time.

Evolution that occurs at slow and steady pace over time

Adaptive Radiation and Convergent Evolution

Write the letter of the correct answer on the line at the left.

___C___ 10. The process in which a single species or a small group of species evolves into diverse forms that live in different ways is called

    A. coevolution.   **C.** adaptive radiation.

    B. macroevolution.   **D.** convergent evolution.

___D___ 11. The process by which unrelated organisms come to resemble one another is

    A. coevolution.   **C.** adaptive radiation.

    B. macroevolution.   **D.** convergent evolution.

___B___ 12. What contributed to the adaptive radiation of mammals?

    A. the evolution of plants   **C.** the decrease in ocean depth

    B. the extinction of most dinosaurs   **D.** continental drift

___C___ 13. Which of the following is an example of convergent evolution?

    A. bird's wing and fish's fin   **C.** shark's fin and dolphin's limb

    B. human's arm and bird's wing   **D.** human's leg and dolphin's limb

Coevolution

14. What is coevolution? *Coevolution is the process by which two species evolve in response to changes in each other over time.*

15. 'I'iwi birds have long, curved beaks that enable them to get nectar from tubular lobelia flowers. Explain how these two species might have coevolved. What might happen if the lobelia die out?

The beak of the 'i'iwi bird has coevolved to match the shape of the lobelia flowers. Over time 'i'iwi birds with long, curved beaks were more successful at surviving and producing offspring than birds without these traits. If the lobelia flowers die out, the 'i'iwi birds would have to adapt to a new food source or they would also die out.

Apply the Big idea

16. What is the relationship between environmental change and the following macroevolutionary patterns: speciation, mass extinction, and adaptive radiation?

The success of a new species depends on its ability to cope with the conditions of a changing environment. During mass extinctions, numbers of species become extinct when their environment suddenly changes drastically. Adaptive radiation is indirectly related to environmental change. Adaptive radiation may occur when species migrate to a new environment or after a large extinction clears the environment of a large number of organisms.

19.3 Earth's Early History

Lesson Objectives

- Identify some of the hypotheses about early Earth and the origin of life.
- Explain the endosymbiotic theory.
- Explain the significance of sexual reproduction in evolution.

Lesson Summary

The Mysteries of Life's Origins Earth's early atmosphere contained toxic gases. The atmosphere also contained little or no oxygen.

▶ In the 1950s, Stanley Miller and Harold Urey set out to determine if organic molecules could assemble under eartly Earth conditions. They filled a container with water and gases that they thought represented the composition of Earth's early atmosphere. They passed electric sparks through the mixture to simulate lightning. Soon, organic compounds formed. The experiment showed that molecules needed for life could have arisen from simpler compounds.

▶ Under some conditions, large organic molecules form tiny bubbles called proteinoid microspheres. Structures similar to proteinoid microspheres might have become the first living cells. RNA and DNA also could have evolved from simple organic molecules.

▶ The first known life forms evolved about 3.5 billion years ago. They were single celled and looked like modern bacteria. Eventually, photosynthetic bacteria became common. During photosynthesis, the bacteria produced oxygen. The oxygen accumulated in the atmosphere. The rise of oxygen drove some life forms to extinction. At the same time, other life forms evolved that depended on oxygen.

Origin of Eukaryotic Cells The first eukaryotes, or organisms with nuclei, evolved from prokaryotes that began to develop internal cell membranes. One explanation for how eukaryotes evolved is the **endosymbiotic theory**. This theory proposes that smaller prokaryotes began living inside larger cells and evolved a symbiotic relationship with the larger cells.

Sexual Reproduction and Multicellularity Sexual reproduction evolved after eukaryotic cells. Sexual reproduction increased genetic variation, so evolution could occur more quickly. Several hundred million years after sexual reproduction evolved, multicellular life evolved.

The Mysteries of Life's Origins

1. What are protenoid microspheres?

   They are tiny bubbles formed from large organic molecules that have some characteristics of living cells.

2. Why do scientists think that RNA may have evolved before DNA?

   Experiments show that small sequences of RNA could have formed and replicated on their own in the conditions present on early Earth.

Use the diagram of the Miller-Urey experiment to answer Questions 3–5.

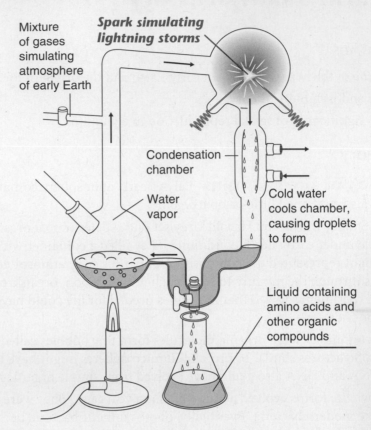

Mixture of gases simulating atmosphere of early Earth

Spark simulating lightning storms

Condensation chamber

Water vapor

Cold water cools chamber, causing droplets to form

Liquid containing amino acids and other organic compounds

3. **THINK VISUALLY** Label the diagram to show which part of Miller and Urey's apparatus simulated lightning storms on early Earth.

4. What was the purpose of Miller and Urey's experiment? *to determine whether organic molecules could assemble under the conditions of early Earth*

5. Explain the results of the Miller-Urey experiment. What did these findings suggest?
The experiment produced several amino acids, which suggested that mixtures of organic compounds could have arisen from substances found on early Earth. Evidence now suggests that the composition of Earth's early atmosphere was different from the one used in their experiment. However, more recent experiments with different mixes of gases have produced similar results.

Origin of Eukaryotic Cells

6. Explain the endosymbiotic theory. *The endosymbiotic theory proposes that prokaryotic cells entered early eukaryotic organisms. Over time a symbiotic relationship evolved between primitive eukaryotic cells and the prokaryotic cells within them.*

7. **THINK VISUALLY** Draw the step in the endosymbiotic theory that shows the origin of chloroplasts. Label the structures in your drawing.

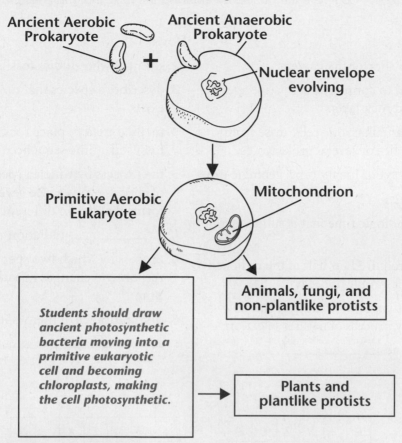

Ancient Aerobic Prokaryote + Ancient Anaerobic Prokaryote

Nuclear envelope evolving

Primitive Aerobic Eukaryote

Mitochondrion

Students should draw ancient photosynthetic bacteria moving into a primitive eukaryotic cell and becoming chloroplasts, making the cell photosynthetic.

Animals, fungi, and non-plantlike protists

Plants and plantlike protists

Primitive Photosynthetic Eukaryote

Sexual Reproduction and Multicellularity

8. How did sexual reproduction speed up the evolutionary process?
Sexual reproduction shuffles and reshuffles genes in each generation. This increase in genetic variation greatly increases the chances of evolutionary change due to natural selection.

9. What is the most likely cause of the great amount of diversity currently seen in multicellular life forms? *Early multicellular life most likely underwent a series of adaptive radiations.*

Apply the Big idea

10. Once DNA evolved, what could have caused it to become the primary means of transmitting genetic information instead of RNA?
SAMPLE ANSWER: DNA was a more stable information-storing molecule than RNA.

_____

_____

Chapter Vocabulary Review

Crossword Puzzle *Complete the puzzle by entering the term that matches the description.*

Across

1. time span shorter than an era
2. fossil used to compare the relative ages of fossils and rock layers
7. theory that eukaryotic cells arose from communities of several prokaryotes
9. measures evolutionary time: geologic time _____
10. span of geologic time that is subdivided into periods
11. the time required for half of the radioactive atoms in a sample to decay
12. a species dying out because of the slow but steady process of natural selection: background _____

Down

1. scientist who studies fossils
3. describes a species that no longer exists
4. method used to place rock layers and their fossils in a time sequence (2 words)
5. the process by which a species or group of species evolves into several different forms that live in different ways: _____ radiation
6. process by which two species evolve in response to changes in each other over time
8. disappearance of many species at the same time: _____ extinction

¹P	E	R	I	O	D		²I	N	³D	E	X		⁴R				
A									X		T		E				
L		⁵A					⁶C		T				L				
⁷E	N	D	O	S	Y	M	B	I	O	T	I	C	A				
O		A					E		N				T				
N		P		⁸M			V		C				I				
T		T		A			O		T				V				
O		I		⁹S	C	A	L	E					E				
L		V		S			U						D				
O		E					T			¹⁰E	R	A					
G			¹¹H	A	L	F	L	I	F	E		T					
I							O					I					
S			¹²E	X	T	I	N	C	T	I	O	N					
T												G					

CHAPTER MYSTERY

MURDER IN THE PERMIAN

21st Century Learning

Geologists are still working on solving the 250-million-year-old Permian murder mystery. To accomplish this, they piece together clues from the past that are preserved in rocks.

The Story Is in the Rocks

In the Chapter Mystery, geologists and other scientists examine rocks to help them uncover the story behind a catastrophic destruction of species and ecosystems. Rocks are extremely useful in revealing what happened on Earth long ago.

The type of rock in a rock layer indicates how the rock formed. Rocks are made up of minerals. The minerals in rocks tell a story. For example, igneous rocks with small mineral crystals are formed during a volcanic eruption because the lava cooled too quickly for large crystals to form. In contrast, igneous rock with large crystals formed underground. Some types of mineral crystals can only form in open spaces, such as a cave, while other crystals can only be deposited in an aquatic environment.

When looking for clues about the past, geologists also look at the shape and size of a rock layer. An unconformity, or a disturbed sequence of rock layers, gives information about events that happened after a rock layer formed. For example, an earthquake can cause a rock layer to snap in two. And slanted rock layers may indicate that uplift occurred in the area.

Most of what we know about Earth's ancient past comes from Earth's rocks. Thus, as the interpretive sign below from Yellowstone National Park shows, discussions of Earth's history are typically based on geological information.

From Yellowstone National Park
BURIED ALIVE

Excelsior Geyser's rugged crater was created by rare massive geyser eruptions. Surprisingly, it also preserves a record of early life.

For thousands of years, microbes have grown in the runoff channels extending from nearby Grand Prismatic Spring. These vast communities were buried alive as the flowing hot water deposited a crust of silica minerals. The resulting deposit, called sinter, preserves the shape of the microbial mat it entombed. As new mats grew, more layers developed. Today's formation is the result of this interplay between its living and nonliving components.

Yellowstone's hydrothermal features provide a glimpse into the distant past, when intense volcanism was widespread on the young Earth. The life forms found here help scientists understand the types of life that likely arose and diversified billions of years ago on our planet.

Continued on next page ▶

21st Century Themes — Science Literacy

1. What is an unconformity?

   An unconformity is a disturbed sequence of rock layers.

   _____

   _____

2. Using the information on the sign, infer how the crusts of silica minerals at Excelsior Geyser formed.

   SAMPLE ANSWER: *Silica in the rock around the underground source of the geyser's water became dissolved in the water. The geyser spewed the water on the surface. As the water cooled and evaporated, the dissolved silica precipitated out of the water and formed a layer of silica.*

3. Why do the rocks around Excelsior Geyser give scientists information about the history of life on Earth?

   Over time, many mats of microbial life were buried alive by deposited minerals. They then became fossilized. This created a record of the microbial life that has existed at the geyser over a long period of time.

4. Suppose a massive volcanic eruption occurred millions of years ago near Excelsior Geyser. What sort of evidence of this eruption would you expect to find?

   SAMPLE ANSWER: *a thick layer of ash and igneous rocks that have very small crystals between the layers of microbial mats and silica crusts*

5. After studying these signs, what else would you have liked to learn about Excelsior Geyser and Grand Prismatic Springs?

   SAMPLE ANSWER: *I would like to have learned more about where the water in the geyser and springs comes from, how long the geyser has been erupting, and what type of microbes are found in the runoff channels.*

21st Century Skills — Geology of Your Region

The skills used in this activity include **information and media literacy, communication skills, critical thinking and systems thinking, creativity and intellectual curiosity, interpersonal and collaborative skills,** and **accountability and adaptability.**

Working in small groups, research the geological history of your town or region. Choose one geological site that particularly interests you and research it. Your research should include geological information found in the library, on the Internet, and from other sources. List the geological conditions at the site and note any interesting or unique features it has and how they formed.

Design a sign that would educate visitors to the site about its geology. Include text, photographs, and a map on your sign.

   Evaluate students' signs based on the uniqueness of the site chosen, the thoroughness and correctness with which its geology is described, and the clarity and completeness of the text, pictures, and map students include in their sign.

20 Viruses and Prokaryotes

 Big idea **Cellular Basis of Life**

Q: Are all microbes that make us sick made of living cells?

WHAT I KNOW	WHAT I LEARNED
20.1 What is a virus?	*SAMPLE ANSWER:* **A virus is a tiny particle that can make people sick.**	*SAMPLE ANSWER:* **A virus is a nonliving particle made of proteins, nucleic acids, and sometimes lipids. Viruses can reproduce only by infecting a host's living cells.**
20.2 What are prokaryotes and why are they important?	*SAMPLE ANSWER:* **Prokaryotes are often referred to as bacteria, and some of them cause diseases.**	*SAMPLE ANSWER:* **Prokaryotes are unicellular organisms that lack a nucleus. Prokaryotes are essential in maintaining every aspect of the ecological balance of the living world. In addition, some species have specific uses in human industry.**
20.3 How can we prevent bacterial and viral diseases from spreading?	*SAMPLE ANSWER:* **Good hygiene helps prevent the spread of bacterial and viral diseases.**	*SAMPLE ANSWER:* **Many bacterial and viral diseases can be prevented by stimulating the body's immune system with vaccines, fighting infections with antibiotics, and maintaining clean and healthy habits.**

20.1 Viruses

Lesson Objectives

Explain how viruses reproduce.

Explain how viruses cause infection.

Lesson Summary

The Discovery of Viruses In 1935, the American biochemist Wendell Stanley isolated a virus for the first time.

▶ A **virus** is a particle made of nucleic acid, protein, and, in some cases, lipids.

▶ A typical virus is composed of a core of DNA or RNA surrounded by a protein coat called a **capsid**.

▶ Viruses that infect bacteria are called **bacteriophages**. They enter living cells and, once inside, use the machinery of the infected cell to produce more viruses.

Viral Infections Viruses have two methods of infection once inside a host cell.

▶ In a **lytic infection**, a virus enters a cell, makes copies of itself, and causes the cell to burst, releasing new virus particles that can attack other cells. In the case of bacteriophage *T4*, viral DNA directs the synthesis of new viruses using materials in the cell.

▶ In a **lysogenic infection**, a virus integrates part of its DNA called a **prophage** into the DNA of the host cell. The viral genetic information replicates along with the host cell's DNA. Eventually, the prophage will remove itself from the host cell DNA and make new virus particles.

In a **retrovirus**, the genetic information is copied backward—from RNA to DNA instead of from DNA to RNA. The virus that causes the disease AIDS is a retrovirus.

Viruses must infect a living cell in order to reproduce. Although viruses are parasites, they are not made of cells and are not considered living things.

The Discovery of Viruses

1. What is a bacteriophage?
   a virus that attacks bacteria

2. What are viruses?
   They are particles of nucleic acid, protein, and in some cases lipids that can
   reproduce only by infecting living cells.

3. What is a capsid?
   a virus's protein coat

4. How does a typical virus get inside a cell?
   The capsid proteins "trick" the cell by binding to receptors on its surface.

5. What occurs when viruses get inside cells?
   Once inside, the viral genes are expressed. This may lead to the cell's destruction.

Viral Infections

6. **VISUAL ANALOGY** In the visual analogy, why is the outlaw locking up the sheriff, instead of the other way around?

The outlaw is locking up the sheriff because, like a

virus, the outlaw has come in and taken over. The

sheriff is basically hostage to the outlaw—as is a cell's

DNA once a virus has entered a cell.

7. **THINK VISUALLY** The diagram below shows the lytic cycle of a viral infection. Label the bacterial DNA, host bacterium, viral DNA, and virus. Then, circle the step that shows lysis of the host cell.

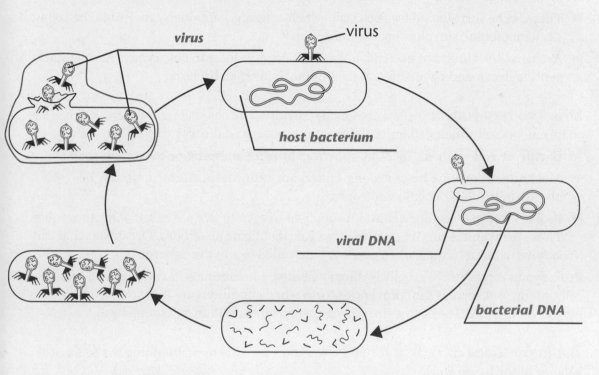

virus

virus

host bacterium

viral DNA

bacterial DNA

8. In a lysogenic infection, how can one virus infect many cells?

The viral DNA is inserted into the host cell's DNA. It remains there and is copied

each time the cell multiplies.

9. How is the common cold like the HIV virus?

They are both RNA viruses.

Apply the Big idea

10. What would happen to a virus that never came in contact with a living cell? Explain your answer.

The virus would never reproduce. Viruses do not have the structures necessary to

metabolize, grow, repair damages, or reproduce without a host.

20.2 Prokaryotes

Lesson Objectives

🔑 Explain how the two groups of prokaryotes differ.

🔑 Describe how prokaryotes vary in structure and function.

🔑 Explain the role of bacteria in the living world.

Lesson Summary

Classifying Prokaryotes The smallest and most common microorganisms are **prokaryotes**, which are unicellular organisms that lack a nucleus. Prokaryotes are classified either in domain Bacteria or domain Archaea.

▶ They can be surrounded by a cell wall, which contains peptidoglycan. Inside the cell wall is a cell membrane surrounding the cytoplasm.

▶ Archaea look similar to bacteria, but are genetically closer to eukaryotes. Archaea lack peptidoglycan and have different membrane lipids than bacteria.

Structure and Function Prokaryotes are identified by characteristics such as shape, the chemical nature of their cell walls, the way they move, and the way they obtain energy.

▶ **Bacilli** are rod-shaped. **Cocci** are spherical. **Spirilla** are spiral or corkscrew-shaped.

▶ Most prokaryotes are heterotrophs. Others are autotrophs. Autotrophs may be photoautotroph, or chemoautotrophs.

▶ Prokaryotes that require a constant supply of oxygen to live are called obligate aerobes. Those that cannot survive in oxygen are called obligate anaerobes. Organisms that can survive without oxygen when necessary are called facultative anaerobes.

Prokaryotes reproduce asexually by **binary fission**, which results in two identical "daughter" cells. Many prokaryotes can form **endospores** when conditions are unfavorable in order to protect their DNA. They can also exchange genetic information by **conjugation**.

The Importance of Prokaryotes Prokaryotes are vital to maintaining the ecological balance of the living world.

▶ Some are decomposers that break down dead matter.

▶ Others are producers that carry out photosynthesis.

▶ Some soil bacteria convert natural nitrogen gas into a form plants can use through a process called nitrogen fixation.

▶ Humans use bacteria in industry, food production, and other ways.

Classifying Prokaryotes

For Questions 1–5, complete each statement by writing the correct word or words.

1. Unicellular organisms that lack a nucleus are called ___prokaryotes___ .

2. The two different domains of prokaryotes are ___Bacteria___ and ___Archaea___ .

3. A cell wall made of ___peptidoglycan___ protects some bacteria from damage.

4. Archaea are more closely related to ___*eukaryotes*___ than ___*bacteria*___ .

5. Some bacteria have a second ___*membrane*___ outside the cell wall.

6. `THINK VISUALLY` Use the box to draw and label a diagram of a typical bacterium.

Students' diagrams should resemble the diagram of a bacterium in the textbook.

Structure and Function

Write the letter of the correct answer on the line at the left.

___B___ **7.** What are rod-shaped bacteria called?

    A. cocci   **C.** spirilla

    B. bacilli   **D.** endospores

___A___ **8.** What are spherical bacteria called?

    A. cocci   **C.** spirilla

    B. bacilli   **D.** endospores

___C___ **9.** Whiplike structures on a bacterium that produce movement are called

    A. pilli.   **C.** flagella.

    B. capsids.   **D.** endospores.

10. Complete the table about the different ways prokaryotes obtain energy.

Energy Capture by Prokaryotes	
Group	**Description**
Photoautotroph	Organism that carries out photosynthesis in a manner similar to that of plants
Chemoautotroph	*Organism that obtains energy directly from chemical reactions*
Heterotroph	Organism that takes in organic molecules and then breaks them down
Photoheterotroph	*Organism that uses light energy in addition to processing organic molecules*

11. What occurs in the process of binary fission?

It is a type of asexual reproduction in which a prokaryote grows to nearly double its

size, replicates its DNA, and divides in half, producing two identical "daughter" cells.

12. What occurs during conjugation?

A hollow bridge forms between two bacterial cells, and genes move from one cell to

the other.

The Importance of Prokaryotes

13. How do decomposers help the ecosystem recycle nutrients when a tree dies?

They feed on and digest the dead tissue, breaking it down into its raw materials,

which are released back into the environment.

14. What would happen to plants and animals if decomposers did not recycle nutrients?

Plants would drain the soil of minerals and die, and animals that depend on plants

for food would starve.

15. Why do all organisms need nitrogen?

They need nitrogen to make proteins and other molecules.

16. Why is the process of nitrogen fixation important?

Nitrogen fixation by bacteria converts nitrogen into a form that can be used by

plants or that can be attached to amino acids that all organisms use.

17. What kind of relationship do many plants have with nitrogen-fixing bacteria?

They have a symbiotic relationship.

18. Describe three different ways that humans use bacteria.

Humans use bacteria to produce foods, such as yogurt; to synthesize drugs and

chemicals; and to clean up waste.

Apply the Big idea

19. Suppose you were studying an infectious unicellular organism with a cell wall under a microscope. How could you confirm that the organism was a prokaryote? How could scientists determine whether it should be classified in domain Bacteria or domain Archaea?

If the organism were a prokaryote, it would not have a nucleus. Its DNA would be in

its cytoplasm. If the organism were a member of the domain Bacteria, its cell wall

would have peptidoglycan.

20.3 Diseases Caused by Bacteria and Viruses

Lesson Objectives

🔑 Explain how bacteria cause disease.

🔑 Explain how viruses cause disease.

🔑 Define emerging disease and explain why emerging diseases are a threat to human health.

Lesson Summary

Bacterial Diseases Microorganisms that cause diseases are known as **pathogens**. Bacterial pathogens can produce many diseases that affect humans and other animals. They do so in one of two general ways:

▶ They destroy living cells and tissues directly or by causing an immune response that destroys tissue.

▶ They damage the cells and tissues of the infected organism directly by breaking down the cells for food.

▶ They release toxins (poisons) that travel throughout the body, interfering with the normal activity of the host.

Many bacterial pathogens can be controlled by washing, using disinfectants, preparing and storing food safely, or sterilizing exposed items. Bacterial diseases can be prevented and treated through the following methods:

▶ A **vaccine** is a preparation of weakened or killed pathogens or inactivated toxins. A vaccine can prompt the body to produce immunity to the disease. Immunity is the body's natural way of killing pathogens.

▶ When a bacterial infection does occur, **antibiotics** can be used to fight the disease. Antibiotics are compounds that block the growth and reproduction of bacteria.

Viral Diseases Viruses produce disease by directly destroying living cells or by affecting cellular processes in ways that disrupt homeostasis. In many viral infections, viruses attack and destroy certain body cells, causing the symptoms of the disease. Viral diseases in humans include the common cold, influenza, AIDS, chicken pox, and measles. Viruses produce other serious diseases in other animals and in plants. Protection against viruses, either by hygiene or vaccination, is the best way to avoid viral illness. A handful of antiviral drugs have been developed that help reduce the symptoms of specific viruses.

Emerging Diseases An unknown disease that appears in a population for the first time or a well-known disease that suddenly becomes harder to control is called an **emerging disease**. The increase of worldwide travel and food shipments is one reason new diseases are spreading. Another is virus and bacteria evolution. Scientists are struggling to keep up with changes. They recently discovered **prions**, which are disease-causing forms of proteins. Prions cause disease in animals, including humans.

Bacterial Diseases

For Questions 1–5, complete each statement by writing the correct word or words.

1. One way bacteria can cause disease is by breaking down and damaging _cells (or tissues)_ of the infected organism.

2. Bacteria can also cause disease by releasing _toxins_ that harm the body.

3. A(n) _pathogen_ is a disease-causing agent.

4. One way to control bacterial growth is by subjecting the bacteria to high temperatures during a process known as _sterilization_ .

5. A(n) _vaccine_ is a preparation of weakened or killed pathogens or inactivated toxins that can prompt the body to produce immunity to a disease.

6. What organs do the bacteria that cause tuberculosis typically damage?
   the lungs

7. What are antibiotics?
   They are compounds that block the growth and reproduction of bacteria.

8. How are the causes of tuberculosis and diphtheria similar? How are they different?
   Both are caused by bacteria. However, the bacteria that cause tuberculosis break down tissue, whereas the bacteria that cause diphtheria release toxins.

9. Describe the similarities and differences of antibiotics and disinfectants.
   Both kill bacteria. Antibiotics are compounds that kill bacteria in an organism.
   Disinfectants are chemical solutions that kill bacteria on surfaces.

10. Why should meat be cooked until it is well-done?
    Cooking meats until they are well done raises the temperature of the meat to a point at which bacteria are killed.

Match the bacterial control method with an example of the method.

Bacterial Control Method		Example
_D_	11. physical removal	A. Putting milk in a refrigerator
_B_	12. disinfectant	B. Using bleach to clean a countertop
_A_	13. safe food storage	C. Using boiling water to clean dishes
_E_	14. safe food processing	D. Washing hands
_C_	15. sterilization by heat	E. Boiling soup

Viral Diseases

16. What are some human diseases caused by viruses?

SAMPLE ANSWER: **AIDS, influenza, and the common cold**

17. How do antiviral medications work? Why don't they also kill host cells?

They attack specific viral enzymes. Hosts do not have these enzymes.

Write the letter of the correct answer on the line at the left.

___B___ **18.** A person has a low helper-T cell count. What viral disease does he or she most likely have?

    A. HPV   **C.** hepatitis B

    B. AIDS   **D.** chicken pox

___D___ **19.** A person has blister-like lesions on the skin. What viral disease does he or she most likely have?

    A. HPV   **C.** hepatitis B

    B. AIDS   **D.** chicken pox

Emerging Diseases

For Questions 20–24, write True if the statement is true. If the statement is false, change the underlined word or words to make the statement true.

___True___ **20.** Pathogens are able to <u>evolve</u> over time.

___emerging___ **21.** A(n) <u>noninfectious</u> disease is an unknown disease that appears in a population for the first time.

___antibiotics___ **22.** The widespread use of <u>vaccines</u> has led to the emergence of resistant strains of bacteria.

___True___ **23.** Slight genetic changes would be needed for the bird flu virus to become infectious to <u>humans</u>.

___prions___ **24.** Scrapie is most likely caused by pathogens known as <u>viroids</u>.

Apply the Big idea

25. RNA viruses have shown an ability to evade antiviral drugs. How do you suppose this is possible, when viruses are not alive? How may the reproductive methods of viruses help the process?

SAMPLE ANSWER: **Viruses reproduce quickly, so their genetic makeup can also change**

quickly. The DNA of RNA viruses must be translated by the host cell. This allows the

opportunity for mutations to occur. Also, many RNA viruses are made inside one cell

before bursting forth. They may exchange genetic information at that time. This

genetic variation allows them to evolve.

Chapter Vocabulary Review

1. The picture shows three different bacteria shapes. Label each shape.

__*bacillus*__ __*spirillum*__ __*coccus*__

Match the term with its definition.

Term

___F___ **2.** lysogenic infection
___B___ **3.** prion
___K___ **4.** bacteriophage
___A___ **5.** antibiotic
___E___ **6.** virus
___J___ **7.** prokaryote
___C___ **8.** prophage
___G___ **9.** pathogen
___I___ **10.** lytic infection
___D___ **11.** endospore
___L___ **12.** binary fission
___H___ **13.** vaccine

Definition

A. Compound that can block the growth and reproduction of bacteria

B. Misfolded protein that causes disease in animals

C. Bacteriophage DNA that is embedded in the host's DNA

D. Protective structure formed by a prokaryote when growth conditions are unfavorable

E. A particle made of nucleic acid, protein, and in some cases, lipids that can replicate only by infecting living cells

F. Process in which viral DNA becomes part of a host cell's DNA

G. Disease-causing microorganism

H. Preparation of weakened or killed pathogens or inactivated toxins used to produce immunity

I. Process in which a host cell bursts after being invaded by a virus

J. Organism consisting of one cell that lacks a nucleus

K. Virus that infects bacteria

L. Process in which a bacterium replicates its DNA and divides in half

Complete each statement by writing the correct word or words.

14. A protein coat surrounding a virus is a(n) ___*capsid*___.

15. Viruses that have RNA as their genetic material are called ___*retroviruses*___.

16. Some bacteria exchange genetic material through the process of ___*conjugation*___.

17. SARS, MRSA, Ebola, and bird flu are all examples of ___*emerging diseases*___.

CHAPTER MYSTERY
THE MAD COWS

The Chapter Mystery investigated the 1986 outbreak of "mad cow" disease (also known as bovine spongiform encephalopathy, or BSE) in the United Kingdom. Subsequent outbreaks occurred around the world, and controversy about how to deal with the disease continues today.

21st Century Learning

Assuring the Safety of the Beef Supply

The Kansas-based beef producer Creekstone Farms Premium Beef, Inc. filed a lawsuit against the United States Department of Agriculture (USDA) over BSE testing. Creekstone Farms claims that its export sales plummeted after a cow infected with BSE was found in the United States in 2003. To combat its losses, Creekstone sought to conduct its own BSE testing on every cow it slaughtered to assure consumers, and especially foreign buyers, of the beef's safety. Creekstone argued that this would be an improvement over the USDA's testing procedures because the USDA only tests approximately 1 percent of all U.S. beef.

However, the USDA argues that the regulation of U.S. beef falls solely under its jurisdiction and that it cannot allow a private company to conduct its own testing because the agency cannot oversee the testing to insure its reliability. Furthermore, a beef producer would have a conflict of interest in reporting accurate results of any BSE tests it conducts.

As it currently stands, the appeals court sided with the USDA, preventing Creekstone from conducting its own BSE tests on its meat. Read the document below, which is adapted and excerpted from the appeals court verdict:

United States Court of Appeals

No. 07-5173
Creekstone Farms Premium Beef, L.L.C.
v.
Department of Agriculture

Bovine Spongiform Encephalopathy, or BSE, was first diagnosed in the United Kingdom in 1986. Since then, more than 189,000 confirmed cases of BSE in cattle worldwide have been reported. While almost all of the cases (95 percent) have occurred in the United Kingdom, BSE has been found in cattle raised in at least 25 other countries as well. Despite prevention efforts by the U.S. government, three BSE-infected cows have been found in the United States. The first was reported in December 2003 in Washington State. Two more BSE-infected cattle were found—one in Texas in June 2005 and one in Alabama in March 2006.

Following the discovery of the first BSE-infected cow in Washington State, several major beef importing countries, including Japan, South Korea and Mexico, (at the time, three of the four largest importers), banned the importation of U.S. beef. Creekstone claims to have suffered $200,000 per day in lost revenue as a result of the diminished export market.

To allay the concerns of consumers and importers, in 2004 Creekstone made a "business decision" to perform a rapid BSE test on each cow it slaughtered. Creekstone sought to purchase rapid BSE test kits from Bio-Rad Laboratories, Inc. Bio-Rad informed Creekstone, however, that it could not sell Creekstone the kits without USDA authorization. On February 19, 2004, Creekstone requested USDA permission to purchase the test kits. USDA denied Creekstone's requests. Creekstone challenged the USDA's action in court.

Continued on next page ▶

21st Century Themes Science and Civic Literacy; Science and Health Literacy

1. Where and when was BSE first diagnosed?

BSE was first diagnosed in the United Kingdom in 1986.

2. How many BSE-infected cows have been found to date in the United States? When and where did the incidents occur?

To date there have been three cases of BSE-infected cows in the United States:

one in Washington State in 2003, one in Texas in 2005, and one in Alabama

in 2006.

3. Which countries stopped importing beef from the United States after the first U.S. incident of a BSE-infected cow in December, 2003?

Japan, South Korea and Mexico banned imports of U.S. beef in the aftermath of the

2003 BSE incident.

4. How much does Creekstone contend it lost in revenue each day from the drop in exports?

Creekstone says it lost $200,000 per day as a result of diminished exports.

5. Infer what the key arguments on each side of the case are. Why does Creekstone think it should be able to conduct its own additional BSE testing? Why does the USDA oppose the idea?

SAMPLE ANSWER: Creekstone wants to conduct its own tests to assure customers of its

beef's safety, especially the export market. The USDA does not want to set the

precedent of allowing beef producers to regulate themselves.

BSE Testing Debate

21st Century Skills The skills used in this activity include **information and media literacy; communication skills; critical thinking and systems thinking; problem identification, formulation, and solution; and creativity and intellectual curiosity.**

Search the Internet to find the actual U.S. appeals court verdict in the Creekstone case. The verdict is filled with legal terminology, but it also offers a wealth of information about the case. Skim the main decision by Judge Karen Henderson, the concurring opinion by Judge Rogers, and the dissenting opinion by Chief Judge Sentelle. Then look for news articles about the case. The legal details might seem complicated, but the underlying issues in the case are clear. Both sides make strong arguments: Creekstone wants more testing to assure its customers; USDA feels that the safety of the beef supply must be regulated by a government agency because companies should not be trusted to regulate their own products. What do you think? Identify some of the different aspects of the problem raised in this case.

Divide into working groups to debate the issue in class.

Evaluate students' participation in the debate by their inclusion of facts supporting their decision. They should be able to distinguish fact from opinion and supporting arguments from opposing arguments.

21 Protists and Fungi

 Big idea **Interdependence in Nature**

Q: How do protists and fungi affect the homeostasis of other organisms and ecosystems?

WHAT I KNOW	WHAT I LEARNED
21.1 Why are "protists" difficult to classify?	*SAMPLE ANSWER:* **Protists have many different body forms and ways of living.**	*SAMPLE ANSWER:* **Protists display a great degree of diversity. Many protists are far more closely related to members of other eukaryotic kingdoms than they are to other protists.**
21.2 How do protists move and reproduce?	*SAMPLE ANSWER:* **Protists move and reproduce in a similar way to bacteria.**	*SAMPLE ANSWER:* **Some protists move by changing their cell shape. Some move by specialized organelles. Other protists do not move actively. Some protists reproduce asexually by mitosis, and some undergo conjugation. Other protists combine asexual and sexual reproduction.**
21.3 What roles do protists play in the environment?	*SAMPLE ANSWER:* **Protists are at or near the bottom of many food chains.**	*SAMPLE ANSWER:* **Some protists are autotrophs, and others are heterotrophs. Many protists engage in symbiotic relationships.**
21.4 What are fungi, and what roles do they play in the environment?	*SAMPLE ANSWER:* **Fungi include mushrooms and molds. They are decomposers.**	*SAMPLE ANSWER:* **Fungi are heterotrophic eukaryotes with cell walls that contain chitin. Many fungi help ecosystems maintain homeostasis by breaking down dead organisms. Many fungi carry on symbiotic relationships with other organisms.**

21.1 Protist Classification—The Saga Continues

Lesson Objectives

🔑 Explain what a "protist" is.

🔑 Describe how protists are related to other eukaryotes.

Lesson Summary

The First Eukaryotes Protists are eukaryotes that are not members of the plant, animal, or fungi kingdoms. The first eukaryotes were protists.

▶ Most protists are unicellular.

▶ Protists are a very diverse group of species.

▶ Many species of protists are more closely related to plants, fungi, or animals than they are to other protists. Because of this, some scientists think the members of the kingdom Protista should be reclassified.

Protists—Ancestors and Descendants All eukaryotes are descended from early protists, but modern protists are very different from their ancestors. Like other eukaryotes, they have been evolving over the last 2.5 billion years.

The First Eukaryotes

1. What is a protist?

   It is any organism that is not a plant, an animal, a fungus, or a prokaryote.

   _____

2. Why are brown algae considered protists even though they are multicellular?

   They are more closely related to some unicellular protists than any other kingdom.

   _____

3. Why do scientists no longer use the categories of animal-like, plantlike, and funguslike protists to classify protists?

   These categories do not reflect the evolutionary history of protists.

For Questions 4–7, complete each statement by writing the correct word or words.

4. Most single-celled eukaryotes are currently classified as _____*protists*_____.

5. Genetic analyses of protists indicate that they belong in six different _____*clades*_____.

6. Protists were the first _____*eukaryotes*_____.

7. Unlike most protists, which are unicellular, kelp has _____*differentiated*_____ tissues.

For Questions 8–11, use the diagram and legend below.

Six Major Groups

 Excavates

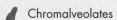 Chromalveolates

Cercozoa, Foraminifera, and Radiolaria

Rhodophyta (red algae)

Amoebozoa

Choanozoa

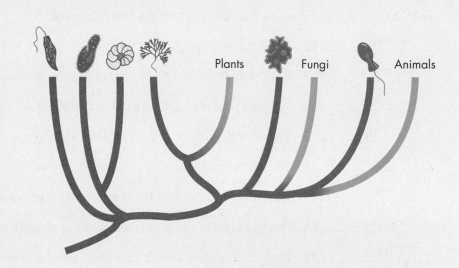

Plants   Fungi   Animals

_C_ **8.** Plants are most closely related to which of the following groups?

  A. Amoebozoa

  B. Cercozoa

  C. Rhodophyta

  D. Choanozoa

_D_ **9.** Brown algae is a member of the clade Chromalveolates. Which of the following is its closest relative?

  A. slime mold, an Amoebozoan   **C.** *Giardia*, an Excavate

  B. red algae, a Rhodophytan   **D.** *Globigerina*, a Foraminiferan

_A_ **10.** Which clade is most primitive?

  A. Excavates

  B. Choanozoa

  C. Cercozoa

  D. Chromalveolates

_A_ **11.** Which statement is true?

  A. Plants, fungi, and animals all emerged from a common protist ancestor.

  B. Only fungi and animals emerged from a common protist ancestor.

  C. Only animals and plants emerged from a common protist ancestor.

  D. Plants, fungi, and animals all emerged from different protist ancestors.

Protists—Ancestors and Descendants

For Questions 12–19, write True or False on the line provided.

___False___ **12.** The first eukaryotes were Archaea.

___False___ **13.** It is possible to find the earliest fungi by looking at modern protists.

___False___ **14.** Modern protists have evolved very little from their ancestral forms.

___True___ **15.** Today, there are as many as 300,000 known species of protists.

___True___ **16.** The oldest known eukaryotic fossils are around 1.5 billion years old.

___False___ **17.** The first protists most likely evolved 3.6 billion years ago.

___True___ **18.** Plants, animals, and fungi most likely evolved from multicellular protists.

___True___ **19.** The protists are more diverse than any other eukaryotic kingdom.

20. Complete the concept map below.

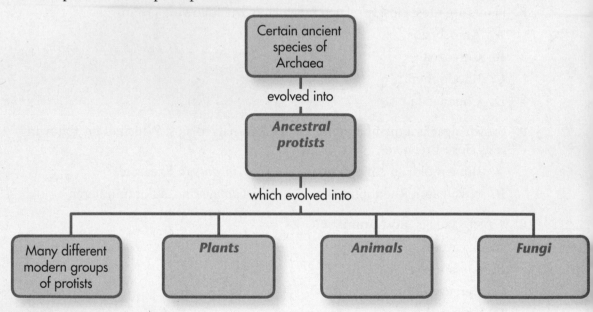

Apply the Big idea

21. *Euglena* are photosynthetic protists that live in fresh water. How would their photosynthetic properties help stabilize a pond ecosystem? Suppose they and all the other photosynthetic organisms disappeared from the pond. How might their disappearance affect other organisms that lived in the pond?

SAMPLE ANSWER: **The photosynthetic properties of Euglena would help stabilize the ecosystem because they would utilize the carbon dioxide excreted by some organisms and provide oxygen for use by the same organisms. If Euglena and all the other photosynthetic organisms disappeared from the pond, all the other organisms would eventually die, since the bases of all of the food chains would be gone.**

21.2 Protist Structure and Function

Lesson Objectives

☑ Describe the various methods of protist locomotion.

☑ Describe how protists reproduce.

Lesson Summary

How Protists Move Protists move in a wide variety of ways.

► Some protists move by extending temporary projections of cytoplasm known as **pseudopods**. These protists, such as amoebas, also use pseudopods for getting prey.

► Some protists swim using **cilia**, numerous short hairlike projections. Others swim using **flagella**, which are similar to cilia, but are longer and fewer in number.

► Some protists do not move on their own. They depend on wind, water, or another organism to move them. They reproduce by means of **spores**.

Protist Reproduction Protists reproduce in a wide variety of ways.

► Some protists reproduce asexually by mitosis.

► Some protists can undergo **conjugation**—a sexual process in which two organisms exchange genetic material. Conjugation helps produce genetic diversity.

► The life cycles of many protists include switching between a diploid and a haploid generation, a cycle called **alternation of generations**.

► Some protist species reproduce asexually by producing spores in a structure called a **sporangium**.

How Protists Move

1. What are pseudopods? How do protists use them? *They are temporary projections of cytoplasm used for feeding and movement.*

2. How do amoebas capture and ingest food? *They use their pseudopods to surround a food particle or cell and take it inside themselves, ingesting it.*

3. What are cilia? How are they used by protists? *They are short hairlike projections used for movement.*

4. **THINK VISUALLY** In the three boxes below, draw pictures of three organisms—one with a pseudopod, one with a flagellum, and one with cilia.

Students' drawings should resemble the amoeba shown in the textbook.	*Students' drawings should resemble the flagellate shown in the textbook.*	*Students' drawings should resemble the ciliate shown in the textbook.*
Pseudopod	**Flagellum**	**Cilia**

5. **VISUAL ANALOGY** The visual analogy compares structures used by cells for movement to boat oars. Explain why a series of oars is compared to cilia, and why only one oar is used to represent flagella.

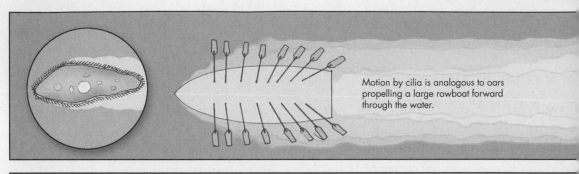

Motion by cilia is analogous to oars propelling a large rowboat forward through the water.

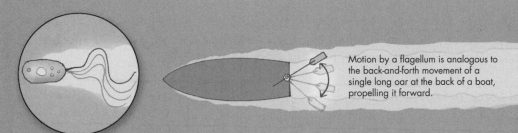

Motion by a flagellum is analogous to the back-and-forth movement of a single long oar at the back of a boat, propelling it forward.

Flagella and cilia are used to move through liquids, such as water. Cilia move rather like oars on a boat, and they are numerous on a protist. Protists with flagella usually only have one or two.

Protist Reproduction

6. How do amoebas reproduce?

They reproduce asexually by means of mitosis.

7. What is conjugation?

It is a process that allows ciliates to exchange genetic information with other individuals.

8. Within a large population, how does conjugation benefit protists?

The process helps to create and maintain genetic diversity.

9. What occurs in the process known as alternation of generations?

Alternation of generations is a means of sexual reproduction in which the reproductive cycle switches back and forth between haploid and diploid stages during an organism's life cycle.

0. Complete the flowchart to show the process of conjugation between two paramecia.

Conjugation begins when two paramecia attach to each other.

↓

Meiosis of their diploid micronuclei produces four haploid micronuclei.

↓

In each cell, three of the micronuclei disintegrate.

↓

The remaining micronucleus in each cell divides by mitosis.

↓

The two cells exchange one haploid micronucleus from each pair.

↓

In each cell, the micronuclei fuse to form a single diploid micronucleus, and the macronuclei disintegrate.

↓

Each cell forms a new macronucleus from its micronucleus.

Apply the Big idea

1. *Plasmodium* is the protist that causes malaria in humans. It is carried by mosquitoes, which transmit the parasite when they bite humans. In the human body, Plasmodia cause red blood cells to break and release spores in the evening. The spores can then travel through the bloodstream. How would this mechanism help spread the parasite throughout an ecosystem? What methods might help prevent its spread?

SAMPLE ANSWER: *Mosquitoes bite in the evening. By releasing spores at that time, the parasite increases its chances of being ingested by the mosquito and carried to another host. Preventative methods may include staying inside in the evening, wearing bug spray or clothes with total coverage, sleeping under nets, and keeping windows and doors screened.*

_____

_____

_____

21.3 The Ecology of Protists

Lesson Objectives

- Describe the ecological significance of photosynthetic protists.
- Describe how heterotrophic protists obtain food.
- Identify the symbiotic relationships that involve protists.

Lesson Summary

Autotrophic Protists Protists that perform photosynthesis are autotrophic. The position of photosynthetic protists at the base of the food chain makes much of the diversity of aquatic life possible.

▶ They feed fish and whales, support coral reefs, and provide shelter to marine life.

▶ In areas where sewage is dumped, protists help recycle the waste. However, when the amount of waste is excessive, algae grow into enormous masses called **algal blooms**.

Heterotrophic Protists Some heterotrophic protists engulf and digest their food, while others live by absorbing molecules from the environment.

▶ Amoebas capture and digest their food, surrounding a cell or particle and then taking it inside themselves to form a food vacuole. A **food vacuole** is a small cavity in the cytoplasm that temporarily stores food.

▶ *Paramecia* and other ciliates use their cilia to sweep food particles into the **gullet**, an indentation in one side of the organism.

▶ Slime molds and water molds are important recyclers of organic material. At one stage of their life cycle, some slime molds fuse to form large cells with many nuclei. These structures are known as **plasmodia**. Sporangia develop from a plasmodium.

Symbiotic Protists—Mutualists and Parasites Some protists have symbiotic relationships with other organisms. *Trichonympha* has a mutualistic relationship with termites. It lives within their digestive system and helps them digest wood. Other protists are parasitic and cause disease. The protist *Trypanosoma* causes African sleeping sickness. The protist *Plasmodium* causes malaria.

Autotrophic Protists

1. How do autotrophic protists make the diversity of aquatic life possible?

They are at the base of the food chain.

2. What are phytoplankton?

Phytoplankton are small photosynthetic organisms found near the surface of the ocean; many are autotrophic protists.

3. How do protists help maintain equilibrium in coral reef ecosystems?

The protists called red algae support coral reefs by providing much needed nutrients for coral animals. Red algae also produces minerals corals need to form reefs.

4. How can algal blooms be harmful?

A bloom can quickly deplete the water of nutrients. The decomposition of the dead

algae can rob the water of its oxygen, choking resident fish and invertebrate life.

_____

Heterotrophic Protists

5. What is the function of a food vacuole?

It temporarily stores food until it can be digested.

6. Label the illustration of a paramecium.

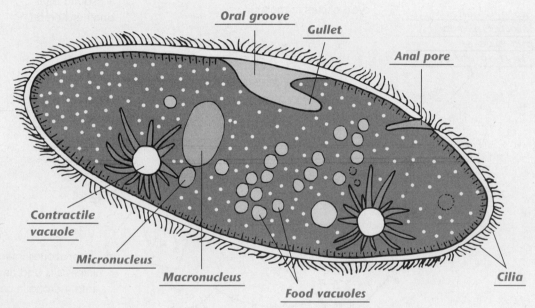

Oral groove

Gullet

Anal pore

Contractile
vacuole

Micronucleus

Macronucleus

Food vacuoles

Cilia

7. What are slime molds?

They are heterotrophic protists that thrive on decaying organic matter.

8. By what process are haploid spores made by a water mold? Where does the process occur?

Spores are made by meiosis inside the sporangium.

9. What structure does a plasmodium eventually develop into and what is the function of that structure?

A plasmodium eventually changes into sporangia, which produce haploid spores.

For Questions 10–13, write True if the statement is true. If the statement is false, change the underlined word or words to make the statement true.

___*food*___ **10.** In amoebas, indigestible materials remain inside <u>contractile</u> vacuoles.

___*feeding*___ **11.** A gullet is a structure used by a paramecium for <u>reproduction</u>.

___*True*___ **12.** In a slime mold's life cycle, germinating spores release <u>amoeba-like</u> cells.

___*True*___ **13.** <u>Water molds</u> grow on dead or decaying plants and animals.

Symbiotic Protists—Mutualists and Parasites

14. How does the protist *Trichonympha* make it possible for termites to eat wood?
<u>*Termites do not have enzymes to break down the cellulose in wood.*</u>

<u>*The protists in a termite's gut manufacture the enzyme cellulase, which breaks*</u>

<u>*the chemical bonds in cellulose. With the help of their protist partners, then, the*</u>

<u>*termites can digest wood.*</u>

15. What causes malaria? _____ **Plasmodium** _____

16. Complete the flowchart showing the cycle of malarial infection.

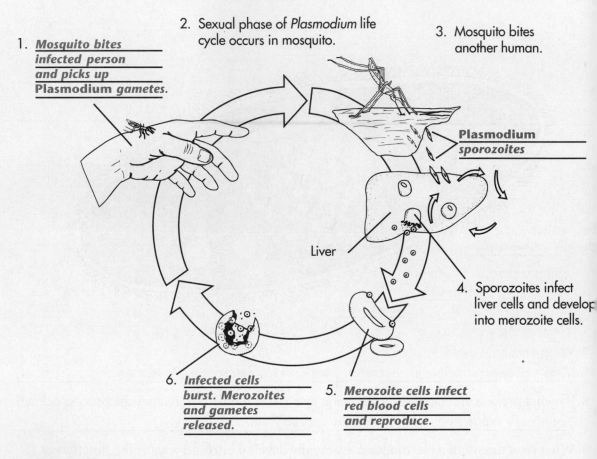

1. <u>*Mosquito bites infected person and picks up Plasmodium gametes.*</u>

2. Sexual phase of *Plasmodium* life cycle occurs in mosquito.

3. Mosquito bites another human.

<u>**Plasmodium sporozoites**</u>

Liver

4. Sporozoites infect liver cells and develop into merozoite cells.

5. <u>*Merozoite cells infect red blood cells and reproduce.*</u>

6. <u>*Infected cells burst. Merozoites and gametes released.*</u>

Apply the Big idea

17. Slime molds are heterotrophic protists that thrive on decaying matter. How would they help maintain homeostasis within their ecosystems? How do they benefit an ecosystem? Why is their role so important?

SAMPLE ANSWER: <u>*They would help decompose decaying plant and animal matter.*</u>

<u>*They therefore help recycle nutrients throughout an ecosystem, which benefits any*</u>

<u>*ecosystem. Without them, there would be fewer nutrients being recycled, and the*</u>

<u>*ecosystem would be smothered by decaying matter.*</u>

21.4 Fungi

Lesson Objectives

Identify the defining characteristics of fungi.

Describe how fungi affect homeostasis.

Lesson Summary

What Are Fungi? Fungi are eukaryotic heterotrophs that have cell walls. The cell walls of fungi contain **chitin**, a complex carbohydrate.

► Most fungi are composed of thin filaments called **hyphae**. The **fruiting body** of a fungus—such as the above-ground part of a mushroom—is a reproductive structure that you can see. It grows from many hyphae tangled underground in a thick mass called a **mycelium**.

► Most fungi reproduce both asexually and sexually. Asexual reproduction can occur when cells or hyphae break off and begin to grow on their own. Some fungi also reproduce asexually by means of spores.

► Most fungi can also reproduce sexually. Spores are produced in structures called sporangia. Many fungi have minus (-) and plus (+) types that can reproduce sexually by fusing their nuclei when they meet.

The Ecology of Fungi Fungi do not ingest their food as animals do. Instead, fungi digest food outside their bodies and then absorb it. Many fungi feed by absorbing nutrients from decaying matter. Some fungi are parasites.

► Fungi help maintain equilibrium in nearly every ecosystem by recycling nutrients by breaking down the bodies and wastes of other organisms.

► Parasitic fungi cause serious plant and animal diseases. Fungal diseases in humans include athlete's foot, thrush, and yeast infections of the female reproductive tract.

► Some fungi form mutualistic relationships in which both partners benefit.

► **Lichens** are symbiotic associations between a fungus and a photosynthetic organism. The photosynthetic organism provides a source of energy. The fungus provides water and minerals.

► Mutualistic associations of plant roots and fungi are called **mycorrhizae**. The plant's roots are woven into a partnership with the web of fungal hyphae.

What Are Fungi?

1. Why do scientists think that fungi are more closely related to animals than to plants?
   The cells walls of fungi contain chitin. Similarly, insect exoskeletons contain chitin.

2. Describe two types of hyphae.
   One type has cross walls that divide it into compartments like cells, and the other does not.

3. Label the parts of the fungus.

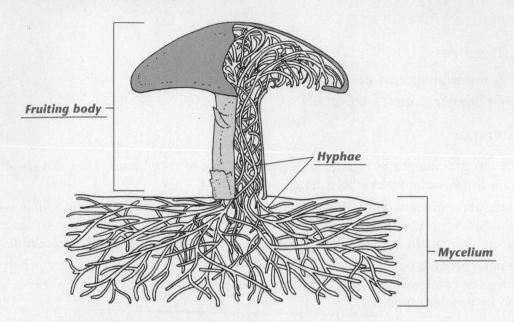

Fruiting body

Hyphae

Mycelium

4. What is the function of a fruiting body?

It is the reproductive structure of the mushroom.

5. What is a fairy ring, and why does it form?

A fairy ring is composed of the fruiting bodies of mushrooms that developed

at the outer edges of a single mycelium. It forms because as time goes by soil

nutrients near the center of the mycelium become depleted and fruting bodies sprout

only at the edges.

6. The diagram below shows the life cycle of *Rhizopus stolonifer* fungi. Shade the arrows that show sexual reproduction. Cross-hatch the arrows that show asexual reproduction.

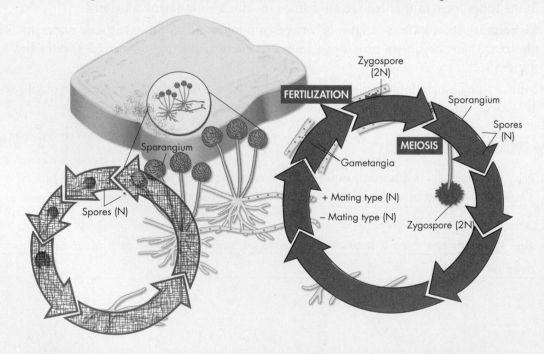

Sporangium

Spores (N)

Zygospore (2N)

FERTILIZATION

Gametangia

+ Mating type (N)

− Mating type (N)

Zygospore (2N)

Sporangium

Spores (N)

MEIOSIS

The Ecology of Fungi

7. How do fungi break down leaves, fruit, and other organic material into simple molecules?

They release digestive enzymes that speed the breakdown of

these materials.

8. How can fungi disrupt the homeostasis of plants?

They can cause diseases, such as corn smut and wheat rust.

9. Lichens and mycorrhizae are both examples of what kind of symbiotic relationship?

mutualism

10. How do plants benefit from mycorrhizae? How do fungi benefit?

The fungi collect water and nutrients and bring them to the plant roots as

well as freeing nutrients in the soil; the plants provide photosynthesis products

to fungi.

11. **THINK VISUALLY** In the diagram of a lichen, label the alga and the fungus. Then, on the lines below, describe what benefits the fungus and alga each derive from their association in the lichen.

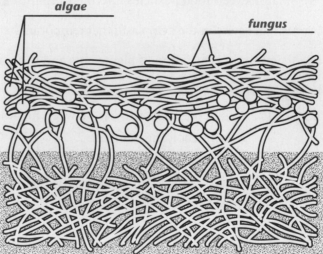

algae

fungus

The photosynthetic organisms provide fungus with a source of energy. The fungus pro-

vides the alga with water, minerals, and protection.

Apply the Big idea

12. A fungus-killing chemical soaks into the ground and is absorbed through the roots of a plant with a fungal disease. How might this help infected plants regain homeostasis? How might it damage the homeostasis of other plants in the area?

SAMPLE ANSWER: *The chemical would kill the fungus that was harming the plants,*

restoring them to homeostasis. It could, however, harm other plants in the area, if

it killed mycorrhizal fungi on their roots.

Chapter Vocabulary Review

Match the term with its definition.

Term   **Definition**

_D_ 1. mycelium   A. Complex carbohydrate that makes up the cell walls of fungi

_B_ 2. lichen   B. An example of a symbiotic association

_C_ 3. sporangium   C. A structure that contains spores

_A_ 4. chitin   D. Mass of tangled fungus hyphae

_E_ 5. algal bloom   E. A rapid growth in algae in a body of water with a great deal

_F_ 6. flagella   of sewage

F. Structures that protists use for motion

Complete each statement by writing the correct word or words.

7. Multicellular fungi are composed of thin filaments called _____hyphae_____.

8. A(n) ____fruiting body____ is a fungal reproductive structure growing from the mycelium.

9. Ciliates sweep food particles into their cell into a _____gullet_____.

10. A small cavity in the cytoplasm that temporarily stores food is a food _____vacuole_____.

11. A symbiotic association of plant roots and fungi is called a(n) _____mycorrhiza_____.

Write the letter of the correct answer on the line at the left.

_D_ 12. A life cycle that switches between haploid and diploid stages is called
    A. amoeboid movement.   C. meiotic binary fission.
    B. conjugation.   D. alternation of generations.

_A_ 13. The single structure with many nuclei that is formed by a mass of amoeba-like slime molds is a(n)
    A. plasmodium.   C. pseudopod.
    B. cilium.   D. sporangium.

_A_ 14. Amoebas move and feed by using their
    A. pseudopods.   C. cilia.
    B. gullets.   D. flagella.

_B_ 15. Some ciliates exchange genetic material through a process called
    A. amoeboid movement.   C. fruiting bodies.
    B. conjugation.   D. alternation of generations.

_A_ 16. A reproductive cell made by some protists is called a
    A. spore.   C. sporangium.
    B. cilium.   D. hypha.

_C_ 17. A paramecium moves by using hairlike projections called
    A. gullets.   C. cilia.
    B. contractile vacuoles.   D. pseudopods.

CHAPTER MYSTERY
"A BLIGHT OF UNUSUAL CHARACTER"
21st Century Learning

In the Chapter Mystery you investigated the water mold *Phytophthora* that led to the Irish potato famine in the 1840s. In recent years, experts have warned that the modern-day banana crop might soon face a similar threat.

A Threat to the World's Banana Crop

Juan Fernando Aguilar is a leading banana breeder at the Honduran Foundation for Agricultural Investigation (FHIA). He believes that the worldwide banana trade is currently highly vulnerable to a blight known as Fusarium wilt, or Panama disease, which is caused by the *Fusarium* fungus. As Aguilar explains, the modern-day banana, a variety known as the Cavendish, is highly susceptible to the disease, which has already destroyed plantations in Southeast Asia and now threatens crops elsewhere.

Read the fact sheet below, compiled from information from banana growers like Aguilar, to learn more about bananas and the threat they face from Fusarium wilt.

Facts About the Banana Trade and the Threat Posed by Fusarium Wilt

▶ The Cavendish banana, nutritious and convenient, is a monoculture. Almost all commercial banana farming relies on the Cavendish.

▶ As many as 100 billion Cavendish bananas are consumed worldwide each year.

▶ The global trade in Cavendish bananas is a $4-billion-per-year business.

▶ Americans eat more bananas than any other kind of fresh fruit. Average consumption in the U.S. equals 26.2 pounds of bananas per year.

▶ Fusarium wilt, once called Panama Disease, is caused by *Fusarium* fungi that invade young roots of the banana plant and cause its leaves to wilt and die.

▶ Some varieties of the fungus have proven resistant to existing fungicides and continue to thrive in surrounding soil, preventing the success of future plantings.

▶ Fusarium wilt wiped out the Gros Michel banana, which once was the most widely consumed banana. The Gros Michel became extinct by 1960.

▶ The Cavendish banana does not appear to be safe from the latest strain of Fusarium wilt which first appeared in 1992 and has spread throughout Southeast Asia. It has not reached the Western Hemisphere yet, but experts predict it will.

▶ Scientists have found no cure for Fusarium wilt.

▶ Fusarium wilt is so virulent that a single clump of dirt carried on a tire or shoe can spark an outbreak.

Continued on next page ▶

21st Century Themes Science and Global Awareness, Science and Economic Literacy

1. How big is the global trade in bananas? What figures illustrate the popularity of bananas and their commercial importance?

   The global trade in bananas accounts for some $4 billion in sales annually, with 100 billion bananas consumed worldwide each year. Americans eat an average of more than 26 pounds of bananas each year, more than any other fresh fruit.

2. What characteristic of the current banana crop makes it particularly vulnerable to a blight?

   Bananas are particularly vulnerable to a blight because they are farmed as a monoculture: the Cavendish variety is virtually the only type commercially grown. The lack of diversity makes bananas particularly susceptible to widespread damage from a single strain of a disease.

3. What is Fusarium wilt? What causes it and how does it affect the banana crop?

   Fusarium wilt, or Panama disease, is caused by the Fusarium fungus, which thrives in the soil and invades the young roots of banana plants, causing the plants' leaves to wilt and die.

4. What characteristics of the current strain of Fusarium wilt make banana growers particularly worried?

   They worry especially because the latest strain infects Cavendish bananas, is resistant to fungicides, and is virulent. It can potentially be spread by a single clump of infected dirt carried on a tire or shoe.

5. Based on the facts presented, how vulnerable do you think the world's banana crop is to a widespread blight? Why or why not?

   Student viewpoints and rationale are encouraged here. Based on the facts presented, however, including the lack of diversity in the banana crop and the virulence of the disease, students should conclude that the banana crop is quite vulnerable.

21st Century Skills Investigate Fusarium Wilt

The skills used in this activity include **problem identification, formulation, and solution; information and media literacy;** and **communication skills**.

Use library and Internet resources to conduct further research about this topic. Try to find out more about the science of Fusarium wilt and expert assessment of the threat posed to the world's banana crops. How does the current situation compare to the Irish potato famine in the 1840s? Based on your research, write a newspaper article on the threat posed to the world trade in bananas and suggest what you think banana growers ought to do about it.

Evaluate students' articles by their choice of appropriate Web sites, inclusion of all the necessary facts, and a clear explanation of Fusarium wilt and the threat it presents to the banana trade. Students should draw apt comparisons with the Irish potato famine. They should also include a well-reasoned opinion of what should be done.

22 Introduction to Plants

Unity and Diversity of Life

Q: What are the five main groups of plants, and how have four of these groups adapted to life on land?

WHAT I KNOW	WHAT I LEARNED
22.1 What are the characteristics of plants?	SAMPLE ANSWER: **Plants are green because of chlorophyll, and they have roots and stems.**	SAMPLE ANSWER: **Plants are eukaryotes with cell walls made of cellulose and that use chlorophyll in photosynthesis. They have adaptations for absorbing sunlight, exchanging gases, and obtaining water and minerals.**
22.2 What are the characteristics of seedless plants?	SAMPLE ANSWER: **Seedless plants are plants that do not make seeds.**	SAMPLE ANSWER: **Seedless plants are the green algae and the mosses and ferns and their relatives. Some have tubes for transporting food and water. They require water to complete their life cycles.**
22.3 What are the characteristics of seed plants?	SAMPLE ANSWER: **Seed plants reproduce with seeds.**	SAMPLE ANSWER: **Seed plants include gymnosperms, which have cones, and angiosperms, which have flowers. Both types have special reproductive structures, such as gametophytes and sporophytes.**
22.4 What are the characteristics of flowering plants?	SAMPLE ANSWER: **Flowering plants have flowers, leaves, and stems.**	SAMPLE ANSWER: **Flowering plants have flowers with ovaries that develop into fruits that surround, protect, and help disperse the seeds. Some have woody stems and some have smooth, nonwoody stems.**

22.1 What Is a Plant?

Lesson Objectives

- Describe what plants need to survive.
- Describe how the first plants evolved.
- Explain the process of alternation of generations.

Lesson Summary

Characteristics of Plants

▶ Plants are eukaryotes that have cell walls containing cellulose. Mostly autotrophs, plants use chlorophyll *a* and *b* to carry out photosynthesis.

▶ Without moving about, plants get what they need from the environment.

- Sunlight: gathered by leaves arranged in ways that maximize absorption
- Gas exchange: brings in oxygen and carbon dioxide and releases excess oxygen
- Water: absorbed mostly from the soil and transported internally
- Minerals: absorbed along with water from the soil

The History and Evolution of Plants Ancestors of today's land plants were water-dwellers similar to today's green algae. Over time, the demands of life on land favored the evolution of plants more resistant to the drying rays of the sun, more capable of conserving water, and more capable of reproducing without water.

▶ The first land plants were dependent on water and lacked leaves and roots.

▶ Five major groups of plants are classified based on four important features:

- embryo formation
- specialized water-conducting tissues
- seeds
- flowers

The Plant Life Cycle The life cycle of land plants has two alternating phases, a diploid (2N) phase and a haploid (N) phase. This shift between haploid and diploid is known as the **alternation of generations**.

▶ **Sporophyte**: the multicellular diploid phase, a spore-producing plant

▶ **Gametophyte**: the multicellular haploid phase, a gamete-producing plant

Characteristics of Plants

For Questions 1–8, write True if the statement is true. If the statement is false, change the underlined word or words to make the statement true.

_____True_____	1.	Both grasses and <u>mosses</u> are examples of plants.
_____plants_____	2.	Green algae are now considered to be <u>protists</u>.
_____A few_____	3.	<u>Most</u> plants are either parasites or saprobes.
_____True_____	4.	In plants, chlorophyll *a* and *b* are located in <u>chloroplasts</u>.

_____sunlight_____ 5. Besides <u>oxygen</u>, plants need water and carbon dioxide for photosynthesis.

_____True_____ 6. Plants require <u>oxygen</u> for cellular respiration.

_____limit_____ 7. Land plants evolved with structures that <u>promote</u> water loss.

_____roots_____ 8. Plants usually take in water and minerals through their <u>leaves</u>.

The History and Evolution of Plants

For Questions 9–12, complete each statement by writing the correct word or words.

9. The ancestors of land plants lived in _____water_____.

10. The oldest fossils of land plants are roughly _____425 million_____ years old.

11. The greatest challenge faced by early land plants was obtaining _____water_____.

12. Early land plants obtained enough water because they grew close to the ground in _____damp_____ places.

13. Describe why biologists now classify green algae as plants.

   Green algae have cell walls and photosynthetic pigments identical to those of plants.

   They also have reproductive cycles similar to those of plants. Finally, studies of the

   genomes of green algae suggest that they are part of the plant kingdom.

14. Describe three characteristics of plants that helped them meet the demands of life on land.

   more resistant to the drying rays of the sun, capable of conserving water, more capable

   of reproducing without water

15. Identify the important features that separate the five major groups of plants by writing each correct answer on the corresponding line provided.

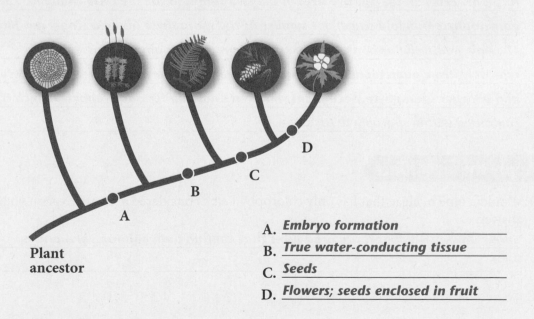

Plant ancestor

A. *Embryo formation*

B. *True water-conducting tissue*

C. *Seeds*

D. *Flowers; seeds enclosed in fruit*

The Plant Life Cycle

16. What is the shift between haploid and diploid phases in the sexual life cycle of a plant called?

alternation of generations

17. Complete the diagram below by writing the name of each phase in a plant's life cycle. Also indicate whether the phase is haploid (N) or diploid (2N).

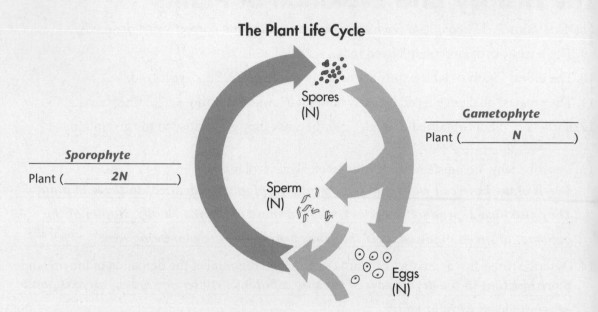

The Plant Life Cycle

Spores
(N)

Gametophyte

Plant (_____ N _____)

Sporophyte

Plant (_____ 2N _____)

Sperm
(N)

Eggs
(N)

18. What evolutionary trend is observable in the relative sizes of the stages in the life cycles of plants, starting with green algae and ending with seed plants?

As plants evolved, the relative sizes of the two stages in the life cycle changed. The gametophyte (haploid stage) got smaller as the sporophyte (diploid stage) got larger. The only multicellular bodies of green algae are gametophytes. Mosses have a relatively large gametophyte and smaller sporophytes. Ferns have a small gametophyte and a larger sporophyte. Seed plants have an even smaller gametophyte, which is contained within sporophyte tissues.

Apply the Big idea

19. Would a type of algae that has only chlorophyll *a* be considered a plant? Explain your answer.

SAMPLE ANSWER: **No. Plants are organisms that contain both chlorophyll a and b.**

22.2 Seedless Plants

Lesson Objectives

- Identify the characteristics of green algae.
- Describe the adaptations of bryophytes.
- Explain the importance of vascular tissue.

Lesson Summary

Green Algae Green algae are mostly aquatic. They are found in fresh and salt water, and in some moist areas on land.

▶ Most do not contain the specialized tissues found in other plants.

▶ Some may not alternate between haploid and diploid stages with every generation.

▶ Green algae form colonies providing a hint about how multicellular plants evolved. Although most cells in a *Volvox* colony are identical, a few are specialized for reproduction.

Mosses and Other Bryophytes The **bryophytes** have specialized reproductive organs.

▶ Bryophytes are small because they lack **vascular tissue**, which is specialized for conducting water.

▶ Bryophytes display alternation of generations:

- Gametophytes produce eggs in **archegonia** and sperm in **antheridia**. Sperm and egg cells fuse to produce a diploid zygote.

- The zygote is the beginning of the sporophyte stage. The sporophyte grows out of the gametophyte and develops a long stalk and a spore-producing capsule called a **sporangium**. Here, haploid spores are produced by meiosis. When the capsule opens, the haploid spores are scattered to start the cycle again.

Vascular Plants These plants are also known as **tracheophytes**.

▶ Vascular plants have vascular tissues that make it possible to move fluids through their bodies against the force of gravity.

- **Tracheids** are hollow tubelike water-conducting cells with thick cell walls strengthened by lignin. Tracheids are found in **xylem**, a tissue that carries water upward from the roots to every part of a plant.

- **Phloem** is a vascular tissue that carries nutrients and carbohydrates produced by photosynthesis.

▶ In a fern life cycle, spores grow into haploid gametophytes that produce eggs in archegonia and sperm in antheridia. The diploid zygote develops into a sporophyte. Haploid spores will develop on the undersides of a fern's fronds, actually the diploid sporophyte stage of the life cycle, and the cycle continues.

Green Algae

For Questions 1–7, complete each statement by writing the correct word or words.

1. *Alga* is the Latin word for ___seaweed___.

2. Large mats of green algae lived during the ___Cambrian___ Period, more than 550 million years ago.

3. Green algae are mostly aquatic, but some live in ___moist___ areas on land.

4. ___Chlamydomonas___ is an example of a single-celled green alga.

5. The ___zygotes___ of a green alga are able to survive freezing or drying conditions.

6. ___Spirogyra___ is a colonial green alga shaped like a filament.

7. *Volvox* is a colonial green alga that shows some cell ___specialization___.

Mosses and Other Bryophytes

For Questions 8–14, write True if the statement is true. If the statement is false, change the underlined word or words to make the statement true.

___bryophytes___ 8. Mosses and their relatives belong to a group called <u>sporophytes</u>.

___water___ 9. The moss life cycle is highly dependent on <u>fertile soil</u>.

___True___ 10. Bryophytes stay small because they lack true <u>vascular tissue</u>.

___True___ 11. The <u>gametophyte</u> is the dominant stage of bryophytes.

___sperm___ 12. Bryophytes must live in places where there is standing water for at least part of the year because, for fertilization to occur, <u>eggs</u> must swim.

___archegonia___ 13. The egg producing organs of bryophytes are called <u>antheridia</u>.

___gametophyte___ 14. When a moss spore germinates, it grows into a <u>sporangium</u>.

15. **THINK VISUALLY** Label the gametophyte and sporophyte in the illustration of a moss plant below.

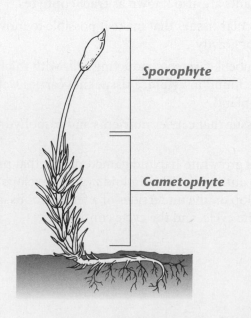

Sporophyte

Gametophyte

Vascular Plants

16. What is vascular tissue?

Vascular tissue is plant tissue that is specialized for carrying water and other

materials.

17. Complete the compare and contrast table for the two main types of vascular tissue.

Xylem and Phloem	
Similarities	**Differences**
Both contain long cells through which fluids can move. The tubular cells are stacked end to end.	**Xylem carries water and minerals absorbed by the roots upward to all the parts of the plant. The tubular cells of xylem are reinforced by lignin. Phloem carries solutions of carbohydrates produced by photosynthesis and other nutrients throughout the plant body.**

18. What is the dominant stage in the life cycle of ferns?

The sporophyte is the dominant stage in ferns.

19. **THINK VISUALLY** Label the parts of a fern in the illustrations below. Then label each drawing as either the sporophyte or the gametophyte.

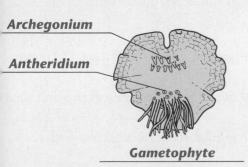

Archegonium

Antheridium

Gametophyte

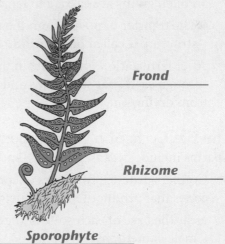

Frond

Rhizome

Sporophyte

Apply the Big idea

20. Which type of plant reproductive cell—spore or gamete—is better adapted for dispersing, or spreading, bryophytes and ferns to other places? Justify your answer.

SAMPLE ANSWER: _Spores are better adapted for dispersing, or spreading, mosses and ferns_

on land. They are small, lightweight, and easily carried away by wind or water.

22.3 Seed Plants

Lesson Objectives

- Describe the reproductive adaptations of seed plants.
- Identify the reproductive structures of gymnosperms.

Lesson Summary

The Importance of Seeds A **seed** is a plant embryo and a food supply, encased in a protective covering. The embryo is an early stage of the sporophyte.

▶ Ancestors of seed plants evolved with many adaptations that allow seed plants to reproduce without open water. These include a reproductive process that takes place in cones or flowers, the transfer of sperm by pollination, and the protection of embryos in seeds. These adaptations enabled plants to survive on dry land.

▶ The gametophytes of seed plants grow and mature within the sporophyte.
- The **gymnosperms** are seed plants that bear their seeds directly on the scales of cones.
- The **angiosperms** are seed plants that bear their seeds in flowers inside a layer of tissue that protects the seed.

▶ In seed plants, the entire male gametophyte is contained in a tiny structure called a **pollen grain**.
- The sperm are produced inside pollen grains and do not have to swim.
- Pollen grains are carried to female reproductive structures by wind or animals.
- The transfer of pollen from the male reproductive structure to the female reproductive structure is called **pollination**.

▶ After fertilization, the zygote in the seed grows into a tiny plant—the sporophyte embryo. A tough **seed coat** surrounds and protects the embryo and keeps the contents of the seed from drying out.

The Life Cycle of a Gymnosperm The word *gymnosperm* means "naked seed." Gymnosperms include cycads, ginkgoes, and conifers such as pines and firs.

▶ Conifers produce two types of cones: pollen cones that produce the pollen grains and seed cones that produce female gametophytes.

▶ Near the base of each scale of the seed cones are two **ovules**, the structures in which the female gametophytes develop.

▶ Wind carries pollen from pollen cones to new female cones.

▶ In gymnosperms, the direct transfer of pollen to the female cone allows fertilization to take place without the need for open water.

▶ If a pollen grain lands near an ovule, the grain begins to grow a structure called a **pollen tube**, which allows the pollen to travel without water and which contains two haploid sperm nuclei.

▶ Once the pollen tube reaches the female gametophyte, one sperm nucleus disintegrates, and the other fertilizes the egg contained within the gametophyte.

▶ Fertilization produces a zygote, which grows into an embryo. The embryo is then encased in a seed and is ready to be dispersed.

The Importance of Seeds

For Questions 1–4, complete each statement by writing the correct word or words.

1. Acorns, pine nuts, and beans are examples of _____seeds_____ .

2. The living plant within a seed represents the early developmental stage of the _____sporophyte_____ phase of the plant life cycle.

3. In seed formation, fertilization does not require _____water_____ .

4. The gametophytes usually develop in reproductive structures known as _____cones_____ or _____flowers_____ .

5. Complete the Venn diagram by correctly placing terms in the diagram. Use the terms that follow: cones, fertilization, flowers, pollen grains, pollination, seeds, and seed coats.

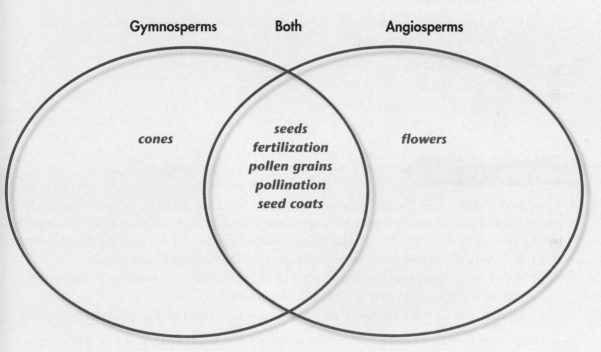

The Life Cycle of a Gymnosperm

For Questions 6–10, write the letter of the correct answer on the line at the left.

__A__ 6. In which part of a pine tree are pollen grains produced?

    A. pollen cones

    B. male flowers

    C. seed cones

    D. female flowers

__D__ 7. Which is one entire male gametophyte of a gymnosperm?

    A. a diploid cell

    B. a haploid nucleus

    C. a pollen cone

    D. a pollen grain

_____B_____ 8. The structures of gymnosperms in which the female gametophytes develop are called

    A. needles.

    B. ovules.

    C. pollen grains.

    D. pollen tubes.

_____C_____ 9. How much time does the conifer life cycle typically take to complete?

    A. 2 days

    B. 2 months

    C. 2 years

    D. 2 centuries

_____D_____ 10. In gymnosperm reproduction, which of these takes the place of water in the transfer of sperm to eggs?

    A. haploid cells

    B. male cones

    C. small gametophytes

    D. pollen tubes

Apply the Big idea

11. The dominant phase of the life cycle of seed plants is the sporophyte, or spore-producing plant. Like all plants, seed plants produce spores. However, the spores are never released from the body of the sporophyte. The spores remain inside of the cones of gymnosperms and the flowers of angiosperms, where they develop into the male and female gametophytes. In what ways has this change in the plant life cycle been an evolutionary advantage to seed plants as they adapted to life on land?

SAMPLE ANSWER: *Because the spores of seed plants are not released, the gametophytes that develop from the spores are protected from drying out by the tissues of the sporophyte. This enables seed plants to survive and reproduce in environments that have limited amounts of water. The gametophytes do not dry out and can still complete the reproductive process without having to wait for an abundance of water for the transfer of sperm to eggs. Additionally, since the zygote also remains within structures of the sporophyte (cones in gymnosperms and flowers in angiosperms), the embryo that develops from it is protected from drying out. The embryo and the tissues that surround and protect it become a seed, which is also able to survive in dry conditions for long periods of time.*

22.4 Flowering Plants

Lesson Objectives

⊂▭ Identify the reproductive structures of angiosperms.

⊂▭ Identify some of the ways angiosperms can be categorized.

Lesson Summary

Flowers and Fruits Angiosperms reproduce sexually by means of flowers.

▶ Flowers contain **ovaries**, which surround and protect the seeds. *Angiosperm* means "enclosed seed."

▶ Flowers are an evolutionary advantage because they attract animals that carry pollen with them as they leave flowers.

▶ After fertilization, ovaries within flowers develop into fruits that surround, protect, and help disperse the seeds.

▶ A **fruit** is a structure containing one or more matured ovaries.

▶ For many years, angiosperms were classified according to the number of seed leaves, or **cotyledons**.

  • **Monocots** have one seed leaf.

  • **Dicots** have two seed leaves.

  • Scientific classification now places the monocots into a single group and dicots in a variety of categories. Recent discoveries are used to place angiosperms in clades. Five of these clades are *Amborella*, water lilies, magnoliids, monocots, and eudicots.

Angiosperm Diversity Scientific classification reflects evolutionary relationships. Farmers, gardeners, and other people who work with plants group angiosperms according to the number of their seed leaves, the strength and composition of their stems, and the number of growing seasons they live.

▶ Monocots and dicots, grouped according to the number of cotyledons they produce, differ in several other characteristics, including:

  • the distribution of vascular tissue in stems, roots, and leaves

  • the number of petals per flower

▶ Plants are also grouped by the characteristics of their stems.

  • **Woody plants** have stems that are made primarily of cells with thick cell walls that support the plant body.

  • **Herbaceous plants** have smooth and nonwoody stems.

▶ Plants are grouped according to life span as annuals, biennials, or perennials. Annuals live one year; biennials live two years; and perennials can live for several years.

Flowers and Fruits

For Questions 1–4, complete each statement by writing the correct word or words.

1. ___Angiosperms___ are seed plants that produce flowers and fruits.

2. Flowering plants first appeared during the ___Cretaceous___ Period.

3. The seeds of flowering plants are encased in ___fruits___ .

4. The success of angiosperms on land is attributed to their flowers, which attract animal ___pollinators___, and to their fruits, which disperse ___seeds___ .

For Questions 5–6, write the letter of the correct answer on the line at the left.

___A___ **5.** Which plant's discovery caused botanists to rearrange the classification of plants?

    A. *Amborella*

    B. *Archaefructus*

    C. *Cooksonia*

    D. *Magnolia*

___B___ **6.** Which major group of angiosperms is by far the largest?

    A. *Amborella*

    B. Eudicots

    C. Magnoliids

    D. Monocots

Angiosperm Diversity

7. Complete the table about groups of angiosperms.

Groups of Angiosperms Based on Seed Structure			
Group	**Number of Seed Leaves**	**Other Characteristics**	**Examples**
Monocots	*1*	*Parallel leaf veins, floral parts often in multiples of 3, vascular bundles scattered throughout stem, fibrous roots*	*Corn, wheat, lilies, orchids, palms, grasses*
Dicots	*2*	*Branched leaf veins, floral parts often in multiples of 4 or 5, vascular bundles in stem arranged in a ring, taproot*	*Roses, clover, tomatoes, oaks, daisies*

For Questions 8–11, match each example with the type of plant it is. Each type may be used more than once.

Example

_B_ **8.** Rose shrubs

_B_ **9.** Oaks

_A_ **10.** Sunflowers

_A_ **11.** Dandelions

_B_ **12.** Grape vines

_A_ **13.** Petunias

Type of Plant

A. Herbaceous

B. Woody

14. Complete the table about plant life spans.

Plant Types Based on Life Spans		
Category	**Definition**	**Examples**
Annuals	*Angiosperms that have a life span of one year*	*Marigolds, petunias, pansies, wheat*
Biennials	*Angiosperms that have a life span of two years*	*Parsley, celery, evening primroses, foxgloves*
Perennials	*Angiosperms that live more than two years and reproduce many times*	*Peonies, asparagus, many grasses, palm trees, honeysuckle, maple trees*

Apply the Big idea

15. Could the terms *woody* and *herbaceous* be used to describe other types of plants besides angiosperms? Justify your answer.

SAMPLE ANSWER: **Yes. Most gymnosperms are trees with woody trunks and, therefore, could be referred to as woody plants. All green algae, bryophytes, and most ferns do not produce wood, and, therefore, could be referred to as herbaceous plants.**

Chapter Vocabulary Review

Crossword Puzzle *Complete the puzzle by entering the term that matches the description.*

Across

5. a moss or its relative
8. plant with two seed leaves in seeds
9. sugar-conducting vascular tissue
10. structure in which a female gametophyte develops
11. sperm-producing organ of seedless plants
12. plant with vascular tissues
13. spore-producing structure of seedless plants

Down

1. egg-producing organ of seedless plants
2. spore-producing stage of plant life cycles
3. water-conducting vascular tissue
4. embryo plant, food supply, and protective covering
6. gamete-producing stage of the plant life cycle
7. the transfer of pollen
10. egg-containing structure of flowering plants

CHAPTER MYSTERY

STONE AGE STORYTELLERS

21st Century Learning

In the Chapter Mystery, you learned about Iceman, who died 5300 years ago. His body is the oldest naturally preserved mummy ever recovered. Many plant materials were preserved along with Iceman. It's very unusual for plant materials to survive that long.

Iceman of the Future?

The environmental conditions where Iceman died were unique. The glacial ice he was found in helped to preserve him and many of his belongings for thousands of years before hikers discovered him in 1991. Consider what might happen to a climber today who died on a mountaintop and whose body became trapped in ice. The article below is a fictional broadcast account of the discovery of Iceman II in the year 3008.

> **Afternoon Mindcast, January 8, 3008**—Hikers on Pike's Glacier literally stumbled upon a major anthropological discovery this morning. When Klendon Deel, 85, tripped over something in the trail, his hiking companion and mother, Mender Yayv Akong, 122, helped him up and then looked for the partially hidden obstacle. It turned out to be an ancient electronic device called a "Hype-Odd," which was used for listening to music aurally. But the most amazing part of the discovery was the skeletal hand still clutching the device.
>
> Akong and Deel beamed the authorities, and within an hour scientists had uncovered the remains of an adult male human. Preliminary tests indicate the man died in February or March of 2016. At that time the glacier did not cover the mountain, which is in an area that was then called "Colorado."
>
> Scientists say that unfortunately most of the man's soft tissue disintegrated through the 100-Year Heat Wave of the 22nd century, the Crustal Shocks of the 24th century, and the Kelvin Ice Age of the 29th century. But according to spokesbeing Nkavrjdn*w, the skeleton, nails, hair, and many of the belongings were all remarkably well preserved. "The lead scientist studying the find is particularly fascinated with the objects remaining in the man's pack," Nkavrjdn*w says. "For example, she thinks she has found what is left of an ancient apple. While the actual fruit is gone, a stem and a pile of seeds remained in the pack."
>
> In addition, a clear bottle was found in the pack. Scientists are planning on doing tests to try to determine what the bottle contained. The only marking they could find on the bottle was a small triangular shape composed of three arrows. Scientists are unsure what this mysterious symbol meant.

Continued on next page ▶

21st Century Themes Science and Global Awareness

1. Consider the items you take with you when hiking. Suppose Iceman II had these items. Which of these items do you think would survive?

   SAMPLE ANSWER: *plastic items, items made of synthetic material such as nylon, metal items*

2. Which of the items that Iceman II possibly took with him on his hike do you think would *not* survive? Explain your answer.

   SAMPLE ANSWER: *foods such as bread, cheese, and lettuce; paper; cotton clothing; straw hat. These items would probably not survive because they have a high water content or are made of relatively fragile fibers that can easily disintegrate.*

3. Describe what future scientists might be able to learn about the 21st century by studying Iceman II's belongings. What type of evidence would be difficult for them to interpret?

   SAMPLE ANSWER: *Scientists would be able to learn about 21st-century clothing, material technology, diet, music, and other information about human culture during that period. Scientists may have a hard time interpreting the symbols and brand names found on many objects. They also may no longer be able to read or translate 21st-century languages.*

21st Century Skills Pondering Plant Products

The skills used in this activity include **information and media literacy, communication skills, creativity and intellectual curiosity,** and **social responsibility.**

Synthetic materials, such as nylon and plastic, tend to be more durable than plant-based materials, such as cotton and paper. Because of this, many modern products are made out of synthetic materials. However, most synthetic materials are made from nonrenewable resources. Use library and Internet resources to compare plant-based materials to synthetic materials. For example, visit the Web sites of companies that manufacture plastic, nylon, paper, or cotton fabric. Consider the following questions:

- How do the costs of plant products compare with those of synthetic products?
- What sort of business opportunities are there in manufacturing products out of plant materials instead of synthetic materials?

With a group, come up with a new plant-based product. Identify potential customers for the product and discuss how you would market the product to them.

Evaluate students' work based on the accuracy of their information, the clarity of their product description, and the effectiveness of their marketing proposal.

23 Plant Structure and Function

Structure and Function

Q: How are cells, tissues, and organs organized into systems that carry out the basic functions of a seed plant?

WHAT I KNOW	WHAT I LEARNED
23.1 How are plant tissues organized?	*SAMPLE ANSWER:* **The tissues of plants are organized into roots, stems, and leaves.**	*SAMPLE ANSWER:* **Dermal tissue, vascular tissue, and ground tissue make up the roots, stems, and leaves of plants.**
23.2 How do the structure and function of roots help a plant carry out life processes?	*SAMPLE ANSWER:* **Roots are long and thin, and they absorb water and minerals.**	*SAMPLE ANSWER:* **The outside layer of a mature root, the epidermis, is covered with root hairs that allow water and minerals to enter. Ground tissue just inside stores food. Vascular tissue at the center transports water and nutrients.**
23.3 How do the structure and function of stems help a plant carry out life processes?	*SAMPLE ANSWER:* **Stems have vascular tissues and help get water and nutrients from roots to leaves.**	*SAMPLE ANSWER:* **Stems produce leaves, branches, and flowers; hold leaves up to the sun, allowing photosynthesis to occur; and transport substances throughout a plant.**
23.4 How do the structure and function of leaves help a plant carry out life processes?	*SAMPLE ANSWER:* **Leaves contain the chlorophyll for photosynthesis.**	*SAMPLE ANSWER:* **The structures of a leaf have many adaptations that enable them to absorb light so that they can carry out photosynthesis.**
23.5 How do plants move materials through their bodies?	*SAMPLE ANSWER:* **Materials move through the bodies of vascular plants in xylem and phloem.**	*SAMPLE ANSWER:* **Transpiration and capillary action pull water through xylem to the top of a plant. Active transport and osmosis move the contents of phloem through a plant.**

23.1 Specialized Tissues in Plants

Lesson Objectives

🔑 Identify the principal organs of seed plants.

🔑 Explain the primary functions of the main tissue systems of seed plants.

🔑 Contrast meristems with other plant tissues.

Lesson Summary

Seed Plant Structure All seed plants have three principal organs:

► Roots anchor plants in the ground and absorb water and dissolved nutrients.

► Stems provide a support system for the plant body, a transport system that carries nutrients, and a defensive system that protects the plant.

► Leaves conduct photosynthesis and exchange gases with the air.

Plant Tissue Systems Plants have three main tissue systems:

► Dermal tissue is the protective outer covering of a plant. In young plants it consists of a single layer of cells called the epidermis. A waxy cuticle often covers epidermis and protects against water loss. In older plants, dermal tissue may be many cell layers deep and may be covered with bark.

► Vascular tissue supports the plant body and transports water and nutrients throughout the plant. The two kinds are xylem, a water-conducting tissue, and phloem, a tissue that carries dissolved nutrients.

  • Xylem contains cells called tracheids, which have cell walls with lignin, a complex molecule that resists water and gives wood much of its strength. Angiosperms have a second form of xylem tissue called vessel elements, which are arranged end to end on top of one another.

  • Phloem contains sieve tube elements, which are arranged end to end. Companion cells support the phloem cells and aid in the movement of substances in and out of the phloem.

► Ground tissue produces and stores sugars, and helps support the plant.

  • Parenchyma cells have a thin cell wall and a large central vacuole.

  • Collenchyma cells have strong, flexible cell walls that help support plant organs.

  • Sclerenchyma cells have extremely thick, rigid cell walls that make ground tissue tough and strong.

Plant Growth and Meristems Meristems are regions of unspecialized cells in which mitosis produces new cells that are ready for differentiation.

► Apical meristems are found in the tips of stems and roots.

► Floral meristems produce the tissues of flowers.

Seed Plant Structure

1. List the three principal organs of seed plants, and state the function of each one.

Roots anchor plants in the ground and absorb water and nutrients.

Stems support the plant body, transport materials, and produce leaves and other organs.

Leaves absorb sunlight, conduct photosynthesis, and exchange gases with the air.

2. What adaptation helps leaves conserve water?

They have adjustable pores that let gases in and out of the leaf.

Plant Tissue Systems

For Questions 3–6, complete each statement by writing the correct word or words.

3. The three main tissue systems of plants are ___*dermal*___ tissue, ___*vascular*___ tissue, and ___*ground*___ tissue.

4. The cuticle protects against ___*water*___ loss.

5. Some epidermal cells have tiny projections known as ___*trichomes*___, which may give a leaf a fuzzy appearance.

6. Dermal tissue in roots contains ___*root hair*___ cells that help absorb water.

For Questions 7–11, match the vascular-tissue elements with their descriptions.

Vascular-Tissue Elements

___B___ **7.** Tracheids

___E___ **8.** Lignin

___D___ **9.** Vessel elements

___A___ **10.** Sieve tube elements

___C___ **11.** Companion cells

Description

A. The main phloem cells

B. Long, narrow xylem cells with openings in their cell walls

C. Cells that support the phloem cells and aid in the movement of substances

D. Xylem cells arranged end to end on top of one another

E. The substance in the cell walls of dead tracheids that makes wood tough

12. How can water move from one tracheid into a neighboring cell?

The cell walls of tracheids have many openings that connect neighboring cells to one another and allow water to flow from cell to cell.

13. How can materials move from one sieve tube element into the next?

The end walls of sieve tube elements have many small holes in them. Materials move through these holes from one cell to the next.

14. Complete the table that compares ground-tissue cells.

Ground-Tissue Cells		
Type of Cell	**Structure**	**Function**
Parenchyma	**Cells with thin cell walls and large central vacuoles**	Photosynthesis in leaves
Collenchyma	Cells with strong, flexible cell walls	**Support for plant organs**
Sclerenchyma	Cells with extremely thick, rigid cell walls	**Strong and tough support and protection**

Plant Growth and Meristems

For Questions 15–19, write True if the statement is true. If the statement is false, change the underlined word or words to make the statement true.

_____**True**_____ 15. <u>Meristems</u> are regions of the plant that produce new cells by mitosis.

_____**True**_____ 16. <u>Apical meristems</u> are found in the growing tip of a root or stem.

**unspecialized** 17. The <u>specialized</u> cells that result from cell division in meristems have thin cell walls.

**differentiation** 18. Newly produced plant cells undergo <u>fertilization</u> as they mature into different cell types.

_____**True**_____ 19. An apical meristem changes into a <u>floral meristem</u> when its pattern of gene expression changes.

Apply the Big idea

20. Plants are the source of many useful fibers, such as cotton and linen. Fibers are long, thin structures that have strength and flexibility. Which plant tissue system produces fibers such as cotton and linen? Justify your answer.

Plant fibers such as cotton and linen are produced by the vascular tissue system of plants.

The vascular tissue contains many long, slender cells that form long tubes and have

walls that are reinforced by lignin. These characteristics are similar to those of fibers

such as cotton and linen. Neither dermal nor ground tissue consists of cells with these

characteristics.

_____

23.2 Roots

Lesson Objectives

Describe the main tissues in a mature root.

Describe the different functions of roots.

Lesson Summary

Root Structure and Growth The root is the first part of a plant to emerge from a seed.

▶ Plants have two main types of root systems:

- Taproot systems are found mainly in dicots and consist of a large primary root that has many smaller branches.

- Fibrous root systems are found mainly in monocots and consist of many equally sized branch roots. They help prevent topsoil from being washed away.

▶ Roots contain cells from the three tissue systems. A mature root has an outside layer, called the epidermis, and also contains vascular tissue and a large area of ground tissue. The root system is important to water and mineral transport.

- The root's epidermis performs the dual functions of protection and absorption. Its surface is covered with thin cellular projections called **root hairs**, which produce a large surface area that allows water and minerals to enter.

- Ground tissue called **cortex** stores products of photosynthesis, such as starch. Water and minerals move through the cortex. A layer called the **endodermis** encloses the vascular cylinder.

- The xylem and phloem together make up a region called the **vascular cylinder** at the center of the root.

- Apical meristems produce new cells near the root tip, which is covered by a tough **root cap** that protects the root tip as it grows into the soil.

Root Functions Roots support a plant, anchor it in the ground, store food, and absorb water and dissolved nutrients from the soil.

▶ Roots take in many essential inorganic nutrients, such as nitrogen and potassium.

▶ Active transport brings the mineral ions of dissolved nutrients from the soil into the plant.

▶ Cells of the root epidermis create conditions under which osmosis causes water to "follow" ions and flow into the root.

▶ The waterproof **Casparian strip** enables the endodermis to filter and control the water and nutrients that enter the vascular cylinder, as well as ensuring that nutrients do not leak out.

▶ Root pressure, produced within the vascular cylinder by active transport, forces water through the vascular cylinder and into the xylem.

Root Structure and Growth

1. Complete the table that compares the types of root systems.

Types of Root Systems			
Type of Root	**Description**	**Mainly in Dicots or Monocots?**	**Examples**
Taproot	Long and thick primary roots that grow deep into the soil	*Dicots*	*Carrots, dandelions, beets*
Fibrous roots	Equally sized branch roots that grow separately from the base of the stem	*Monocots*	*Grasses*

For Questions 2–6, complete each statement by writing the correct word or words.

2. A mature root has a large area of _____ground_____ tissue between its dermal and vascular tissues.

3. A root's surface area for absorption of water is increased by _____root hairs_____.

4. One function of the _____cortex_____ is the storage of starch.

5. The _____vascular_____ cylinder, made up of xylem and phloem, is found at the center of a root.

6. A root's apical meristem can be found just behind the _____root cap_____.

7. **THINK VISUALLY** Complete the illustration of a cross section of a root by adding labels for the parts indicated.

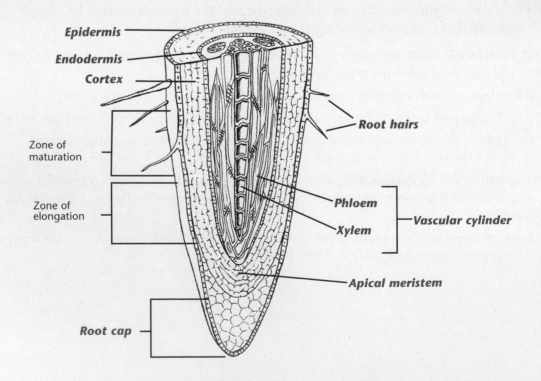

Epidermis

Endodermis

Cortex

Zone of maturation

Zone of elongation

Root hairs

Phloem

Xylem

Vascular cylinder

Apical meristem

Root cap

Root Functions

8. Name at least two functions, besides uptake of water and nutrients, of a plant's roots.

SAMPLE ANSWER: *support of a plant, anchoring a plant in the ground, and food storage*

9. What is the role of active transport in the uptake of water by plant roots?

Energy from ATP is used to pump mineral ions of dissolved nutrients from the soil into the plant. This increases the concentration of mineral ions in the root cells. As a result, water moves into the plant by osmosis.

10. Where in roots are active transport proteins located?

They are located in the cell membranes of root hairs and other cells in the root epidermis.

11. What happens to water and dissolved minerals after they move across the epidermis of a root?

The water and dissolved minerals move from the epidermis through the cortex into the vascular cylinder.

12. Why is there a one-way passage of materials into the vascular cylinder in plant roots?

Because water and minerals cannot pass through the waxy Casparian strip, once they pass through the endodermis, they are trapped in the vascular cylinder.

13. How do water and nutrients cross the endodermis that surrounds the vascular cylinder?

The water and nutrients pass through the cell membranes of the endodermis cells instead of flowing between the cells.

14. What is root pressure?

It is the force that causes water and dissolved nutrients to move out of the root's vascular cylinder and upward into the xylem of a stem.

Apply the Big idea

15. People often give potted houseplants more fertilizer than they need. As a result, the plants begin to wilt and eventually die instead of getting larger and healthier. What could be the reason for this result?

Roots are adapted for taking in water by osmosis, which is the movement of water toward an area with a higher solute content. If the concentration of solutes in the soil around a plant's roots gets too high, water will begin to move in the opposite direction—out of the roots and into the soil.

23.3 Stems

Lesson Objectives

⚷ Describe the main functions of stems.

⚷ Contrast the processes of primary growth and secondary growth in stems.

Lesson Summary

Stem Structure and Function Aboveground stems have three main functions:

▶ Stems produce leaves, branches, and flowers.

▶ Stems hold leaves up to the sun.

- Growing stems contain distinct **nodes**, where leaves are attached.

- **Buds** contain apical meristems that can produce new stems and leaves.

▶ Stems transport substances throughout the plant.

- Vascular tissues are arranged in clusters of xylem and phloem called **vascular bundles**. In monocots, vascular bundles are scattered throughout the stem; in dicots they are arranged a cylinder, or ring.

- In a young dicot, the parenchyma cells inside the ring of vascular tissue are known as **pith**.

Growth of Stems One type of growth adds length to a plant's stems and roots. The other adds width, or thickens stems and roots.

▶ **Primary growth** of stems is the result of elongation of cells produced in the apical meristem. It takes place in all seed plants.

▶ **Secondary growth** is an increase in the thickness of stems and roots that is common among dicots and gymnosperms but rare in monocots. In conifers and dicots, secondary growth takes place in meristems called the vascular cambium and cork cambium.

- The **vascular cambium** produces vascular tissues and increases the thickness of stems over time.

- The **cork cambium** produces the outer covering of stems.

- "Wood" is actually layers of secondary xylem produced by the vascular cambium. **Heartwood**, near the center of the stem, contains old xylem that no longer conducts liquids. **Sapwood** surrounds heartwood and is active in fluid transport.

- In most of the temperate zone, tree growth is seasonal. Tree rings can be used to estimate a tree's age and provide information about past climate and weather conditions. In a mature stem, all of the tissues found outside the vascular cambium make up the **bark**.

Stem Structure and Function

1. What are the three main functions of stems?

Stems produce organs (leaves and flowers), hold leaves up to the sun, and transport *materials throughout the plant.*

2. What is an example of a stem that conducts photosynthesis and stores water?

A desert cactus stem conducts photosynthesis and stores water.

3. What is a node?

In plants, a node is where leaves are attached to the stem.

4. What kind of plant tissue does a bud contain?

A bud contains apical meristems.

5. What does a vascular bundle contain?

A vascular bundle contains xylem and phloem tissue.

6. Complete the cross-section diagrams by writing labels for the structures indicated.

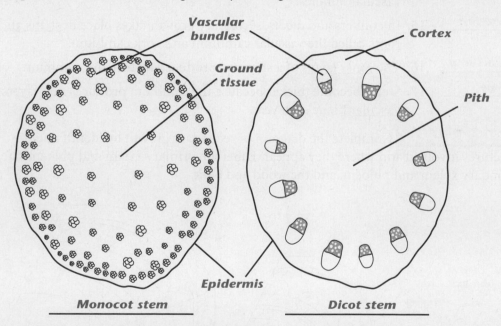

Vascular bundles

Cortex

Ground tissue

Pith

Epidermis

Monocot stem

Dicot stem

7. Complete the compare and contrast chart.

Structure of Monocot Stems and Dicot Stems	
Similarities	**Differences**
Composed of vascular tissue, ground tissue, and epidermal tissue. Vascular tissues are in vascular bundles.	*In monocots, vascular bundles are scattered in ground tissue, which is fairly uniform. In dicots, the vascular bundles are arranged in a ring near the epidermis.*

Growth of Stems

For Questions 8–17, write True if the statement is true. If the statement is false, change the underlined word or words to make the statement true.

different from   8. Plants grow in a way that is <u>the same as</u> the way animals grow.

True   9. The number of legs an animal will have is predetermined, but the number of <u>branches</u> a plant will have is not predetermined.

apical meristem   10. Primary growth of stems is the result of elongation of cells produced in the <u>ground tissue</u>.

secondary   11. The increasing thickness of stems and roots in dicots and gymnosperms is called <u>new</u> growth.

rare   12. Secondary growth is <u>common</u> in monocots.

True   13. Dicots can grow to great heights because the increase in <u>width</u> supports the weight.

True   14. Vascular cambium forms <u>between</u> the xylem and phloem of the vascular bundles.

meristems   15. In conifers and dicots, secondary growth takes place in <u>stems and roots</u> called the vascular cambium and cork cambium.

outer covering   16. The <u>inner layers</u> of a stem are produced by the cork cambium.

True   17. Stems become thicker because the cambium produces new layers of <u>vascular</u> tissue each year.

18. **THINK VISUALLY** Complete the diagram of secondary growth by identifying the structures involved and where they appear. Label the primary xylem and phloem, the secondary xylem and phloem, and the wood and bark.

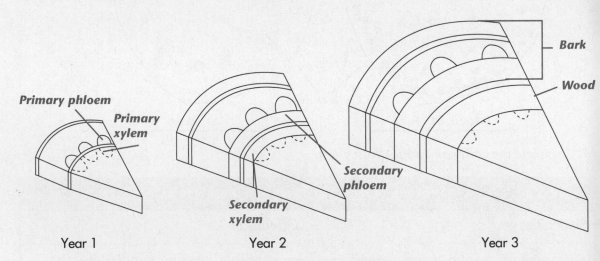

For Questions 19–23, complete each statement by writing the correct word or words.

19. Most of what we call "wood" is made up of layers of _____secondary_____ xylem.

20. The dark wood that no longer conducts water is called _____heartwood_____.

21. The wood that is active in fluid transport is called _____sapwood_____.

22. The lighter wood in tree rings contains _____larger_____ cells with thin cell walls compared with the cells in darker wood.

23. Alternating layers of light wood and dark wood are used to estimate a tree's _____age_____.

24. **THINK VISUALLY** Complete the illustration showing the formation of wood and bark. Use the following terms: wood, bark, cork, cork cambium, vascular cambium, phloem, heartwood, and sapwood.

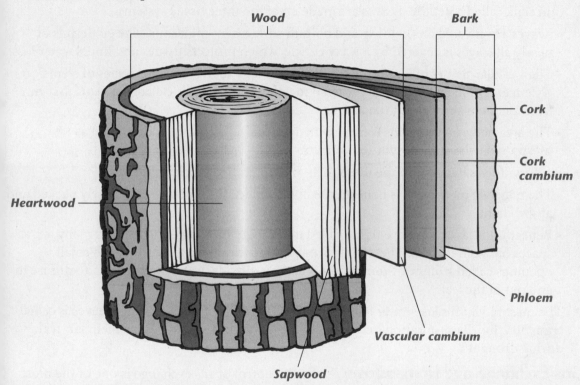

Wood   Bark

Cork

Cork cambium

Heartwood

Phloem

Vascular cambium

Sapwood

Apply the Big idea

25. "Girdling" is a term that refers to removing the bark of a tree in a complete ring around the trunk or a branch. Predict the effect that girdling will have on a tree. Explain.

Girdling will eventually cause the parts of the tree above the injury to die. This happens because the phloem vessels that conduct products of photosynthesis to other parts of the tree, including its roots, will be cut and no fluids will be able to flow. In addition, the cork cambium will be gone in the damaged area and unable to replace the bark that keeps the tree from losing water from the sapwood just under the bark.

23.4 Leaves

Lesson Objectives

🔑 Describe how the structure of a leaf enables it to carry out photosynthesis.

🔑 Explain how gas exchange in leaves relates to homeostasis.

Lesson Summary

Leaf Structure and Function The structure of a leaf is optimized to absorb light and carry out photosynthesis.

▶ Most leaves have a thin, flattened part called a **blade**, which is attached to the stem by a thin stalk called a **petiole**. Leaves are made up of the three tissue systems.

- Leaves are covered on their top and bottom surfaces by epidermis. The epidermis of nearly all leaves is covered by a waxy cuticle, which protects tissues and limits water loss.

- The vascular tissues of leaves are connected directly to the vascular tissues of stems. Xylem and phloem tissues are gathered together into bundles called leaf veins that run from the stem throughout the leaf.

- The area between leaf veins is filled with a specialized ground tissue known as **mesophyll**, where photosynthesis occurs.

▶ Photosynthesis happens in the mesophyll, which has two specialized layers:

- The **palisade mesophyll** is beneath the upper epidermis. The cells are closely packed and absorb light.

- Beneath this layer is a loose tissue called the **spongy mesophyll**, which has many air spaces between its cells. These air spaces connect with the exterior through small openings called **stomata**. Stomata allow carbon dioxide, water, and oxygen to diffuse in and out of the leaf.

▶ The mesophyll cells lose water by evaporation. This loss of water through leaves is called **transpiration**. Transpiration helps to cool the leaves, but also threatens their survival during droughts.

Gas Exchange and Homeostasis A plant's control of gas exchange is one of the most important elements of homeostasis.

▶ Plant leaves allow gas exchange between air spaces in the spongy mesophyll and the exterior by opening their stomata.

▶ Plants maintain homeostasis by keeping their stomata open just enough to allow photosynthesis to take place but not so much that they lose an excessive amount of water.

▶ **Guard cells** are highly specialized cells that surround the stomata and control their opening and closing depending on environmental conditions.

▶ Wilting results from the loss of water and pressure in a plant's cells. The loss of pressure causes a plant's cell walls to bend inward. When a plant wilts, its stomata close so the plant can conserve water.

Leaf Structure and Function

For Questions 1–4, complete each statement by writing the correct word or words.

1. The structure of a leaf is optimized for the purposes of absorbing _____*light*_____ and carrying out _*photosynthesis*_.

2. The _____*epidermis*_____ of nearly all leaves is covered by a waxy _____*cuticle*_____.

3. The vascular tissues of leaves are connected directly to the vascular tissues of _____*stems*_____.

4. The area between leaf veins is filled with a specialized ground tissue known as _____*mesophyll*_____.

For Questions 5–10, match the description with the leaf structure.

Description		**Structure**
_*F*_	5. A layer of mesophyll cells that absorb light that enters the leaf	A. leaf vein
_*D*_	6. Small openings in the epidermis	B. blade
_*B*_	7. The thin, flattened part of a leaf	C. petiole
_*A*_	8. A bundle of xylem and phloem tissues in a leaf	D. stomata
_*C*_	9. A stalk that attaches a leaf to a stem	E. spongy mesophyll
_*E*_	10. A loose tissue with many air spaces between its cells	F. palisade mesophyll

Gas Exchange and Homeostasis

11. Why can't stomata be kept open all the time?

Water loss would be so great that few plants would be able to take in enough water to survive.

12. Complete the flowchart that summarizes how guard cells help maintain homeostasis.

> Guard cells are forced into a curved shape when water pressure _____*increases*_____.

⬇

> The thick inner walls of the guard cells pull away from one another, opening the _____*stoma*_____. Water is lost by transpiration.

⬇

> Guard cells straighten out when water pressure _____*decreases*_____.

⬇

> The inner walls of the guard cells pull together, closing the _____*stoma*_____.

For Questions 13–17, write the letter of the correct answer on the line at the left.

___D___ **13.** Which is likely to happen to a plant if it starts losing more water than it can take in?

    A. It will reproduce.

    B. It will flower.

    C. It will grow.

    D. It will wilt.

___B___ **14.** Which is a plant that has narrow leaves with a waxy epidermis?

    A. cactus

    B. spruce

    C. rock plant

    D. rose bush

___C___ **15.** A pitcher plant's leaves are adapted for

    A. conducting photosynthesis.

    B. limiting transpiration.

    C. catching and digesting insects.

    D. pollination and fertilization.

___C___ **16.** A rock plant adapts to hot, dry conditions by having very few

    A. thorns.

    B. leaves.

    C. stomata.

    D. nutrients.

___A___ **17.** A cactus's thorns are actually its

    A. leaves.

    B. stems.

    C. roots.

    D. bark.

Apply the Big idea

18. The inside of the glass or plastic walls of a greenhouse full of plants is very wet on cool days. Where does this water come from?

The inside surfaces of the walls of a greenhouse are wet because of water vapor from the air condensing on the cool glass or plastic. The water vapor in the air comes from the plants through the process of transpiration.

23.5 Transport in Plants

Lesson Objectives

- Explain the process of water movement in a plant.
- Describe how the products of photosynthesis are transported throughout a plant.

Lesson Summary

Water Transport The pressure created by water entering the tissues of a root push water upward in a plant stem, but this pressure is not enough. Other forces are much more important.

▶ The major force is provided by the evaporation of water from leaves during transpiration. Its pull extends into vascular tissue so that water is pulled up through xylem.

▶ Both the force of attraction between water molecules, cohesion, and the attraction of water molecules to other substances, **adhesion**, help with water transport. The effects of cohesion and adhesion of water molecules are seen in **capillary action**, which is the tendency of water to rise in a thin tube. Capillary action is important because xylem tissue is composed of tracheids and vessel elements that form hollow, connected tubes.

Nutrient Transport The leading explanation of phloem transport is known as the **pressure-flow hypothesis**.

▶ Active transport moves sugars into the sieve tube from surrounding tissues.

▶ Water then follows by osmosis, creating pressure in the tube at the source of the sugars.

▶ If another region of the plant needs sugars, they are actively pumped out of the tube and into the surrounding tissues. Pressure differences move the sugars to tissues where they are needed.

▶ Changes in nutrient concentration drive the movement of fluid through phloem tissue in directions that meet the nutritional needs of the plant.

Water Transport

For Questions 1–2, refer to the Visual Analogy of clowns being pulled up a ladder compared to water being pulled up a tree.

1. **VISUAL ANALOGY** In the visual analogy of the climbing circus clowns, what makes it possible for the falling clowns to pull others up the ladder?
   The rope that ties the clowns to each other transfers the force of gravity pulling on the falling clowns back through the chain to the ones still climbing.

2. How are water molecules similar to the clowns?

SAMPLE ANSWER: *A force between water molecules is keeping them together and transferring the pull of transpiration back through the rising column of water.*

3. Complete the table about the types of attraction between molecules.

Attraction Between Molecules	
Type of Attraction	Definition
Cohesion	*The attraction between molecules of the same substance*
Adhesion	*The attraction between unlike molecules*

For Questions 4–8, complete each statement by writing the correct word or words.

4. Water cohesion is especially strong because water molecules tend to form ___*hydrogen*___ bonds with each other.

5. The tendency of water to rise in a thin tube is called ___*capillary action*___.

6. The height to which water can rise in a tube is determined by its ___*diameter*___.

7. ___*Vessel elements*___ in xylem form many hollow, connected tubes through which water moves.

8. The pull of transpiration extends from the leaves to the ___*roots*___ of a plant.

Nutrient Transport

9. According to the pressure-flow hypothesis, why must sieve-tube elements in phloem be living cells?

   Sugars are moved across cell membranes in phloem tissue by active transport. This process requires ATP, which is made by the cell during cellular respiration. Only living cells can conduct cellular respiration.

10. Where sugar concentration is high, what is the source of water taken in by phloem?

   The water drawn in by osmosis in areas of high sugar concentration comes from xylem tissue.

11. How does the structure of the vascular bundles in stems and roots and of the veins in leaves make the process of pressure-flow possible?

   The vascular bundles and veins in leaves contain both xylem and phloem. The two are close together, which means that water can move from xylem to phloem without having to pass through many cells.

12. Complete the flowchart that summarizes the movement of sugars in plants.

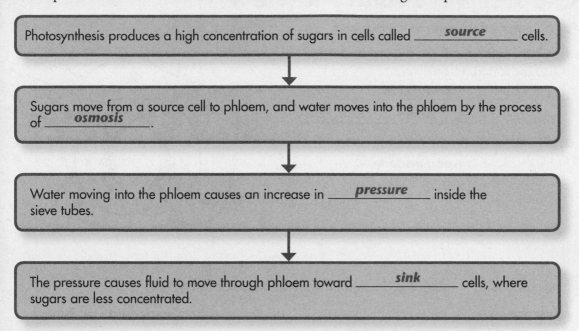

Photosynthesis produces a high concentration of sugars in cells called _____*source*_____ cells.

Sugars move from a source cell to phloem, and water moves into the phloem by the process of _____*osmosis*_____.

Water moving into the phloem causes an increase in _____*pressure*_____ inside the sieve tubes.

The pressure causes fluid to move through phloem toward _____*sink*_____ cells, where sugars are less concentrated.

13. What is one importance of the cell walls of xylem to the capillary action that occurs during transpiration?

The cell walls of the tracheids and vessel elements in the xylem are made of cellulose,

and water adheres very strongly to cellulose.

14. According to the pressure-flow hypothesis, what process prompts rapid spring growth in a plant?

Chemical signals stimulate phloem cells in the roots to pump sugars back into phloem

sap. These sugars are raised into stems and leaves to support growth.

Apply the Big idea

15. Leaves range in size from very large to very tiny. In what type of environment would you expect to find the most plants with very large leaves? Very small leaves? Explain.

Plants that live in warm, wet places tend to have larger leaves. They take in a lot of

water and need to give off a lot of water by transpiration to maintain homeostasis.

Plants that live in hot, dry places tend to have very tiny leaves. They conserve water

by limiting the amount of surface area through which transpiration can occur.

Chapter Vocabulary Review

For Questions 1–2, refer to the diagram.

1. What are the names of the two parts of a leaf indicated in the diagram?

   A. _____*Guard cells*_____

   B. _____*Stoma*_____

2. What process do the structures control?

   _____*transpiration*_____

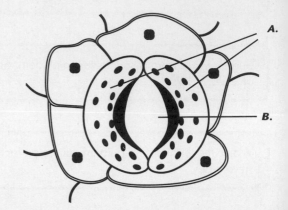

For Questions 3–9, match the description with the tissue or cell type.

Description		Tissue and Cell Types
_D_	3. Ground tissue specialized for photosynthesis	A. sclerenchyma
_G_	4. Layer of ground tissue that encloses the vascular cylinder	B. collenchyma
_B_	5. Thick-walled cells in ground tissue	C. parenchyma
_F_	6. Dermal tissue in leaves and young plants	D. mesophyll
_E_	7. Region of actively dividing unspecialized cells	E. meristem
_A_	8. Very thick-walled cells that make ground tissue such as seed coats tough and strong	F. epidermis
_C_	9. Thin-walled cells in ground tissue	G. endodermis

For Questions 10–16, complete each statement by writing the correct word or words.

10. Most leaves have a flattened part called a _____*blade*_____, which is attached at a _____*node*_____ on the stem by a _____*petiole*_____.

11. The root _____*hairs*_____ increase a root's surface area for absorption, while the root _____*cap*_____ protects the growing tip of the root.

12. The cells of the _____*palisade*_____ mesophyll are tightly packed, but many air spaces separate the cells of the _____*spongy*_____ mesophyll.

13. The meristem between xylem and phloem cells is called _____*vascular cambium*_____ and forms wood by _____*secondary growth*_____.

14. In a mature stem, the tissues outside the vascular cambium make up the _____*bark*_____; the tissues include phloem, cork, and the _____*cork cambium*_____.

15. Water is drawn to the material in cell walls by the process called _____*adhesion*_____.

16. Monocot stems have scattered _____*vascular bundles*_____ while dicots form a ringlike pattern around the _____*pith*_____.

CHAPTER
MYSTERY

THE HOLLOW TREE

In the Chapter Mystery, you learned about a tree that begins growing in the branches of other trees. Its roots get nutrients from materials that collect in the folds in the host tree's bark.

21st Century Learning

Scale Drawings

Engineers often look to nature for inspiration. Early designers of airplane wings examined birds. Modern camera lens engineers are using the human eye for inspiration. Similarly, an engineer interested in extracting water or oil from the ground might look to a plant's roots for ideas. The engineer might start by making a model of a root.

Often, the first step in building a model is making a scale drawing of the object. A scale drawing is a drawing that is the same shape but not the same size as the actual object. Maps and blueprints are examples of scale drawings.

Scale drawings are often used to show objects that are too large or too small to be shown in detail in their actual sizes. For example, the root used for the blueprint below is actually 1/1,000 the size of the drawing. This makes the scale of the drawing 1 cm = 0.001 cm.

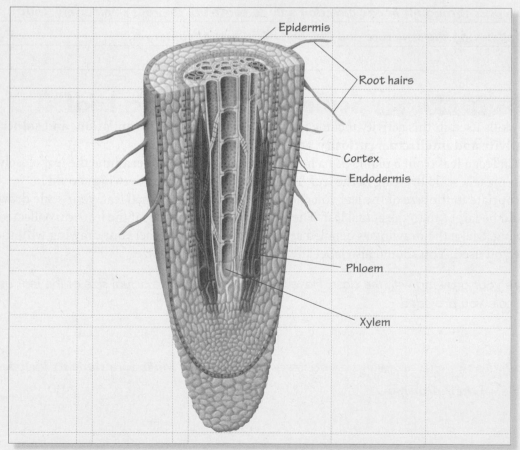

Epidermis

Root hairs

Cortex

Endodermis

Phloem

Xylem

Continued on next page ▶

21st Century Themes Science Literacy

1. Considering the scale of the root blueprint, approximately how long would the root hairs on the actual root be?

   Students' answers may vary, but should be near 0.0015 cm and 0.002 cm.

2. If you were building a working model of a root, what properties would you want the root hairs to have?

   They should be long and thin, and capable of absorbing water.

3. Suppose the root blueprint is reduced to half its current size. What would the scale then be?

   1 cm = 0.002 cm

4. The root used to draw the blueprint is very small, thus the drawing is bigger than the actual object. Give an example of a plant part that you would most likely need to draw on a smaller scale if you were making a blueprint of that part.

   SAMPLE ANSWER: *a tree trunk*

5. Suppose you were going to use the root blueprint to build a model. Give some examples of materials you might use when making your model. Explain your answer.

   SAMPLE ANSWER: *I might use small tubes to represent the vascular structures of the roots*

   so that liquids could flow through them. I might use a ground cloth that allows water

   to pass through it in one direction only to construct the root's epidermis, thus

   mimicking the structure and function of an actual epidermis.

21st Century Skills Scale Drawing of a Leaf

The skills used in this activity include **problem identification, formulation, and solution**; **creativity and intellectual curiosity**; and **self-direction**.

Collect a leaf from a plant. Use a hand lens or microscope to examine the leaf closely. Then make a scale drawing of the leaf. The scale you use in your drawing should be appropriate to the size of the leaf you chose. If you collected a small leaf, your scale drawing should be larger than the actual leaf. The opposite should be true if the leaf you collected is very big. Make the drawing as detailed as possible. Be sure to label your drawing with the scale you used. You should also label any structures you recognize.

Share your drawing with the class. Have the class calculate the actual size of the leaf using the scale you provided.

Evaluate students' drawings on accuracy and neatness. Make sure students included a

scale on their drawings.

24 Plant Reproduction and Response

Big idea **Growth, Development, and Reproduction**

Q: How do changes in the environment affect the reproduction, development, and growth of plants?

WHAT I KNOW	WHAT I LEARNED
24.1 How do flowering plants reproduce?	SAMPLE ANSWER: *Flowering plants reproduce by making seeds in flowers.*	SAMPLE ANSWER: *Flowering plants produce male and female gametophytes in flowers. Pollen grains transfer sperm to the stigma of a flower. Double fertilization in an ovule produces a zygote and endosperm. The ovule becomes a seed.*
24.2 How are fruits and seeds important adaptations for plants?	SAMPLE ANSWER: *Fruits protect seeds, and seeds grow into new plants.*	SAMPLE ANSWER: *Fruits are adaptations for seed dispersal. Seeds enable plant embryos to be transported over long distances and remain dormant until the environment is favorable for growth.*
24.3 How do plants respond to their environments?	SAMPLE ANSWER: *Plants respond to light and other environmental factors such as temperature.*	SAMPLE ANSWER: *Plants make hormones that affect cell growth. Some hormones cause stems to bend toward or away from light or gravity. Others regulate the growth of buds, fruits, flowers, and seeds or stimulate fruit ripening.*
24.4 In what ways do humans depend on plants?	SAMPLE ANSWER: *Humans depend on plants for food.*	SAMPLE ANSWER: *In addition to food, plants provide humans with wood for building and fuel, fibers for making paper and cloth, and medicines.*

24.1 Reproduction in Flowering Plants

Lesson Objectives

🔑 Identify the functions of various structures of a flower.

🔑 Explain how fertilization differs between angiosperms and other plants.

🔑 Describe vegetative reproduction.

Lesson Summary

The Structure of Flowers Four different kinds of specialized leaves form flowers.

▶ Sepals form the outermost circle of flower parts. They protect a flower bud.

▶ Petals form a ring just inside the sepals. Some are brightly colored, which attracts pollinators.

▶ **Stamens** are the male reproductive structures and form a ring inside of the petals. Pollen is produced in an **anther**, which is the sac at the tip of a stamen. Each pollen grain contains a male gametophyte.

▶ **Carpels** are the female reproductive structures at the center of flowers. The female gametophytes develop inside the ovules that form in a carpel's ovary.

  • The sticky tip of a carpel, called the **stigma**, captures pollen.

  • A **pistil** is a structure that is made up of one or more carpels.

The Angiosperm Life Cycle The life cycle involves alternation of generations. Meiosis in stamens and carpels produces haploid cells (spores) that develop into gametophytes.

▶ The haploid cells in a stamen's anther undergo mitosis and form pollen grains, the male gametophytes, that contain 2 sperm nuclei.

▶ A haploid cell in each ovule of a carpel undergoes mitosis to produce an **embryo sac**, or female gametophyte, which contains 8 haploid nuclei. One of these nuclei becomes the egg.

▶ Pollen grains are transported to the stigmas of carpels during pollination.

▶ Both sperm nuclei fuse with nuclei in the embryo sac in a process called **double fertilization**. One sperm fuses with the egg to form a diploid (2N) zygote. The other sperm fuses with 2 other nuclei to form the triploid (3N) **endosperm**.

Vegetative Reproduction Asexual reproduction is common in plants.

▶ **Vegetative reproduction** leads to offspring that are identical to the parent. The offspring develop by mitotic cell division of cells in stems, leaves, and roots.

▶ Horticulturists use vegetative reproduction to propagate (grow) many identical plants. Making cuttings of stems and roots is one example. **Grafting** involves attaching a bud or a stem of one woody plant to the stems of another.

The Structure of Flowers

For Questions 1–10, match the floral part with its description.

Floral Part

_B_	1.	anthers
_F_	2.	carpels
_E_	3.	filament
_C_	4.	ovary
_I_	5.	petals
_G_	6.	pollen
_D_	7.	sepals
_H_	8.	stamen
_J_	9.	stigma
_A_	10.	style

Description

A. Stalk with a stigma at the top

B. Structures that produce male gametophytes

C. Structure that contains one or more ovules

D. Outermost circle of green floral parts

E. Long, thin structure that supports an anther

F. Floral parts that produce female gametophytes

G. Yellowish dust that contains male gametophytes

H. Male structure with an anther and a filament

I. Brightly colored parts just inside the sepals

J. Sticky, top portion of style

11. Complete the illustration by labeling the parts of the flower indicated.

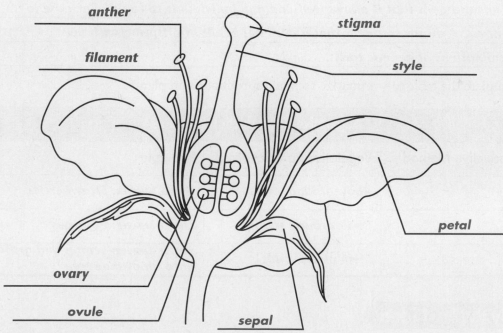

The Angiosperm Life Cycle

For Questions 12–15, complete each statement by writing the correct word or words.

12. The body of an adult plant with flowers is the ___*sporophyte*___ generation of the plant's life cycle.

13. The gametophytes of angiosperms have cells with nuclei that have the ___*haploid*___ number of chromosomes.

14. A male ___*gametophyte*___ of an angiosperm is a pollen grain.

15. A(n) ___*ovule*___ contains a female gametophyte of an angiosperm.

For Questions 16–20, write True if the statement is true. If the statement is false, change the underlined word or words to make the statement true.

___*stigma*___ **16.** In pollination, pollen grains are transferred to the <u>ovary</u> of a flower.

___*two*___ **17.** A pollen tube delivers <u>one</u> sperm to an ovule.

___*True*___ **18.** The fertilized egg in an ovule becomes the <u>zygote</u> of a new sporophyte.

___*True*___ **19.** Triploid tissue, called <u>endosperm</u>, forms in double fertilization.

___*ovule*___ **20.** A fertilized <u>embryo sac</u> then develops into a seed.

Vegetative Reproduction

21. What is vegetative reproduction in plants?

It is the production of offspring from one parent that results from mitotic cell division in nonreproductive parts such as leaves, stems, and roots.

22. Give an advantage and a disadvantage of vegetative reproduction to plants.

An advantage is that it allows well-adapted individuals to rapidly increase in numbers. A disadvantage is that it does not result in offspring with new combinations of genetic traits.

23. Complete the table to summarize asexual reproduction in plants.

Vegetative Reproduction in Plants		
Reproductive Method	**Vegetative Parts Involved**	**Example**
Stolons	*Aboveground stems*	SAMPLE ANSWER: *Strawberries*
Tubers	*Underground stems*	SAMPLE ANSWER: *Potatoes*
Grafts	*Stem pieces, buds*	SAMPLE ANSWER: *Lemon bud grafted onto an orange tree*

Apply the Big idea

24. How might a long period of rainy weather affect reproduction in wind-pollinated plants?

SAMPLE ANSWER: *A long period of rainy weather may prevent wind-pollinated plants from being pollinated and developing fruits and seeds. Pollen floats on the wind; however, if it were wet, the pollen would fall to the ground and never reach the stigmas of the plants. Without pollination, there will be no fertilization and no seeds produced.*

24.2 Fruits and Seeds

Lesson Objectives

- Describe the development of seeds and fruits.
- Explain how seeds are dispersed.
- List the factors that influence the dormancy and germination of seeds.

Lesson Summary

Seed and Fruit Development Seeds develop in the fruit of angiosperms.

► A seed protects and provides nourishment for a plant embryo.

► An ovary matures into a fruit as an embryo develops within each of its seeds. Some fruits are fleshy, and others are dry. Many foods are fruits.

Seed Dispersal Fruits are adaptations for seed dispersal that have been favored by natural selection.

► Animals disperse seeds for many plants that make edible fruits or fruits that cling to animal bodies.

► Wind and water disperse seeds for plants that make fruits with adaptations for gliding on the wind or floating on water.

Seed Dormancy and Germination Some seeds sprout right away, and others lie dormant for a period of time.

► In a period of **dormancy**, the embryo of a seed is alive but not growing.

► **Germination** is the resumption of growth by the embryo. Seeds absorb water before germinating. The water causes tissues in a seed to swell, causing the seed coat to crack. The embryonic root emerges first.

► Monocots and dicots have different patterns of germination.

► Dormancy helps the embryos in seeds survive until the environment is favorable for plant growth.

Seed and Fruit Development

For Questions 1–6, complete each statement by writing the correct word or words.

1. The function of a seed is to nourish and _____**protect**_____ a plant embryo.

2. After fertilization, _____**nutrients**_____ flow into the flower to support the growing embryo.

3. A fruit is a matured _____**ovary**_____ of a flower.

4. Fruits are adaptations for _____**spreading (dispersing)**_____ seeds.

5. Peas, corn, green beans, tomatoes, and rice are all examples of the _____**fruits**_____ of angiosperms.

6. In a peanut, the _____**shell**_____ is the fruit and the nut is the _____**seed**_____.

Seed Dispersal

For Questions 7–11, write the letter of the correct answer on the line at the left.

_____B_____ 7. Which tissue formed in plant reproduction nourishes the embryo?

   A. nectar   C. ovary wall

   B. endosperm   D. seed coat

_____D_____ 8. In evolutionary terms, seed dispersal is important because it

   A. allows plants to produce more offspring.

   B. keeps the number of plants in an area high.

   C. helps plants form new communities.

   D. reduces competition with parent plants.

_____A_____ 9. Seeds encased in fleshy, nutritious fruits are usually dispersed by

   A. animals.   C. water.

   B. gravity.   D. wind.

_____C_____ 10. Which fruit would be adapted for dispersal by water?

   A. a dry fruit with feathery branches

   B. a greenish fruit with a sticky surface

   C. a large, lightweight fruit with a thick, waxy covering

   D. a small, round fruit with a sweet, jellylike covering

_____C_____ 11. Which is an adaptation of a fruit for dispersal by wind?

   A. a tough, hard seed coat

   B. a ring of fleshy projections

   C. a pair of papery wings

   D. a hollow, air-filled center

Seed Dormancy and Germination

12. Complete the flowchart to summarize the process of seed germination.

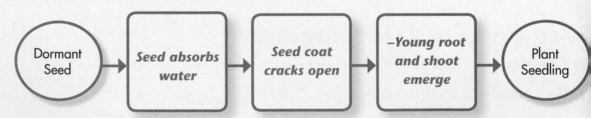

For Questions 13–20, write True if the statement is true. If the statement is false, change the underlined word or words to make the statement true.

_____True_____ 13. In most <u>monocots</u>, the cotyledon remains underground.

_____sheath_____ 14. In monocots, a <u>cotyledon</u> protects the young shoot as it emerges.

_____True_____ 15. The <u>hook</u> of the new shoot of a germinating dicot protects the new leaves from injury by the soil.

_____True_____ **16.** The <u>primary</u> root is the first root of a new plant.

_____germinate_____ **17.** Dormancy enables seeds to <u>live</u> under ideal growing conditions.

_____spring_____ **18.** The seeds of most plants in temperate regions germinate in the <u>fall</u>.

_____True_____ **19.** For many seeds, a <u>long period of cold</u> is required before dormancy can end.

_____fire_____ **20.** The cones of some pine trees must be exposed to <u>light</u> in order to release their seeds.

21. **THINK VISUALLY** Complete the illustration comparing seed germination in corn (monocot) and a bean (dicot). Under each drawing, identify the kind of plant that is shown, and make a sketch of the missing stage for each in the appropriate circle.

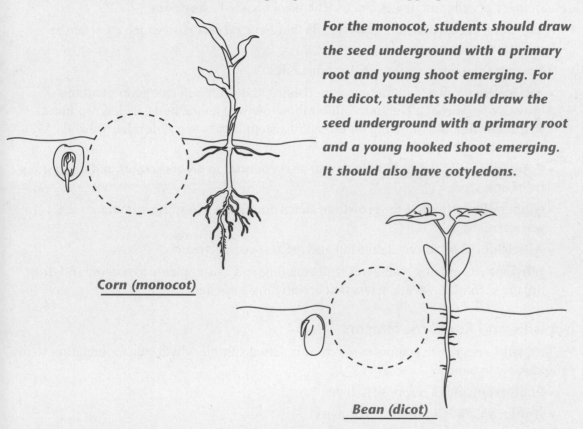

For the monocot, students should draw the seed underground with a primary root and young shoot emerging. For the dicot, students should draw the seed underground with a primary root and a young hooked shoot emerging. It should also have cotyledons.

Corn (monocot)

Bean (dicot)

Apply the Big idea

22. Lupines are flowering plants that make seeds with a thick, hard seed coat. Seeds collected from wild lupines are difficult to grow. What could be the cause of this difficulty? How might a hard seed coat be an adaptation that helps lupines survive?

SAMPLE ANSWER: *A hard seed coat makes it difficult for a seed to take in water, which is the first step in seed germination. This would be an adaptation for surviving the passage through an animal's digestive tract, or for surviving extremely low temperatures.*

_____

24.3 Plant Hormones

Lesson Objectives

🔑 Describe the effects of hormones on plant growth and development.

🔑 Identify three tropisms exhibited in plants.

🔑 Describe how plants respond to seasonal change.

Lesson Summary

Hormones Living organisms produce chemical signals that affect the growth, activity, and development of cells and tissues. Such a chemical is called a **hormone**.

▶ A hormone affects particular **target cells** that have **receptors** to which a particular hormone can bind.

▶ There are five major classes of plant hormones.

- **Auxins** are produced in the apical meristems and cause cell elongation and the growth of new roots. They also inhibit the growth of lateral buds, which produces **apical dominance**. Snipping off the tip of a stem breaks apical dominance and enables branches to develop.
- **Cytokinins** stimulate cell division and are produced in growing roots and developing fruits and seeds.
- **Gibberellins** stimulate the growth of stems and fruits. They also stimulate seed germination.
- **Abscisic acid** inhibits cell division and causes seed dormancy.
- **Ethylene** is a gas that stimulates fruit ripening and causes plants to seal off and drop organs such as leaves and fruits that are no longer needed.

Tropisms and Rapid Movements

▶ **Tropisms** are growth responses to environmental stimuli, which cause elongating stems and roots to bend.

- **Phototropism** is a response to light.
- **Gravitropism** is a response to gravity.
- **Thigmotropism** is a response to touch.

▶ Rapid movements such as the closing of leaves when touched are caused by changes in cell walls and in osmotic pressure in certain cells.

Response to Seasons Plants have regular cycles in their patterns of growth, development and flowering that are tied to seasonal changes. One environmental stimulus that changes with the seasons is the **photoperiod**, the relative length of the light and dark periods in a day. A plant pigment called phytochrome causes a plant's response to the photoperiod.

▶ The timing of flowering is one plant response to the photoperiod.

▶ Preparations for winter dormancy, which include leaf loss and the formation of scales around terminal buds, are also responses to the photoperiod.

Hormones

1. What is a hormone?

A hormone is a chemical signal produced by a living organism that affects the growth, activity, and development of cells and tissues.

2. What are the functions of hormones in plants?

Plant hormones control the development of cells, tissues, and organs. They also coordinate a plant's response to the environment.

3. What is a target cell?

A target cell is one that has receptors for and is affected by a hormone.

4. Briefly describe the experiments that Charles and Francis Darwin performed on grass seedlings.

SAMPLE ANSWER: Charles and Francis Darwin studied the mechanisms behind a seedling's tendency to bend toward light. They cut off the tips of some grass seedlings and blocked light from reaching the tips of other grass seedlings. Only the seedlings with tips that were exposed to light grew toward the source of the light.

For Questions 5–19, match the action with the plant hormone that produces it. Hormones may be used more than once.

Action

C	**5.**	May oppose the effects of auxins
B	**6.**	Promotes cell elongation
D	**7.**	Causes petals and leaves to drop
E	**8.**	Promotes seed germination
A	**9.**	Promotes seed dormancy
C	**10.**	Stimulates cell division
E	**11.**	Causes the enlargement of fruits
B	**12.**	Causes apical dominance
D	**13.**	Stimulates fruit ripening
C	**14.**	Forms in growing roots
D	**15.**	Forms in aging leaves and flowers
E	**16.**	Opposes the effects of abscisic acid
E	**17.**	Stimulates dramatic stem growth
B	**18.**	Stimulates new root growth
A	**19.**	Inhibits cell division

Plant Hormone

A. abscisic acid

B. auxin

C. cytokinins

D. ethylene

E. gibberellin

Tropisms and Rapid Movements

20. What is a tropism?

A tropism is a growth response of a plant to a stimulus from the environment.

21. What causes the bending of stems and roots in tropisms? Give an example.

The bending of stems and roots is caused by the difference in concentration of auxins on one side of the stem or root, which causes that side to grow longer than the other side. For example, auxin moves toward the dark side of a stem, causing the cells on that side to elongate more than the cells on the lighted side and making the stem bend in the direction of the light.

22. Complete the table about plant tropisms.

Plant Tropisms		
Tropism	**Definition**	**Example**
Gravitropism	*The response of a plant to gravity*	SAMPLE ANSWER: *Roots growing downward*
Phototropism	*The response of a plant to light*	*A stem bending toward a light source*
Thigmotropism	The response of a plant to touch	SAMPLE ANSWER: *A tendril of a vine coiling around a trellis*

23. How are the speed and causes of rapid movements of plants different from the speed and causes of tropisms?

Rapid movements happen in a few seconds and are caused by changes in cell walls and the osmotic pressure of certain cells. Tropisms take much longer to appear because they involve the growth of a plant.

24. List two examples of rapid movements that occur in plants.

The closing of the leaves of "sensitive plants" and the closing of a Venus' flytrap leaf around an insect are examples of rapid movements.

Response to Seasons

For Questions 25–28, complete each statement by writing the correct word or words.

25. Plants that flower when nights are longer than days are called ___*short-day*___ plants.

26. Irises that flower in summer when nights are short are called ___*long-day*___ plants.

27. The relative lengths of the light and dark times in a day are a stimulus called the ___*photoperiod*___ .

28. The chemical that causes the seasonal responses of plants is a type of light-sensitive chemical called a(n) ___*pigment*___ .

29. Complete the concept map that summarizes the role of phytochrome in plants.

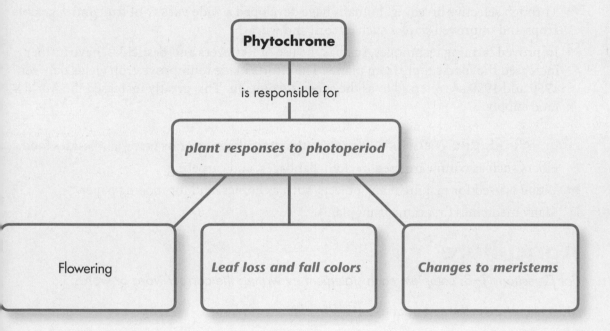

Phytochrome

is responsible for

plant responses to photoperiod

Flowering   *Leaf loss and fall colors*   *Changes to meristems*

Apply the Big idea

30. You have been asked to suggest a flowering plant that would bloom and beautify a lighted parking lot. The parking lot is only dark between midnight and sunrise. What information should you research about the plants you consider? Explain your answer.

SAMPLE ANSWER: *It will be crucial to know what kind of photoperiod stimulates the plants to flower. The plants will have to be long-day plants (or day-neutral), otherwise flowering will be inhibited by the short dark period.*

_____

_____

24.4 Plants and Humans

Lesson Objectives

Identify the major food-supply crops for humans.

Describe how humans benefit from plants.

Lesson Summary

Agriculture The systematic cultivation of useful plants is called agriculture.

▶ The beginning of human civilization is linked to the development of agriculture. Worldwide, a few crop plants such as rice, wheat, soybeans, and corn provide the bulk of the food supply for humans and livestock.

▶ Through selective breeding, humans have developed a wide variety of fruit and vegetable crops and improved staples such as corn and wheat.

▶ Improved farming techniques, such as the use of fertilizers and pesticides, have further increased the food supply from plants. The efforts made to improve crop yields between 1950 and 1970 are referred to as the **green revolution**. This greatly increased the world's food supply.

Fiber, Wood, and Medicine Plants are the source of many raw materials besides food.

▶ Fibers such as cotton are used in cloth, bandages, and carpeting.

▶ Wood is used for making many objects, such as homes, and for making paper.

▶ Many medicines first came from plants.

Agriculture

For Questions 1–8, complete each statement by writing the correct word or words.

1. Agriculture is the systematic _____*cultivation*_____ of plants.

2. The foundation on which human society is built is modern _____*farming*_____.

3. Evidence suggests that agriculture developed between _____*10,000*_____ and _____*12,000*_____ years ago.

4. Nearly all agricultural plants belong to the group of plants called _____*angiosperms*_____.

5. The _____*seeds*_____ produced by crop plants such as wheat, rice, and corn are the source of most of the food humans eat.

6. Humans changed wild food plants into productive crops through the practice of *selective breeding*.

7. Cabbage, broccoli, and Brussels sprouts were all developed from the wild _____*mustard*_____ plant.

8. The green revolution greatly increased _____*crop yields*_____.

9. Complete the concept map.

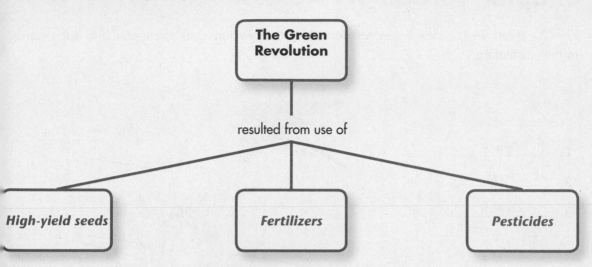

Fiber, Wood, and Medicine

For Questions 10–13, write the letter of the correct answer on the line at the left.

__C__ **10.** Which is an example of a plant that is a source of food?

A. *Aloe vera*   C. maize

B. cotton   D. Sitka spruce

__A__ **11.** Cotton fibers are outgrowths of the

A. seed coat epidermis.   C. vascular cambium.

B. ripened ovary wall.   D. vascular bundles.

__D__ **12.** The wood used to make chairs and musical instruments is made up of which plant tissue?

A. the cortex   C. the mesophyll

B. the cambium   D. the xylem

__A__ **13.** Which plant contains chemicals that can help burns and other wounds?

A. *Aloe vera*   C. maize

B. cotton   D. Sitka spruce

Apply the Big idea

14. What effect is global climate change likely to have on agriculture?

SAMPLE ANSWER: *Global climate change is likely to change the types of crops that are grown in particular areas of the world. It is also likely to cause the development of new crop varieties and methods of farming that could enable people to grow crops in less than ideal conditions.*

Chapter Vocabulary Review

For Questions 1–3, on the lines provided, label the structure that corresponds to each number in the illustration.

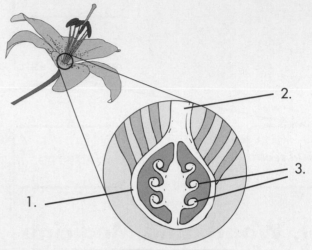

1. _____Ovary_____

2. _____Style_____

3. _____Ovules_____

For Questions 4–15, complete each statement by writing the correct word or words.

4. The female structure of a flower that can be made up of a single carpel or two or more fused carpels is called a _____pistil_____.

5. A plant hormone that causes stem and fruit growth as well as seed _____germination_____ is called _____gibberellin_____.

6. A _____target_____ cell has _____receptors_____ for a particular hormone.

7. The female gametophyte of an angiosperm is a small structure called the _____embryo sac_____.

8. The food storage tissue that results from double _____fertilization_____ in angiosperms is called _____endosperm_____.

9. Seed _____dormancy_____ is a period during which a plant embryo stops growing.

10. _____Grafting_____ is the method of propagating many identical woody plants using the buds of a desirable plant.

11. The ripening of fruits is one effect of the plant hormone called _____ethylene_____.

12. Identical offspring produced by a single parent plant result from _____vegetative_____ reproduction.

13. _____Apical_____ dominance is a major effect of the plant hormone _____auxin_____.

14. Pollination occurs when pollen grains land on the _____stigma_____ of a flower.

15. The _____anthers_____ of flowers are the tiny sacs that produce the male gametophytes of angiosperms.

CHAPTER MYSTERY

THE GREEN LEMONS

21st Century Learning

In the Chapter Mystery, you learned how one factor could disrupt a plant's ripening schedule. Many factors affect a plant's growth and reproduction, as well as its taste and nutrition. Today's consumers are becoming increasingly conscious of the factors that affect the food they eat.

Organic Food Farming and Labeling

Organic farming is a type of agricultural production system that uses natural methods, such as compost instead of synthetic fertilizers, biological pest control instead of synthetic pesticides, and crop rotation instead of plant growth regulators. Organic farmers are not allowed to use certain products that conventional farmers use. All organic food products must be certified by independent state or private agencies accredited by the U.S. Department of Agriculture.

Many consumers think that organic food tastes better and is more nutritious and healthful. Therefore, they are willing to pay more for food labeled organic. Scientists, however, have not proven that organic food is more nutritious.

Rules for Labeling Food as Organic

1. Animals producing meat, poultry, eggs, and dairy products must not be given antibiotics or growth hormones. They also cannot be fed animal byproducts, such as feathers and ground-up chicken parts.
2. Cows on organic farms must graze on grass that has not been treated with pesticides.
3. Vegetables must be grown without using conventional pesticides.
4. The use of conventional pesticides, petroleum-based fertilizers, bioengineering, and ionizing radiation is prohibited from all organic food production.

Before any food receives an organic label, a government-approved certifier must inspect the farm where the food is produced as well as the companies that process and transport the food.

21st Century Themes ## Science and Global Awareness

1. Why are organic food products considered more "natural" than conventional food products?

   Organic farming produces food using natural methods. It does not use synthetic, or

   human-made, fertilizers, pesticides, and other chemicals.

2. Why are many consumers willing to pay more for food items labeled "organic"?

   They think the food tastes better and is more nutritious and healthful.

Continued on next page ▶

3. Why do you think the U.S. Department of Agriculture deems it important to regulate which foods get the "organic" label?

SAMPLE ANSWER: *Because stores can get more money for items labeled "organic," they may be willing to put that label on food that is not organic. Food that is not organic is often cheaper for the stores to buy. Therefore, stores would make more money by mislabeling food, but the consumer would be cheated.*

4. The first rule states that animals producing organic foods cannot be fed animal byproducts. Why do you think this rule is included? Give an example to support your reasoning.

SAMPLE ANSWER: *Animal byproducts could include the very chemicals not allowed for animals producing organic food. For example, a chicken could have been raised on a farm using synthetic pesticides. If byproducts from this chicken are fed to an animal on an organic farm, those pesticides could be passed on in the food.*

5. Why is important to inspect companies transporting the food as well as those producing the food?

SAMPLE ANSWER: *A transportation company might transport non-organic food one week and organic the next. Traces of synthetic pesticides and fertilizers may be left in the truck from the non-organic food. These chemicals could then get on the organic food. Inspectors have to inspect everything that comes in contact with organic food before that food can be labeled as truly organic.*

21st Century Skills History of Organic Food

The skills used in this activity include **information and media literacy, communication skills, critical thinking and systems thinking, creativity and intellectual curiosity,** and **interpersonal and collaborative skills.**

Work in a small group to find out about the history of organic food. Decide on a graphic to present to the class. For example, your group may want to make a graph to show how the amount of organic food produced in the U.S. has changed over the past few decades. Or, your group might choose to make a poster or a timeline that shows the evolution of what food is considered "organic." Then, present your graphic to the class.

Evaluate students' work by whether the presentation uses current data and refers to current processes and regulations.

25 Introduction to Animals

Big idea

Unity and Diversity of Life

Q: What characteristics and traits define animals?

WHAT I KNOW	WHAT I LEARNED
25.1 What is an animal?	SAMPLE ANSWER: *Animals are different from other living things (bacteria, protists, fungi, and plants).*	SAMPLE ANSWER: *All animals are multicellular, eukarytotic, and heterotrophic. Their cells lack cell walls. Chordates exhibit four characteristics during some stage of their development: a dorsal, hollow nerve cord; a notochord; a tail that extends beyond the anus; and pharyngeal pouches.*
25.2 How have different animal body plans evolved?	SAMPLE ANSWER: *Each animal group evolved a group of structures or "body plan" that is unique to that group.*	SAMPLE ANSWER: *The features of a body plan include levels of organization (cells, tissues, organs, organ systems); body symmetry; differentiation of germ layers; formation of a cavity between the digestive tract and the body wall; patterns of embryological development; segmentation; cephalization; and limb formation. The features of body plans provide evidence needed to build a cladogram, or phylogenetic tree, of animals.*

25.1 What Is an Animal?

Lesson Objectives

List the characteristics that all animals share.

Differentiate between invertebrates and chordates.

List and discuss the essential functions that animals perform in order to survive.

Lesson Summary

Characteristics of Animals All animals are multicellular, heterotrophic, and eukaryotic. Their cells lack cell walls.

Types of Animals Animals are often classified into two broad categories: invertebrates and chordates.

▶ **Invertebrates** do not have a backbone, or vertebral column.

- More than 95 percent of all animal species are invertebrates.
- Invertebrates are classified in at least 33 phyla, the largest taxonomic groups of animals. Examples of invertebrates are sea stars, jellyfishes, and insects.

▶ **Chordates** exhibit four characteristics during some stage of development: a dorsal, hollow nerve cord; a notochord; a tail that extends beyond the anus; and pharyngeal pouches.

- A **notochord** is a supporting rod that runs through the body just below the nerve cord.
- **Pharyngeal pouches** are paired structures in the throat region.
- Most chordates develop a backbone, or vertebral column. They are **vertebrates**.

What Animals Do to Survive Animals must maintain homeostasis in order to survive. One important way to maintain homeostasis is **feedback inhibition**, also called negative feedback, in which the product or result of a process limits the process itself. In order to maintain homeostasis, animals must

▶ gather and respond to information;

▶ obtain and distribute oxygen and nutrients;

▶ collect and eliminate carbon dioxide and other wastes.

They also reproduce.

Characteristics of Animals

1. Complete the graphic organizer to summarize the characteristics of animals.

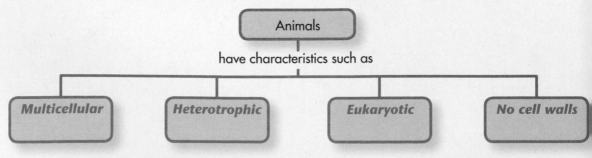

Types of Animals

2. Are invertebrates rare? Explain your answer.

No, they are common. More than 95 percent of animal species are invertebrates.

_____

3. What is an invertebrate?

An invertebrate is an animal that lacks a backbone, or vertebral column.

_____

4. Why do invertebrates not form a clade?

They are not a clade because they are defined by the absence of a characteristic.

_____

5. What are some examples of invertebrates?

Sea stars, worms, jellyfishes, and insects are invertebrates.

6. Look at the diagram of a chordate. Write the name of the labeled structure on the lines below.

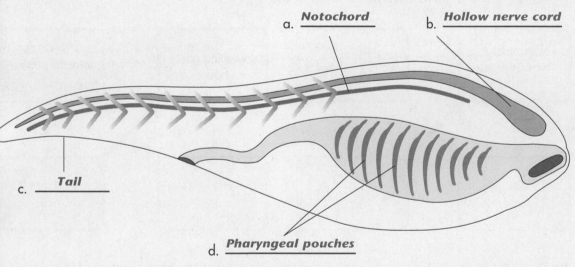

a. *Notochord*   b. *Hollow nerve cord*

c. *Tail*

d. *Pharyngeal pouches*

7. Are all chordates vertebrates? Explain your answer.

No, some chordates never develop a backbone.

_____

8. What groups of animals are vertebrates?

Vertebrates include fishes, amphibians, reptiles, birds, and mammals.

_____

9. Both snakes and earthworms have long, streamlined body shapes, but snakes are vertebrates and earthworms are not. Why are they classified differently despite their similarity in appearance?

Animals are classified based on body plans, not similarity of appearance. Earthworms do not have the characteristics of a chordate, so they are considered invertebrates.

_____

What Animals Do to Survive

10. Complete the graphic organizer to define three ways that animals maintain homeostasis.

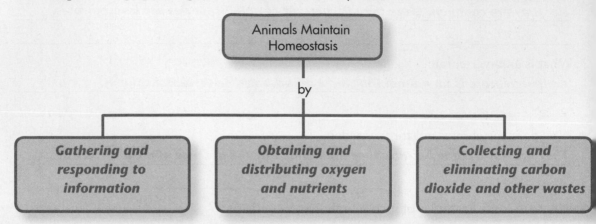

11. The diagram on the left below shows the feedback inhibition that maintains temperature in a house. Complete the blank boxes in the diagram on the right below to show how body temperature is maintained in a human being.

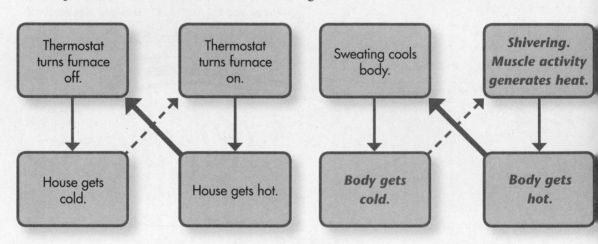

12. Describe generally how an animal's nervous and musculoskeletal systems work together to allow it to escape a predator.

The animal's sensory receptors, which are part of the nervous system, sense a

predator. Its nervous system then sends signals to the musculoskeletal system to flee.

The animal's muscles work with its skeleton to allow it to move away from the predator.

_____

13. In complex animals, what system collects metabolic wastes and delivers them to the respiratory and excretory systems?

the circulatory system

14. In complex animals, which three body systems work together to obtain and distribute oxygen and nutrients?

the respiratory, digestive, and circulatory systems

For Questions 15–24, write the letter of the correct answer on the line at the left.

___D___ 15. What system gathers information through receptors for sound, light, chemicals, and other stimuli?

    A. respiratory

    B. circulatory

    C. musculoskeletal

    D. nervous

___C___ 16. Most chordates have a large number of nerve cells concentrated into a

    A. backbone.

    B. notochord.

    C. brain.

    D. pharyngeal pouch.

___B___ 17. How does muscle tissue generate force?

    A. It stretches.

    B. It shortens.

    C. It inflates.

    D. It dilates.

___B___ 18. How do the skeletons of insects and vertebrates differ?

    A. Insects have fluid skeletons. Vertebrates have external skeletons.

    B. Insects have external skeletons. Vertebrates have internal skeletons.

    C. Insects have internal skeletons. Vertebrates have external skeletons.

    D. Insects have external skeletons. Vertebrates have fluid skeletons.

___A___ 19. What process allows some aquatic animals to "breathe" through their skin?

    A. diffusion

    B. digestion

    C. excretion

    D. circulation

___D___ 20. Which structure performs a function most similar to that of gills?

    A. heart

    B. intestine

    C. blood vessel

    D. lung

___D___ 21. Which of these functions requires the coordinated actions of the digestive, circulatory, and excretory systems?

    A. gathering O_2 and distributing it to body systems

    B. collecting and eliminating CO_2 from tissues

    C. acquiring nutrients and distributing them to body systems

    D. collecting and eliminating metabolic wastes

_____A_____ **22.** How do the respiratory system and excretory system differ in the wastes they eliminate?

    A. The respiratory system eliminates carbon dioxide. The excretory system eliminates ammonia.

    B. The respiratory system eliminates wastes that contain nitrogen. The excretory system eliminates carbon-based wastes.

    C. The respiratory system eliminates oxygen and nitrogen. The excretory system eliminates ammonia.

    D. The respiratory system eliminates ammonia. The excretory system eliminates carbon dioxide.

_____C_____ **23.** Which activity is required for survival of the species but not survival of the organism?

    A. digestion

    B. excretion

    C. reproduction

    D. circulation

_____B_____ **24.** What is an advantage of asexual reproduction?

    A. It increases genetic diversity in a population.

    B. It produces large numbers of offspring rapidly.

    C. It increases a species' ability to evolve.

    D. It produces offspring that are genetically different from the parents.

Apply the Big idea

25. In what ways do invertebrates differ from vertebrates? Identify at least three groups of invertebrates.

SAMPLE ANSWER: *Invertebrates have no backbones. They don't have a nerve cord, a notochord, a tail, or pharyngeal pouches. Invertebrate groups include insects, worms, sea stars, and jellyfishes.*

26. Suppose you were studying the cell walls of a multicellular organism under a microscope. Were you studying an animal? Explain your answer.

No, it wasn't an animal, because animal cells have no cell walls.

25.2 Animal Body Plans and Evolution

Lesson Objectives

▱ Discuss some trends in animal evolution.

▱ Explain the differences among the animal phyla.

Lesson Summary

Features of Body Plans Each animal phylum has a unique organization of body structures called its "body plan." The features of a body plan include

► levels of organization: cells, tissues, organs, organ systems

► body symmetry:
  • **radial symmetry:** body parts extend from a central point
  • **bilateral symmetry:** left and right sides are mirror images, with front and back ends

► differentiation of germ layers:
  • **endoderm**, the innermost layer
  • **mesoderm**, the middle layer
  • **ectoderm**, the outermost layer

► formation of a cavity, or fluid-filled space between the digestive tract and the body wall:
  • a true **coelom** (found in most complex animal phyla) develops in the mesoderm and is lined with tissue derived from the mesoderm
  • a **pseudocoelom** is only partially lined with mesoderm
  • Some invertebrates lack a body cavity and some have only a primitive, jellylike layer between the ectoderm and endoderm.

► patterns of embryological development
  • Sexually reproducing animals begin life as a **zygote**, or fertilized egg.
  • The zygote develops into a hollow ball of cells, the **blastula**.
  • The blastula folds in on itself and creates a tube that becomes the digestive tract; the tube has a single opening, the blastopore:
    ▷ In **protostomes** (most invertebrates), the blastopore becomes the mouth.
    ▷ In **deuterostomes** (chordates and echinoderms), the blastopore becomes the anus.

► segmentation: repeated parts, such as the segments of worms

► **cephalization**: the concentration of sense organs and nerves near the anterior (head) end

► limb formation: external appendages such as legs, flippers, and wings

The Cladogram of Animals The features of body plans provide the evidence needed to build a cladogram, or phylogenetic tree, of all animals. Animal phyla are usually defined by their adult body plans and patterns of embryological development.

► The characteristics of animals vary within each phylum.

► Each phylum may be thought of as an "evolutionary experiment." Phyla with successful body plans have survived.

Features of Body Plans

1. Complete the table of main ideas and details about animal body plans. Use the boxes to list and summarize the features of animal body plans.

Features of Body Plans	
Main Idea: Feature of Body Plan	**Details: Important structures or patterns of development**
Levels of organization	*Cells, tissues, organs, organ systems*
Body symmetry	None, radial, or bilateral
Germ layers	*Endoderm, mesoderm, ectoderm*
Body cavity	*None, pseudocoelom, or true coelom*
Patterns of embryological development	*The zygote develops into a hollow ball of cells, the blastula.* • *Protostomes: the blastopore becomes the mouth.* • *Deuterostomes: the blastopore becomes the anus.*
Segmentation	Repeated parts, such as the segments of worms
Cephalization	*The concentration of sense organs and nerves near the anterior (head) end*
Limb formation	*External appendages such as legs, flippers, and wings*

2. **THINK VISUALLY** Sketch two common objects that show the difference between radial symmetry and bilateral symmetry. Label your sketches and explain them.

One sketch (bilateral) should show and explain an object that can be divided into two matching halves along one axis. The other (radial) should show an object that can be divided into equivalent segments by drawing a line through its center.

3. **THINK VISUALLY** Label each of these organisms with the kind of symmetry it exhibits.

bilateral symmetry
_____

radial symmetry
_____

radial symmetry
_____

bilateral symmetry
_____

4. **THINK VISUALLY** Draw three sketches that show the difference between acoelomate, pseudocoelomate, and coelomate animals. Label ectoderm, mesoderm, and endoderm in your sketches.

The acoelomate sketch should show mesoderm and a digestive cavity, as in a flatworm. The pseudocoelomate sketch should show a pseudocoelom and a digestive tract, as in a roundworm. The coelomate sketch should have a coelom and a digestive tract, as in an earthworm.

5. Label the diagram showing the difference between deuterostomes and protostomes. Label the following structures: blastula, blastopore, ectoderm, endoderm, mesoderm, mouth, protostome.

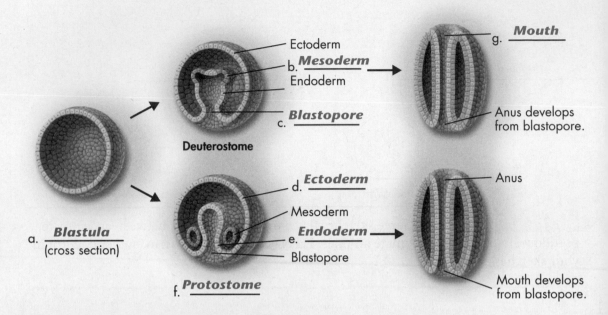

Ectoderm

b. *Mesoderm*

Endoderm

c. *Blastopore*

Deuterostome

g. *Mouth*

Anus develops from blastopore.

a. *Blastula* (cross section)

d. *Ectoderm*

Mesoderm

e. *Endoderm*

Blastopore

f. *Protostome*

Anus

Mouth develops from blastopore.

For Questions 6–14, complete each statement by writing the correct word or words.

6. Deuterostomes that show radial symmetry in their adult form are called ___*echinoderms*___.

7. ___*Flatworms*___ are bilaterally symmetrical animals with three germ layers and no coelom.

8. ___*Mollusks*___ are protostomes with a true coelom and cephalization without segmentation.

9. Members of the ___*sponge*___ phylum have no body symmetry.

10. Animals in the ___*cnidarian*___ phylum have specialized cells and tissues, but no organs.

11. Both ___*annelids*___ and ___*arthropods*___ are segmented protostomes with bilateral symmetry.

12. In addition to echinoderms, ___*chordates*___ are also deuterostomes.

13. An important way in which the body plan of mollusks differs from that of arthropods is that mollusks lack ___*segmentation*___.

14. Only members of the ___*roundworm*___ phylum have a pseudocoelom.

The Cladogram of Animals

Use the cladogram to answer Questions 15–17.

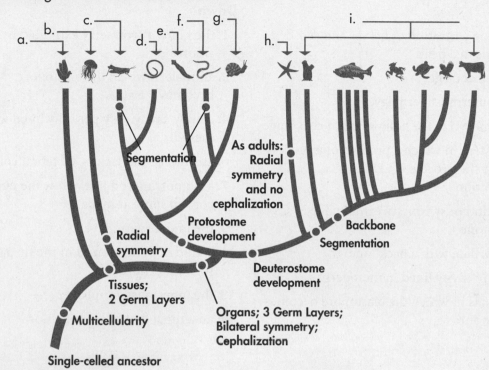

15. On the lines provided, label the names of the animal phyla that correspond to the letters in the diagram.

a. _____Sponges_____   d. _____Roundworms_____   g. _____Mollusks_____

b. _____Cnidarians_____   e. _____Flatworms_____   h. _____Echinoderms_____

c. _____Arthropods_____   f. _____Annelids_____   i. _____Chordates_____

16. What characteristics define the branch of the cladogram that leads to the mollusks?

The characteristics are organs, three germ layers, bilateral symmetry, cephalization,

and protostome development.

17. Is a chordate a "better" animal than a sponge? Explain your answer.

No, it simply has a different body plan that has made it well adapted to survive and

reproduce in its environment.

Apply the Big idea

18. Cows, hawks, and whales are all vertebrates. However, their forelimbs are noticeably different. Explain how "evolutionary experiments" that yield variations on a body plan have produced such diversity among vertebrates. Use forelimb structures as an example.

Those variations that promoted survival and reproduction were maintained in what

eventually became new classes of chordates. For example, the forelimb has evolved

as a leg in the cow, while it is a wing on a bird. The whale's forelimb is adapted for

swimming in water; the bird's is adapted for flying in air.

Chapter Vocabulary Review

Across

2. the concentration of nerves and sense organs in a head
5. a fertilized egg
8. the outermost germ layer
10. an embryo at the hollow ball of cells stage
12. A system in which a product of a process limits the process is _____ inhibition.
15. the kind of symmetry exhibited by a sea anemone
16. a chordate with a backbone
17. a body cavity lined in mesoderm
18. animals in which the blastopore becomes the mouth

Down

1. the kind of symmetry exhibited by a horse
3. animals in which the blastopore becomes the anus
4. a body cavity only partially lined with mesoderm
6. an animal that lacks a vertebral column
7. a supporting rod just below the nerve cord in some animals
9. the middle germ layer
11. a kind of pouch found in the throat region of chordates
13. the innermost germ layer
14. an animal that has a notochord

Crossword solution:

- 2 Across: CEPHALIZATION
- 1 Down: BILATERAL
- 5 Across: ZYGOTE
- 6 Down: INVERTEBRATE
- 7 Down: NOTOCHORD
- 4 Down: PSEUDOCOELOMS
- 3 Down: DEUTEROSTOMES
- 8 Across: ECTODERM
- 9 Down: MESODOM
- 10 Across: BLASTULA
- 11 Down: PHARYNGEAL
- 12 Across: FEEDBACK
- 13 Down: ENDODERM
- 14 Down: CHORDATE
- 15 Across: RADIAL
- 16 Across: VERTEBRATE
- 17 Across: COELOM
- 18 Across: PROTOSTOMES

CHAPTER MYSTERY

SLIME DAY AT THE BEACH

21st Century Learning

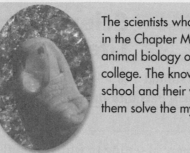

The scientists who helped identify the salp in the Chapter Mystery probably studied animal biology or marine biology in college. The knowledge they acquired at school and their work experience helped them solve the mystery of the slime.

Working with Animals

Some people who are interested in animals and love to be around them own pets or volunteer at local animal shelters. Other people, however, want to devote their careers to caring for or studying animals.

People who want to work with animals must decide what level of education and training they are willing to pursue to achieve their goal. Some jobs that involve caring for and understanding animals require extensive education or intensive training, such as that of the scientists in the Chapter Mystery. Other careers that involve working with animals require less experience and education. For example, animal control officers might be required to have a two-year degree, rather than a four-year degree or a graduate degree. Below is an example of a job description for an animal control officer.

County Animal Control Officer Job Opening

• •

JOB DESCRIPTION

Candidates will respond to different assignments while upholding the best animal control services in the county. Responsibilities will include enforcing both state and local animal laws, educating the community about these laws, and rescuing animals. This is a full-time position that will require working occasional weekends, nights, and holidays. Candidates will also be on-call at times. Continuing education provided on the job.

QUALIFICATIONS

Candidate must have excellent equipment, computer, and management skills. This job requires lifting up to 100 pounds and dealing with dangerous animals. Applicant must have a valid driver's license. Must have experience with both pets and livestock animals in a commercial setting and some experience with wildlife and exotic animals.

EDUCATION

Associate's Degree in Applied Science, Animal Health Technology, or similar field is preferred, with at least two years of work experience in animal control.

STATUS

Full time

SALARY

Depends on qualifications and experience

Continued on next page ▶

21st Century Themes Science and Economic Literacy

1. What work experience should a candidate for this job opening have?

experience working with pets and livestock, as well as wildlife

2. What might be a commercial setting in which a candidate worked with animals?

SAMPLE ANSWER: *Veterinary clinics, zoos, animal shelters, farms*

3. Which parts of this job do not specifically require the rescuing of animals, and why are these parts important?

Animal control officers must educate the public about state and local animal laws

and enforce those laws. These responsibilities are important because they help

citizens become aware of the importance of treating animals well.

4. This ad states that an Associate's Degree is preferred. What do you think might be an alternative to this degree?

SAMPLE ANSWER: *An alternative might be more experience in the field of animal control*

and animal handling with a proven record of mastering the job qualifications and

responsibilities.

5. What danger might an animal control officer face when rescuing an animal?

SAMPLE ANSWER: *An animal control officer might have to deal with an aggressive and*

frightened animal or an animal with rabies, or might have to face angry citizens.

21st Century Skills Investigate a Career

The skills used in this activity include **information and media literacy, critical thinking and systems thinking, creative and intellectual curiosity,** and **self-direction.**

Work with a group to investigate how a person would become an animal control officer. Then create a chronological plan to become an animal control officer. Do an online search to identify community colleges, state colleges, and private institutions that offer courses and degrees that satisfy the job description on the previous page. (Alternatively, you could call local animal shelters to discuss the educational programs completed by its staff members.) In your group's plan, identify the courses a person would need to complete the program. Include any high school experiences, internships, and summer jobs that would be helpful to secure a job after college graduation. Your group should also create a budget that includes tuition, room and board, application fees, meal plans, textbooks, and other supplies. Submit your group's plan and budget to your teacher.

Evaluate groups' plans based on how realistic they are, and how complete they are in terms of taking all the factors involved in preparing for this career into account. Plans should be clear and chronological and presented in an easy-to-understand format.

26 Animal Evolution and Diversity

 Evolution

Q: How have animals descended from earlier forms through the process of evolution?

WHAT I KNOW	WHAT I LEARNED
26.1 How did invertebrates evolve?	*SAMPLE ANSWER: **Invertebrates evolved before vertebrates, millions of years ago.***	*SAMPLE ANSWER: **The first animals began evolving before the Cambrian Explosion. Over a period of 10–15 million years, animals evolved complex body plans, appendages, skeletons, and other hard body parts. By the end of the Cambrian Period, all the basic body plans of modern animal phyla had been established.***
26.2 How did chordates evolve?	*SAMPLE ANSWER: **Chordates evolved more recently than invertebrates.***	*SAMPLE ANSWER: **Each time chordate ancestors evolved a new adaptation in their body plan, a major adaptive radiation occurred. Today, there are six groups of modern chordates—one group of nonvertebrate chordates and five groups of vertebrate chordates (fishes, amphibians, reptiles, birds, and mammals).***
26.3 How did primates evolve?	*SAMPLE ANSWER: **Primates evolved later than other animals. There are many different kinds of primates, including monkeys, apes, and humans.***	*SAMPLE ANSWER: **Humans and other primates evolved from a common ancestor that lived more than 65 million years ago. Many species of the genus Homo existed before our species, Homo sapiens, appeared. Our genus originated in Africa and spread to the rest of the world.***

26.1 Invertebrate Evolution and Diversity

Lesson Objectives

Explain what fossil evidence indicates about the timing of the evolution of the first animals.

Interpret the cladogram of invertebrates.

Lesson Summary

Origins of the Invertebrates It is not known when the first multicellular animals evolved from single-celled eukaryotes.

▶ Animals probably evolved from ancestors they shared with choanoflagellates. Fossil evidence indicates that animals began evolving long before the Cambrian Explosion, which occurred between 530 and 515 million years ago.

▶ Fossils from the Ediacara Hills of Australia date from roughly 565 to 544 million years ago. Their body plans are different from those of anything alive today. Some seem to be related to invertebrates such as jellyfishes and worms.

▶ Cambrian fossils (dating back about 542 million years ago) show how animals evolved complex body plans over a span of 10–15 million years. Many had body symmetry, a front and back end, specialized cells, and **appendages**, structures such as legs or antennae protruding from the body. Some had hard body parts that became fossilized.

▶ By the end of the Cambrian, the basic body plans of the modern phyla were established.

▶ Today, invertebrates are the most abundant animals on Earth.

Cladogram of Invertebrates The cladogram of invertebrates presents current hypotheses about evolutionary relationships among major groups of modern invertebrates.

▶ The major invertebrate phyla are the sponges, cnidarians, arthropods, nematodes (roundworms), flatworms, annelids, mollusks, and echinoderms.

• Sponges have pores in their bodies.

• Cnidarians are radially symmetrical animals with stinging tentacles.

• Arthropods have segmented bodies, a hard external skeleton, jointed appendages, and cephalization.

• Nematodes, or roundworms, are nonsegmented worms with pseudocoeloms. Their digestive tracts have two openings.

• Platyhelminthes, or flatworms, are the simplest animals to have three germ layers, bilateral symmetry, and cephalization.

• Annelids are worms with segmented bodies and a true coelom.

▶ **Larvae** are the immature stages of development in some animals, such as mollusks. Many mollusks have a free-swimming larval stage called a **trochophore**. The trochophore is also characteristic of many annelids, indicating that annelids and mollusks are closely related.

• Mollusks are soft-bodied animals that usually have a shell. They also have a true coelom and complex organ systems.

• Echinoderms have spiny skin and exhibit radial symmetry.

Origins of the Invertebrates

1. How much time passed between the appearance of the first prokaryotic cells and the emergence of multicellular organisms?

About three billion years passed

2. What are choanoflagellates? What is their significance in animal evolution?

They are single-celled eukaryotes that sometimes grow in colonies. They may have

evolved from ancestors they shared with animals.

3. How old is our oldest evidence of multicellular life?

roughly 600 million years old

For Questions 4–9, write the letter of the correct answer on the line at the left.

_____ B _____ **4.** The first animals were tiny and soft-bodied, so

    A. no fossilized bodies exist.

    B. few fossilized bodies exist.

    C. fossilized bodies are plentiful.

    D. the only fossils that exist are "trace fossils."

_____ B _____ **5.** Fossil evidence indicates that the first animals began evolving

    A. during the Cambrian Period.   **C.** after the Cambrian Explosion.

    B. before the Cambrian Explosion.   **D.** after the Cambrian Period.

_____ A _____ **6.** Why are the fossils of the Ediacara Hills of Australia important?

    A. Their body plans are different from those of anything alive today.

    B. Some had cells, tissues, and specialized organs.

    C. Some were differentiated into a front and back end.

    D. Some were autotrophic.

_____ C _____ **7.** Over a period of 10–15 million years in the Cambrian Period, animals evolved

    A. into eukaryotic, photosynthetic forms.

    B. the ability to survive on the bottom of shallow seas.

    C. complex body plans, including cells, tissues, and organs.

    D. into modern, vertebrate forms.

_____ B _____ **8.** Structures such as legs or antennae that protrude from the body are

    A. trace fossils.

    B. appendages.

    C. shells, skeletons, and other hard body parts.

    D. evidence of an extinct phylum.

_____ D _____ **9.** Which animals are the most abundant on Earth?

    A. arthropods   **C.** sponges

    B. mollusks   **D.** invertebrates

Cladogram of Invertebrates

10. Write "yes" or "no" to indicate how certain features distinguish each phylum of multicellular invertebrates. The first row is completed as an example.

	Tissues	Radial	Bilateral symmetry	Protostome development	Deuterostome development
Sponges	no	no	no	no	no
Cnidarians	*yes*	*yes*	*no*	*no*	*no*
Arthropods	*yes*	*no*	*yes*	*yes*	*no*
Nematodes (Roundworms)	*yes*	*no*	*yes*	*yes*	*no*
Flatworms	*yes*	*no*	*yes*	*yes*	*no*
Annelids	*yes*	*no*	*yes*	*yes*	*no*
Mollusks	*yes*	*no*	*yes*	*yes*	*no*
Echinoderms	*yes*	*yes*	*yes*	*no*	*yes*

Apply the Big idea

11. Describe three evolutionary trends you see in invertebrates.

Invertebrates developed complex body plans, including specialized tissues; they also

developed body symmetry such as bilateral or radial symmetry; arthropods, annelids,

and mollusks developed a protostome, while echinoderms developed a deuterostome.

_____

_____

26.2 Chordate Evolution and Diversity

- Describe the most ancient chordates.
- Interpret the cladogram of chordates.

Lesson Summary

Origins of the Chordates Embryological studies suggest that the most ancient chordates were related to the ancestors of echinoderms.

▶ Fossils of the earliest chordates (Cambrian Period) show muscles arranged in a series, traces of fins, sets of feathery gills, a head with paired sense organs, and a skull and skeletal structures likely made of cartilage, a strong connective tissue that is softer and more flexible than bone. Cartilage supports all or part of a vertebrate's body.

▶ Modern chordates are very diverse, consisting of six groups: the nonvertebrate chordates and the five groups of vertebrates—fishes, amphibians, reptiles, birds, and mammals.

Cladogram of Chordates The cladogram of chordates presents current hypotheses about relationships among chordate groups. Major groups are:

▶ Nonvertebrate chordates: The tunicates and the lancelets lack backbones.

▶ Jawless fishes: Lampreys and hagfishes lack vertebrae and have notochords as adults.

▶ Sharks and their relatives: They have jaws and skeletons made of cartilage.

▶ Bony fishes: These animals have skeletons made of true bone. Most modern bony fishes are ray-finned fishes. One group of ancient lobe-finned fishes evolved into the ancestors of tetrapods, which are four-limbed vertebrates.

▶ Amphibians: Amphibians live in water as larvae but on land as adults. They breathe with lungs as adults, but most require water for reproduction.

▶ Reptiles: Reptiles have dry, scaly skin, well-developed lungs, strong limbs, and shelled eggs that do not develop in water.

▶ Birds: Birds can regulate their internal body temperature. They have an outer covering of feathers, strong yet lightweight bones, two legs covered with scales that are used for walking or perching, and front limbs modified into wings.

▶ Dinosaurs and birds are now considered to be in one clade, which is part of the larger reptiles clade. Modern birds are, therefore, reptiles. The traditional class Reptilia, which is not a clade, includes living reptiles and dinosaurs but not birds.

▶ Mammals: Mammals produce milk from mammary glands, have hair, breathe air, have four-chambered hearts, and regulate their internal body temperature.

Origins of the Chordates

For Questions 1–8, write True if the statement is true. If the statement is false, change the underlined word to make the statement true.

_____True_____ 1. Embryological evidence suggests that the most ancient chordates were related to the ancestors of echinoderms.

_____chordate_____ 2. *Pikaia* was an early vertebrate fossil.

___vertebrate___ 3. The earliest known <u>chordate</u> fossil was *Myllokunmingia,* which had muscles arranged in a series, traces of fins, sets of feathery gills, a head with paired sense organs, and a skull and skeletal structures.

___cartilage___ 4. The earliest vertebrate fossils had skeletons made of <u>bone</u>.

___True___ 5. Cartilage is a strong <u>connective</u> tissue that is more flexible than bone.

___True___ 6. Most modern chordates are <u>vertebrates</u>.

___True___ 7. Modern chordates include <u>five</u> groups of vertebrates.

___fishes___ 8. The most numerous group of vertebrates today is the <u>mammals</u>.

Cladogram of Chordates

9. Write "yes" or "no" to indicate how certain features distinguish each subphylum of chordates. The first row is completed as an example.

	Vertebrae	Jaws and Paired Appendages	True Bone	Lungs	Four Limbs	Amniotic Egg	Endothermy
Nonvertebrate chordates	no	no	no	no	no	no	no
Jawless fishes	*yes*	*no*	*no*	*no*	*no*	*no*	*no*
Sharks and their relatives	*yes*	*yes*	*no*	*no*	*no*	*no*	*no*
Bony fishes	*yes*	*yes*	*yes*	*no*	*no*	*no*	*no*
Amphibians	*yes*	*yes*	*yes*	*yes*	*yes*	*no*	*no*
Reptiles	*yes*	*yes*	*yes*	*yes*	*yes*	*yes*	*no*
Birds	*yes*	*yes*	*yes*	*yes*	*yes*	*yes*	*yes*
Mammals	*yes*	*yes*	*yes*	*yes*	*yes*	*yes*	*yes*

10. Sharks and their relatives are the first group of animals with jaws. Why are jaws a significant evolutionary development?

Jaws enabled the sharks and their relatives to more easily feed and defend themselves.

11. What three adaptations were needed for chordates to move from living in water to living on land?

Animals on land needed legs to crawl around on, ways to breathe air, and ways to protect themselves from drying out.

12. One group of feathered dinosaurs led to modern birds. What advantage might feathers have given these dinosaurs?

    Feathers may have evolved as a means of regulating body temperature.

13. How do mammals differ from all other chordates on the cladogram?

    Mammals feed their young with milk.

14. Which chordate groups can regulate their body temperatures?

    Birds and mammals

15. **THINK VISUALLY** Much evidence supports the hypothesis that modern birds share a common ancestor with dinosaurs. Make a sketch to show the probable evolutionary relationships among modern birds, modern reptiles, and extinct dinosaurs. Circle the clades shown in your diagram.

Students' sketches should resemble the bird-evolution cladogram in the textbook. They should circle the dinosaurs and birds as one clade, and the reptiles as a larger clade, which includes the dinosaurs and birds as a subset.

Apply the Big idea

16. The order in which the major groups of chordates evolved makes sense. For example, a bony skeleton had to evolve before a vertebral column. A vertebral column had to develop before four limbs. Fish had to evolve before birds. Explain why certain traits had to evolve before the traits now seen in birds.

    SAMPLE ANSWER: *Certain aspects of the bird body plan are derived from older forms. For example, one group of ancient fishes evolved skeletons of true bone. Another group of fishes evolved into the ancestors of four-limbed vertebrates. Today's birds have bony skeletons and four limbs. Birds could not have evolved before these features became parts of the chordate body plan, as seen in fishes.*

26.3 Primate Evolution

- Identify the characteristics that all primates share.
- Describe the major evolutionary groups of primates.
- Describe the adaptations that enabled later hominine species to walk upright.
- Describe the current scientific thinking about the genus *Homo*.

Lesson Summary

What Is a Primate? In general, a primate is a mammal that has relatively long fingers and toes with nails instead of claws, arms that can rotate around shoulder joints, a strong clavicle, and a well-developed cerebrum.

▶ Many primates have eyes that face forward, giving them **binocular vision**, which is the ability to combine visual images from both eyes to provide three-dimensional views.

▶ The well-developed cerebrum enables complex behaviors.

Evolution of Primates Humans and other primates evolved from a common ancestor that lived more than 65 million years ago. Early in their history, primates split into two groups:

▶ Primates in one group look very little like typical monkeys. This group contains the lemurs and lorises.

▶ Primates in the other group include tarsiers and **anthropoids**, or humanlike primates. Monkeys, great apes, and humans are anthropoids. Anthropoids split into two groups about 45 million years ago.

- The New World monkeys have **prehensile tails**, which can coil tightly around a branch to serve as a "fifth hand."

- Old World monkeys do not have prehensile tails. Great apes, also called **hominoids**, include gibbons, orangutans, gorillas, chimpanzees, and humans.

Hominine Evolution The hominoids in the lineage that led to humans are called **hominines**. The skull, neck, spinal column, hip bones, and leg bones of early hominine species changed shape in ways that enabled later species to walk upright.

▶ The evolution of **bipedal**, or two-footed, locomotion freed both hands to use tools.

▶ The hominine hand evolved an **opposable thumb** that could touch the tips of the fingers, enabling the grasping of objects and the use of tools.

▶ Hominines also evolved much larger brains.

▶ The oldest hominine fossil may be *Sahelanthropus*, roughly seven million years old.

▶ Fossils of one early group of hominines, *Australopithecus*, showed they were bipedal apes that probably spent some time in trees.

▶ *Paranthropus* probably had a diet like that of modern gorillas. This species lived two to three million years ago.

The Road to Modern Humans Many species of the genus *Homo* existed before *Homo sapiens* appeared. At least three other *Homo* species existed at the same time as early humans.

▶ *Homo neanderthalensis* survived in Europe until 28,000–24,000 years ago. *H. sapiens* coexisted with the Neanderthals for several thousand years.

What Is a Primate?

For Questions 1–4, complete each statement by writing the correct word or words.

1. Primates have _____*nails*_____ on their fingers and toes.

2. Primates are good climbers because they have a strong shoulder joint attached to a strong _____*clavicle*_____.

3. The ability to combine vision from both eyes is _____*binocular*_____ vision.

4. The "thinking" part of the brain is the _____*cerebrum*_____.

Evolution of Primates

For Questions 5–11, write the letter of the correct answer on the line at the left.

___A___ 5. How long ago did the common ancestor of all primates live?

    A. 65 million years ago   **C.** 45 million years ago

    B. 56 million years ago   **D.** 28,000 years ago

___D___ 6. Which of these is NOT an anthropoid?

    A. gibbon   **C.** human

    B. orangutan   **D.** tarsier

___B___ 7. What factor contributed to the split of two groups of anthropoids about 45 million years ago?

    A. One group developed a prehensile tail.

    B. The continents where they lived moved apart.

    C. They diverged from the lemurs and tarsiers.

    D. The climate changed from warmer to colder.

___A___ 8. Which characteristic distinguishes the New World monkeys from the Old World monkeys?

    A. prehensile tail   **C.** binocular vision

    B. opposable thumb   **D.** mammary glands

___D___ 9. Which of these is a hominoid?

    A. loris   **C.** tarsier

    B. lemur   **D.** gibbon

___D___ 10. Which primate is the closest relative of humans?

    A. gorilla   **C.** orangutan

    B. gibbon   **D.** chimpanzee

___C___ 11. How did scientists confirm which primate was the closest primate relative to humans?

    A. by comparing the skeletons

    B. by studying behavior

    C. by using DNA analyses

    D. by using geographic analyses

Hominine Evolution

12. Complete the Venn diagram to compare human and gorilla skeletons.

Human	Both	Gorilla

- S-shaped spine
- spinal cord exits at bottom of skull
- arms shorter than legs
- hands don't touch ground when walking
- bowl-shaped pelvis
- thigh bones angled inward, directly below body

- skull atop spine
- spinal cord exits near skull
- have arms and hands
- have pelvis
- angled thigh bones

- C-shaped spine
- spinal cord exits near back of skull
- arms longer than legs
- hands touch ground when walking
- long and narrow pelvis
- thigh bones angled away from pelvis

13. What do Lucy and the Dikika Baby have in common? Which one is more complete?

Both are important fossils of the hominine A. afarensis. The Dikika Baby is more

complete.

14. Why did scientists conclude that *Paranthropus* probably ate a diet that included coarse and fibrous plant foods?

Fossils show that this species had huge grinding back teeth.

15. Why do we now think about human evolution as a shrub with multiple trunks rather than a family tree?

We now see that a series of hominine adaptive radiations produced a number of species

whose relationships are difficult to determine, rather than a series of simple steps.

The Road to Modern Humans

For Questions 16–21, write True if the statement is true. If the statement is false, change the underlined word to make the statement true.

_____Many_____ 16. <u>One</u> species of our genus, *Homo*, existed before our species, *Homo sapiens*.

_____True_____ 17. The earliest fossils that can definitely be assigned to the genus *Homo* are from the species *H. <u>ergaster</u>*.

_____Africa_____ 18. Researchers agree that the genus *Homo* originated in <u>Asia</u> and migrated to other parts of the world.

_____True_____ 19. One way to discover the migration patterns of human ancestors is to compare the <u>mitochondrial</u> DNA of living humans.

_____True_____ 20. Early *Homo sapiens* lived at the same time as another, closely related species, *Homo <u>neanderthalensis</u>*.

_____sapiens_____ 21. The only surviving species of the once large and diverse hominine clade is *Homo <u>erectus</u>*.

Apply the Big idea

22. What evidence do scientists use to classify extinct species of the genus *Homo*? How do scientists differentiate extinct species of *Homo* from each other and from the modern species?

Scientists analyze the fossil record, mostly by comparing differences in bony

structures. From such comparisons, they can infer important characteristics such as

brain size and bipedalism. In some cases, DNA can be analyzed.

_____

_____

_____

Chapter Vocabulary Review

For Questions 1–8, match the term with its definition.

Definition

___F___ **1.** The ability to combine visual images from both eyes

___E___ **2.** Any four-limbed vertebrate

___H___ **3.** Another name for the great apes

___A___ **4.** A structure such as an arm, a leg, or an antenna protruding from the body

___G___ **5.** The group of humanlike primates that includes monkeys and great apes

___B___ **6.** An immature stage of life in some animals; many mollusks have one called a trochophore.

___D___ **7.** Connective tissue that is more flexible than bone

___C___ **8.** The free-swimming larval stage of some mollusks

Term

A. appendage

B. larva

C. trochophore

D. cartilage

E. tetrapod

F. binocular vision

G. anthropoids

H. hominoids

For Questions 9–12, complete each statement by writing the correct word or words.

9. The appendage that can serve as a "fifth hand" in some primates is the __prehensile tail__.

10. A hominoid in the lineage that led to humans is a(n) __hominine__.

11. The evolution of __bipedal__, or two-footed, locomotion freed the hands for tool use.

12. The line that led to humans evolved a(n) __opposable thumb__ that can touch the tips of the fingers.

13. What groups have a trochophore?

__mollusks and annelids__

14. What does the fact that these groups have a trochophore indicate about the relationships between them?

__Mollusks and annelids must be closely related.__

15. What advantage does a primate with an opposable thumb have over a primate without an opposable thumb?

__An opposable thumb enables an animal to grasp objects and use tools.__

16. What advantage does a primate with binocular vision have over a primate without binocular vision?

__Binocular vision provides depth perception and a three-dimensional view of the world.__

__This helps the animal judge the locations of tree branches, from which many primates__

__swing.__

CHAPTER
MYSTERY

FOSSIL QUEST

Josh and Pedro, whom you read about in the Chapter Mystery, have a strong interest in fossils. It can be difficult, however, to pursue this interest if the local area is not rich in fossils.

21st Century Learning

Fossil Education for the Nonscientist

Josh, who is interested in fossils that are over 600 million years old, learned that it was impossible for him to find these fossils nearby. In fact, he would have to travel to China or Australia to find such fossils. Alternatively, Josh could learn about ancient fossils by reading articles published in scientific journals. If he does, he will discover that many of the articles are technical and difficult to understand. But another pathway to such information exists: national park staff members and other science educators help convey complex scientific information to the public with their interpretive activities. They use presentations, workshops, pamphlets, and other materials to educate people about fossils. Below is an example of a pamphlet describing the Grampians mountain range in western Victoria, Australia.

The Grampians Range, Western Victoria

INTRODUCTION
The Grampians Range was not always the incredible mountain range it is today. Over 400 million years ago, this area was actually a relatively flat coastline. To the east of this coastline was a deep ocean, and to the west was a mountain range that has now been eroded away. How did a flat coastline area become a mountain range hundreds of kilometers away from the sea? This pamphlet discusses the sedimentation, the pressure, and the forces that made the Grampians Range.

SEDIMENTATION
Over millions of years, rivers from the mountains and inlets along the shore deposited layers of gravel, sand, and mud. They deposited thousands of meters of material. Each layer of sediment tells a story about the past. Some layers contain fossils, including small plants, vertical worm holes, pieces of primitive jawless fish, brachiopods, and what scientists believe may be algal mats. Petrified ripples and mud cracks indicate the locations of ancient beaches, rivers, and other bodies of water that deposited sediments. These features and other geological evidence help explain the sedimentation story.

PRESSURE AND PLATES
As the layers of sediment accumulated or built up, the pressure and temperature increased, squeezing the water out and turning the sand to stone. Continental drift kept the Earth's tectonic plates moving. Tectonic forces buckled, folded, and uplifted the sediments, creating the Grampians Range, as well as other mountain ranges on Earth.

Continued on next page ▶

21st Century Themes Science and Global Awareness

1. What evidence indicates that some of the land making up the Grampians Range was once under water?

   Fossils of aquatic organisms and petrified ripples indicate that some of the land

   making up the Grampians Range was once under water.

2. What was the topography (surface characteristics) of the land in this region at that time?

   The land was once a relatively flat coastline with a deep ocean to the east and

   mountains to the west.

3. What types of informational material do you think would help explain the geology of the Grampians Range other than what is described in the text?

   SAMPLE ANSWER: Maps, figures, diagrams, and photographs would all help to explain the

   geology of what is described above.

4. Consider the evidence presented in the pamphlet to explain the formation of the Grampians. What type of similar evidence could you collect to study the geological history of landforms in your area?

   SAMPLE ANSWER: I could study the layers of rock, sediment, and fossils in my area to

   learn about what happened at different times during the geologic history of my

   region. I can also look for evidence of folding and uplifting that may have occurred

   to form nearby mountains.

5. Suppose you found a fossilized algal mat in a desert. What could you infer about the probably nature of the ancient environment of this area?

   SAMPLE ANSWER: The ancient environment was much likely much wetter than the modern

   desert environment. For example, it may have once been a lake or wetland.

21st Century Skills Fossils Pamphlet

The skills used in this activity include **information and media literacy, communication skills, critical thinking and systems thinking, creativity and intellectual curiosity,** and **self-direction**.

Research the geology and fossils in your state or region online or by going to a visitor center of nearby state or national park. Museum Web sites are a good place to start, as is the National Park Service Web site. If possible, ask your teacher to arrange a field trip to help you with research. Based on your research, put together a pamphlet describing the fossils in your area. While designing and writing your pamphlet, remember that your audience includes people who may not know much about fossils and geology.

The pamphlet should fold into three parts and include maps, figures, diagrams, and photographs that are appropriately labeled.

   Evaluate students' pamphlets based on how well planned they are, on the accuracy
   and clarity of the text, its readability for an average, nontechnical audience, and the
   appropriateness of the illustrative material, which, along with labels, should empha-
   size or expand what is in the text.

27 Animal Systems I

Big idea **Structure and Function**

Q: How do the structures of animals allow them to obtain essential materials and eliminate wastes?

WHAT I KNOW	WHAT I LEARNED
27.1 How do different animals obtain and digest food?	SAMPLE ANSWER: **Most animals have mouths and digestive tracts.**	SAMPLE ANSWER: **Some invertebrates break down food through intracellular digestion, but many animals use extracellular digestion.**
27.2 How do animals in different environments breathe?	SAMPLE ANSWER: **Animals need oxygen. Some animals obtain oxygen with gills. Others obtain oxygen with lungs.**	SAMPLE ANSWER: **Many aquatic animals exchange gases through gills. Respiratory structures in terrestrial animals include skin, mantle cavities, book lungs, tracheal tubes, and lungs.**
27.3 How have animals evolved complex, efficient ways to move materials through their bodies?	SAMPLE ANSWER: **Blood moves materials through an animal's body.**	SAMPLE ANSWER: **Most vertebrates with gills have a single-loop circulatory system. Most vertebrates that use lungs for respiration have a double-loop circulatory system.**
27.4 How do animals in different environments excrete metabolic wastes?	SAMPLE ANSWER: **Animal wastes are removed by the excretory system.**	SAMPLE ANSWER: **Aquatic animals allow ammonia to diffuse out of their bodies into surrounding water. Some terrestrial invertebrates produce urine in nephridia. Other terrestrial invertebrates convert ammonia into uric acid. Mammals and land amphibians convert ammonia into urea.**

27.1 Feeding and Digestion

Lesson Objectives

⊙▬ Describe the different ways animals get food.

⊙▬ Explain how digestion occurs in different animals.

⊙▬ Describe how mouthparts are adapted for an animal's diet.

Lesson Summary

Obtaining Food Animals obtain food in different ways.

▶ Most filter feeders catch algae and small animals by using modified gills or other structures as nets that filter food items out of water.

▶ Detritivores feed on detritus, or decaying bits of plant and animal material. Detritivores often obtain extra nutrients from the bacteria, algae, and other microorganisms that grow on and around the detritus.

▶ Carnivores eat other animals.

▶ Herbivores eat plants or parts of plants in terrestrial and aquatic habitats.

▶ Many animals rely upon symbiosis for their nutritional needs. Parasites live within or on a host organism, where they feed on tissues or on blood and other body fluids. In mutualistic relationships, both participants benefit.

Processing Food Some invertebrates break down food primarily by intracellular digestion, but many animals use extracellular digestion to break down food.

▶ In **intracellular digestion**, food is digested inside specialized cells that pass nutrients to other cells by diffusion.

▶ In **extracellular digestion**, food is broken down outside cells in a digestive system and then absorbed.

• Some invertebrates, such as cnidarians, have a **gastrovascular cavity** with a single opening through which they both ingest food and expel wastes.

• Many invertebrates and all vertebrates, such as birds, digest food in a tube called a **digestive tract**, which has two openings: a mouth and an anus. Food travels in one direction through the digestive tract.

Specializations for Different Diets The mouthparts and digestive systems of animals have evolved many adaptations to the physical and chemical characteristics of different foods.

▶ Carnivores typically have sharp mouthparts or other structures that can capture food, hold it, and "slice and dice" it into small pieces.

▶ Herbivores typically have mouthparts adapted to rasping or grinding.

▶ Some animals have specialized digestive organs that help them break down certain foods. For example, cattle have a pouchlike extension of their esophagus called a **rumen**, in which symbiotic bacteria digest cellulose.

Obtaining Food

1. Complete the table about types of feeders.

Types of Feeders	
Type of Feeder	**Description**
Filter feeder	*filters food items out of water*
Detritivore	feeds on decaying bits of plant and animal material
Carnivore	*eats other animals*
Herbivore	eats plants or parts of plants
Parasitic symbionts	*live within or on a host organism, where they feed on tissues or on blood and other body fluids*
Mutualistic symbionts	*live within or on a host organism and gain their nutrition in such a way that they do not harm the host*

2. Explain the difference between a parasite and a host.

A parasite lives within or on a host organism and feeds on that host organism. The host is usually harmed by the feeding behavior of the parasite.

3. Give an example of a mutualistic relationship involving a nutritional symbiont.

Some kinds of coral and algae have a mutualistic relationship. The algae produce food for the coral through photosynthesis. In return, the algae use some of the coral's waste products as nutrients.

Processing Food

4. How is the digestion of food different in simple animals compared with more complex animals?

Simple animals break down food primarily through intracellular digestion, but more complex animals use extracellular digestion. Also, simple animals have a gastrovascular cavity through which food enters and wastes are expelled. More complex animals have a one-way digestive tract through which food moves.

5. How is a one-way digestive track like a "disassembly line"?

Food is broken down one step at a time through mechanical and chemical digestion.

6. Label the digestive structures of this cnidarian.

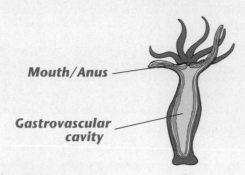

Mouth/Anus

Gastrovascular cavity

Specializations for Different Diets

7. VISUAL ANALOGY

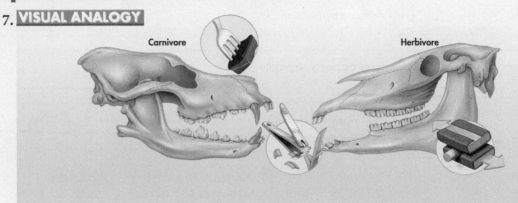

Carnivore

Herbivore

The visual analogy compares different types of teeth with common tools. Complete the table about the different kinds of teeth found in mammals and the tools they are like.

Teeth Adaptations in Mammals		
Type of Teeth	**Description**	**Tool Analogy**
Canines	*pointed teeth used for piercing, gripping, and tearing*	fork
Incisors	chisel-like teeth used for cutting, gnawing, and grooming	*nail clippers*
Molars	*flat teeth used for grinding food*	*pieces of sandpaper*

Apply the Big idea

8. Explain whether organisms with a gastrovacular cavity or organisms with a digestive tract obtain and process nutrients more efficiently.

SAMPLE ANSWER: *Organisms with digestive tracts obtain and process nutrients more efficiently. They are able to take in nutrients and excrete wastes at the same time because their mouth and anus are separate orifices.*

27.2 Respiration

Lesson Objectives

- Describe the characteristics of respiratory structures that all animals share.
- Explain how aquatic animals breathe.
- Identify the respiratory structures that enable land animals to breathe.

Lesson Summary

Gas Exchange Animals have evolved respiratory structures that promote the movement of oxygen and carbon dioxide in the required directions by passive diffusion.

- Gases diffuse most efficiently across a thin, moist membrane.
- Respiratory structures maintain a difference in concentrations of oxygen and carbon dioxide on either side of the respiratory membrane, promoting diffusion.

Respiratory Surfaces of Aquatic Animals Many aquatic invertebrates and most aquatic chordates, other than reptiles and mammals, exchange gases through gills.

- **Gills** are feathery structures that expose a large surface area of thin, selectively permeable membrane to water.
- Aquatic reptiles and aquatic mammals, such as whales, breathe with **lungs**, organs that exchange oxygen and carbon dioxide, and must hold their breath underwater.

Respiratory Surfaces of Terrestrial Animals Terrestrial animals must keep their respiratory membranes moist in dry environments.

- Respiratory structures in terrestrial invertebrates include skin, mantle cavities, book lungs, and tracheal tubes.
- All terrestrial vertebrates breathe with lungs.
  - In mammalian lungs, **alveoli** provide a large surface for gas exchange.
  - In birds, a unique system of tubes and air sacs enables one-way airflow.

Gas Exchange

For Questions 1–5, write True if the statement is true. If the statement is false, change the underlined word or words to make the statement true.

passive	1.	In respiratory systems, gas exchange occurs through <u>active</u> diffusion.
True	2.	Substances diffuse from an area of <u>higher concentration</u> to an area of lower concentration.
moist	3.	Gases diffuse most efficiently across thin, <u>dry</u> surfaces.
True	4.	Respiratory structures have a <u>selectively permeable</u> membrane.
carbon dioxide	5.	Respiratory structures maintain a difference in the relative concentrations of oxygen and <u>nitrogen</u> on either side of the membrane.

6. Respiratory organs have large surface areas. How is this an advantage to an animal?

The more surface area that is exposed to the environment, the greater the amount of

gas exchange that can occur.

7. Respiratory surfaces are moist. How does this enable respiration to take place?

Gases diffuse most efficiently across a moist membrane.

Respiratory Surfaces of Aquatic Animals

8. Complete the flowchart that describes the path of water as it moves through fish.

> Water flows in through the fish's _____*mouth*_____, where muscles pump the
> water across the _____*gills*_____.

> As water passes over the gill filaments, the filaments absorb _____*oxygen*_____
> from water and release *carbon dioxide*.

> Water and carbon dioxide are pumped out behind the _____*operculum*_____.

Respiratory Surfaces of Terrestrial Animals

9. **THINK VISUALLY** Label the book lung, spiracles, and tracheal tubes in the organisms
below. Write a description of these structures on the lines below the organisms.

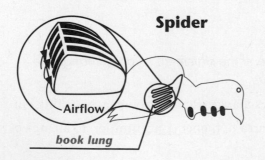

Spider

Airflow

book lung

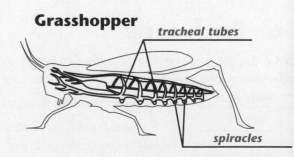

Grasshopper

tracheal tubes

spiracles

Book lungs are made of parallel, sheet-
like layers of thin tissues that contain
blood vessels.

Tracheal tubes extend throughout the
body. Air enters and leaves the system
through openings called spiracles.

10. **THINK VISUALLY** Label the nostrils, mouth, and throat; trachea; and lungs of the animals below.

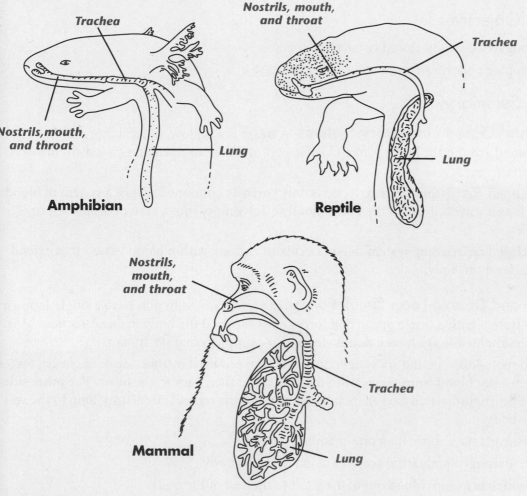

11. Describe the basic process of breathing among land vertebrates.

  Inhaling brings oxygen-rich air through the trachea into the lungs. The oxygen dif-

  fuses into the blood, and carbon dioxide diffuses out of the capillaries into the air.

  Oxygen-poor air is then exhaled.

12. Why are the lungs of birds more efficient than those of most other animals?

  Air flows through bird lungs in only one direction. Thus, gas exchange surfaces are

  continuously in contact with oxygen-rich air.

Apply the Big idea

13. Compare the structure and function of fish gills with the structure and function of bird lungs.

  Both fish gills and bird lungs function to receive a constant supply of oxygen. The

  structure of fish gills allows this one-way flow by pumping water through the mouth,

  over the gill filaments, and out the operculum as a fish swims. A unique system of

  tubes allows the one-way flow of oxygen in bird lungs.

27.3 Circulation

Lesson Objectives

🔑 Compare open and closed circulatory systems.

🔑 Compare patterns of circulation in vertebrates.

Lesson Summary

Open and Closed Circulatory Systems A **heart** is a hollow, muscular organ that pumps blood around the body. A heart can be part of either an open or a closed circulatory system.

▶ In an **open circulatory system**, blood is only partially contained within a system of blood vessels as it travels through the body. Blood vessels empty into a system of sinuses, or cavities.

▶ In a **closed circulatory system**, blood circulates entirely within blood vessels that extend throughout the body.

Single- and Double-Loop Circulation Most vertebrates with gills have a single-loop circulatory system with a single pump that forces blood around the body in one direction. Most vertebrates that use lungs have a double-loop, two-pump circulatory system.

▶ In a double-loop circulatory system, the first loop, powered by one side of the heart, forces oxygen-poor blood from the heart to the lungs, and then back to the heart. The other side of the heart pumps this oxygen-rich blood through the second circulatory loop to the rest of the body.

▶ Some hearts have more than one chamber.

• The **atrium** (plural: atria) receives blood from the body.

• A **ventricle** pumps blood out of the heart to the rest of the body.

▶ Amphibian hearts usually have three chambers: two atria and one ventricle.

• The left atrium receives oxygen-rich blood from the lungs.

• The right atrium receives oxygen-poor blood from the body.

• Both atria empty into the ventricle. Some mixing of oxygen-rich and oxygen-poor blood occurs in the ventricle.

▶ Most reptilian hearts have three chambers. However, most reptiles have a partial partition in the ventricle, so there is little mixing of oxygen-rich and oxygen-poor blood in the ventricle.

▶ Modern mammals have four-chambered hearts that are actually two separate pumps working next to one another.

Open and Closed Circulatory Systems

1. Use the Venn diagram to compare and contrast open and closed circulatory systems.

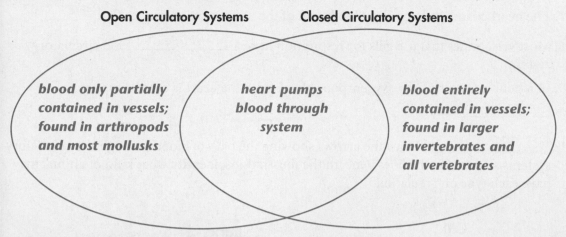

Open Circulatory Systems   Closed Circulatory Systems

blood only partially contained in vessels; found in arthropods and most mollusks

heart pumps blood through system

blood entirely contained in vessels; found in larger invertebrates and all vertebrates

2. **THINK VISUALLY** Label the structures shown on each organism. Then write on the line below the organism whether the organism has an open or a closed circulatory system.

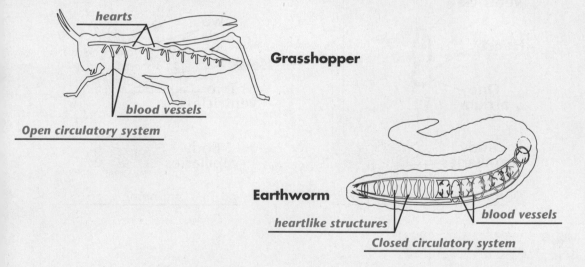

hearts

Grasshopper

blood vessels

Open circulatory system

Earthworm

heartlike structures

blood vessels

Closed circulatory system

Single- and Double-Loop Circulation

3. Identify where the blood is carried in each loop of a double-loop circulatory system.
One loop carries blood between the heart and the lungs. The other loop carries blood between the heart and the body.

4. Why is a four-chambered heart sometimes described as a double pump?
One pump moves blood through the lung loop, and the other moves blood through the body loop.

5. What is the difference between a reptilian heart and an amphibian heart?
The reptilian heart has a partial partition in the ventricle that reduces the mixing of oxygen-rich and oxygen-poor blood.

For Questions 6–9, complete each statement by writing the correct word or words.

6. In most vertebrates with gills, the heart consists of _____*two*_____ chambers.

7. The heart chamber that pumps blood out of the heart is called the ____*ventricle*____.

8. Most vertebrates that use gills for respiration have a _____*single*_____ loop circulatory system.

9. In a double-loop system, oxygen-poor blood from the heart is carried to the _____*lungs*_____.

10. **THINK VISUALLY** Draw the arrows showing the path of blood through the circulatory systems shown. On the lines beneath the illustrations, identify what kind of animal may have each type of circulation.

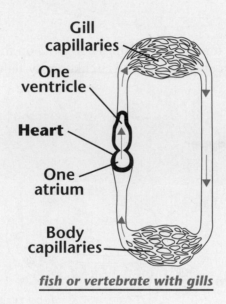

fish or vertebrate with gills

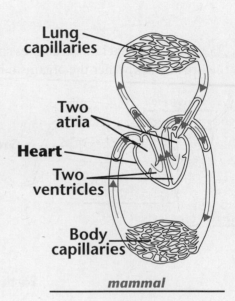

mammal

Apply the Big idea

11. On the basis of what you have learned about circulatory systems, infer how many chambers a bird's heart has. Explain your answer.

SAMPLE ANSWER: **Birds most likely have a four-chambered heart. Their metabolisms are very rapid due to the amount of energy needed to maintain flight and body heat. Their respiratory system brings in a constant supply of oxygen. The most efficient way to handle this supply is with a heart that includes two separate pumps: one to the lungs and one to the rest of the body.**

27.4 Excretion

Lesson Objectives

▭ Describe the methods animals use to manage nitrogenous wastes.

▭ Explain how aquatic animals eliminate wastes.

▭ Explain how land animals eliminate wastes.

Lesson Summary

The Ammonia Problem Ammonia is a waste product that can kill most cells, even in moderate amounts.

► Animals either eliminate ammonia from the body quickly or convert it into other nitrogenous compounds that are less toxic.

► The elimination of metabolic wastes, such as ammonia, is called **excretion**.

► Many animals use **kidneys** to separate wastes and excess water from blood.

Excretion in Aquatic Animals In general, aquatic animals can allow ammonia to diffuse out of their bodies into surrounding water, which dilutes the ammonia and carries it away.

► Many freshwater invertebrates lose ammonia to their environment by simple diffusion across their skin. Many freshwater fishes and amphibians eliminate ammonia by diffusion across the same gill membranes they use for respiration. Freshwater fishes also actively pump salt inward across their gills.

► Marine invertebrates and vertebrates typically release ammonia by diffusion across their body surfaces or gill membranes. These animals also actively excrete salt across their gills.

Excretion in Terrestrial Animals In dry environments, land animals can lose large amounts of water from respiratory membranes that must be kept moist. In addition, they must eliminate nitrogenous wastes in ways that require disposing of water.

► Some terrestrial invertebrates produce urine in **nephridia**, which are tubelike excretory structures that filter body fluid. Urine leaves the body through excretory pores.

► Other terrestrial invertebrates, such as insects and arachnids, convert ammonia into uric acid. Nitrogenous wastes, such as uric acid, are absorbed from body fluids by structures called **Malpighian tubules**, which concentrate the wastes and add them to digestive wastes traveling through the gut.

► Mammals and land amphibians convert ammonia into urea, which is excreted in urine. In most reptiles and birds, ammonia is converted into uric acid.

The Ammonia Problem

1. Why does ammonia build up in organisms? *Ammonia is a waste product caused by the breakdown of proteins by cells.*

2. Why is ammonia a problem in the body of an animal?
   It is poisonous even in moderate amounts.

3. Complete the concept map.

Ways to Store Nitrogenous Waste

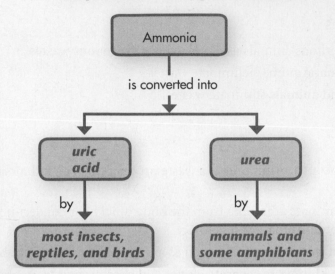

Excretion in Aquatic Animals

4. How do many freshwater invertebrates rid their bodies of ammonia?
Ammonia diffuses from their body tissues into the surrounding water.

5. Describe how flatworms maintain water balance.
Flatworms have flame cells that remove excess water from body fluids. That water travels
through excretory tubules and leaves through pores in the skin.

6. Why do freshwater fishes typically have very dilute urine and marine fishes have very
concentrated urine?
In freshwater environments, the concentration of water is higher than the concentration
of water in fish body fluids. So water moves into fish bodies by osmosis. Salt leaves by
diffusion. Because of the large water intake, urine is dilute. Marine fishes tend to lose
water to their surroundings because their bodies are less salty than the surrounding
water. Their kidneys produce small amounts of concentrated urine to conserve water.

For Questions 7–8, write the letter of the correct answer on the line at the left.

____A____ **7.** Marine organisms tend to lose water to their surroundings because
   A. their bodies are less salty than the water they live in.
   B. their bodies are more salty than the water they live in.
   C. their cells actively pump water across their membranes.
   D. their cells actively pump ammonia across their membranes.

____C____ **8.** Which of the following structures helps remove excess water from an organism's
body?
   A. a gill   **C.** a flame cell
   B. a ventricle   **D.** an operculum

Excretion in Terrestrial Animals

9. **THINK VISUALLY** Label the excretory organs on the organisms shown. Then, describe the function of the labeled organs on the lines below.

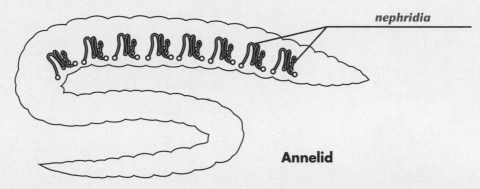

nephridia

Annelid

Nephridia are tubelike excretory structures that filter body fluid. Body fluid enters *through openings called nephrostomes and becomes more concentrated as it moves* *along the tubes.*

_____

Malpighian tubules

Arthropod

Nitrogenous wastes are absorbed from body fluids by Malpighian tubules, which *concentrate the wastes and add them to digestive wastes traveling through the gut.*

For Questions 10–12, complete each statement by writing the correct word or words.

10. In terrestrial vertebrates, excretion is carried out mostly by the ___*kidney*___.

11. In mammals, urea is excreted from the body in a liquid known as ___*urine*___.

12. Most vertebrate kidneys cannot excrete concentrated ___*salt*___.

Apply the Big idea

13. How does the structure of a gill make it an ideal excretory organ?

Gills are feathery structures that expose a large surface area of thin membrane to *water. Inside gill membranes is a network of capillaries. Many substances can pass* *through the thin walls of capillaries. As an animal actively pumps water over the gills,* *wastes in the blood could diffuse out into the water.*

Chapter Vocabulary Review

Match the image with the best term.

Image

<u>*E*</u> 1.

<u>*A*</u> 2.

<u>*B*</u> 3.

<u>*C*</u> 4.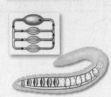

<u>*D*</u> 5.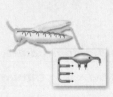

Term

A. lung

B. gill

C. closed circulatory system

D. open circulatory system

E. nephridium

For Questions 6–13, write True if the statement is true. If the statement is false, change the underlined word or words to make the statement true.

<u>*Extracellular*</u> 6. <u>Intracellular</u> digestion is the process in which food is broken down outside cells and then absorbed.

<u>*Malpighian tubules*</u> 7. <u>Kidneys</u> concentrate the wastes and add them to digestive wastes traveling through the gut.

<u>*digestive tract*</u> 8. Many invertebrates and all vertebrates digest food in a <u>gastrovascular cavity</u>, which has two openings.

<u>*True*</u> 9. <u>Excretion</u> is the elimination of metabolic wastes from the body.

<u>*True*</u> 10. A pouchlike extension of a stomach in which symbiotic bacteria digest cellulose is called a <u>rumen</u>.

<u>*Ventricles*</u> 11. <u>Atria</u> pump blood out of the heart.

<u>*True*</u> 12. Circulatory systems contain a pumplike organ called a <u>heart</u>.

<u>*True*</u> 13. <u>Alveoli</u> in lungs provide an enormous surface area for gas exchange.

CHAPTER
MYSTERY

(NEAR) DEATH BY SALT WATER

21st Century Learning

Drinking clean water is a vital part of maintaining your health. The Chapter Mystery showed that drinking the wrong water can have negative health effects.

Why Clean Water?

Clear water may look clean, but it could possibly contain dissolved contaminants. Contaminants include pesticides or other agricultural chemicals, industrial chemicals, disease-causing microorganisms, and high concentrations of minerals. Contaminants often have no taste and can be toxic to humans. You could develop serious health problems by drinking contaminated water. Therefore, it is important to be aware of drinking water regulations and treatment methods. Below are some facts about drinking water.

Important Facts about Clean Drinking Water

1. The Safe Drinking Water Act regulates the supply of public drinking water, or tap water. The regulations protect rivers, reservoirs, springs, and other sources so that the public water supply remains safe. The regulations also set guidelines for testing and treating the public water supply and detail which chemicals and the amount of each chemical that can be present in the supply.
2. The Federal Food, Drug, and Cosmetic Act and individual state laws regulate bottled water. All bottled water must be sampled and analyzed before it is considered safe for drinking.
3. Tap water is treated with filters and/or disinfecting agents such as chlorine. When water flows through filters, many contaminants are removed. Disinfectants such as chlorine help kill bacteria and fungi in water.
4. Bottled water is sealed in sanitary or sterilized plastic bottles according to both federal and state standards. Chemicals and sweeteners cannot be added to bottled water.
5. Bottled water sources include municipal supplies, springs, and wells. Springs and wells are considered natural sources. About 75% of bottled water comes from these natural sources.
6. The FDA has defined different kinds of bottled water. Definitions are based on the source of the water and on the chemicals in the water at its source. FDA classifications include artesian well water, mineral water, spring water, and well water.
7. Before water is bottled, it can be treated using distillation, reverse osmosis, filtration, and ozonation. Not all bottled water is treated this way. If a manufacturer treats water using these methods, the manufacturer can sell and label the water as purified.

Continued on next page ▶

21st Century Themes Science and Economic Literacy

1. What federal laws regulate public drinking water and bottled water, and how are these laws similar?

The Safe Drinking Water Act regulates tap water. The Federal Food, Drug, and Cosmetic Act regulates bottled water. Both acts require that drinking water and bottled water must be tested and deemed safe to drink.

2. How is tap water treated to prevent consumers from getting sick?

Filters eliminate many contaminants, and disinfection with chlorine removes fungi and bacteria.

3. What do you think most public water is used for?

SAMPLE ANSWER: I think most of it is used by people for drinking; cooking; bathing; and washing dishes, clothing, cars, and so on.

4. Suppose a city's tap water became temporarily unsafe. What would be the likely consequences?

SAMPLE ANSWER: Some people drinking the unsafe water may become ill. Many people would turn to bottled water for their drinking supply.

5. If you wanted to start a bottled water company, what would be the first thing you would do?

SAMPLE ANSWER: I would review state and federal water regulations and learn more about the kinds of bottled-water sources and the types of water treatment.

21st Century Learning Bottled Water Business Plan

The skills used in this activity include **information and media literacy; communication skills; critical thinking and systems thinking; problem identification, formulation, and solution; interpersonal and collaborative skills; accountability and adaptability;** and **social responsibility.**

Working in small groups, create a business plan to sell bottled water. Research and enhance the facts given on the previous page about bottled drinking water. Start by visiting the FDA's Web site to learn more about how the FDA regulates bottled water. Create a name for your company and assign roles to each team member. Your business plan should include the following: a summary description of the business, product description, an analysis of the bottled water market, strategy and implementation of the business plan, management team, and a financial or budgetary plan.

Present your business plan to your class.

Evaluate students' business plans based on their comprehensiveness (including information about each factor mentioned above), the organization and clarity of the writing, the accuracy of any researched information the plan contains, the students' argument for feasibility, and how realistic the budget is.

28 Animal Systems II

 Big idea **Structure and Function**

Q: How do the body systems of animals allow them to collect information about their environments and respond appropriately?

WHAT I KNOW	WHAT I LEARNED
28.1 How do animals sense and respond to the environment?	*SAMPLE ANSWER:* **Animals have sensory organs that help them sense their environment.**	*SAMPLE ANSWER:* **Animal nervous systems help them sense and respond to the environment. Sensory systems range from individual sensory neurons to sense organs.**
28.2 How are different animals adapted to move through their environments?	*SAMPLE ANSWER:* **Most aquatic animals have fins. Most land animals have legs.**	*SAMPLE ANSWER:* **In animals, muscles work together in pairs that are attached to different parts of a skeleton. This helps animals move their locomotive structures.**
28.3 What are the different strategies animals have evolved to help them produce offspring?	*SAMPLE ANSWER:* **Most animals reproduce sexually through either external or internal fertilization.**	*SAMPLE ANSWER:* **Asexual reproduction requires only one parent, so individuals may reproduce rapidly. Sexual reproduction maintains genetic diversity by creating individuals with new combinations of genes.**
28.4 How do animals maintain homeostasis?	*SAMPLE ANSWER:* **Animals have feedback mechanisms that help them maintain a stable internal environment**	*SAMPLE ANSWER:* **Animals have different body systems and different techniques, such as ectothermy and endothermy, to maintain a stable internal environment.**

28.1 Response

Lesson Objectives

- Describe how animals respond to stimuli.
- Summarize the trends in the evolution of nervous systems in animals.
- Describe some of the different sensory systems in animals.

Lesson Summary

How Animals Respond Information in the environment that causes an organism to react is called a **stimulus**. A specific reaction to a stimulus is called a **response**. The nervous systems of animals help animals respond to stimuli. Nervous systems are composed of specialized nerve cells, or **neurons**.

- Neurons that respond to stimuli are **sensory neurons**.
- Neurons that typically pass information to still other neurons are called **interneurons**.
- **Motor neurons** carry "directions" from interneurons to muscles.

Trends in Nervous System Evolution Animal nervous systems exhibit different degrees of cephalization and specialization.

- Cnidarians, such as jellyfishes, have simple nervous systems called nerve nets.
- Other invertebrates have a number of interneurons that are grouped together into small structures called **ganglia**.
- Bilaterally symmetric animals often exhibit cephalization, the concentration of sensory neurons and interneurons in a "head."
- In some species, cerebral ganglia are further organized into a structure called a brain. Vertebrate brains include the following structures:
  - The **cerebrum** is the "thinking" region of the brain.
  - The **cerebellum** coordinates movement and controls balance.
  - The medulla oblongata controls the functioning of many internal organs.

Sensory Systems Sensory systems range from individual sensory neurons to sense organs that contain both sensory neurons and other cells that help gather information.

- Many invertebrates have sense organs that detect light, sound, vibrations, movement, body orientation, and chemicals in air or water.
- Most vertebrates have highly evolved sense organs. Many vertebrates have very sensitive organs of taste, smell, and hearing.

How Animals Respond

1. What is a response?

   A response is a single, specific reaction to a stimulus.

2. What body systems interact to produce a behavior in response to a stimulus?

   The sense organs, nervous system, and muscles interact to produce the behavior.

Write the letter of the correct answer on the line at the left.

___B___ **3.** Which of the following is the best example of a stimulus?

    A. sneezing   **C.** swallowing food

    B. a bell ringing   **D.** holding your breath

___D___ **4.** Which of the following is the best example of a response?

    A. hunger pains   **C.** a breeze blowing

    B. a hot sidewalk   **D.** answering a phone

5. Complete the table about types of neurons.

Types of Neurons	
Type of Neuron	**Description**
Interneurons	neurons that pass information from one neuron to another
Sensory neurons	*neurons that respond to stimuli*
Motor neurons	*neurons that control the movement of muscles*

Trends in Nervous System Evolution

6. **THINK VISUALLY** Label the nervous system structures in the following invertebrates. Circle the organism that does NOT show cephalization.

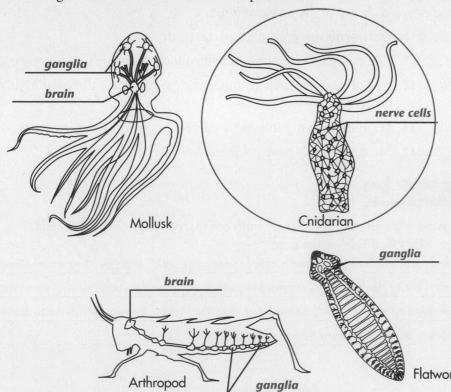

7. **THINK VISUALLY** Use the terms in the box below to label the diagrams of the reptile, bird, and mammal brains. Then, circle the brain with the most complex cerebrum.

| Cerebellum | Cerebrum | Medulla oblongata | Olfactory bulb | Optic lobe |

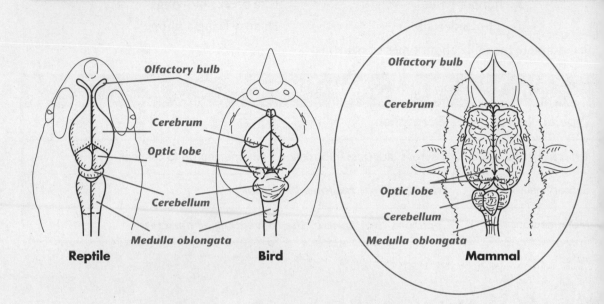

Reptile   Bird   Mammal

Sensory Systems

For Questions 8–12, write True if the statement is true. If the statement is false, change the underlined word or words to make the statement true.

_____ **True** _____ **8.** Flatworms use <u>eyespots</u> to detect light.

_____ **lenses** _____ **9.** The complex eyes of many arthropods are made up of many <u>eyespots</u>.

_____ **vertebrates** _____ **10.** Out of all the animal groups, <u>invertebrates</u> have the most highly evolved sensory organs.

_____ **True** _____ **11.** Many aquatic organisms can detect <u>electric currents</u> in water.

_____ **True** _____ **12.** Most mammals have <u>color</u> vision.

Apply the Big idea

13. Humans have a relatively small olfactory bulb compared with other mammals. Hypothesize why this might be the case.

SAMPLE ANSWER: *Ancient humans needed their senses of sight and hearing more than their sense of smell while hunting and scavenging for food. Humans with better eyesight and hearing survived and produced more offspring. Over time, humans evolved to have stronger senses of eyesight and hearing than sense of smell.*

28.2 Movement and Support

Lesson Objectives

- Describe the three types of skeletons in animals.
- Explain how muscles produce movement in animals.

Lesson Summary

Types of Skeletons There are three main types of animal skeletons:

▶ Some invertebrates, such as cnidarians and annelids, have hydrostatic skeletons. A **hydrostatic skeleton** consists of fluids held in a gastrovascular cavity that can alter the animal's body shape drastically by working with contractile cells in its body wall.

▶ An **exoskeleton**, or external skeleton, of an arthropod is a hard body covering made of a complex carbohydrate called chitin. Most mollusks have exoskeletons, or shells, made of calcium carbonate. To increase in size, arthropods break out of their exoskeleton and grow a new one in a process called **molting**.

▶ An **endoskeleton** is a structural support system within the body. Vertebrates have an endoskeleton made of cartilage or a combination of cartilage and bone.

▶ Arthropods and vertebrates can bend because many parts of their skeletons are connected by **joints**. In vertebrates, bones are connected at joints by strong connective tissues called **ligaments**.

Muscles and Movement Muscles are attached to and pull on different parts of an organism's skeleton. This causes movement.

▶ Muscles are attached to bones around the joints by tough connective tissue called **tendons**.

▶ The shapes and relative positions of bones and muscles, and the shapes of joints, are linked very closely to the functions they perform.

▶ Muscles often work in opposing groups. Flexors bend a joint. Extensors straighten a joint.

Types of Skeletons

1. What are the three main kinds of skeletal systems?
   hydrostatic skeletons, exoskeletons, and endoskeletons

2. What does a cnidarian's hydrostatic skeleton consist of?
   It consists of a layer of contractile cells as well as fluids held in the gastrovascular
   cavity.

3. What is chitin?
   a protein that makes up the hard exoskeleton of arthropods

4. Which invertebrates have endoskeletons?
   echinoderms

Match the organism with its skeleton. A skeleton type may be used more than once.

Organism		Skeleton Type
_C_	5. cow	A. hydrostatic skeleton
_B_	6. grasshopper	B. exoskeleton
_A_	7. jellyfish	C. endoskeleton
_C_	8. hawk	
_C_	9. sea star	
_B_	10. crab	
_A_	11. earthworm	
_B_	12. ant	
_C_	13. dog	

For Questions 14–16, write the letter of the correct answer on the line at the left.

_A_ **14.** What is the process by which an arthropod breaks out of an exoskeleton it has outgrown?

  A. molting   **C.** shedding

  B. excreting   **D.** metamorphosing

_B_ **15.** The pieces of an exoskeleton move against each other along

  A. chitin.   **C.** tendons.

  B. joints.   **D.** cavities.

_C_ **16.** What type of structure connects one bone to another in a vertebrate skeleton?

  A. a muscle   **C.** a ligament

  B. a tendon   **D.** a tube foot

Muscles and Movement

17. Explain how arthropods move.

Arthropods move using groups of muscles that are attached to their exoskeleton. When the muscle contracts, it bends or flexes the joint. The exoskeleton moves along the joint.

18. What are tendons?

A tendon is a tough connective tissue that attaches a muscle to a bone around a joint.

19. What muscle pairs with the hamstring to move your leg?

quadricep

20. Complete the Venn diagram comparing arthropod movement with vertebrate movement.

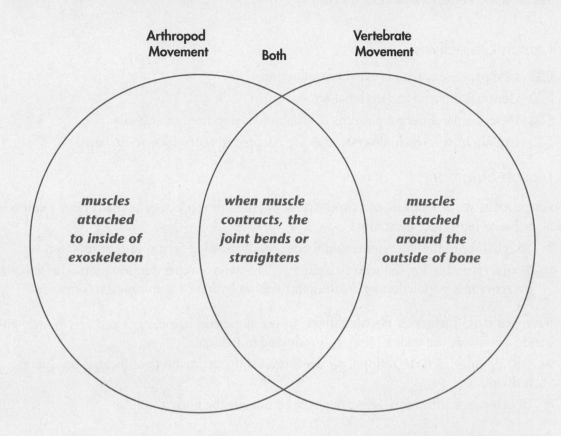

Arthropod Movement   Both   Vertebrate Movement

muscles attached to inside of exoskeleton

when muscle contracts, the joint bends or straightens

muscles attached around the outside of bone

For Questions 21–27, complete each statement by writing the correct word or words.

21. Specialized tissues that produce physical force by contracting, or getting shorter, when they are stimulated are called _____*muscles*_____.

22. When they are not being stimulated, muscles _____*relax*_____.

23. In many animals, muscles work in _____*pairs*_____ on opposites sides of a joint.

24. Muscles are attached to bones around the joints by tough connective tissue called _____*tendons*_____.

25. When muscles contract, tendons pull on _____*bones*_____.

26. Arthropod muscles are attached to the inside of the _____*exoskeleton*_____.

27. Paleontologists can reconstruct how an extinct mammal moved by looking at the shape of its _____*leg or limb bones*_____.

Apply the Big idea

28. Hypothesize how a bird's skeleton might be different from reptile and mammal skeletons in order to help the bird fly.

SAMPLE ANSWER: *A bird's skeleton is probably made up of less-dense bones than the bones*

in a reptile's or mammal's skeleton.

_____

28.3 Reproduction

Lesson Objectives

🔑 Compare asexual and sexual reproduction.

🔑 Contrast internal and external fertilization.

🔑 Describe the different patterns of embryo development in animals.

🔑 Explain how terrestrial vertebrates are adapted to reproduction on land.

Lesson Summary

Asexual and Sexual Reproduction Most animals reproduce sexually. Some animals are also able to reproduce asexually.

▶ Asexual reproduction requires only one parent allowing for rapid reproduction.

▶ Sexual reproduction requires two parents. This type of reproduction maintains genetic diversity in a population by creating individuals with new combinations of genes.

Internal and External Fertilization In sexual reproduction, eggs and sperm meet either inside or outside the body of the egg-producing individual.

▶ During internal fertilization, eggs are fertilized inside the body of the egg-producing individual.

▶ In external fertilization, eggs are fertilized outside the body.

Development and Growth Embryos develop either inside or outside the body of a parent in various ways.

▶ **Oviparous** species are those in which embryos develop in eggs outside the parents' bodies.

▶ In **ovoviviparous** species, embryos develop within the mother's body, but they depend entirely on the yolk sac of their eggs.

▶ **Viviparous** species' embryos obtain nutrients from the mother's body. Some mammals nourish their embryos by means of a **placenta**—a specialized organ that enables exchange of respiratory gases, nutrients, and wastes between the mother and her developing young.

▶ As invertebrates, nonvertebrate chordates, fishes, and amphibians develop, they undergo **metamorphosis**, resulting in changes to their shape and form.

▶ Some insects undergo gradual or incomplete metamorphosis. Immature forms, or **nymphs**, resemble adults, but they lack functional sexual organs and some adult structures.

▶ Other insects undergo complete metamorphosis. Larvae change into a **pupa**, the stage in which an insect larva develops into an adult.

Reproductive Diversity in Chordates Chordates had to adapt to reproduction on land. Most chordates need a wet or moist environment for their eggs.

▶ The eggs of most aquatic organisms must develop in water. Reptiles, birds, and a few mammals have evolved **amniotic eggs** in which an embryo can develop outside its mother's body, and out of water, without drying out.

▶ Mammals have various reproductive adaptations. But all mammalian young are nourished by milk produced by the mother's **mammary glands**.

Asexual and Sexual Reproduction

1. What does asexual reproduction allow animals to do?

It allows animals to increase their numbers rapidly.

2. What is an advantage of sexual reproduction?

It helps a species maintain genetic diversity.

3. **THINK VISUALLY** Shade the arrows showing haploid stage of the life cycle. Draw small dots in the arrows showing diploid stages.

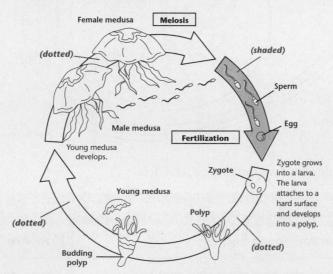

Internal and External Fertilization

4. What is the difference between external and internal fertilization?

In external fertilization, eggs are fertilized outside the body of the egg-producing

individual. In internal fertilization, eggs are fertilized inside the body of the egg-

producing individual.

Development and Growth

Write the letter of the correct answer on the line at the left.

___B___ **5.** In which mode of reproduction do the embryos develop inside the mother's body using the egg yolk for nourishment?

    A. oviparous   **C.** viviparous

    B. ovoviviparous   **D.** herbivorous

___C___ **6.** Organisms that develop placentas are

    A. oviparous.   **C.** viviparous.

    B. ovoviviparous.   **D.** herbivorous.

7. Explain the difference between complete and incomplete metamorphosis.

In complete metamorphosis, the insect goes through immature stages that do not

look like the adult form. In incomplete metamorphosis, the immature form, the

nymph, looks similar to the adult form.

Reproductive Diversity in Chordates

8. **THINK VISUALLY**

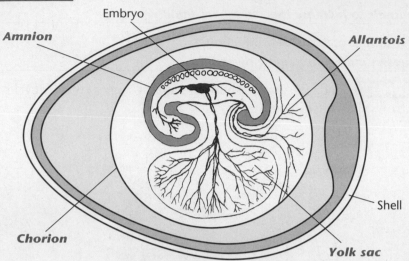

9. Complete the table about mammal reproduction.

Types of Mammalian Reproduction and Development		
Group	**How Are Young Born?**	**How Are Young Fed?**
Monotremes	Young hatch from soft-shelled eggs laid outside the mother's body.	*Young get milk from pores on the mother's abdomen.*
Marsupials	*Embryo is born at a very early stage of development and attaches to a nipple inside a pouch.*	Young drink from a nipple inside the mother's pouch.
Placental mammals	*Embryos develop inside the mother. Wastes and nutrients pass through the placenta.*	Young are generally nursed by the mother.

Apply the Big idea

10. How might the shape of an amniotic egg complement its function?

SAMPLE ANSWER: *The slightly elongated, pointed shape may help the mother lay the egg more easily. In addition, the shape keeps the egg from rolling far from a nest.*

_____

_____

28.4 Homeostasis

Lesson Objectives

Explain how homeostasis is maintained in animals.

Describe the importance of body temperature control in animals.

Lesson Summary

Interrelationship of Body Systems Homeostasis is the maintenance of a relatively stable internal environment. All body systems work together to maintain homeostasis. Fighting disease-causing agents is a large part of maintaining homeostasis. Most animals have an immune system that attacks pathogens.

▶ Vertebrates and many invertebrates regulate many body processes using a system of chemical controls.

▶ **Endocrine glands**, which produce and release hormones, regulate body activities by releasing hormones into the blood.

Body Temperature Control Control of body temperature is important for maintaining homeostasis, particularly in areas where temperature varies widely with time of day and with season.

▶ An **ectotherm** is an animal whose regulation of body temperature depends mostly on its relationship to sources of heat outside its body. Most reptiles, invertebrates, fishes, and amphibians are ectothermic.

▶ An **endotherm** is an animal whose body temperature is regulated, at least in part, using heat generated by its body. Birds and mammals are endothermic.

Interrelationship of Body Systems

1. Complete the graphic organizer about body systems working together.

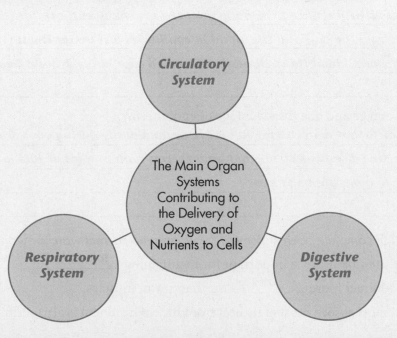

2. What is homeostasis?

Homeostasis is the ability of an animal to maintain a stable internal environment.

3. Name the body system that helps protect mammals from disease and describe how it accomplishes this task.

The immune system protects mammalian bodies from disease. It does this by distin-
guishing between "self" and "other." Once the immune system discovers "others" in
the body, it attacks the invaders.

4. What are endocrine glands?

Endocrine glands are part of the body system that regulates many body processes
using chemical controls. Endocrine glands release chemicals called hormones that
affect other organs and tissues.

Body Temperature Control

5. List three features that animals need in order to control their body temperature.

Animals need a way to generate heat, a way to conserve heat, and a way to eliminate
excess heat.

6. How do ectotherms control their body temperature?

They rely on interactions with the environment.

7. Explain how the human body cools itself.

Humans sweat to help reduce their body temperature. As sweat evaporates, it
removes heat from the skin and the blood in capillaries just under the surface of the
skin. Thus, as warm blood flows through the cooled capillaries, it loses heat.

8. Name one advantage and one disadvantage of endothermy.

One advantage is that endotherms can move around easily during cool nights or in
cold weather. One disadvantage is that endotherms require a lot of fuel in the form of
food in order to generate body heat.

For Questions 9–15, complete each statement by writing the correct word or words.

9. Control of body temperature is important for maintaining ___homeostasis___.

10. Cold muscles contract more ___slowly___ than warm muscles.

11. An animal that must absorb most of its heat from the environment is a(n) ___ectotherm___.

12. An animal that uses heat generated by its own body to maintain its body temperature is a(n) __endotherm__.

13. Endotherms have a higher __metabolic__ rate than ectotherms.

14. Endothermy evolved __after__ ectothermy.

15. Mammals use __body fat__ and __hair__ as insulation in order to stay warm.

Match each organism with the method of controlling body heat. Methods may be used more than once.

Organism

__B__ 16. mammals

__A__ 17. fish

__A__ 18. amphibian

__A__ 19. invertebrate

__B__ 20. birds

__A__ 21. reptiles

Body Heating Method

A. Ectothermy

B. Endothermy

For Questions 22–25, write True if the statement is true. If the statement is false, change the underlined word or words to make the statement true.

__True__ 22. The first land vertebrates were <u>ectotherms</u>.

__True__ 23. Some scientists hypothesize that some <u>dinosaurs</u> were endotherms.

__twice__ 24. Current evidence suggests that endothermy evolved at least <u>four times</u>.

__endotherms__ 25. Most animals living in polar regions are <u>ectotherms</u>.

Apply the Big idea

26. Explain how an organism's circulatory, digestive, or excretory system helps the organism maintain homeostasis.

SAMPLE ANSWER: *The excretory system of an organism helps it maintain homeostasis by regulating water balance and getting rid of toxic waste products. For example, the kidneys excrete or retain excess liquid, but they filter waste products out of the bloodstream so that the waste products will not poison cells.*

_____

_____

_____

_____

Chapter Vocabulary Review

1. In the box below, draw a picture of the arrangement of a joint, including at least one ligament and at least one tendon. Label your picture.

> *Students' drawings should show the articulation point of two bones. This point should be labeled as a joint. Connective tissues should be drawn connecting the two bones. This tissue should be labeled as a ligament. Another connective tissue should connect a bone to a muscle. This tissue should be labeled as a tendon.*

For Questions 2–7, complete each statement by writing the correct word or words.

2. A single, specific reaction to a stimulus is a(n) _____response_____.

3. A structure called a(n) _____placenta_____ forms when an embryo's tissues join with the tissues from the mother's body.

4. One of the most important adaptations to life on land is the _____amniotic egg_____, which protects the growing embryo and keeps it from drying out.

5. In _____ovoviviparous_____ animals, the eggs develop inside the mother's body, and the embryo uses the yolk for nourishment.

6. A(n) _____exoskeleton_____ is a tough external covering of the body.

7. A(n) _____endoskeleton_____ is an internal skeleton.

For Questions 8–11, write True if the statement is true. If the statement is false, change the underlined word or words to make the statement true.

_____True_____ **8.** A <u>stimulus</u> is any kind of signal that carries information and can be detected.

_____viviparous_____ **9.** In <u>oviparous</u> animals, the embryos develop inside the mother's body and obtain their nourishment from their mother, not the egg.

_____pupa_____ **10.** In complete metamorphosis, the stage in which an insect changes from larva to adult is called a(n) <u>nymph</u>.

_____True_____ **11.** A group of nerve cells that control the nervous system in many invertebrates is called a(n) <u>ganglion</u>.

Write the letter of the correct answer on the line at the left.

___C___ **12.** Mammals are characterized by hair and
  A. lungs.   C. mammary glands.
  B. prehensile tails.   D. four-chambered hearts.

___B___ **13.** Animals that can generate their own body heat are known as
  A. ectotherms.   C. chordates.
  B. endotherms.   D. invertebrates.

CHAPTER
MYSTERY

SHE'S JUST LIKE HER MOTHER

21st Century Learning

After the incredible birth of the bonnethead shark at the Doorly Zoo, the zoo's public relations department was probably working overtime. The birth of this shark provided a perfect opportunity to promote the zoo.

Promoting Zoo Births

Zoos work responsibly to foster the reproduction of animals. The birth of a zoo animal is something to be celebrated and promoted, especially when it involves an endangered or threatened animal. Zoo births are helpful to zoos in many ways. For example, they can bring in additional visitors and encourage donations to the zoo.

A zoo's public relations department can find many ways to promote the birth of an animal. They may create and issue press releases, posters, pamphlets, commercials, and billboards. Their efforts may lead local television and radio stations to cover the animal birth in news reports. The following is an example of what a transcript of a live report by a local television station might have been like after a Sumatran tiger gave birth to triplets at the San Francisco Zoo.

Live at 5 - San Francisco News REPORTING LIVE FROM THE SAN FRANCISCO ZOO

March 14, 2008 - I'm reporting live from the San Francisco Zoo. Zookeepers were in for a couple of surprises today at the San Francisco Zoo. The zoo has been buzzing with excitement and activity since their 230-pound Sumatran tiger, Leanne, gave birth to one cub on March 6. But just this week, the zoo revealed that Leanne actually had triplets! The zoo's chief veterinarian did not suspect that there was more than one cub until 6 days ago.

How could this be? Well, Leanne had decided to take a tiger-size lick of the camera that was monitoring her, fogging up part of the lens. The birthing box was not completely visible, either. It was not until the thirsty new mom left the box to get a drink that the zookeeper noticed the two other cubs. Zookeepers do not want to disturb the mother and her young yet. Leanne is doing a great job of taking care of her babies—even protecting them from the camera lens. Sumatran tigers are an endangered species, with only about 600 remaining in the wild. Zoo officials hope that these web-footed cubs will soon be swimming just as fast as other Sumatran tigers.

Continued on next page ▶

21st Century Themes Science and Global Awareness

1. What is the tone of this television report, and how is it intended to make you feel?

SAMPLE ANSWER: **The tone is one of excitement. It is probably intended to make the viewer want to visit the zoo to see the tiger triplets.**

2. Suppose you were giving this report. What information would you add to the report? Explain your answer.

SAMPLE ANSWER: **I would give more information about the cubs, which is the main focus of the story, and thus the reason people are watching the report. I would give details about how big they were when they were born, when they will be moving about, and how healthy they are.**

3. What do you think is the purpose of this television report?

SAMPLE ANSWER: **I think the purpose is to get viewers excited. They left out just enough information to keep viewers interested, which may serve to encourage viewers to visit the zoo.**

4. What are some words and phrases in the broadcast that appeal to listeners' emotions and make them want to visit the zoo?

Examples of words and phrases in this report that appeal to a listener's emotions include surprises, buzzing with excitement, and new mom. These words and phrases are all emotionally charged.

5. What are two facts you learned about Sumatran tigers from this report?

SAMPLE ANSWER: **Sumatran tigers have webbed feet and can swim fast. There are only about 600 left in the wild.**

21st Century Skills Promote Zoo News

The skills used in this activity include **information and media literacy, creativity and intellectual curiosity.**

Find out about the latest news at a zoo close to your town or in your area by calling the zoo and asking to speak with its public relations department, visiting the zoo, or looking at the zoo's Web site. Choose an event, such as the recent birth or acquisition of an animal, that you can promote to encourage more people to visit the zoo. After researching the event, create a poster to promote it. Your poster should include persuasive text, photographs or illustrations, contact information, and how to visit the zoo.

Display copies of your poster around your school. You may also want to contact the zoo and encourage them to use your poster.

Evaluate students' posters based on the organization of the text and art, the appeal of the art as an enticement to visit the zoo, the succinctness and completeness of the text, and the information it contains.

29 Animal Behavior

Big idea: Evolution

Q: How do animals interact with one another and their environments?

WHAT I KNOW	WHAT I LEARNED
29.1 What are the elements of animal behavior?	*SAMPLE ANSWER:* **Animal behavior involves the way an animal acts and how an animal learns.**	*SAMPLE ANSWER:* **Behavior is the way an organism responds to stimuli in its environment. Behaviors that are influenced by genes that increase an individual's reproductive fitness spread throughout a population and increase a population's fitness. An innate behavior is an instinct. Learned behaviors include habituation, classical conditioning, operant conditioning, and insight learning. Complex behaviors combine innate and learned behaviors.**
29.2 How do the environment and other organisms affect an animal's behavior?	*SAMPLE ANSWER:* **The environment affects behavior. Animals communicate and interact with one another.**	*SAMPLE ANSWER:* **Many animals demonstrate daily or seasonal cycles in their behavior. Interactions among animals of the same species are called social behavior. Communication is important to social behavior.**

29.1 Elements of Behavior

Lesson Objectives

- Identify the significance of behavior in the evolution of a species.
- Explain what an innate behavior is.
- Describe the major types of learning.
- Explain what types of behaviors are usually considered complex.

Lesson Summary

Behavior and Evolution Behavior is the way an organism reacts to stimuli in its environment.

- ▶ Behaviors essential to survival and reproduction include finding and catching food, selecting a habitat, avoiding predators, and finding a mate.
- ▶ Some behaviors are influenced by genes and can be inherited.
- ▶ Certain behaviors evolve under the influence of natural selection:
  - If a behavior increases an individual's fitness and is influenced by genes, it tends to spread through a population.
  - Over many generations, adaptive behaviors can prove important in the survival of populations and species.

Innate Behavior An innate behavior, also called an instinct, is fully functional the first time it is performed, although the animal has no previous experience with the stimulus. All innate behaviors depend on patterns of nervous system activity that develop through complex interactions between genes and the environment.

Learned Behavior Acquiring changes in behavior during one's lifetime is called learning. There are four types:

- ▶ Habituation is the process by which an animal decreases or stops its response to a repetitive stimulus that neither rewards nor harms the animal.
- ▶ In classical conditioning, a certain stimulus comes to produce a particular response, usually through an association with a positive or negative experience.
- ▶ Operant conditioning (a form of trial-and-error learning) is the use of a reward or punishment to teach an animal to behave in a certain way through repeated practice.
- ▶ Insight learning occurs when an animal applies to a new situation something that it learned previously in another context.

Complex Behaviors Many complex behaviors combine innate behavior with learning. Imprinting is a complex behavior. Imprinting is the process by which some animals, such as birds, recognize and follow the first moving object they see during a critical period in their early lives.

Behavior and Evolution

For Questions 1–5, write True if the statement is true. If the statement is false, change the underlined word or words to make the statement true.

behavior   1. An <u>adaptation</u> is the way an animal responds to a stimulus in its environment.

True   2. An animal's <u>nervous</u> system makes behaviors possible.

True   3. Certain behaviors are influenced by <u>genes</u> and can therefore be inherited.

increases   4. If a behavior <u>decreases</u> fitness, it may spread in a population.

True   5. <u>Adaptive</u> behaviors can play a role in the survival of a species.

6. How are behaviors affected by natural selection?

Many behaviors are influenced by genes and can be inherited. Natural selection can influence these behaviors to evolve the way physical traits do. If a behavior increases an animal's fitness, the animal will be more likely to survive and produce offspring.

Innate Behavior

7. Does learning play a role in innate behavior? Explain your answer.

No. Learning plays no role in innate behavior. The innate behavior is performed properly the first time a stimulus is encountered.

8. Give three examples of innate behaviors.

SAMPLE ANSWER: Innate behaviors include the suckling of a newborn, the weaving of a spider web, or the construction of a hanging nest by a weaver bird.

Learned Behavior

9. What is learning? Why is it important for survival?

Learning is acquiring changes in behavior during one's lifetime. Learning is the result of experience or practice. Learning is important for survival because it allows animals to respond to changing situations. Animals that have the ability to learn a new behavior are more likely to survive in an unpredictable environment.

10. Complete the graphic organizer to summarize the four types of learning.

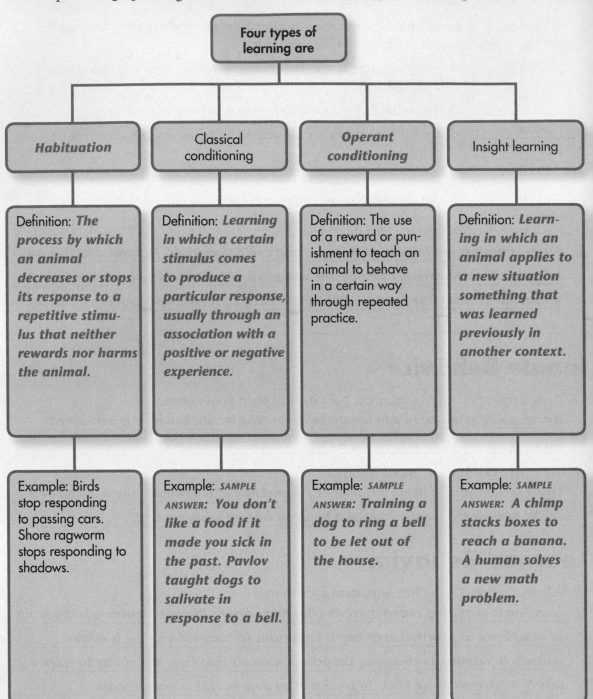

Four types of
learning are

Habituation	Classical conditioning	Operant conditioning	Insight learning
Definition: *The process by which an animal decreases or stops its response to a repetitive stimulus that neither rewards nor harms the animal.*	**Definition:** *Learning in which a certain stimulus comes to produce a particular response, usually through an association with a positive or negative experience.*	**Definition:** The use of a reward or punishment to teach an animal to behave in a certain way through repeated practice.	**Definition:** *Learning in which an animal applies to a new situation something that was learned previously in another context.*
Example: Birds stop responding to passing cars. Shore ragworm stops responding to shadows.	**Example:** SAMPLE ANSWER: *You don't like a food if it made you sick in the past. Pavlov taught dogs to salivate in response to a bell.*	**Example:** SAMPLE ANSWER: *Training a dog to ring a bell to be let out of the house.*	**Example:** SAMPLE ANSWER: *A chimp stacks boxes to reach a banana. A human solves a new math problem.*

11. In Pavlov's experiment, a dog produced salivation in reaction to a bell associated with food. Which type of learning does this describe? Explain your answer.

Pavlov's experiment is an example of classical conditioning. Classical conditioning occurs when a certain stimulus comes to produce a particular response through the association with an experience. In Pavlov's experiment, the dog's salivating was a response to the bell (the stimulus), which was associated with food.

12. What is a "Skinner box"? Explain how it is used in learning.

The American psychologist B.F. Skinner invented the Skinner box to help animals learn

by operant conditioning. In operant conditioning, an animal learns through repeated

practice to receive a reward or avoid a punishment. The Skinner box contains a

colored button. When the button is pressed, food is delivered to the test subject as a

reward. After an animal is rewarded several times, it learns that it gets food whenever

the button is pressed.

Complex Behavior

For Questions 13–17, write the letter of the correct answer on the line at the left.

___A___ **13.** Birds that are born recognizing the songs of their own species are exhibiting

    A. innate behavior.   **C.** operant conditioning.

    B. habituation.   **D.** insight learning.

___A___ **14.** Young birds following their mother is an example of

    A. imprinting.   **C.** operant conditioning.

    B. classical conditioning.   **D.** habituation.

___C___ **15.** What do newly hatched salmon imprint on?

    A. Sounds of the stream where they hatched

    B. Sights of the stream where they hatched

    C. Odors of the stream where they hatched

    D. Feel of the stream where they hatched

___D___ **16.** Imprinting is considered a complex behavior because

    A. it is adaptive.

    B. it is instinctual.

    C. it combines classical conditional and instinct.

    D. it combines innate behavior with learning.

___B___ **17.** Once imprinting has occurred, the behavior becomes

    A. complex.   **B.** fixed.   **C.** conditioned.   **D.** innate.

Apply the Big idea

18. Lloyd has two goldfish in a bowl he keeps on his desk. Every morning when he arrives
at work, he turns on his office lights. The instant the lights come on, the fish rise to the
surface of the water and move their mouths. Lloyd always feeds them before he begins
work. What kind of behavior are the fish exhibiting before Lloyd drops food into the
water? How is this type of behavior adaptive? Explain.

The fish have learned through classical conditioning to associate the lights with the food

that is to come. They rise to the top of the water and move their mouths in response

to the lights, just as they would in response to food alone. This behavioral response is

adaptive because it helps the fish obtain food, which then enables the fish to survive.

29.2 Animals in Their Environments

Lesson Objectives

🔑 Explain how environmental changes affect animal behavior.

🔑 Explain how social behaviors increase the evolutionary fitness of a species.

🔑 Summarize the ways that animals communicate.

Lesson Summary

Behavioral Cycles Many animals demonstrate daily or seasonal cycles in their behavior.

▶ **Circadian rhythms** are behavioral cycles that occur daily.

▶ **Migration** is the seasonal movement from one environment to another. For example, many birds find food and nesting sites in the north in summer, but they fly south to warmer climates for the winter.

Social Behavior Interactions among animals of the same species are social behavior. There are several types:

▶ Animals (usually the males) perform **courtship** behaviors to attract a mate. An elaborate series of courtship behaviors is a courtship ritual.

▶ Many animals occupy a specific area, or **territory**, that they defend against competitors. Animals may use threatening behaviors, or **aggression**, to defend their territories. Animals also may use aggression when they compete for resources.

▶ Some animals form a **society**, or a group that interacts closely and often cooperatively. The theory that helping a relative survive increases the chance of transmitting one's own genes is **kin selection**.

▶ The most complex animal societies are those formed by social insects such as ants, bees, and wasps. All animals in the society cooperate closely to perform complex tasks, such as nest construction.

Communication The passing of information from one individual to another is **communication**.

▶ Animals use a variety of signals for communication, including visual, chemical, and sound.

▶ **Language** is a system of communication that combines sounds, symbols, and gestures according to rules about sequence and meaning.

Behavioral Cycles

For Questions 1–6, complete each statement by writing the correct word or words.

1. Many animals respond to periodic changes with _____daily_____ or _____seasonal_____ cycles of behavior.

2. Behavioral cycles that occur daily are called _____circadian rhythms_____.

3. Seasonal dormancy in mammals is called _____hibernation_____.

4. The seasonal movement from one environment to another is _____migration_____.

5. Migration allows animals to take advantage of favorable __environmental__ conditions.

6. During northern winters, many birds live in tropical environments where _____food_____ is plentiful.

7. **THINK VISUALLY** Draw a diagram that shows the migration pattern of green sea turtles. Label your diagram. Then, on the lines below, describe the migration pattern followed by these animals.

> *Students' diagrams should resemble the illustration in the textbook.*

Each year green sea turtles migrate between their feeding grounds on the coast of
Brazil and their nesting grounds on Ascension Island.

Social Behavior

8. Complete the table of main ideas and details about the social behavior of animals. Explain and give an example of each type of social behavior.

Social Behaviors of Animals		
Type of Social Behavior	**Definition**	**Example**
Courtship	A member of one sex advertises willingness to mate.	SAMPLE ANSWER: The "trill" of a tree frog is a breeding call.
Territoriality	Animals occupy an area that they defend against competitors.	SAMPLE ANSWER: A grizzly bear marks its territory with its fur and scent.
Animal Societies	Animal societies are groups that interact closely and often cooperate.	SAMPLE ANSWER: African dogs guard the young and hunt for food cooperatively.

9. What are rituals? How do rituals help a species' survival?

A ritual involves an elaborate series of courtship behaviors. Rituals help animals of the

same species communicate that they are ready to mate. This type of behavior helps a spe-

cies' survival by ensuring reproductive success. Rituals ensure that male and female mem-

bers of a species will recognize one another and be ready to mate at the same time.

10. Suppose you find a stray cat. As you approach, the cat begins to hiss, arch its back, and flatten its ears. Which type of behavior is this cat exhibiting? How would this behavior help this cat survive?

The cat is exhibiting aggression. It is showing threatening behaviors to try to exert

dominance over another animal. This type of behavior could help a cat that was com-

peting with another animal for resources or territory. By showing aggression, the cat

can scare off its competition and protect its resources.

11. Coyotes are predators. Prairie dogs are prey. Prairie dogs live in large colonies. When a coyote nears, one prairie dog may spot the predator and make a high-pitched sound that alerts other members of the colony. In the process of making the sound, the alarm-calling prairie dog draws the coyote's attention, so that animal faces the greatest risk of predation. How does the theory of kin selection explain this behavior?

The alarm-calling prairie dog risks its own life in sounding the call, but many of its

relatives may be saved as a result. So some of the prairie dog's genes are passed on

to the next generation via close relatives, even though the individual animal may be

eaten by the coyote.

Communication

For Questions 12–20, complete each statement by writing the correct word or words.

12. __Communication__ is the passing of information from one individual to another.

13. Communication is important to ____social____ behavior, which involves more than one individual.

14. The kinds of signals that animal species send and receive depend on the stimuli they can detect with their ____senses____.

15. Visual signals may be used by animals that can detect color, shape, or ____light____.

16. Some animals may change ____color____ to signal readiness to mate.

17. The use of chemical signals requires a well-developed sense of ____smell____.

18. A chemical messenger that affects the behavior or another individual of the same species is a(n) ____pheromone____.

19. Some animals send and receive sound signals that they do not hear but they can ____feel____.

20. Rules of sequence and meaning are required for the form of communication called
_____*language*_____.

21. Complete the concept map to show the kinds of signals animals can use to communicate.

Apply the Big idea

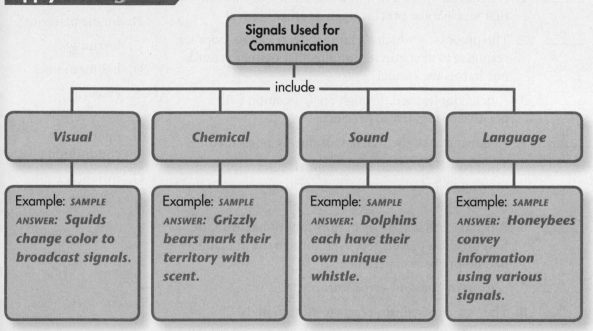

22. Explain how social behaviors can increase evolutionary fitness.

Whether it is finding a mate, defending a territory, or cooperating in a hunt, social

behaviors increase the chance that individuals will survive and reproduce. Enhanced

survival and reproduction ensure that animals exhibiting successful social behaviors

pass their genes on to their offspring. Those offspring, also equipped with successful

social behaviors, acquired through heredity and/or learning, are also more likely to

survive and reproduce.

Chapter Vocabulary Review

For Questions 1–8, match the term with its definition.

Definition

Term

___G___ 1. A behavior applied to a new situation from something that was learned previously in another context

___D___ 2. The process by which an animal decreases or stops its response to a repetitive stimulus that neither rewards nor harms the animal

___E___ 3. A behavior learned through an association with a positive or negative experience

___C___ 4. Acquiring changes in behavior during one's lifetime

___H___ 5. The process by which some animals follow the first moving object they see during a critical period in their early lives

___B___ 6. A behavior that appears in fully functional form the first time it is performed, even though the animal has had no previous experience

___F___ 7. A form of trial-and-error learning

___A___ 8. The way an organism reacts to stimuli in its environment

A. behavior
B. innate behavior
C. learning
D. habituation
E. classical conditioning
F. operant conditioning
G. insight learning
H. imprinting

For Questions 9–13, complete each statement by writing the correct word or words.

9. The behavior used to attract a mate is called _____courtship_____.

10. The area that animals occupy and defend against competitors is their _____territory_____.

11. Any threatening behavior is a form of _____aggression_____.

12. A _____society_____ is the term for a group of animals of the same species that interact.

13. Helping a relative survive may be explained by the theory of _____kin selection_____.

Write the letter of the correct answer on the line at the left.

___A___ 14. What are behavioral cycles that occur daily?
 A. circadian rhythms   C. migration
 B. courtship   D. learned behaviors

___D___ 15. Each year, green sea turtles travel back and forth between their feeding and nesting grounds. This is an example of
 A. kin selection.   C. hibernation.
 B. circadian rhythms.   D. migration.

___C___ 16. The system that combines sounds, symbols, and gestures to communicate meaning is
 A. society.   C. language.
 B. kin selection.   D. territory.

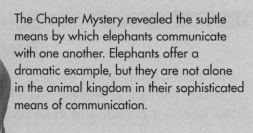

CHAPTER MYSTERY

ELEPHANT CALLER ID

21st Century Learning

The Chapter Mystery revealed the subtle means by which elephants communicate with one another. Elephants offer a dramatic example, but they are not alone in the animal kingdom in their sophisticated means of communication.

The Impact of Ocean Noise on Marine Mammals

Marine mammals and fish have sensitive hearing. They use sound for most of the important aspects of their survival, including reproduction, feeding, navigation, and the avoidance of predators.

For some time, ocean noise has been increasing because of huge ocean tankers, offshore oil drilling, naval sonar, and other human activity. Many marine biologists have worried about the impact of this noise on marine species. In 2004, the National Oceanic and Atmospheric Administration (NOAA) in the United States held the first international symposium to draw together experts from government, academia, and the commercial shipping industry to address this issue.

Read the symposium's summary report below to learn more about the effect of noise on marine mammals.

Shipping Noise and Marine Mammals
2004 International Symposium
Sponsored by the U.S. National Oceanic and Atmospheric Administration
18-19 May 2004, Arlington, Virginia, USA

There is currently considerable interest in whether human-generated sound produced in the marine environment impacts animals and, if so, how. It is clear from scientific investigations of many marine mammals that the production and reception of certain sounds are critical to their survival and well being. It is also evident that ocean noise has the potential to interfere with these marine mammals' normal functioning.

The symposium found evidence that noise levels in the ocean have risen dramatically over the past several decades. Researchers reported, for instance, that the worldwide fleet of commercial shipping vessels, such as tankers and container ships, has more than doubled over the past several decades. In one study, scientists continuously sampled ocean noise in a single location off southern California and determined that noise levels have increased at a rate of approximately 3 decibels per decade over the past thirty years.

Although ocean noise is getting louder, it remains largely unclear exactly what kind of disruption and threat the noise pollution may cause to populations of marine mammals. Marine biologists have studied the hearing capabilities of at least 22 of the approximately 125 species of living marine mammals, although usually in very small sample sizes. Most of these studies have determined that these marine species can be very sensitive to sound. In addition, noise can induce physical trauma to non-auditory structures. In fish, noise can increase egg mortality.

One scientist argued that the most important effect of vessel noise on marine animals is that it masked sounds that were biologically significant. Nonetheless, the evidence remains sparse and limited. While participants at the symposium raised a number of issues about the possible effects of noise on marine life, they agreed that more research is badly needed to better understand the effects of ocean noise on marine mammals.

Continued on next page ▶

21st Century Themes Science and Global Awareness

1. Why did the National Oceanic and Atmospheric Administration hold the meeting discussed above, and who was invited?

The National Oceanic and Atmospheric Administration held the symposium in 2004 to determine what was known about the impact of ocean noise on marine mammals. The meeting drew an international collection of experts from government, academia, and commercial shipping.

2. What evidence do scientists have that ocean noise is increasing?

Commercial shipping fleets have grown significantly, doubling over the past several decades. In addition, one study monitored ocean noise in a single location over time and found that it had increased by 3 decibels each decade over the past 30 years.

3. What role does sound play in the survival of marine mammals?

Marine mammals have sensitive hearing and make use of sounds in reproduction, feeding, navigation, and the avoidance of predators.

4. What may be the most important effect of shipping-vessel noise on marine animals?

Shipping-vessel noise masks sounds that are biologically significant.

5. What has limited scientists' ability to learn more about the effect of noise on marine mammals?

Information about these populations is sparse and hard to come by because of the size of the oceans and the inaccessibility of marine mammal species.

21st Century Skills Listing Research Priorities

The skills used in this activity include **problem identification, formulation, and solution; creativity and intellectual curiosity;** and **self-direction.**

NOAA officials seek to spur new research on the impacts of noise on marine mammals. What research do you think is needed? Find the final report of the symposium on the Internet. It suggests many ideas for future research. Which ideas do you think should have the highest priority? Using the online symposium report, make a list of the top three ideas for possible research projects that you think could best help scientists learn more about this subject. Justify your choices in writing. Then work with three other students to arrive at one list of three priorities and present your list to the class.

Evaluate students' lists by their choices of three priorities from the suggestions in the report. Their justifications should include information from the report, and may include opinion based on fact.

30 Digestive and Excretory Systems

 Big idea **Homeostasis**

Q: How are the materials that enter and leave your body related to the processes that maintain homeostasis?

WHAT I KNOW	WHAT I LEARNED
30.1 How is the human body organized and regulated?	*SAMPLE ANSWER:* **The body is organized into systems.**	*SAMPLE ANSWER:* **The levels of organization in the body are cells, tissues, organs, and organ systems. At each level of organization, these parts work together to carry out life functions and to maintain homeostasis.**
30.2 Why are the essential nutrients important?	*SAMPLE ANSWER:* **Nutrients supply the body with building blocks for growth, repair, and everyday functioning.**	*SAMPLE ANSWER:* **The essential nutrients, which include water, carbohydrates, fats, proteins, vitamins, and minerals, supply the energy and materials the body uses for growth, repair, and maintenance. Diets lacking essential nutrients result in serious health consequences.**
30.3 How does the human body convert food into useful molecules?	*SAMPLE ANSWER:* **Digestion breaks food down into molecules.**	*SAMPLE ANSWER:* **The digestive system converts food into small molecules that can be used by the cells of the body. Food is processed by the digestive system in four phases—ingestion, digestion, absorption, and elimination.**
30.4 How does the human body get rid of wastes?	*SAMPLE ANSWER:* **Liquid wastes are eliminated in urine and solid wastes are removed as feces.**	*SAMPLE ANSWER:* **The excretory system, which includes the skin, liver, lungs, and kidneys, excretes metabolic wastes from the body.**

30.1 Organization of the Human Body

Lesson Objectives

🔑 Describe how the human body is organized.

🔑 Explain homeostasis.

Lesson Summary

Organization of the Body The levels of organization in a multicellular organism include cells, tissues, organs, and organ systems.

▶ A cell is the basic unit of structure and function in living things. Specialized cells are uniquely suited to perform particular functions.

▶ Groups of similar cells that perform a single function are called tissues. There are four basic types of tissue in the human body: **epithelial tissue** lines the interior and exterior body surfaces; **connective tissue** provides support for the body and connects its parts; **nervous tissue** carries messages in the form of nerve impulses throughout the body; and **muscle tissue** is responsible for voluntary and involuntary movement.

▶ Groups of different kinds of tissue that work together to carry out complex functions are called organs.

▶ A group of organs that performs closely related functions is called an organ system.

Homeostasis The different organ systems work together to maintain a controlled, stable internal environment called **homeostasis**. Homeostasis describes the internal physical and chemical conditions that organisms maintain despite changes in internal and external environments.

▶ **Feedback inhibition**, or negative feedback, is the process in which a stimulus produces a response that opposes the original stimulus. An example of feedback inhibition is the way in which the body maintains a constant temperature.

▶ The liver is important for homeostasis. It converts toxic substances into compounds that can be removed from the body safely. It also helps regulate the body's glucose levels.

Organization of the Body

Complete each statement by writing the correct word or words.

1. The tissue that lines the interior and exterior of the body is called ___*epithelial*___ tissue.

2. Connective tissue includes fat cells, ___*bone*___ cells, and blood cells.

3. The brain, ___*spinal cord*___, and nerves are made up of nervous tissue.

4. Voluntary and involuntary movements are controlled by ___*muscle*___ tissue.

5. Complete the table about the organization of the human body.

Organization of the Human Body		
Level of Organization	**Description**	**Example**
Cell	Basic unit of structure and function in living things	*SAMPLE ANSWER:* **muscle cells**
Tissue	**Group of cells that perform a particular function**	*SAMPLE ANSWER:* **nervous tissue**
Organ	Group of different types of tissue that function together	*SAMPLE ANSWER:* **brain**
Organ system	**Group of organs that perform closely related functions**	Nervous system

For Questions 6–16, match the function(s) with the organ system.

Function

_____I_____ 6. Eliminates waste products from the body

_____K_____ 7. Produces gametes

_____H_____ 8. Breaks down food

_____C_____ 9. Protects the body from disease

_____A_____ 10. Recognizes and coordinates the body's response to changes

_____E_____ 11. Transports oxygen to cells

_____D_____ 12. Produces voluntary movement

_____B_____ 13. Guards against ultraviolet light

_____G_____ 14. Brings in oxygen for cellular respiration

_____F_____ 15. Protects internal organs

_____J_____ 16. Controls growth and metabolism

Organ System

A. nervous system

B. integumentary system

C. immune/lymphatic systems

D. muscular system

E. circulatory system

F. skeletal system

G. respiratory system

H. digestive system

I. excretory system

J. endocrine system

K. reproductive system

Homeostasis

17. All of the organ systems in the human body work together to maintain homeostasis. What is homeostasis?

Homeostasis describes the relatively stable conditions the body maintains despite

changes in the internal and external environments.

18. What is a feedback inhibition? Give an example of how it is used in the human body.

Feedback inhibition is the process in which a stimulus produces a response that

opposes the original stimulus. One example is the maintenance of body temperature.

19. Why is the liver important for homeostasis?

The liver converts ammonia and many other dangerous substances, such as drugs,

into compounds that can be removed from the body safely. It also regulates the

body's glucose levels.

20. THINK VISUALLY Fill in the missing labels in the diagram to show how a thermostat uses feedback inhibition to maintain a stable temperature in a house.

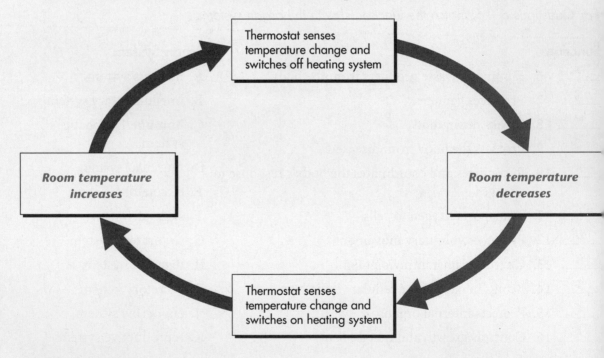

Thermostat senses temperature change and switches off heating system

Room temperature decreases

Thermostat senses temperature change and switches on heating system

Room temperature increases

Apply the Big idea

21. Which organ systems work together to maintain body temperature?

The nervous system and the endocrine system work together to maintain body

temperature.

30.2 Food and Nutrition

Lesson Objectives

- Explain how food provides energy.
- Identify the essential nutrients your body needs and tell how each is important to the body.
- Explain how to plan a balanced diet.

Lesson Summary

Food and Energy Molecules in food contain chemical energy that cells use to produce ATP. Food also supplies raw materials cells need to build and repair tissues.

▶ The energy in food is measured in dietary Calories. One **Calorie** is equal to 1000 calories. A calorie is the amount of heat needed to raise the temperature of 1 gram of water by 1 degree Celsius.

▶ A healthy diet provides the body with raw materials to build and repair body tissues and make enzymes, lipids, and DNA.

Nutrients Nutrients are substances in food that supply the body with energy and raw materials needed for growth, repair, and maintenance. The nutrients that the body needs are water, carbohydrates, fats, proteins, vitamins, and minerals.

▶ Many of the body's processes take place in water. Water makes up a large part of blood and other body fluids.

▶ Simple and complex **carbohydrates** are the body's main source of energy. Complex carbohydrates, such as starches, must be broken down into simple sugars to be used for energy.

▶ **Fats** are formed from fatty acids and glycerol. Fats help the body absorb fat-soluble vitamins and are a part of cell membranes, nerve cells, and certain hormones.

▶ **Proteins** supply raw materials for growth and repair of structures such as skin and muscle. Many enzymes and hormones are proteins.

▶ **Vitamins** are organic molecules that the body needs in very small amounts. They are needed to help the body perform chemical reactions.

▶ **Minerals** are inorganic nutrients the body needs in small amounts. Examples of minerals include calcium and iron.

Nutrition and a Balanced Diet The science of nutrition is the study of food and its effects on the body. A balanced diet provides nutrients in adequate amounts and enough energy for a person to maintain a healthful weight.

▶ Food labels provide general information about nutrition as well as specific information about a food.

▶ Exercising about 30 minutes a day, eating a balanced diet, and controlling fat intake can help maintain a healthful weight.

Food and Energy

Write True if the statement is true. If the statement is false, change the underlined word or words to make the statement true.

_____raise_____ 1. A calorie is the amount of heat needed to <u>lower</u> the temperature of 1 gram of water by 1 degree Celsius.

_____1000_____ 2. One dietary Calorie is equal to <u>2000</u> calories.

_____True_____ 3. The energy stored in food molecules is used to produce <u>ATP</u>.

_____True_____ 4. The body needs raw materials from food to build body tissues and make enzymes, lipids and <u>DNA</u>.

Nutrients

For Questions 5–16, match each description with the nutrient. Each nutrient may be used more than once.

Description	Nutrient
_D_ 5. Provide the body with building materials for growth and repair	A. water
_C_ 6. Needed to build cell membranes, produce certain hormones, and store energy	B. carbohydrates
_B_ 7. Major source of food energy	C. fats
_A_ 8. Makes up the bulk of most body fluids	D. proteins
_F_ 9. Inorganic nutrients	E. vitamins
_E_ 10. Organic molecules used by the body to help regulate body processes	F. minerals
_C_ 11. May be saturated or unsaturated	
_F_ 12. Required to produce the compound that makes up bones and teeth	
_E_ 13. May be fat-soluble or water-soluble	
_D_ 14. Polymers of amino acids	
_B_ 15. May be monosaccharides, disaccharides, or polysaccharides	
_A_ 16. The most important nutrient	

17. What are three ways the body loses water?

The body loses water through sweat, urine, and exhaling breaths.

_____

Nutrition and a Balanced Diet

18. What is the science of nutrition?

the study of food and its effects on the body _____

_____

Complete each statement by writing the correct word or words.

19. A gram of fat has more Calories than a gram of carbohydrate because carbon atoms in fat have more carbon to ___*hydrogen*___ bonds than the carbon atoms in carbohydrates.

20. Nutrient needs are affected by age, ___*gender*___, and lifestyle.

21. When a person stops growing or becomes less active, energy needs ___*decrease*___.

22. Percent Daily Values found on food labels are based on a ___*2000-Calorie*___ diet.

23. Eating a balanced diet and exercising ___*30 minutes*___ a day can help maintain a healthful weight.

24. Physical activity can ___*strengthen*___ the heart, bones, and muscles.

25. Diets that are high in ___*saturated fat*___ and trans fat increase a person's risk of developing heart disease and Type II diabetes.

Apply the Big idea

26. How can poor food choices negatively affect a person's health?

The body requires particular nutrients for energy and raw materials. Someone who _____

eats an unhealthy diet deprives their body of the materials needed to adequately _____

build and repair body tissue, produce ATP for energy, and make enzymes, lipids, and _____

DNA. Diets high in fats and sugars can lead to problems such as vitamin deficiencies, _____

obesity, heart disease, and diabetes. _____

_____

30.3 The Digestive System

Lesson Objectives

🔑 Describe the organs of the digestive system and explain their functions.

🔑 Explain what happens during digestion.

🔑 Describe how nutrients are absorbed into the bloodstream and wastes are eliminated from the body.

Lesson Summary

Functions of the Digestive System The digestive system converts food into small molecules that can be used by body cells. Food is processed by the digestive system in four phases: ingestion, digestion, absorption, and elimination.

▶ Ingestion is the process of putting food into your mouth.

▶ **Mechanical digestion** is the physical breakdown of large pieces of food into smaller pieces. During **chemical digestion**, enzymes break down food into molecules the body can use.

▶ Food molecules are absorbed into the circulatory system by cells in the small intestine.

▶ Materials the body cannot digest travel through the large intestine and are eliminated as feces.

The Process of Digestion During digestion, food travels through the mouth, esophagus, stomach, and small intestine.

▶ Mechanical digestion begins as teeth tear and grind food. Saliva contains **amylase**, an enzyme that breaks down starches into sugars. This begins the process of chemical digestion. Once food is chewed, it is pushed into the pharynx.

▶ The tube leading from the pharynx to the stomach is called the **esophagus**. Contractions of smooth muscles, called **peristalsis**, move food through the esophagus to the **stomach**, a large muscular sac that continues digestion.

  • Glands in the stomach lining release hydrochloric acid and the enzyme **pepsin**, which breaks proteins into smaller polypeptide fragments.

  • Contractions of stomach muscles churn the stomach contents, which forms **chyme**, a mixture with an oatmeal-like consistency.

▶ As chyme moves out of the stomach, it enters the duodenum, the uppermost portion of the **small intestine**. Here, digestive fluids from the pancreas, liver, and lining of the duodenum are added to the chyme.

Absorption and Elimination Most nutrients from food are absorbed by the small intestine. The large intestine absorbs water and prepares waste for elimination from the body.

▶ The small intestine has fingerlike projections (**villi**) that are covered with microvilli, which absorb nutrients. Most nutrients are absorbed into the blood, but fats are absorbed into the lymph.

▶ When chyme leaves the small intestine, it enters the **large intestine**, or colon. The large intestine absorbs water and some vitamins that are produced by bacteria in the large intestine. The remaining waste material leaves the body through the anus.

Functions of the Digestive System

1. What is the function of the organs of the digestive system?

Their function is to help convert foods into simpler molecules that can be absorbed

and used by body cells.

2. What are the four phases of digestion?

ingestion, digestion, absorption, and elimination

3. What is mechanical digestion?

Mechanical digestion is the physical breakdown of large pieces of food into smaller

pieces.

4. How do absorbed food molecules travel to the rest of the body?

Once the molecules are absorbed by the small intestines, they enter the circulatory

system. The circulatory system transports the molecules throughout the body.

The Process of Digestion

Write the letter of the correct answer on the line at the left.

___C___ **5.** Where does chemical digestion begin?

    A. the stomach   **C.** the mouth

    B. the small intestine   **D.** the esophagus

___A___ **6.** Saliva eases the passage of food through the digestive system and contains

    A. amylase.   **C.** sodium bicarbonate.

    B. pepsin.   **D.** bile.

___C___ **7.** Which is the correct order of passage of food through the digestive system?

    A. mouth, stomach, esophagus, large intestine, small intestine

    B. mouth, stomach, esophagus, small intestine, large intestine

    C. mouth, esophagus, stomach, small intestine, large intestine

    D. mouth, esophagus, stomach, large intestine, small intestine

___B___ **8.** Which of the following is not a role of the pancreas?

    A. produces sodium bicarbonate

    B. produces bile

    C. produces hormones that regulate blood sugar

    D. produces enzymes that break down carbohydrates, proteins, lipids, and nucleic acids

9. Complete the table about the effects of digestive enzymes.

Active Site	Enzyme	Effect on Food
Mouth	*Salivary amylase*	Breaks down starches into disaccharides
Stomach	Pepsin	*Breaks down proteins into large peptides*
Small intestine (released from pancreas)	*Pancreatic amylase*	Continues the breakdown of starch
	Trypsin	*Continues the breakdown of protein*
	Lipase	Breaks down fat
Small intestine	Maltase, sucrase, lactase	*Breaks down remaining disaccharides into monosaccharides*
	Peptidase	Breaks down dipeptides into amino acids

10. **THINK VISUALLY** Draw and label the digestive system. Include the salivary glands, mouth, epiglottis, esophagus, stomach, liver, gallbladder, small intestine, and large intestine.

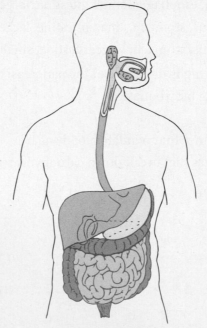

Student drawings should show and label salivary glands, mouth, epiglottis, esophagus, stomach, liver, gallbladder, small intestine, and large intestine.

Absorption and Elimination

For Questions 11–16, complete each statement by writing the correct word or words.

11. The folded surface and fingerlike projections of the __small intestine__ provide a large surface area for absorption of nutrient molecules.

12. The fingerlike projections are called _____villi_____.

13. Capillaries in the villi absorb the products of ____carbohydrate____ and ____protein____ digestion.

14. Fats and fatty acids are absorbed by ____lymph vessels____.

15. In some animals, the _____appendix_____ processes cellulose, but not in humans.

16. Once chyme leaves the small intestine, it enters the large intestine, or _____colon_____.

17. The small intestine is longer than the large intestine. How did the large intestine get its name?

   Although the large intestine is much shorter than the small intestine, its diameter is

   much greater than the small intestine's diameter.

18. What is the primary function of the large intestine?

   The large intestine absorbs water from undigested material.

19. What happens to waste materials when they leave the colon?

   Wastes pass into the rectum and are released from the body through the anus.

Apply the Big idea

20. What role does the large intestine play in maintaining homeostasis?

   The primary function of the large intestine is to absorb water. Water is the most

   important nutrient. The large intestine works with other organ systems to maintain

   water balance in the body.

30.4 The Excretory System

Lesson Objectives

🔑 Describe the structures of the excretory system and explain their functions.

🔑 Explain how the kidneys clean the blood.

🔑 Describe how the kidneys maintain homeostasis.

Lesson Summary

Structures of the Excretory System Cells produce wastes such as salts, carbon dioxide, and ammonia. For homeostasis to be maintained, these wastes need to be removed from the body. **Excretion** is the process by which metabolic wastes are eliminated from the body.

▶ The skin excretes excess water, salts, and a small amount of urea in sweat.

▶ The lungs excrete carbon dioxide and water vapor.

▶ The liver converts potentially dangerous nitrogen wastes to urea.

▶ The kidneys are the major organs of excretion. They remove excess water, urea, and metabolic wastes from the blood. **Ureters** carry urine from the kidneys to the **urinary bladder**, where it is stored until it leaves the body through the **urethra**.

Excretion and the Kidneys The kidneys remove excess water, minerals, and other waste products from the blood. The cleansed blood returns to circulation. Each kidney has nearly a million processing units called **nephrons**. Filtration and reabsorption occur in the nephrons.

▶ **Filtration** is the passage of a fluid or gas through a filter to remove wastes. The filtration of blood in the nephron takes place in the **glomerulus**, a small, dense network of capillaries. Each glomerulus is encased by a cuplike structure called **Bowman's capsule**. Pressure in the capillaries forces fluids and wastes from the blood into Bowman's capsule. This fluid is called filtrate.

▶ Most of the material that enters Bowman's capsule is returned to circulation. The process by which water and dissolved substances are taken back into the blood is called **reabsorption**.

▶ A section of the nephron tubule, called the **loop of Henle**, conserves water and minimizes the volume of filtrate. The fluid that remains in the tubule is called urine.

The Kidneys and Homeostasis The kidneys remove wastes, maintain blood pH, and regulate the water content of the blood.

▶ The activity of the kidneys is controlled in part by the composition of blood. For example, if blood glucose levels rise well above normal, the kidneys excrete glucose into the urine.

▶ Disruption of kidney function can lead to health issues such as kidney stones and serious health issues such as kidney damage, and kidney failure.

• Kidney stones occur when minerals or uric acid salts crystallize and obstruct a ureter.

• Kidney damage is often caused by high blood pressure or diabetes.

• When a patient's kidneys can no longer maintain homeostasis, the patient is said to be in kidney failure.

Structures of the Excretory System

1. Why does the body need an excretory system?

The human body produces chemical waste products. Some of these waste products can be toxic and may cause death if they are not eliminated from the body. The excretory system eliminates these harmful waste products.

2. What is excretion?

Excretion is the process by which metabolic wastes are eliminated from the body to maintain homeostasis.

3. What waste compounds are produced by every cell in the body?

excess salts, carbon dioxide, and ammonia

4. What organs are included in the excretory system?

skin, lungs, liver, kidneys, ureters, urinary bladder, and the urethra

5. Complete the table about the excretory system.

Organs of the Excretory System	
Organ	**Function**
Skin	*Excretes excess water, salts, and urea in sweat*
Lungs	*Excrete carbon dioxide and water vapor when you exhale*
Liver	Converts dangerous nitrogen wastes into urea
Kidneys	*Remove excess water, urea, and metabolic wastes from the blood; produce urine*
Ureters	Transport urine from kidneys to the bladder
Urinary bladder	Stores urine
Urethra	*Releases urine from the body*

Excretion and the Kidneys

6. Complete the concept map.

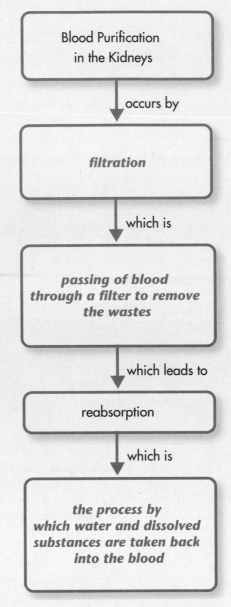

For Questions 7–10, write True if the statement is true. If the statement is false, change the underlined word or words to make the statement true.

___nephrons___ **7.** Each kidney has nearly a million individual processing units called <u>capillaries</u>.

___True___ **8.** The material that is filtered from the blood contains water, urea, <u>glucose</u>, salts, amino acids, and some vitamins.

___active transport___ **9.** A number of materials, including salts, are removed from the filtrate by <u>osmosis</u> and reabsorbed by the capillaries.

___loop of Henle___ **10.** The <u>glomerulus</u> is responsible for conserving water and minimizing the volume of the filtrate.

11. THINK VISUALLY Label the diagram of a nephron.

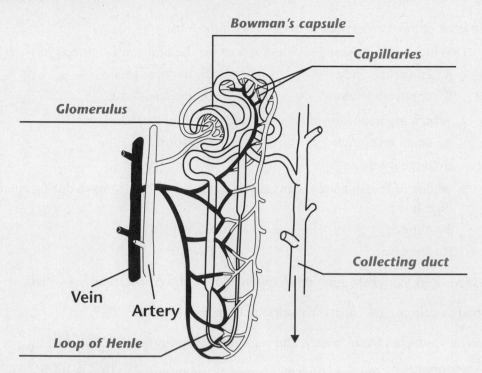

Bowman's capsule

Capillaries

Glomerulus

Collecting duct

Vein

Artery

Loop of Henle

The Kidneys and Homeostasis

12. Describe three ways that the kidneys help maintain homeostasis.

The kidneys help maintain homeostasis by regulating water balance, pH, and blood

glucose.

13. Explain how the kidneys regulate the levels of salt in the blood.

The kidneys respond to the composition of the blood. If the level of salt in the blood is

too high, the kidneys will return less salt to the blood during reabsorption.

14. How does dialysis work?

During dialysis, a machine performs the role of the kidneys. The patient's blood is

pumped through the machine, cleansed, and pumped back into the body.

Apply the Big idea

15. Urine testing is a common way that doctors can monitor a patient's health. Suppose a urine test reveals that there are proteins in the patient's urine. What might be wrong with this patient? What part of the excretory system might not be functioning properly?

The presence of protein in the urine can indicate high blood pressure or diabetes.

Within each nephron is a cluster of capillaries, called a glomerulus, that filters blood.

Usually, proteins do not pass through the walls of the capillaries and into the filtrate

in the Bowman's capsule. If proteins are found in the urine, this indicates that the

capillaries may be damaged.

Chapter Vocabulary Review

Write the letter of the correct answer on the line at the left.

__B__ 1. Which type of tissue provides support for the body and connects its parts?

    A. epithelial tissue   C. nervous tissue

    B. connective tissue   D. muscle tissue

__A__ 2. Which organ absorbs most of the nutrients during digestion?

    A. small intestine   C. stomach

    B. large intestine   D. esophagus

__C__ 3. Which of the following is an enzyme released by the stomach during chemical digestion?

    A. chime   C. pepsin

    B. amylase   D. bile

For Questions 4–8, complete each statement by writing the correct word or words.

4. The body's systems are constantly working to maintain __homeostasis__.

5. The sugars found in fruits, honey, and sugar cane are simple __carbohydrates__.

6. The __esophagus__ is a long tube that connects the mouth and the stomach.

7. The __large intestine__ absorbs water from undigested material that will be eliminated.

8. The process by which metabolic wastes are eliminated is called __excretion__.

For Questions 9–18, match the term with its definition.

Terms	Definitions
__G__ 9. Calorie	A. Inorganic molecule needed by the body in small quantities
__J__ 10. proteins	B. Functional unit of the kidney
__F__ 11. vitamins	C. Mixture of stomach fluids and partially digested food
__E__ 12. amylase	D. Section of a nephron that conserves water and minimizes urine volume
__A__ 13. mineral	
__H__ 14. peristalsis	E. Enzyme that breaks down carbohydrates
__C__ 15. chyme	F. Organic molecules that regulate body processes
__B__ 16. nephron	G. Unit equal to 1000 calories of heat or 1 kilocalorie
__I__ 17. Bowman's capsule	H. Smooth muscle contractions that squeeze food through the esophagus into the stomach
__D__ 18. loop of Henle	I. Cup-shaped structure that surrounds a glomerulus
	J. Nutrients that provide the body with the building materials it needs for growth and repair

CHAPTER MYSTERY

THE TELLTALE SAMPLE

In the Chapter Mystery, you learned how evidence of illegal drug use can be found by testing a person's urine. In this activity, you'll learn about other substances that athletes should possibly be tested for.

21st Century Learning

Dietary Supplements

Some athletic organizations test competing athletes for illegal drug use. Dietary supplements, on the other hand, are not tested for by most athletic organizations, because they are legal. But since many supplements claim to improve health or boost physical performance, should they be included in athletes' drug tests as well? Are dietary supplements even safe or effective? The following Web page presents one view on supplements.

SportsMedForum > Home > Fitness > Dietary Supplements

Dietary Supplements: Helpful or Hazardous?

Do you agree with the following two statements about the safety and effectiveness of dietary supplements?

> *"If it weren't safe, they wouldn't be allowed to sell it."*
> *"They can't claim it in their ad if it's not true."*

The fact is, both statements are false an awful lot of the time. Neither statement is true, for instance, when you see an ad for a dietary supplement claiming that it will help you lose weight, build muscles, or be happier. Why?

Here's the thing. Before a drug—defined as any substances intended for use in the diagnosis, cure, mitigation, treatment, or prevention of disease—can be sold in this country, the manufacturer has to prove to the Food and Drug Administration that the drug is safe and effective. If it doesn't, the FDA won't approve the drug. But dietary supplements are not drugs, and so the rules are different.

Manufacturers are not allowed to sell dietary supplements—defined as substances that are added to a person's diet, but don't have proven disease-treating effects—that are unsafe and/or ineffective. However, the manufacturers don't have to prove to anyone that their product actually is safe and effective. The FDA can only ban a product if it performs its own tests to prove that the product is dangerous or fraudulent. Needless to say, the FDA can't afford to test all of the roughly 29,000 supplements on the market. This means unsafe and ineffective supplements may slip by.

The FDA does have rules about what a manufacturer can claim, but these rules are very easy to get around. For example, product labels are not allowed to include any "false or misleading claims." But is anybody going to test the claims to see if they are false or misleading? No. Manufacturers can't claim that a supplement will "treat, mitigate, or cure a disease," a label reserved for drugs. So they can't say a product will treat high blood pressure but to get around it, they can say it will "promote blood-vessel health." They can't say a supplement will treat depression, but they can say it will "promote a feeling of well-being."

And then there's the phrase I hate the most—"all natural." In how many ads does someone say, "It's all natural, so you know it's safe"? Oh yeah? Poison ivy is "natural," but I wouldn't eat it. Foxglove is "natural," but if you eat it, be prepared for nausea, diarrhea, vomiting, irregular heartbeat, convulsions, and maybe death. Monkshood is "natural," but you can die if you handle it, never mind ingest it.

As always, friends, don't believe everything you read. Even here.

Murray Gelb, D. Jur,. is a practicing attorney.

This column is for entertainment only. Nothing in it should be construed as legal advice.

Continued on next page ▶

21st Century Themes Science and Economic Literacy, Science and Health Literacy

1. What is the difference between a drug and a dietary supplement?

   A drug is any substance intended for use in the diagnosis, cure, mitigation, treatment, or prevention of disease, while a dietary supplement is a substance that can be added to a person's diet, but that does not have any proven disease-treating effects.

2. What are two FDA rules about labeling on packages of dietary supplements?

   The label can't contain any "false or misleading claims," or any claim to "treat, mitigate, or cure a disease."

3. An ad for a dietary supplement says a product builds muscle mass and improves athletic performance. Why should you approach such claims with skepticism? Explain your answer.

   SAMPLE ANSWER: *Such claims may not be true—a manufacturer does not have to prove that its product is safe or effective, and the product has probably not been tested by the FDA.*

4. A dietary supplement's label has the phrase "all natural." Can you assume that the product is safe? Explain your answer.

   SAMPLE ANSWER: *No, you cannot assume the product is safe. Just because an ingredient is natural does not mean it is safe.*

5. If a product label says it will "treat and prevent heartburn and acid indigestion," what does that tell you about the product?

   Because it "treats" a condition, the product should be a drug that has been proven to be safe and effective.

21st Century Skills Evaluate Products

The skills used in this activity include **information and media literacy**, **communication skills**, **creativity and intellectual curiosity**, and **social responsibility**.

Go to a local mall, pharmacy, or health food store and look for products taken to improve one's health or well-being that are not FDA-approved. Read the labels. Look at any advertising you see nearby—signs, brochures, pamphlets, and so on. Look at the wording that is used, and how things are phrased.

Write a short essay about these products, giving your opinion on what the products most likely can and cannot do.

Students should use their knowledge of science to identify any possible false claims made by the product's advertising. Evaluate students' essays on the clarity with which they present their opinions.

31 The Nervous System

 Big idea **Structure and Function**

Q: How does the structure of the nervous system allow it to regulate functions in every part of the body?

WHAT I KNOW	WHAT I LEARNED
31.1 What is the basic function of the nervous system?	*SAMPLE ANSWER:* **The nervous system controls functions throughout the body by carrying signals.**	*SAMPLE ANSWER:* **The nervous system collects information about the body's internal and external environment, processes that information, and responds to it.**
31.2 What does the central nervous system do?	*SAMPLE ANSWER:* **The central nervous system processes information the body receives.**	*SAMPLE ANSWER:* **The central nervous system is made up of the brain and spinal cord. The brain is made up of the cerebrum, cerebellum, and brain stem. Each part of the brain is responsible for processing and relaying specific information. The spinal cord is the link between the brain and the rest of the body.**
31.3 How does the central nervous system send and receive information?	*SAMPLE ANSWER:* **The central nervous system receives information from the peripheral nervous system.**	*SAMPLE ANSWER:* **The sensory division of the peripheral nervous system transmits impulses from sense organs to the central nervous system. The motor division transmits impulses from the central nervous system to the muscles.**
31.4 How do humans sense changes in their environment?	*SAMPLE ANSWER:* **Different senses respond to touch, smells, flavors, sounds, and sight.**	*SAMPLE ANSWER:* **There are five types of sensory receptors: those that respond to pain, temperature, pressure, chemicals, and light.**

31.1 The Neuron

Lesson Objectives

- Identify the functions of the nervous system.
- Describe the function of neurons.
- Describe how a nerve impulse is transmitted.

Lesson Summary

Functions of the Nervous System The nervous system collects information about the body's internal and external environment, processes that information, and responds to it.

▶ The **peripheral nervous system** consists of nerves and supporting cells. It collects information about the body's internal and external environment.

▶ The **central nervous system** consists of the brain and spinal cord. It processes information and creates a response that is delivered through the peripheral nervous system.

Neurons Nervous system impulses are transmitted by cells called neurons. The three types of neurons are sensory, motor, and interneurons. All neurons have certain features:

▶ The **cell body** contains the nucleus and much of the cytoplasm.

▶ **Dendrites** receive impulses from other neurons and carry impulses to the cell body.

▶ The **axon** is the long fiber that carries impulses away from the cell body. In some neurons, the axon is surrounded by an insulating membrane called the **myelin sheath**.

The Nerve Impulse Nerve impulses are similar to the flow of an electric current through a wire.

▶ Neurons have a charge, or electric potential, across their membranes. When resting, the inside of a neuron has a negative charge compared to the outside. This difference is called the **resting potential**.

▶ When a neuron is stimulated, the inside of its membrane temporarily becomes more positive than the outside. This reversal of charges is called an **action potential**, or nerve impulse. The nerve impulse moves along the axon.

▶ Not all stimuli are capable of starting an impulse. The minimum level of a stimulus that is required to start an impulse in a neuron is called its **threshold**.

▶ At the end of the axon, impulses can be transmitted to the next neuron. The point at which a neuron transfers an impulse to another cell is called a **synapse**. When an impulse arrives at the synapse, **neurotransmitters**, chemicals that transmit an impulse across a synapse to another cell, are released from the axon.

Functions of the Nervous System

1. What are the main functions of the nervous system?

   The nervous system collects information about the body's internal and external envi-

   ronment, processes that information, and responds to it.

2. Name the two parts of the nervous system and explain what each part does.

Peripheral nervous system and central nervous system. The peripheral nervous

system collects information about the body's environment. The central nervous system

processes that information and creates a response that is delivered by the peripheral

nervous system.

Neurons

3. THINK VISUALLY Draw and label a diagram of a neuron. Be sure to include the
following features in your drawing: axon, axon terminals, cell body, dendrites, myelin
sheath, nodes, and nucleus.

Students should draw a picture of a neuron similar to the textbook's illustration of

a neuron. Check to make sure that the labeling is complete and the labels are posi-

tioned correctly.

For Questions 4–8, complete each statement by writing the correct word or words.

4. Neurons that carry impulses from the eyes to the spinal cord and brain are called
  sensory neurons .

5. Motor neurons carry impulses from the brain and spinal cord to ____muscles____ and
  ____glands____.

6. The neuron's cell body has short, branched extensions called ____dendrites____ which
  receive impulses from other neurons.

7. In most animals, ____axons____ and ____dendrites____ of different neurons are
  clustered in bundles called nerves.

8. The insulating membrane that surrounds a single axon in some neurons is called the
  ____myelin sheath____.

The Nerve Impulse

9. Describe the role of sodium ions in propagating a nerve impulse.

   Sodium ions flow into the cell, temporarily making the inside of the cell membrane

   more positive than the outside. This reversal of charges causes an action potential.

   _____

   _____

For Questions 10–11, use the Visual Analogy comparing falling dominoes to a moving impulse.

10. **VISUAL ANALOGY** Dominoes require a push to begin falling. What "push" starts a nerve impulse?

    the movement of positively charged sodium ions

    into the neuron

    _____

11. What is the threshold of a neuron, and how is it similar to a row of falling dominoes?

    The threshold is the minimum level of a stimulus

    that is required to cause an impulse in a neuron.

    Any stimulus that is weaker than the threshold will not produce an impulse. A

    push strong enough to cause the first domino to fall into the second is similar to a

    threshold stimulus.

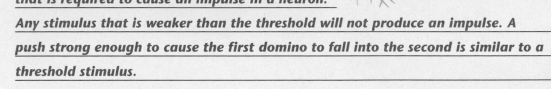

Action Potential

12. What are neurotransmitters, and how do they function?

    Neurotransmitters are chemicals that transmit an impulse across a synapse to

    another cell. When an impulse arrives at the synapse, neurotransmitters are released

    from the axon and diffuse across the synaptic cleft. They then bind to receptors on the

    membrane of the receiving cell causing the cell's ion channels to open.

    _____

Apply the Big idea

13. How is the structure of a neuron suited to its function?

    SAMPLE ANSWER: *Both axons and dendrites are slender, like wires; this structure facili-*

    tates the collection and transmission of nerve impulses. Dendrites often form a net-

    work that enables them to collect sensory information from a large area. The myelin

    sheaths that are present on some axons speed up the transmission of impulses.

    _____

31.2 The Central Nervous System

Lesson Objectives

⬚ Discuss the functions of the brain and spinal cord.

⬚ Describe the effects of drugs on the brain.

Lesson Summary

The Brain and Spinal Cord The central nervous system consists of the brain and spinal cord. Some kinds of information, including some reflexes, are processed directly in the spinal cord. A **reflex** is a quick, automatic response to a stimulus.

▶ The largest region of the human brain is the **cerebrum**, which controls learning, judgment, and voluntary actions of muscles.

   • The cerebrum is divided into right and left hemispheres. Each deals primarily with the opposite side of the body.

   • The outer layer of the cerebrum is the **cerebral cortex**. It processes information from the sense organs and controls body movements.

▶ The limbic system controls functions such as emotion, behavior, and memory.

▶ The **thalamus** receives messages from sensory receptors throughout the body and sends the information to the proper region of the cerebrum for processing.

▶ The **hypothalamus** controls the recognition and analysis of hunger, thirst, fatigue, anger, and body temperature. It helps coordinate the nervous and endocrine systems.

▶ The **cerebellum** is the second largest region of the brain. It receives information about muscle and joint position and coordinates the actions of these muscles.

▶ The **brain stem** connects the brain and spinal cord. It regulates the flow of information between the brain and the rest of the body.

Addiction and the Brain Almost all addictive substances affect brain synapses.

▶ Many drugs cause an increase in the release of the neurotransmitter **dopamine**. The brain reacts to high dopamine levels by reducing the number of receptors.

▶ With fewer dopamine receptors available, larger amounts of drugs are required to produce a high. This can result in an addiction.

The Brain and Spinal Cord

Write the letter of the correct answer on the line at the left.

___B___ **1.** What is the main link between the brain and the rest of the body?

    A. cerebrum   **B.** spinal cord   **C.** cerebellum   **D.** brain stem

___D___ **2.** Which of the following is the best example of a reflex?

    A. jumping up and down

    B. running in a race

    C. slowly putting your foot into cool water

    D. pulling your hand away from a hot pot

_____A_____ 3. Which part of the brain controls blood pressure, heart rate, breathing, and swallowing?

      A. brain stem

      B. limbic system

      C. cerebral cortex

      D. thalamus

_____A_____ 4. Which of the following is a function of the frontal lobe?

      A. making judgments

      B. hearing and smelling

      C. reading and speech

      D. vision

_____C_____ 5. Which part of the brain is the site of intelligence, learning, and judgment?

      A. brain stem

      B. cerebellum

      C. cerebrum

      D. limbic system

For Questions 6–10, match the part of the brain with its function.

Part of Brain	Function
_____C_____ 6. cerebrum	**A.** Coordinates and balances the actions of the muscles
_____A_____ 7. cerebellum	**B.** Regulates the flow of information between the brain and the rest of the body
_____B_____ 8. brain stem	**C.** Controls voluntary activities of the body
_____E_____ 9. thalamus	**D.** Controls hunger, thirst, fatigue, anger, and body temperature
_____D_____ 10. hypothalamus	**E.** Receives and relays messages from the sense organs

11. What connects the two hemispheres of the brain?

    a band of tissue called the corpus callosum

12. Identify the four lobes of the brain and their functions.

    frontal lobe: evaluating consequences, making judgments, forming plans; temporal

    lobe: hearing and smell; parietal lobe: reading and speech; occipital lobe: vision

13. What is the cerebral cortex and what is its function?

    The cerebral cortex is the outer layer of the cerebrum. It consists of densely packed

    nerve cell bodies known as gray matter. The cerebral cortex processes information

    from the sense organs and controls body movements.

Addiction and the Brain

14. What parts of the brain are changed by drug use?

Drugs cause changes to synapses that use the neurotransmitter dopamine.

15. What is dopamine?

Dopamine is a neurotransmitter that is associated with the brain's pleasure and reward centers. When you engage in activity that brings pleasure, neurons in the hypothalamus and the limbic system release dopamine.

16. How do drugs cause addiction?

Drugs initially cause the dopamine levels in the brain to increase. The brain reacts to the excessive dopamine levels by reducing the number of receptors for the neurotransmitter. With fewer receptors, larger amounts of drugs are required to produce the same high, leading to addiction.

17. Complete the table.

Effects of Drugs on the Body	
Drug	**Effects on the Body**
Methamphetamine	Releases a flood of dopamine, produces an instant high
Cocaine	Keeps dopamine in the synaptic region longer, intensifying pleasure and suppressing pain
Heroin	**Stimulates receptors elsewhere in the brain leading to a dopamine release**
Nicotine and alcohol	**Increased release of dopamine**

Apply the Big idea

18. What might be the effects on someone who seriously injured his or her cerebellum? Explain your answer.

The cerebellum controls muscle, joint, and sensory inputs. A person with a serious cerebellum injury might experience loss of balance and coordination. The cerebellum coordinates the actions of muscles and enables the body to move gracefully. The person may also have difficulty mastering new tasks or actions because the cerebellum learns new movements and coordinates the actions of the muscles involved.

31.3 The Peripheral Nervous System

Lesson Objectives

🔑 Describe the functions of the sensory division of the peripheral nervous system.

🔑 Describe the functions of the motor division of the peripheral nervous system.

Lesson Summary

The Sensory Division The peripheral nervous system consists of all the nerves and associated cells that are not part of the brain or spinal cord. It is made up of the sensory division and the motor division.

▶ The sensory division transmits impulses from sense organs to the central nervous system.

▶ Sensory receptors are cells that transmit information about changes in the internal and external environment. Chemoreceptors respond to chemicals. Photoreceptors respond to light. Mechanoreceptors respond to touch, pressure, vibrations, and stretch. Thermoreceptors respond to temperature change. Pain receptors respond to tissue injury.

The Motor Division The motor division, which is divided into the somatic and autonomic nervous systems, transmits impulses from the central nervous system to muscles and glands.

▶ The **somatic nervous system** regulates processes under voluntary control.

▶ Actions of the somatic nervous system called reflexes occur automatically. The impulses controlling these actions travel on a pathway called a **reflex arc**. An impulse travels through a sensory neuron, to the spinal cord, and then back through a motor neuron.

▶ The **autonomic nervous system** regulates activities that are involuntary. It consists of two parts, the sympathetic nervous system and the parasympathetic nervous system.

• In general, the sympathetic nervous system prepares the body for intense activity. It prepares the body to "fight or flee" in response to stress.

• The parasympathetic nervous system causes the "rest and digest" response.

The Sensory Division

1. Which nerves go through openings in the skull and stimulate the head and neck?
   cranial nerves

2. What are ganglia?
   Ganglia are clusters of cell bodies of cranial and spinal nerves.

3. What is the function of the sensory division of the peripheral nervous system?
   It transmits impulses from sense organs to the central nervous system.

4. What are sensory receptors?
   Cells that transmit information about changes in the internal and external
   environment.

Match the sensory receptor with the stimuli to which it responds.

Sensory Receptor		Stimuli
_E_	5. chemoreceptor	A. light
_B_	6. mechanoreceptor	B. touch and pressure
_D_	7. pain receptor	C. temperature changes
_A_	8. photoreceptor	D. tissue injury
_C_	9. thermoreceptor	E. chemicals

The Motor Division

For Questions 10–12, write True or False on the line provided.

___False___ 10. The motor division of the peripheral nervous system transmits impulses directly from the sensory receptors to muscles or glands.

___True___ 11. The somatic nervous system regulates body activities that are under conscious control.

___True___ 12. Brain impulses are carried to motor neurons and then to muscles.

13. Complete a flowchart showing the reflex arc that occurs when you step on a sharp object.

> Sensory receptors react to a stimulus and send an impulse to sensory neurons.

↓

> *Sensory neurons relay the information to the spinal cord.*

↓

> *An interneuron in the spinal cord processes the information and forms a response.*

↓

> *A motor neuron carries impulses to the muscle it stimulates.*

↓

> *The muscle contracts, causing movement.*

14. Complete the concept map.

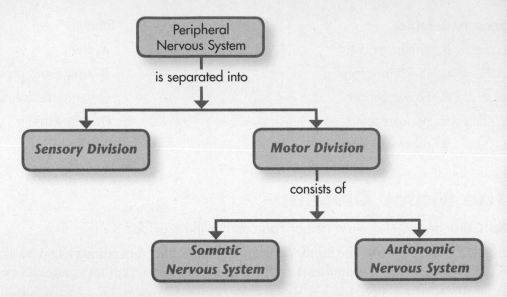

15. What is the function of the autonomic nervous system?
It regulates activities that are involuntary or not under conscious control.

16. How might the autonomic nervous system prepare your body during rigorous exercise?
It prepares the body by speeding up the heart rate and blood flow to the skeletal muscles. It stimulates sweat glands and slows the digestive system.

17. What is the function of the parasympathetic nervous system?
It prepares the body for relaxation or the "rest and digest" response. It lowers heart rate and blood pressure, activates digestion, and activates pathways that store food.

18. What situation might trigger a response from the sympathetic nervous system? Explain.
SAMPLE ANSWER: *Life-threatening experience would cause it to respond. It prepares the body by increasing blood pressure and releasing energy-rich sugar into the blood.*

Apply the Big idea

19. Suppose someone was playing baseball and trying to catch a pop fly ball. Explain how the different parts of the nervous system would respond in this situation.
The sensory division would respond to the sight and sound of the baseball. Mechanoreceptors in the ears would be stimulated by the noise of the bat hitting the ball. Photoreceptors in the eyes would be stimulated by the sight of the ball. These cells would produce nerve impulses that travel to the central nervous system. Interneurons in the brain would then pass the impulses to motor neurons. The motor neurons carry the impulses to the muscles. This would cause a contraction of the muscles in the arm, allowing the person to catch the ball.

31.4 The Senses

Lesson Objectives

- Discuss the sense of touch and identify the various types of sensory receptors in the skin.
- Explain the relationship between smell and taste.
- Identify the parts of the ears that make hearing and balance possible.
- Describe the major parts of the eye and explain how the eye enables us to see.

Lesson Summary

Touch and Related Senses Different sensory receptors in the body respond to touch, temperature, and pain.

▶ Skin contains at least seven types of sensory receptors that respond to touch.

▶ Thermoreceptors respond to heat and cold. They are found in the skin and hypothalamus.

▶ Pain receptors are found throughout the body. They respond to physical injuries.

Smell and Taste Sensations of smell and taste are the result of impulses sent to the brain by chemoreceptors. Sense organs that detect taste are called **taste buds**. Sensory cells in taste buds respond to salty, bitter, sweet, sour, and savory foods.

Hearing and Balance Mechanoreceptors found in parts of the ear transmit impulses to the brain. The brain translates the impulses into sound and information about balance.

▶ Vibrations cause pressure waves in the fluid-filled **cochlea** of the inner ear. Tiny hair cells in the cochlea are pushed back and forth by the pressure waves. The hair cells send nerve impulses to the brain, which interprets them as sound.

▶ The ears also help maintain balance. The **semicircular canals** and two fluid-filled sacs behind them monitor the position of the body in relation to gravity.

Vision Vision occurs when photoreceptors in the eyes transmit impulses to the brain, which translates these impulses into images.

▶ The **cornea** is a tough, transparent layer of cells. The cornea helps focus the light, which passes through a chamber filled with fluid called aqueous humor.

▶ The **iris** is the colored portion of the eye. In the middle of the iris is a small opening called the **pupil**, through which light enters the eye.

▶ The **lens** is located behind the iris. The shape of the lens is changed by tiny muscles to adjust the eye's focus.

▶ The lens focuses light on the **retina**, the inner layer of the eye. Photoreceptors in the retina convert light energy into nerve impulses that are carried to the brain via the optic nerve. There are two kinds of photoreceptors:

- **Rods** are very sensitive to light but do not distinguish colors.
- **Cones** are less sensitive to light, but do distinguish colors.

Touch and Related Senses

Write True or False on the line provided.

_____True_____ 1. Unlike other senses, the sense of touch is not found in one particular place.

_____False_____ 2. The greatest density of touch receptors is found on the arms and legs.

_____True_____ 3. Touch is detected by mechanoreceptors.

_____False_____ 4. Thermoreceptors which respond to heat and cold are found in the thalamus region of the brain.

_____False_____ 5. The brain has pain receptors that respond to chemicals released during infection.

Smell and Taste

Complete each statement by writing the correct word or words.

6. Chemical-sensing cells known as ___chemoreceptors___ in the nose and mouth are responsible for the senses of _____taste_____ and _____smell_____.

7. The sense organs that detect taste are the _____taste buds_____.

8. Taste buds respond to _____salty_____, bitter, sweet, and _____sour_____ foods.

9. The _____umami_____ receptors are stimulated by MSG, meat, and cheese.

10. People with head colds may have difficulty tasting foods. Explain why this happens.
    During a cold, the nose and sinuses are stuffed with mucus. This blocks the chemore-ceptors in the nose from detecting chemicals. When the sense of smell is blocked, the taste of food is barely detectable.

Hearing and Balance

11. Name the two sensory functions of the human ear.
    hearing and detecting positional changes associated with movement

12. What is sound? *vibrations moving through the air around us*

13. After you spin around and around, you usually become dizzy. What part of the ear is involved in this sensation? Explain.
    The semicircular canals monitor the position of the body and the head. The semicir-cular canals are filled with fluid. As the head changes position, the fluid in the canals also changes position. This sends impulses to the brain that enable it to determine body motion and position.

14. Complete the flowchart showing how we process sound.

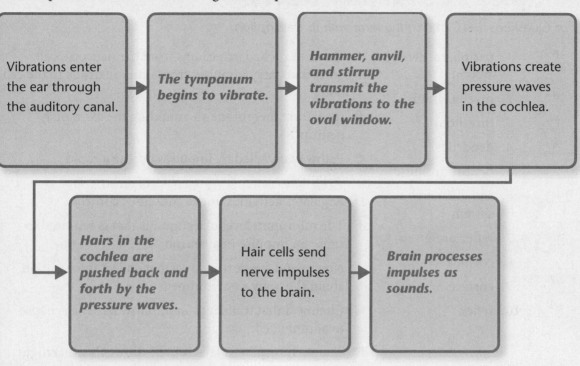

Vibrations enter the ear through the auditory canal.	*The tympanum begins to vibrate.*	*Hammer, anvil, and stirrup transmit the vibrations to the oval window.*	Vibrations create pressure waves in the cochlea.

Hairs in the cochlea are pushed back and forth by the pressure waves.	Hair cells send nerve impulses to the brain.	*Brain processes impulses as sounds.*

Vision

15. Label the diagram of the eye.

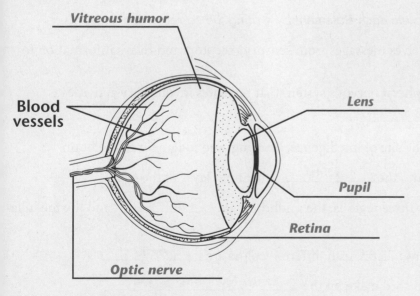

Vitreous humor

Blood vessels

Lens

Pupil

Retina

Optic nerve

Apply the Big idea

16. How does the shape and structure of the lens relate to its function in the eye?

The thin lens is flexible and transparent; tiny muscles change its shape. This allows

it to perform its function of adjusting the eye's focus and enabling light to reach the

retina.

Chapter Vocabulary Review

For Questions 1–10, match the term with its description.

F	1. peripheral nervous system	**A.** Short, branched extensions from the neuron's cell body that carry impulses from other neurons to the cell body
B	2. myelin sheath	
E	3. threshold	**B.** Insulating membrane surrounding the axon of a neuron
A	4. dendrites	
G	5. neurotransmitter	**C.** Pathway travelled by impulses during a rapid response
D	6. somatic nervous system	
		D. Regulates activities under conscious control
C	7. reflex arc	**E.** The minimum level of a stimulus that is required to cause an impulse in a neuron
I	8. cochlea	
H	9. cornea	**F.** Nerves and supporting cells that collect information about the body's environment
J	10. reflex	**G.** Chemical that transmits an impulse across a synapse to another cell

H. Tough, transparent layer of cells through which light enters the eye

I. Fluid-filled inner ear structure lined with hair cells

J. Quick, automatic response to a stimulus

For Questions 11–20, complete each statement by writing the correct word or words.

11. The ____thalamus____ receives messages from sensory receptors and relays information to the cerebrum.

12. The division of the peripheral nervous system that regulates involuntary activities is the ____autonomic nervous system____.

13. The ____cerebrum____ is the site of intelligence, learning, and judgment in the brain.

14. The lens focuses light onto the ____retina____, the inner layer of the eye.

15. The ____brain stem____ has three regions, the midbrain, the ____pons____, and the medulla oblongata.

16. Photoreceptors that do not distinguish different colors are ____rods____.

17. The brain and the spinal cord make up the ____central nervous system____.

18. The ____cerebral cortex____ is made up of densely packed nerve cell bodies called gray matter.

19. Most addictive substances act on synapses that use ____dopamine____ as a neurotransmitter.

20. A nerve impulse, or ____action potential____, begins when a neuron is stimulated by another neuron or the environment.

CHAPTER MYSTERY

POISONING ON THE HIGH SEAS

21st Century Lea

The Chapter Mystery focused on the likelihood that eating the Silverstripe blaasop may have poisoned the men on Captain James Cook's ship the HMS *Resolution* in 1774. Bacteria that live in the fish produce the poison tetrodotoxin.

Poison Safety at Home

The effects of tetrodotoxin are deadly and dramatic. Thankfully, tetrodotoxin poisoning is rare. Many other poisons however, while perhaps not as deadly, surround us each day. In fact, in the United States, roughly one million possible poisonings are reported each year for children under the age of six. Approximately 90 percent of poisonings occur in the home.

Small children may eat pills such as analgesics, or pain relievers, in doses that can be toxic to them. Other poisonings can occur when people accidentally ingest household cleaners, cosmetic or personal care products, pesticides, or prescription drugs.

The table below is adapted from the 2006 Annual Report of the American Association of Poison Control Centers. It shows the number of cases handled by poison control centers in the United States that year by poison category:

Poisons Most Frequently Involved in Human Exposures

Substance	Number of cases/yr	%
Analgesics	284,906	11.9
Cosmetics/personal care products	214,780	8.9
Cleaning substances (household)	214,091	8.9
Sedatives/hypnotics/antipsychotics	141,150	5.9
Foreign bodies/toys/miscellaneous	120,752	5.0
Cold and cough preparations	114,559	4.8
Topical preparations	108,308	4.5
Pesticides	96,811	4.0
Antidepressants	95,327	4.0
Chemicals	47,557	2.0

Continued on next page ▶

21st Century Themes Science and Health Literacy

1. How many possible poisonings are reported each year in the United States for children under the age of six?

   Roughly one million

2. Where do most poisonings tend to occur?

   Ninety percent of the reported poisonings occur in the home.

3. According to the table, what percent of poisoning cases in the United States involve household cleaning substances?

   8.9 percent

4. According to the table, what portion of all poisoning cases involve all the categories of drugs—analgesics, sedatives, cold medicines, and antidepressants? How many of these cases are reported each year?

   Accidental poisonings by all categories of drugs account for 26.6 percent

   (11.9 + 5.9 + 4.8 + 4.0) of all poisoning cases listed on the table. Taken together,

   these poisonings made up some 635,942 individual cases.

5. Were you surprised to learn about the most common poisonings in the United States? Which category surprised you the most? Why?

   Answers will vary. Student viewpoints and rationale encouraged here.

21st Century Skills Letter to the FDA

The skills used in this activity include **problem identification, formulation, and solution; creativity and intellectual curiosity; information and media literacy;** and **social responsibility.**

Sometimes substances believed to be safe raise concerns about toxic effects. This happened recently with the chemical bisphenol-A (BPA). BPA was suspected of being hazardous to humans as early as the 1930s. But, until recently, it was widely used as a component in polycarbonate plastic water bottles and baby bottles. In 2008, concerns about the use of BPA in consumer products grabbed headlines when several governments issued reports questioning its safety, and some retailers voluntarily pulled products made with it off their shelves. The chemical is still widely used in the lining of cans and many other products. Scientists remain divided about the health risks posed by BPA. The Canadian government has moved to restrict it, but the U.S. Food and Drug Administration (FDA) has not. Using the Internet, find at least two news articles about the controversy over the potentially toxic effects of BPA. Weigh the evidence for yourself. Then write a letter to the FDA recommending what you think the FDA should do about BPA. Include your reasoning.

Evaluate students' letters by their choice of news articles, inclusion of facts about BPA, and the logical consistency of their reasoning to support their position. Evaluation should also include the organization of their letter and how clearly it states facts and opinion.

32 Skeletal, Muscular, and Integumentary Systems

 Big idea **Structure and Function**

Q: What systems form the structure of the human body?

WHAT I KNOW	WHAT I LEARNED
32.1 How does the structure of the skeletal system allow it to function properly?	*SAMPLE ANSWER:* **Bones are hardened, which makes them strong. They are connected at joints, which allows for bending.**	*SAMPLE ANSWER:* **Bones act like levers that are moved by muscles. Bones contain living cells and tissues. Bone cells secrete minerals that cause bones to harden. Bones are constantly remodeled throughout life.**
32.2 How do muscles help you move?	*SAMPLE ANSWER:* **Muscles work with bones, which move when muscles contract.**	*SAMPLE ANSWER:* **Muscles are attached to bones by tendons. Opposing muscles of pairs contract to pull ends of bones back and forth, creating movement around the joints.**
32.3 Why is the integumentary system a necessary organ system?	*SAMPLE ANSWER:* **The integumentary system is necessary because it covers the body and keeps it from drying out.**	*SAMPLE ANSWER:* **The integumentary system provides protection by serving as a barrier to pathogens. It works with many other body systems to help maintain homeostasis by regulating temperature, excreting wastes, and conserving water.**

32.1 The Skeletal System

Lesson Objectives

🔑 List the structures and functions of the skeletal system.

🔑 Describe the structure of a typical bone.

🔑 List the different kinds of joints and describe the range of motion of each.

Lesson Summary

The Skeleton The human skeleton, like that of other vertebrates, is an endoskeleton.

▶ The adult human skeleton consists of 206 bones. Some bones are considered part of the axial skeleton and others of the appendicular skeleton.

• The skull, vertebral column, and rib cage form the **axial skeleton**, which supports the central axis of the body.

• The bones of the arms, legs, shoulders, and hips make up the **appendicular skeleton**.

▶ The skeleton supports the body, protects internal organs, produces movement by acting as levers, stores minerals, and produces blood cells.

Bones A solid network of living cells and protein fibers surrounded by calcium salts forms the bones of the human body.

▶ Bones have a complex structure. A layer of tough connective tissue called the periosteum covers a bone. Bones are made up of two types of bone tissue.

• Compact bone is a dense outer layer that is arranged around **Haversian canals**— channels through which blood vessels and nerves run.

• Spongy bone is a less dense layer found at the ends of long bones and in the center of flat bones, which adds strength without adding excess mass.

• Soft tissue called **bone marrow** fills cavities in some bones. Yellow marrow stores fat. Red marrow contains stem cells, which make most types of blood cells.

▶ In infants, the skeleton is almost all **cartilage**, which is a dense tissue built around protein fibers. Bone replaces cartilage by a process called **ossification**, during which cells called **osteoblasts** secrete minerals. Osteoblasts mature into cells called **osteocytes**, which maintain the minerals in bone and strengthen the bone.

▶ Mature bone contains some osteoblasts, which build new bone, and cells called **osteoclasts**, which break down bone minerals. These cells enable the repair of broken or damaged bones and keep bone from becoming brittle and weak.

Joints Bones meet at **joints**, which contain connective tissues that hold the ends together. Joints permit bones to move without damaging each other.

▶ Joints are classified into three types:

• Immovable, or fixed, joints allow no movement. These joints are found between bones in the skull.

• Slightly movable joints, such as those found between vertebrae, permit some movement.

• Freely movable joints, such as those found in the elbows and knees, permit movement in two or more directions.

► Cartilage covers the ends of the bones in a joint. **Ligaments**, tough strips of connective tissue, hold bones together. Synovial fluid reduces friction between moving bones. Bursae are sacs of synovial fluid that also act as shock absorbers.

► Joint injuries include ligament damage, inflammation, or loss of cartilage. Bursitis is inflammation of the bursae. Osteoarthritis is a painful stiffening of joints caused by the breakdown of cartilage.

The Skeleton

1. Complete the concept map that summarizes the parts of the human skeleton.

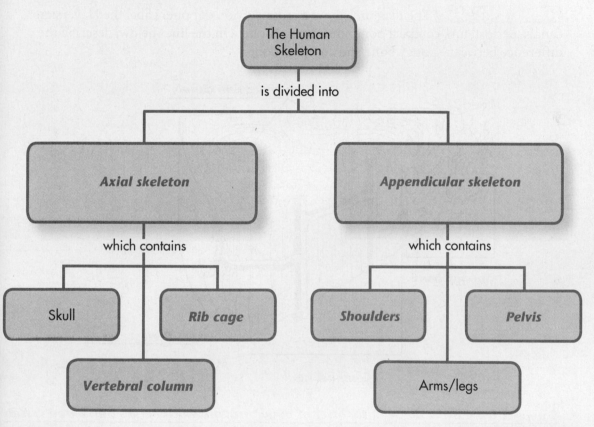

For Questions 2–3, refer to the Visual Analogy comparing the skeleton to the wooden frame of a house.

2. **VISUAL ANALOGY** What would happen to a house if its upright beams were not strong and sturdy? Compare that to what would happen in the human body if upright bones were not strong and sturdy.

Beams that are not strong and sturdy would bend under the

weight of the house and the shape of the house would change. If bones that hold the

human frame upright were not strong and sturdy, the bones would bend under the

weight of the person and change the person's shape.

_____

3. Suggest another possible analogy for the structure and function of the skeleton.

SAMPLE ANSWER: *the vascular bundles of a plant*

4. List five functions of the skeletal system.

Functions of the skeleton include supporting and giving shape to the body, protecting internal organs, producing movement by acting as levers on which muscles can act, storing minerals, and producing new blood cells.

Bones

5. **THINK VISUALLY** The diagram shows a cross-section of bone. Label the Haversian canals, periosteum, compact bone, and spongy bone. On the lines below, describe the difference between spongy bone and compact bone.

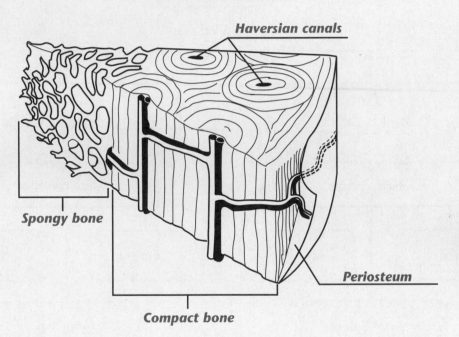

Haversian canals

Spongy bone

Periosteum

Compact bone

Compact bone is the dense outer layer of bone through which nerves and blood vessels run. Spongy bone is beneath compact bone. It is less massive than compact bone, but its latticework structure adds additional strength to the ends of long bones.

For Questions 6–12, complete each statement by writing the correct word or words.

6. A tough layer of connective tissue called the ___*periosteum*___ surrounds a bone.

7. Nerves and blood vessels run through the ___*Haversian canals*___ in bones.

8. Bone ___*marrow*___ is soft tissue in bone cavities that ___*stores fat*___ (yellow) or produces blood cells (red).

9. Bone with a latticework structure is called ___*spongy*___ bone.

10. During the process of ___ossification___, cartilage is replaced by bone.

11. Cells that secrete mineral deposits that form bone are called ___osteoblasts___.

12. A disorder called ___osteoporosis___ results when ___osteoclasts___ break down bone minerals more quickly than they can be deposited.

Joints

13. What is a joint?

A joint is a place where one bone attaches to another.

14. List the three classifications of joints, based on their type of movement.

immovable, slightly movable, and freely movable

For Questions 15–19, match each joint with the category of joints that it represents.

Joint

___B___ 15. Ankle

___E___ 16. Between two vertebrae

___A___ 17. Shoulder

___D___ 18. Elbow

___C___ 19. Between skull bones

Category

A. Ball-and-socket joint

B. Hinge joint

C. Immovable joint

D. Pivot joint

E. Slightly movable joint

For Questions 20–22, write True or False on the line provided.

___False___ 20. Ligaments protect the ends of bones as they move against each other at joints.

___False___ 21. Synovial fluid prevents the ends of bones from slipping past each other at joints.

___True___ 22. Osteoarthritis is joint pain and stiffness caused by loss of cartilage.

Apply the Big idea

23. Plumbers use the word *joint* to refer to the place where two pipes are joined together. How are the structure and function of pipe joints similar to and different from the skeletal system's joints?

SAMPLE ANSWER: *Pipe joints have a similar function to human joints because they both join two pieces together, but they have different structures and do not allow movement of the pieces on either side.*

32.2 The Muscular System

Lesson Objectives

- Describe the structure and function of each of the three types of muscle tissue.
- Describe the mechanism of muscle contraction.
- Describe the interaction of muscles, bones, and tendons to produce movement.

Lesson Summary

Muscle Tissue About one third of the mass of the body is muscle. There are three different types of muscle tissue.

▶ Skeletal muscle, which has alternating light and dark bands called striations, makes up muscles that are usually attached to bones. Movements of most skeletal, or striated, muscle are consciously controlled by the central nervous system. The cells in skeletal muscle are often called **muscle fibers**.

▶ Smooth muscle, which lacks striations and is made up of spindle-shaped cells, lines the walls of hollow structures such as the stomach and blood vessels. Movements of smooth muscle are usually involuntary.

▶ Cardiac muscle, which is also striated but has smaller cells than skeletal muscle, is found only in the heart. The control of cardiac muscle is involuntary.

Muscle Contraction Skeletal muscles produce movements by contracting from end to end. The contractions result from the interaction of two kinds of muscle protein filaments—actin and myosin.

▶ Skeletal muscle fibers are tightly packed with **myofibrils**, which are bundles of protein filaments. Thick filaments of the protein **myosin** and thin filaments of the protein **actin** are arranged in an overlapping pattern, which creates the striations of skeletal muscle. Actin filaments are bound together in areas called Z lines. Two Z lines and the filaments between them make up a unit called a **sarcomere**.

▶ During a muscle contraction, myosin filaments (powered by ATP) form connections called cross-bridges with actin filaments. The cross-bridges change shape and pull the actin filaments toward the center of the sarcomere. This action decreases the distance between Z lines, and the sarcomere shortens.

▶ Motor neurons control muscle fiber contractions. A motor neuron meets a muscle fiber at a synapse called a **neuromuscular junction**. The neurotransmitter **acetylcholine** carries nerve impulses across the synapse to the muscle cell.

Muscles and Movement Muscles produce force by contracting in only one direction.

▶ Strips of connective tissue called **tendons** attach skeletal muscles to bones, which act like levers. Controlled movements are possible because muscles work in opposing pairs.

▶ Red muscles, or slow-twitch muscles, contain many mitochondria and can work for long periods of time. White muscles, or fast-twitch muscles, contain fewer mitochondria, but can generate more force than slow-twitch. They are used for quick bursts of strength or speed.

▶ Regular exercise helps maintain muscle strength and flexibility, which makes muscle injuries less likely to occur.

Muscle Tissue

For Questions 1–6, write True if the statement is true. If the statement is false, change the underlined word or words to make the statement true.

True	1.	Large skeletal muscles have long, slender cells with multiple <u>nuclei</u>.
striations	2.	The light and dark bands in skeletal muscles are called <u>Z lines</u>.
spindles	3.	The cells of smooth muscle are shaped like <u>boxes</u>.
True	4.	Smooth-muscle tissue lines the <u>inside</u> of the blood vessels and the digestive tract.
involuntary	5.	Cardiac muscle is under <u>voluntary</u> control.
True	6.	The cells in cardiac muscle are connected to each other by <u>gap</u> junctions that allow electrical impulses to pass from cell to cell.

7. Complete the table that compares and contrasts the three types of muscle tissue.

Types of Muscle Tissue		
Type of Muscle	**Striated/Not Striated**	**Type of Control**
Skeletal	Striated	**Voluntary**
Smooth	**Not striated**	Involuntary
Cardiac	**Striated**	**Involuntary**

Muscle Contraction

For Questions 8–13, complete each statement by writing the correct word or words.

8. Muscle fibers are filled with ____**myofibrils**____, which are bundles of tightly packed protein filaments.

9. The thick protein filaments in muscle fibers are called ____**myosin**____, and the thin protein filaments are called ____**actin**____.

10. The thick filaments in muscle fibers form ____**cross-bridges**____, which cause the filaments to slide past each other.

11. The energy used in muscle contraction is supplied by ____**ATP**____.

12. Impulses passed from motor neurons release ____**calcium**____ ions within the muscle fibers.

13. The difference between a strong muscle contraction and a weak muscle contraction is the ____**number of**____ muscle fibers that contract.

Muscles and Movement

14. **THINK VISUALLY** Complete the illustration showing how the muscles of the upper arm produce movements of the forearm by adding labels for the structures indicated. Then, on the lines below the illustration, explain how the muscles cause the elbow to bend and straighten.

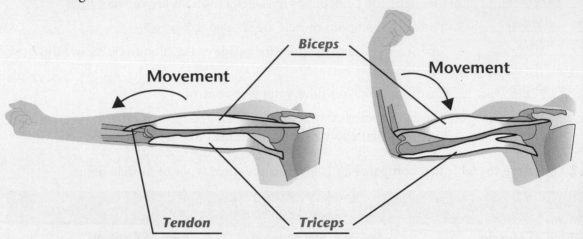

SAMPLE ANSWER **When the triceps contracts, the elbow straightens. When the biceps contracts, the elbow bends.**

For Questions 15–19, complete each statement by writing the correct word or words.

15. While producing movements, muscles supply the force, bones act as ___**levers**___, and a joint acts as a(n) ___**fulcrum**___.

16. Skeletal muscles work in ___**opposing**___ pairs.

17. Red muscle fibers contain ___**myoglobin**___, which stores oxygen.

18. White muscle is also called ___**fast-twitch**___ muscle.

19. Many mitochondria are found in the cells of ___**red**___ muscle, which uses oxygen for aerobic respiration.

Apply the Big idea

20. When viewed under a microscope, a sample of tissue reveals striations and long, thin fibers that contain many nuclei and mitochondria. What type of tissue is most likely being viewed? Explain your answer.

SAMPLE ANSWER: **The tissue is likely to be skeletal muscle that contains red muscle fibers. Skeletal muscle is striated, and the fibers have many nuclei; red muscle fibers contain many mitochondria.**

32.3 Skin—The Integumentary System

Lesson Objectives

State the functions of the integumentary system.

Identify the structures of the integumentary system.

Describe some of the problems that affect the skin.

Lesson Summary

Integumentary System Functions The skin, hair, and nails make up the integumentary system, which functions to protect internal organs, regulate body temperature, excrete wastes, gather information about the environment, and produce vitamin D.

Integumentary System Structures The system consists of skin and its related structures—hair, nails, and several types of glands. Skin consists of two main layers.

▶ The outer layer of the skin is the **epidermis**, which has an upper layer of dead cells and an inner layer of rapidly dividing living cells. Living epidermal cells make **keratin**, the tough fibrous protein that fills dead skin cells. The epidermis also contains cells called **melanocytes**, which make melanin. **Melanin** is the brown pigment that gives skin its color and protects the skin from ultraviolet radiation.

▶ The **dermis** is the thick inner layer of skin that contains structures that interact with other body systems to maintain homeostasis by regulating body temperature. **Sebaceous glands** in the dermis secrete sebum, an oily acidic substance that keeps the epidermis flexible and waterproof and kills bacteria.

▶ Hairs are large columns of cells that have filled with keratin and died. They are produced in **hair follicles**, pockets in the epidermis that extend into the dermis.

▶ Nails grow from rapidly dividing cells at the tips of fingers and toes. The cells fill with keratin and produce the tough, platelike nails.

Skin Problems Many external and internal factors affect the health of the skin.

▶ Acne is a condition that develops when sebum and dead skin cells plug hair follicles.

▶ Hives are red welts that result from allergies to food or medicines.

▶ Skin cancer, the abnormal growth of skin cells, results from excessive exposure to ultraviolet radiation in sunlight and in the lights of tanning beds.

Integumentary System Functions

For Questions 1–5, write True or False on the line provided.

____False____ 1. Protection from pathogens, water loss, and ultraviolet radiation are functions of the dermis.

____True____ 2. The skin releases excess heat but holds in some body heat.

____True____ 3. Sweat contains salts and urea excreted by the skin.

____True____ 4. The skin has sensory receptors for both pressure and pain.

____False____ 5. The skin needs sunlight to produce vitamin B.

Integumentary System Structures

6. THINK VISUALLY Label the structures of the skin.

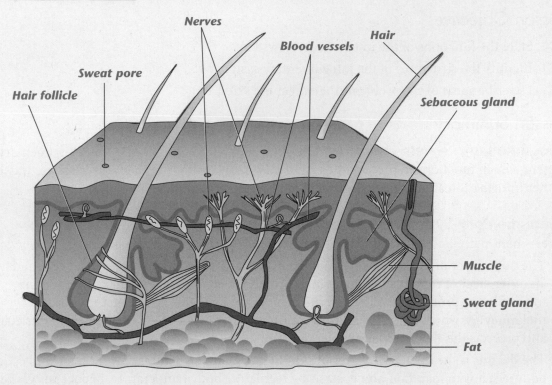

Nerves

Blood vessels

Hair

Sweat pore

Hair follicle

Sebaceous gland

Muscle

Sweat gland

Fat

For Questions 7–14, complete each statement by writing the correct word or words.

7. The outer layer of the skin is called the ___*epidermis*___.

8. The inner layer of the epidermis includes ___*stem*___ cells that divide rapidly, producing new skin cells that push old ones to the surface.

9. Epidermal cells, called ___*melanocytes*___, produce the brown pigment ___*melanin*___.

10. The brown pigment in skin protects it by absorbing ___*ultraviolet radiation*___.

11. The lower layer of skin that contains many specialized structures is the ___*dermis*___.

12. Structures that help maintain homeostasis by excreting salts and urea from the skin are called ___*sweat glands*___.

13. The ___*sebaceous glands*___ produce a fluid that kills bacteria.

14. Both hair and ___*nails*___ contain ___*keratin*___, the same tough, fibrous protein made by skin cells.

15. How does the dermis help regulate body temperature?
   When the body needs to conserve heat, the blood vessels in the dermis narrow, help-
   ing to limit heat loss. When the body needs to lose heat, the blood vessels widen,
   bringing heat from the body's core to the skin and increasing heat loss.

16. How does sweat help keep you cool?
   When sweat evaporates, it takes heat away from your body.

17. What is the function of sebum?

It helps to keep the epidermis flexible and waterproof. It can also kill bacteria on the skin.

18. How does the hair in the nose and ears and around the eyes help protect the body?

It prevents dirt and other particles from entering the body through the nose, ears, and eyes.

19. What causes hair to grow?

Rapid cell growth at the base of the hair follicle causes hair to grow.

20. What is a nail root?

It is an area of rapidly dividing cells near the tips of the fingers and toes where the nails grow.

Skin Problems

21. Complete the table that summarizes types of skin problems and their causes.

Types of Skin Problems		
Skin Problem	**Description**	**Cause**
Acne	Bumps that become red, may contain pus, and may leave scars	*Plugging of hair follicles by sebum and dead skin cells combined with infection by bacteria*
Hives	*Red welts*	*Allergic reactions to food or medicines*
Skin cancer	*Abnormal growths or sores that do not heal*	*Damage to skin cells by exposure to ultraviolet radiation*

Apply the Big idea

22. Why is a third-degree burn, which damages both the epidermis and the dermis of the skin, a very serious injury?

SAMPLE ANSWER: *Third-degree burns leave the body unprotected from pathogens, which can lead to infections. They also disrupt the body's homeostasis by destroying its ability to regulate temperature and water loss and to excrete excess salts and toxic wastes.*

Chapter Vocabulary Review

1. The diagram below shows muscle filaments in a relaxed muscle. Label the myosin, actin, and sarcomere. Then on the lines below, describe how the position of the actin filaments changes during muscle contraction.

Relaxed Muscle

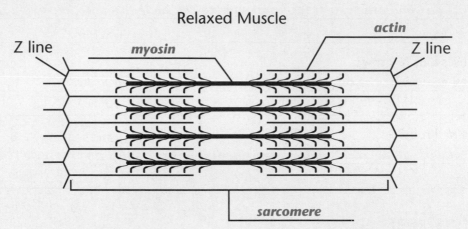

The actin fibers move into the center of the sarcomere, shortening the sarcomere and
contracting the muscle.

For Questions 2–9, match the cell or tissue named with its description.

Cell/Tissue		Description
D	2. Dermis	**A.** Attaches two bones at a joint
F	3. Epidermis	**B.** Attaches muscles to bones
A	4. Ligament	**C.** Bone cell that breaks down minerals in bone
G	5. Melanocyte	**D.** Inner layer of the skin
H	6. Osteoblast	**E.** Mature bone cell that maintains bone
C	7. Osteoclast	**F.** Outer layer of the skin
E	8. Osteocyte	**G.** Skin cell that produces a brown pigment
B	9. Tendon	**H.** Bone cell that builds bone

For Questions 10–15, complete each statement by writing the correct word or words.

10. A(n) ___sarcomere___ is a section of a myofibril that includes two Z lines and the filaments between them.

11. A substance that waterproofs the skin and kills bacteria on it is produced by the ___sebaceous glands___.

12. A(n) ___myofibril___ is a bundle of actin and ___myosin___ filaments.

13. Hair and nails are both made of the protein ___keratin___.

14. The neurotransmitter ___acetylcholine___ is released at neuromuscular junctions of motor neurons and muscle fibers.

15. Nerves and blood vessels in compact bone run through structures called ___Haversian canals___.

CHAPTER MYSTERY

THE DEMISE OF A DISEASE

21st Century Learning

In the Chapter Mystery, you unraveled the link between vitamin D and the scourge of rickets that afflicted many malnourished children in northern climates early in the twentieth century. Though this disease has been largely eradicated in this country, many millions of children worldwide still suffer from vitamin and mineral deficiencies.

Fighting Malnutrition Around the World

The problem of child malnutrition is so pressing and dire that many governmental and nonprofit organizations have pledged to combat it. One such effort is by the nonprofit Bill and Melinda Gates Foundation. The Foundation has announced that it would award $25 million in grants to support "biofortification." This approach involves breeding crops that provide higher levels of micronutrients such as iron, zinc, and vitamin A.

Read the facts below, from a United Nations report, to learn more about the scope of the problem that spurred the Gates Foundation to action:

Report on Childhood Vitamin and Mineral Deficiencies
A Global Problem

• •

- **Iron deficiency**, the most prevalent form of malnutrition worldwide, affects *billions* of people. Iron carries oxygen in the blood, so symptoms of a deficiency include tiredness and pallor. Lack of iron in large segments of the population severely damages a country's productivity. Iron deficiency also impedes cognitive development. In developing countries, it affects over half of children aged 6–24 months, a time when the brain is developing rapidly.
- **Vitamin A deficiency** affects 127 million preschool children and six million pregnant women in developing countries. It is also a leading cause of blindness in children in developing countries. Vitamin A deficiency weakens the immune system, increasing vulnerability to disease and risk of dying from diarrhea, measles, and malaria.
- **Iodine deficiency** affects 780 million people worldwide. The clearest symptom is a swelling of the thyroid gland called a goiter. But the most serious impact is on the brain, which cannot develop properly without iodine. According to UN research, each year 20 million children are born impaired because their mothers did not consume enough iodine. The most severe deficiencies result in mental retardation and physical stunting.
- **Zinc deficiency** contributes to growth failure and weakened immunity in young children. It is linked to a higher risk of diarrhea and pneumonia, resulting in nearly 800,000 deaths per year worldwide.

Continued on next page ▶

21st Century Themes Science and Global Awareness, Science and Health Literacy

1. What are some of the vitamin and mineral deficiencies other than vitamin D that affect children and adults around the world today?

   Some of the most significant include deficiencies in iron, vitamin A, iodine, and zinc.

2. What percentage of children aged six months to two years old are estimated to suffer from a deficiency in iron? *more than 50%*

3. How many preschool children are thought to suffer from a vitamin A deficiency, and what are the health effects associated with it?

   127 million preschool children around the world are deficient in vitamin A. Lack

   of vitamin A is a leading cause of blindness in children in developing countries and

   weakens children's immune systems, leaving them more vulnerable to diseases like

   measles and malaria.

4. What is "biofortification" and how can it help combat vitamin and mineral deficiencies?

   Biofortification is an approach that involves breeding crops that provide higher levels

   of micronutrients such as iron, zinc, and vitamin A.

5. Do you agree that the problem of vitamin and mineral deficiencies among the world's children needs urgent attention? Explain.

   Answers will vary. Student viewpoints and rationale encouraged here.

6. Do you think that a focus on biofortification can help? Why or why not?

   Answers will vary. Student viewpoints and rationale encouraged here.

21st Century Skills Memo to the Gates Foundation

The skills used in this activity include **critical thinking and systems thinking; problem identification, formulation, and solution; creativity and intellectual curiosity; information and media literacy;** and **social responsibility.**

On the Internet, visit Web sites that map problems of hunger and malnutrition around the world. You might try the Web site of the World Food Program of the United Nations. Based on your research, draft a brief letter to the Gates Foundation. State where you think the need is greatest and outline the steps you think the foundation should consider taking to combat vitamin and mineral deficiencies.

Evaluate students' memos based on the quality and extent of their research and the

clear presentation of concrete steps the Foundation should take.

33 Circulatory and Respiratory Systems

 Big idea **Structure and Function**

Q: How do the structures of the circulatory and respiratory systems allow for their close functional relationship?

WHAT I KNOW	WHAT I LEARNED
33.1 What structures transport substances throughout the human body?	SAMPLE ANSWER: **The heart pumps blood, and blood vessels carry blood throughout the body.**	SAMPLE ANSWER: **Pulmonary circulation pumps blood from the heart to the lungs and back. Systemic circulation pumps blood from the heart to the cells of the body. Three types of blood vessels are arteries, capillaries, and veins.**
33.2 What are the roles of blood and the lymphatic system in the body?	SAMPLE ANSWER: **Blood carries oxygen and nutrients throughout the body. The lymphatic system works with the circulatory system.**	SAMPLE ANSWER: **The components of blood transport oxygen, guard against infection, make blood clotting possible, and make up about 55 percent of total blood volume. The lymphatic system screens lymph for microorganisms and is involved in the absorption of nutrients and in immunity.**
33.3 How are oxygen and carbon dioxide exchanged between humans and the environment?	SAMPLE ANSWER: **Breathing brings air into the lungs and exhales wastes.**	SAMPLE ANSWER: **The human respiratory system picks up oxygen from air during inhalation. Carbon dioxide is released during exhalation. Oxygen and carbon dioxide are exchanged across the walls of alveoli and capillaries.**

33.1 The Circulatory System

Lesson Objectives

- Identify the functions of the human circulatory system.
- Describe the structure of the heart and explain how it pumps blood through the body.
- Name three types of blood vessels in the circulatory system.

Lesson Summary

Functions of the Circulatory System The circulatory system transports oxygen, nutrients, and other substances throughout the body, and removes wastes from tissues.

The Heart The muscle layer of the heart is the **myocardium**. Its powerful contractions pump blood through the circulatory system. The human heart has four chambers. A wall called the septum separates the right side of the heart from the left side. On each side of the septum are an upper and lower chamber.

▶ Each upper chamber, or **atrium** (plural: atria), receives blood from the body; each lower chamber, or **ventricle**, pumps blood out of the heart.

▶ Flaps of connective tissue called **valves** are located between the atria and the ventricles and between the ventricles and blood vessels leaving the heart. The valves open and close to keep blood moving in one direction.

The heart pumps blood through two pathways:

▶ **Pulmonary circulation** pumps blood from the heart to the lungs and back to the heart again. Blood picks up oxygen and releases carbon dioxide in the lungs.

▶ **Systemic circulation** pumps blood from the heart to the rest of the body. Cells absorb much of the oxygen and load the blood with carbon dioxide.

The heart muscle beats in an orderly and coordinated way. A small group of cardiac muscle fibers, the sinoatrial node (SA node), is also called the **pacemaker**. When the pacemaker fires, an electrical impulse causes the atria to contract. Another group of muscle fibers, the atrioventricular node (AV node), causes the ventricles to contract. The nervous system influences the SA node, increasing or decreasing heart rate to meet the body's needs.

Blood Vessels Blood flows through the circulatory system in blood vessels:

▶ **Arteries** are large vessels that carry blood away from the heart to the tissues of the body. Except for the pulmonary arteries, all arteries carry oxygen-rich blood.

▶ **Capillaries** are the smallest vessels. Their thin walls allow oxygen and nutrients to pass from blood into tissues and wastes to move from tissues into blood.

▶ **Veins** return blood to the heart. Many have valves that prevent backflow.

The contractions of the heart produce a wave of fluid pressure in the arteries, known as blood pressure. Without that pressure, blood would stop flowing through the body. The body regulates blood pressure through actions of the brain and the kidneys.

Functions of the Circulatory System

1. Why do animals with millions of cells "need" a circulatory system while animals with few cells can do without one?

   If all cells are in direct contact with the environment, diffusion and active transport

   can provide nutrients and oxygen and remove wastes. Large, multicellular organisms

   have cells that are not in direct contact with the environment. A circulatory system is

   required to serve those functions.

2. **VISUAL ANALOGY** Marie lives in a large city. She is disabled and cannot leave her home. Everything she needs must be delivered to her, and all her garbage must be hauled away. Compare how the streets and highways of the city supply Marie's needs with how the circulatory system supplies the needs of individual cells of the human body.

   Marie's food, medicines, and other supplies are brought to her door by delivery

   people who travel along streets and highways. Garbage collectors use those same

   streets and highways to collect and haul away her trash. The same thing happens in

   the body. Delivery people (blood cells) travel along streets and highways (arteries and

   veins). They deliver supplies like oxygen and nutrients. They also collect waste prod-

   ucts like carbon dioxide and haul them away.

The Heart

3. Complete the table.

Circulation Pathway	Side of Heart Pumping	Destination After Leaving Heart	Blood Change
Pulmonary	*Right*	*Lungs*	*Oxygen poor to oxygen rich*
Systemic	*Left*	*Body*	*Oxygen rich to oxygen poor*

4. Label the diagram at the points indicated to show the structures of the human circulatory system. Add arrows to show the direction of blood flow.

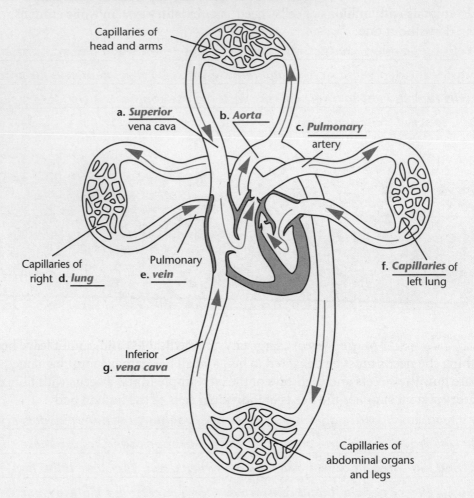

Capillaries of
head and arms

a. *Superior*
vena cava

b. *Aorta*

c. *Pulmonary*
artery

Capillaries of
right **d.** *lung*

Pulmonary
e. *vein*

f. *Capillaries* of
left lung

Inferior
g. *vena cava*

Capillaries of
abdominal organs
and legs

5. Complete the flowchart to show the actions that keep the heart beating in an orderly way.

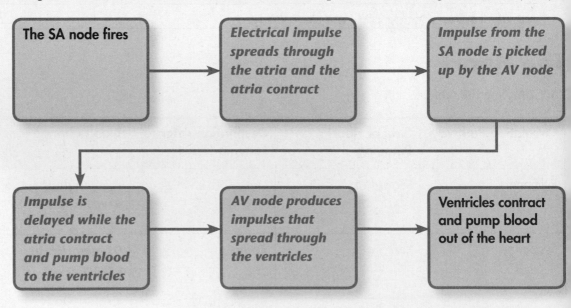

| The SA node fires | Electrical impulse spreads through the atria and the atria contract | Impulse from the SA node is picked up by the AV node |

| Impulse is delayed while the atria contract and pump blood to the ventricles | AV node produces impulses that spread through the ventricles | Ventricles contract and pump blood out of the heart |

Blood Vessels

6. As blood flows through the body, it passes through three types of blood vessels. Complete the table by naming each type and describing its structure and function.

Blood vessels	Structure	Function
Arteries	Thick, elastic walls containing connective tissue, smooth muscle, and endothelium	Carry blood from the heart to the tissues of the body
Capillaries	Smallest blood vessels; extremely thin walls	Allow oxygen and nutrients to diffuse from blood into tissues, and wastes to move from tissues into blood
Veins	Large vessels; many contain valves to ensure that blood flows in one direction	Carry blood toward the heart

7. Complete the feedback diagram to show how the nervous system regulates blood pressure.

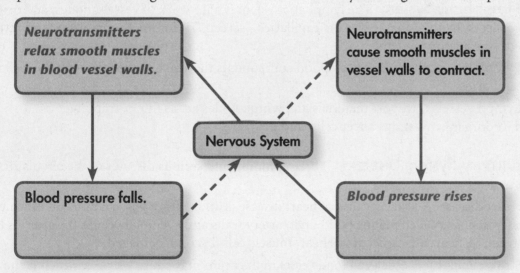

Apply the Big idea

8. The left side of the heart is larger and more muscular than the right side. Also, artery walls are thicker than those of veins. Explain how those differences in structure are important to function.

SAMPLE ANSWER: *The left side of the heart must pump blood through the entire body. It has to be stronger than the right side, which only pumps blood to the lungs. Arteries carry blood away from the heart. They must be stronger and more flexible than veins to withstand the pressure of the pumping heart.*

33.2 Blood and the Lymphatic System

🔑 Explain the functions of blood plasma, red blood cells, white blood cells, and platelets.

🔑 Describe the role of the lymphatic system.

🔑 List three common circulatory diseases.

🔑 Describe the connection between cholesterol and circulatory disease.

Lesson Summary

Blood Blood has four main components:

▶ **Plasma** is a straw-colored fluid. It is about 90 percent water and 10 percent dissolved gases, salts, nutrients, enzymes, hormones, waste products, plasma proteins, cholesterol, and other important compounds. Parts of plasma help control body temperature, transport substances, and fight infection. Plasma proteins are involved in blood clotting.

▶ **Red blood cells** transport oxygen. Blood gets its red color from the iron in **hemoglobin**, a protein that binds oxygen in the lungs and releases it in the capillaries.

▶ **White blood cells** guard against infection, fight parasites, and attack bacteria.

▶ **Platelets** are cell fragments involved in blood clotting.

The Lymphatic System The lymphatic system is a network of vessels, nodes, and organs that collects the fluid that leaves the capillaries, "screens" it for microorganisms, and returns it to the circulatory system.

▶ **Lymph** is fluid that consists of blood components that have moved through the walls of capillaries.

▶ Lymph vessels transport materials and lymph nodes act as filters, trapping microorganisms, stray cancer cells, and debris.

Circulatory System Diseases Three common and serious diseases of the circulatory system are:

▶ Heart disease: A leading cause of heart disease is **atherosclerosis**, a condition in which fatty deposits called plaque build up in artery walls and eventually cause the arteries to stiffen. A heart attack occurs as heart muscle cells become damaged.

▶ Stroke: A clot that blocks a blood vessel in the brain may cause a stroke, which is the sudden death of brain cells when their blood supply is interrupted. A stroke can also occur if a weak vessel breaks and causes bleeding in the brain.

▶ High blood pressure, or hypertension, is usually defined as blood pressure higher than 140/90. Uncontrolled high blood pressure can damage the heart and blood vessels. It can also lead to heart attack, stroke, and kidney damage.

Understanding Circulatory Disease Cholesterol is a lipid that is part of animal cell membranes. It is transported in the blood primarily by two types of lipoproteins: low-density lipoprotein (LDL) and high-density lipoprotein (HDL). The liver manufactures cholesterol, but it also comes from animal product foods. High cholesterol levels, along with other risk factors, lead to atherosclerosis and higher risk of heart attack.

Blood

For Questions 1–5, write True if the statement is true. If the statement is false, change the underlined word or words to make the statement true.

_____True_____ 1. Blood helps regulate body <u>temperature</u> and fight infections.

_____4–6_____ 2. The human body contains <u>8–10</u> liters of blood.

_____90_____ 3. Plasma is about <u>50</u> percent water.

_____proteins_____ 4. Albumin, globulins, and fibrinogen are <u>nucleic acids</u> in blood.

_____True_____ 5. <u>Fibrinogen</u> is necessary for blood clotting.

6. Complete the table to describe the characteristics and functions of blood.

Component	Characteristics	Function
Plasma	It is 90 percent water and 10 percent dissolved gases, salts, nutrients, enzymes, hormones, waste proteins, and other compounds.	Helps control body temperature, transports fatty acids, hormones and vitamins, and helps with osmotic pressure and clotting.
Red blood cells	They are disks that are thinner in their center than along the edges. They get their red color from the iron in hemoglobin.	Hemoglobin binds to oxygen. Red blood cells transport oxygen to cells and some carbon dioxide to the lungs.
White blood cells	There are different types, such as macrophages, B lymphocytes, and T lymphocytes.	Macrophages engulf pathogens. B lymphocytes produce antibodies. T lymphocytes help fight tumors and viruses.
Platelets	They are fragments of the cytoplasm of certain bone marrow cells. They are enclosed in a membrane.	They cluster around a wound and release proteins called clotting factors that start blood clotting.

The Lymphatic System

For Questions 7–14, write the letter of the correct answer on the line at the left.

____D____ 7. Fluid and small particles that leave the blood are collectively called

    A. plasma.   **C.** platelets.

    B. lymphocytes.   **D.** lymph.

____B____ 8. Some of the lymph is collected in a network of vessels, nodes, and organs called the

    A. circulatory system.   **C.** respiratory system.

    B. lymphatic system.   **D.** excretory system.

____A____ 9. How does lymph help protect against infection?

    A. It screens for microorganisms.

    B. It causes fevers when viruses are present.

    C. It removes defective DNA from cells.

    D. It removes toxins from the liver.

____C____ 10. What moves lymph into ducts?

    A. valves in the veins

    B. the pumping action of the heart

    C. pressure from skeletal muscles

    D. the thin walls of capillaries

____A____ 11. Where does lymph return to the bloodstream?

    A. through veins just below the shoulders

    B. through veins in the legs

    C. through arteries in the abdomen

    D. through capillaries in the liver

____A____ 12. What nutrients does the lymphatic system pick up in the digestive tract and transport to the bloodstream?

    A. fats and fat-soluble vitamins

    B. water and water-soluble vitamins

    C. water and proteins

    D. fatty acids and cholesterol

____A____ 13. Which of the following is NOT a function of lymph nodes?

    A. pumping blood to the lungs

    B. trapping microorganisms

    C. collecting cancer cells

    D. gathering debris from the body

____D____ 14. Which organ of the lymphatic system stores platelets?

    A. heart   **C.** thymus

    B. lymph node   **D.** spleen

Circulatory System Diseases

15. Why is the first sign of a circulatory problem an event that affects the heart or brain?

The tissues of these vital organs begin to die within moments if their oxygen supply is interrupted.

16. What is atherosclerosis?

It is a condition in which fatty deposits called plaques build up in artery walls and cause arteries to stiffen.

17. What is angina, and what causes it?

It is chest pain caused by restricted blood flow to the heart.

18. What is one cause of heart failure?

The heart is weakened or damaged by oxygen deprivation.

19. What is a heart attack, and what causes most heart attacks?

A heart attack occurs when blood flow to heart muscle tissue is blocked and the tissue is damaged. A heart attack may occur if the cap of a plaque ruptures, and a blood clot forms that completely blocks an artery.

20. How is a stroke like a heart attack?

A stroke and heart attack may have the same cause: a clot blocks the blood supply to tissue (brain for a stroke, heart for a heart attack).

21. How does high blood pressure damage the heart?

The heart struggles to push blood through the vessels. Also, hypertension causes small tears in blood vessels; the plaques of atherosclerosis can form in the tears.

Understanding Circulatory Diseases

For Questions 22–25, complete each statement by writing the correct word or words.

22. Cholesterol is transported through the body by _____low density_____ lipoprotein and _____high density_____ lipoprotein.

23. A cholesterol level in the range of _____100–200 mg/dL_____ is considered normal.

24. Cholesterol is made in the _____liver_____, but can also be found in foods high in _____fat_____.

25. High cholesterol is one of the risk factors for _____atherosclerosis_____ and heart attack.

26. Fill in the concept map to compare the path of cholesterol in normal liver cells and defective liver cells.

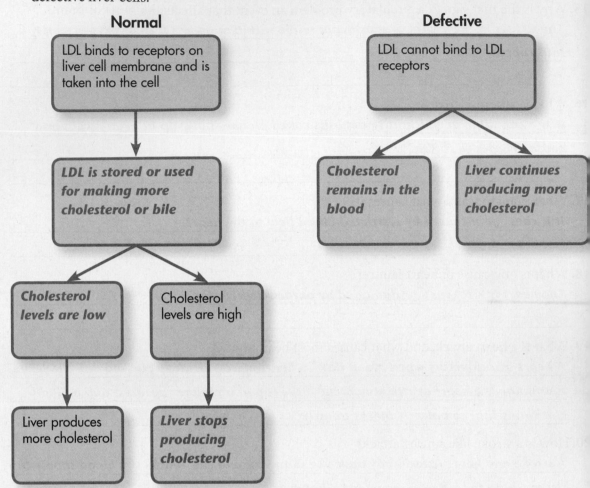

Normal

LDL binds to receptors on liver cell membrane and is taken into the cell

↓

LDL is stored or used for making more cholesterol or bile

Cholesterol levels are low   Cholesterol levels are high

↓   ↓

Liver produces more cholesterol   *Liver stops producing cholesterol*

Defective

LDL cannot bind to LDL receptors

Cholesterol remains in the blood   *Liver continues producing more cholesterol*

27. What did Brown and Goldstein discover about people who eat high-fat diets?

They store extra cholesterol in their liver cells. Those cells then stop making LDL receptors and removing cholesterol from blood. The excess blood cholesterol is then deposited in the arteries.

Apply the Big idea

28. Heart disease, stroke, and high blood pressure are major killers in the United States, yet much can be done to prevent them. How can a healthy diet and exercise keep the circulatory system functioning properly to prevent these diseases?

A healthy diet low in fat prevents LDL levels from rising and leading to atherosclerosis. Exercise keeps the heart muscles strong and pumping blood efficiently.

33.3 The Respiratory System

- Identify the structures of the respiratory system and describe their functions.
- Describe gas exchange.
- Describe how breathing is controlled.
- Describe the effects of smoking on the respiratory system.

Lesson Summary

Structures of the Respiratory System For organisms, *respiration* means the process of gas exchange between a body and the environment. The human respiratory system picks up oxygen from the air we inhale and releases carbon dioxide into the air we exhale. The structures of the respiratory system include the

- nose, where air is filtered, moistened, and warmed.
- **pharynx**, or throat, which serves as a passageway for both air and food.
- **trachea**, or windpipe, and the **larynx**, or vocal cords.
- **bronchi**, two large tubes that lead to the lungs. Each bronchus branches into smaller passageways called bronchioles that end in tiny air sacs called **alveoli** within the lungs.

Gas Exchange and Transport Oxygen and carbon dioxide are exchanged across the walls of alveoli and capillaries. Chemical properties of blood and red blood cells allow for efficient transport of gases throughout the body.

- Carbon dioxide and oxygen are exchanged across capillary and alveolus walls.
- Hemoglobin binds with and transports oxygen that diffuses from alveoli to capillaries. It also increases the efficiency of gas exchange.
- Carbon dioxide is transported in the blood in three ways. Most combines with water and forms carbonic acid. Some dissolves in plasma. Some binds to hemoglobin and proteins in plasma.

Breathing Movements of the diaphragm and rib cage change air pressure in the chest cavity during inhalation and exhalation.

- The dome-shaped muscle at the bottom of the chest cavity is the **diaphragm**. During inhalation, contraction of the diaphragm and rib muscles increases chest volume and air rushes in. In exhalation, these muscles relax and air rushes out.
- The nervous system has final control of the breathing muscles. Breathing does not require conscious control.

Smoking and the Respiratory System Chemicals in tobacco smoke damage structures throughout the respiratory system and have other negative health effects. Smoking causes a number of diseases, including chronic bronchitis, emphysema, and lung cancer.

Structures of the Respiratory System

1. Label each of the structures indicated in this drawing of the human respiratory system.

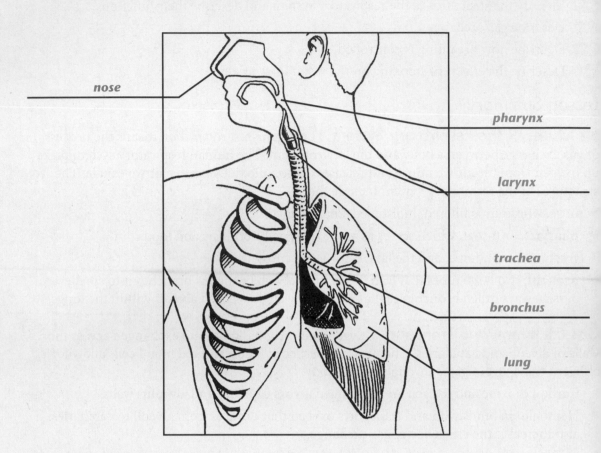

nose

pharynx

larynx

trachea

bronchus

lung

Gas Exchange and Transport

For Questions 2–7, complete each statement by writing the correct word or words.

2. The surface area for gas exchange in the lungs is provided by the ___*alveoli*___.

3. The gases exchanged in the lungs are carbon dioxide and ___*oxygen*___.

4. The process that exchanges gases across the walls of capillaries is ___*diffusion*___.

5. Oxygen diffuses from an area of ___*greater*___ concentration to an area of lesser concentration.

6. ___*Hemoglobin*___ binds with oxygen and increases the blood's oxygen-carrying capacity.

7. Most carbon dioxide combines with ___*water*___ in the blood, forming carbonic acid.

Breathing

8. Complete the flowchart to show how breathing works.

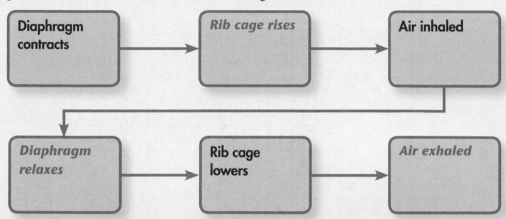

Diaphragm contracts →	*Rib cage rises* →	**Air inhaled**
Diaphragm relaxes →	**Rib cage lowers** →	*Air exhaled*

Smoking and the Respiratory System

9. Complete the table to describe the health effects of three substances in tobacco smoke.

Substance	Effect
Nicotine	*Nicotine is addictive. It increases heart rate and blood pressure.*
Carbon monoxide	*Carbon monoxide is a poisonous gas that blocks hemoglobin from binding with oxygen, thus interfering with oxygen transport in the blood.*
Tar	*Tar contains at least 60 compounds known to cause cancer.*

10. What causes smoker's cough?

Tobacco smoke paralyzes cilia in the trachea. Inhaled particles stick to the walls of the respiratory tract or enter the lungs. Smoke-laden mucus is trapped along the airways. Irritation from all this triggers a cough as the smoker tries to clear the airways.

11. Smoking even a few cigarettes on a regular basis can lead to chronic bronchitis. What happens to people with this disease?

They often find simple activities, like climbing stairs, difficult.

Apply the Big idea

12. Smoking and secondhand smoke damage both the respiratory system and the circulatory system. Explain how the close structural relationship of these two systems accounts for the effect of smoke on both systems.

Gases are exchanged across the thin membranes of alveoli and the thin walls of the capillaries. Compounds in smoke affect both structures, reducing airflow in the alveoli and interfering with the oxygen-binding capacity of hemoglobin.

Chapter Vocabulary Review

Across

1. the sinoatrial node of the heart
3. fluid and the small particles it contains that leaves blood cells
5. the circulation pathway that sends blood from the heart to the lungs and back to the heart
8. a muscle layer in the heart
10. the build-up of fatty deposits in artery walls
14. the smallest blood vessel
15. Leukocytes, or _____ blood cells, guard against infection.
16. the protein in the blood that binds oxygen

Down

2. an upper chamber of the heart
4. the fluid portion of the blood
6. a blood vessel that returns blood from the body to the heart
7. a structure that keeps blood moving through the heart in one direction
9. a lower chamber of the heart
10. a blood vessel that carries blood from the heart to body tissues
11. Erythrocytes, or _____ blood cells, transport oxygen.
12. the circulation that sends blood from the heart to all the body except the lungs
13. a cell fragment that makes blood clotting possible

For Questions 17–19, complete each statement by writing the correct word or words.

17. The throat is also called the ___pharynx___.
18. The windpipe is also called the ___trachea___.
19. The vocal cords are in the ___larynx___.

Name _____ Class _____ Date _____

CHAPTER
MYSTERY
IN THE BLOOD

The Chapter Mystery focused on a rare genetic disease known as familial hypercholesterolemia. Far more common are diseases that are often directly associated with cigarettes and other types of tobacco use: lung cancer and heart disease.

21st Century Learning

Smoking, Lung Cancer, and Heart Disease: Should the FDA Regulate Tobacco?

Lung cancer and heart disease are among the nation's top killers. Together, they account for the deaths of hundreds of thousands of Americans each year.

Federal lawmakers have long debated how to best regulate tobacco products. A bill passed in the House of Representatives would require the U.S. Food and Drug Administration (FDA) to regulate cigarettes and other tobacco products if it is enacted.

Read the following statement made on the floor of the U.S. House of Representatives by Congressmember Rosa DeLauro (D-CT) urging passage of the bill, called H.R.1108:

HOUSE OF REPRESENTATIVES, JULY 30, 2008

Ms. *DeLAURO*. Madam Speaker, I rise in support of H.R. 1108, the Family Smoking Prevention and Tobacco Control Act. This legislation would grant the Food and Drug Administration (FDA) long-needed authority to regulate the manufacture, sale, distribution and marketing of tobacco products.

As we all know, tobacco use contributes to the death of more than 400,000 Americans and costs the nation's health care system nearly $100 billion each year. The most tragic part of this statistic is that virtually all of these deaths are preventable. It is alarming that preventable diseases such as emphysema, heart disease and cancer all can be attributed to the use of tobacco. In addition to providing consumers with science-based information about tobacco products, granting FDA the authority to regulate tobacco will more importantly help protect our children from using these products. Approximately 90 percent of all adult smokers began their habit while in their teens, or earlier, and two-thirds become regular, daily smokers before they reach the age of 19. According to the American Medical Association, each day, about 4,000 children try smoking a cigarette for the first time and another 1,000 become new, regular, daily smokers. This means that one-third of these children will die prematurely.

Despite their claims to the contrary, the tobacco companies continue to market their products aggressively toward children. This bill will give FDA the authority to impose marketing restrictions, labeling requirements, as well as to ban candy-flavored tobacco products in order to prevent tobacco companies from addicting children to tobacco.

This bill has strong bipartisan support, and is endorsed by key groups including the American Cancer Society, the American Medical Association, the American Heart Association, the American Lung Association, and Campaign for Tobacco-Free Kids.

Continued on next page ▶

21st Century Themes — Science and Civic Literacy, Science and Health Literacy

1. How many deaths in the United States are directly attributed to tobacco use each year?

More than 400,000

2. How much are tobacco-related diseases estimated to cost the United States health care system annually?

Nearly $100 billion each year

3. If the U.S. Food and Drug Administration (FDA) regulated tobacco products, what changes could the agency impose?

The FDA could impose marketing restrictions, labeling requirements, and ban candy-flavored tobacco products.

4. At what age did most adult smokers begin their habit?

Approximately 90 percent of all adult smokers began their habit while in their teens, or earlier.

5. Do you think that bill H.R. 1108 should be passed into law? Why or why not?

Answers will vary. Accept any answers that show logical reasoning and are supported by facts.

21st Century Learning — Letter to Your Senator

The skills used in this activity include **critical thinking and systems thinking, information and media literacy, communication skills,** and **social responsibility.**

Using the Internet, visit the Library of Congress's powerful legislative database called "Thomas," named after the third U.S. President, Thomas Jefferson. Use the database to track the status of bill H.R. 1108. Read the bill, search for comments by other representatives, and review the economic assessment of the bill from the Congressional Budget Office. Based on this research, write a letter to your Senator voicing your opinion about whether the bill should be, or should have been, passed into law. Clearly state your reasons why or why not in your letter.

Evaluate students' letters based on their inclusion of facts about the bill and careful reasoning about its impact. Their arguments for or against the bill should be supported by facts.

34 Endocrine and Reproductive Systems

Big idea Homeostasis

Q: How does the body use chemical signals to maintain homeostasis?

WHAT I KNOW	WHAT I LEARNED
34.1 How does the body send and receive chemical signals?	SAMPLE ANSWER: **The body has hormones that carry chemical signals.**	SAMPLE ANSWER: **Chemical messengers called hormones travel through the blood and bind to receptors on or in target cells. Hormones are produced and released by endocrine glands.**
34.2 What life processes are regulated by hormones?	SAMPLE ANSWER: **Hormones regulate many life processes such as reproduction.**	SAMPLE ANSWER: **Hormones regulate many cycles such as reproductive and sleep cycles. They also help maintain homeostasis through feedback mechanisms that control temperature, blood sugar levels, mineral levels in blood, and water balance.**
34.3 What body structures enable humans to produce offspring?	SAMPLE ANSWER: **Humans have male and female reproductive organs that produce sperm and eggs.**	SAMPLE ANSWER: **Human reproductive organs, ovaries and testes, are endocrine glands regulated by pituitary hormones. These glands produce hormones that help produce eggs and sperm and secondary sex characteristics.**
34.4 How does a human develop from a single cell to a newborn baby?	SAMPLE ANSWER: **The first cell of a new individual forms from the fertilization of an egg by a sperm.**	SAMPLE ANSWER: **Following fertilization, repeated mitosis and the migration of cells into three cell layers lead to the formation of an embryo. The embryo develops into a fetus that emerges through the vagina during childbirth.**

34.1 The Endocrine System

Lesson Objectives

🔑 Describe the structure and function of the endocrine system.

🔑 Explain how hormones work.

Lesson Summary

Hormones and Glands The endocrine system is made up of endocrine glands that release hormones into the blood.

▶ **Hormones** are chemicals made in one part of the body that affect cells in other parts of the body. Hormones travel throughout the body in the bloodstream.

- Hormones bind to **target cells**, which are cells that have specific receptors for a hormone either in the cell membrane or inside the cell.
- A hormone will not affect a cell that does not have receptors for the hormone.

▶ Glands are organs that release secretions. The body has two types of glands.

- **Exocrine glands** release their secretions through ducts either outside the body or into the digestive system.
- **Endocrine glands** release hormones directly into the bloodstream. Other structures that are not usually considered glands, such as bones, fat tissue, the heart, and the small intestine, also produce and release hormones.

▶ All cells, except for red blood cells, produce hormonelike substances called **prostaglandins**. Prostaglandins are modified fatty acids that usually affect only nearby cells and tissues. They are sometimes called "local hormones."

Hormone Action There are two types of hormones.

▶ Steroid hormones are produced from cholesterol. They can cross cell membranes of target cells, bind with their receptors, and enter the nucleus. The hormone-receptor complexes change the expression of genes in the target cell, often resulting in dramatic changes in the cell's activity.

▶ Nonsteroid hormones can be proteins, small peptides, or modified amino acids. They cannot cross cell membranes. The receptors for nonsteroid hormones are on the cell membrane. Compounds called secondary messengers carry the messages of nonsteroid hormones inside target cells.

Hormones and Glands

For Questions 1–4, write True if the statement is true and False if the statement is false.

_____*True*_____ 1. Hormones are chemical messengers that are transported by the bloodstream.

_____*False*_____ 2. Any cell can be a target cell for a hormone.

_____*False*_____ 3. The body's response to hormones is the same as it is for nerve impulses.

_____*True*_____ 4. Insulin and glucagon are two opposing hormones.

5. Complete the table that summarizes major endocrine glands of the human body.

Gland	Hormone(s) Produced	Function
Parathyroid	Parathyroid hormone	*Regulates the level of calcium in the blood*
Pineal	*Melatonin*	Regulates rhythmic activities
Thyroid	Thyroxine	*Regulates the body's metabolism*
Adrenal	Corticosteroids, epinephrine, norepinephrine	*Helps the body respond to stress*
Pancreas	*Insulin, glucagon*	Maintains the level of glucose in the blood
Ovaries	*Estrogen, progesterone*	Regulates formation of eggs and development of secondary female sex characteristics; prepares uterus for fertilization
Testes	Testosterone	*Regulates production of sperm and secondary male sex characteristics*

6. What are prostaglandins? How is their action different from that of hormones?

Prostaglandins are modified fatty acids that are produced by nearly every cell and

that act like hormones. They act only on nearby cells and tissues, whereas hormones

can act on target cells throughout the body.

_____

_____

Hormone Action

7. **THINK VISUALLY** Steroid and nonsteroid hormones affect their target cells in different ways. In the spaces below, draw diagrams that show how each type of hormone affects its target cells. Be sure to label the cell membrane, cytoplasm, nucleus, the hormones, and their receptors.

How Steroid Hormones Work	How Nonsteroid Hormones Work
See the textbook for what this drawing should look like. Drawings should show the hormone binding with the receptor complex inside the cell and then entering the nucleus of the cell.	*See the textbook for what this drawing should look like. Drawings should show the hormone binding with the receptor on the cell membrane of the cell.*

8. Summarize the action of a steroid hormone on a target cell.

A steroid hormone passes through the cell membrane and binds with a receptor inside the cell. The hormone-receptor complex then passes into the nucleus. The complex binds to a region of DNA that controls gene expression. This causes certain genes to be transcribed into mRNA that goes into the cytoplasm and directs protein synthesis.

9. Summarize the action of a nonsteroid hormone on a target cell.

A nonsteroid hormone binds to a receptor on the cell membrane. This activates enzymes inside the cell. The enzymes cause the release of secondary messengers, which are molecules that activate or inhibit cell activities.

Apply the Big idea

10. Compare the release of a hormone to the broadcast of a television commercial.

SAMPLE ANSWER: *A television commercial only affects the behavior of people who are interested in buying the product the commercial advertises (the target audience). A circulating hormone only affects the activities of cells with receptors (target cells) for that hormone. Neither the commercial nor the hormone will affect a "non-target."*

34.2 Glands of the Endocrine System

Lesson Objectives

▸ Identify the functions of the major endocrine glands.

▸ Explain how endocrine glands are controlled.

Lesson Summary

The Human Endocrine Glands Endocrine glands are scattered throughout the body.

▸ The **pituitary gland** is a bean-size structure at the base of the brain. Consisting of two parts, the anterior pituitary and the posterior pituitary, it secretes hormones that regulate body functions and control the actions of other endocrine glands.

▸ The hypothalamus controls the secretions of the pituitary gland and is the link between the central nervous system and the endocrine system. The hypothalamus controls the posterior pituitary through neurosecretory cells. The hypothalamus produces **releasing hormones** that control the secretions of the anterior pituitary.

▸ An adrenal gland sits on top of each kidney. The adrenal glands make hormones that help the body prepare for and deal with stress. They consist of a cortex and a medulla.

  • The adrenal cortex produces more than two dozen **corticosteroids**, which help maintain homeostasis.

  • The adrenal medulla produces the "fight or flight" hormones **epinephrine** and **norepinephrine**, which help the body respond to stress.

▸ The pancreas is both an exocrine gland and an endocrine gland. As an exocrine gland, the pancreas releases digestive enzymes.

▸ Insulin and glucagon, hormones produced by the islets of Langerhans in the pancreas, help keep levels of glucose in the blood stable.

▸ The thyroid gland wraps around the trachea at the base of the neck. The four parathyroid glands are on the back surface of the thyroid gland. **Thyroxine**, produced by the thyroid gland, regulates metabolism. A hormone from the thyroid gland, **calcitonin**, and one from the parathyroid glands, **parathyroid hormone**, work together to maintain blood calcium levels.

▸ Reproductive glands, or gonads, make gametes and secrete sex hormones. The female gonads, ovaries, produce eggs. The male gonads, testes, produce sperm.

Control of the Endocrine System Feedback mechanisms involving hormones help maintain homeostasis. In feedback inhibition, increasing levels of a substance inhibit the process that produced the substance. Secretions of the hypothalamus and pituitary gland regulate the activity of other endocrine glands in this way.

▸ Actions of the hypothalamus and posterior pituitary gland regulate water balance. The hypothalamus signals the posterior pituitary gland to increase (in the case of dehydration) or decrease (in the case of overhydration) its release of anti-diurectic hormone (ADH). In response to ADH levels the kidneys produce less or more urine.

▸ The hypothalamus and anterior pituitary regulate metabolism and body temperature by controlling the amount of thyroxine produced by the thyroid gland.

The Human Endocrine Glands

For Questions 1–4, complete each statement by writing the correct word or words.

1. The pituitary gland is located at the base of the ____brain____ and consists of the ____anterior____ pituitary and the ____posterior____ pituitary.

2. ____Neurosecretory____ cells in the ____hypothalamus____ produce hormones that are released by the ____posterior pituitary____.

3. The two hormones released from the posterior pituitary are oxytocin and ____antidiuretic hormone____.

4. ____Releasing____ hormones secreted into blood vessels leading to the ____anterior____ pituitary control its secretions.

For Questions 5–9, match each pituitary hormone with its action.

Hormone	Action
__E__ 5. MSH	**A.** Stimulates ovaries and testes
__B__ 6. TSH	**B.** Stimulates the release of thyroxine
__A__ 7. LH	**C.** Stimulates release of hormones from adrenal cortex
__D__ 8. GH	**D.** Stimulates protein synthesis and growth in cells
__C__ 9. ACTH	**E.** Stimulates melanocytes to increase production of melanin in the skin

10. Complete the table. Fill in the missing information about each adrenal gland.

Part of the Adrenal Gland	Hormone(s) Produced	Function
Adrenal cortex	**Corticosteroids**	**Regulating blood volume and pressure, metabolism**
Adrenal medulla	**Epinephrine, norepinephrine**	**Producing "fight or flight" response**

11. How does the pancreas use insulin and glucagon together to control blood glucose levels in the body?

   When blood glucose rises after a person eats, the pancreas releases insulin to promote the uptake of glucose from the blood. Once the level drops, the pancreas releases glucagon to stimulate the release of glucose into the blood.

12. What is diabetes mellitus?

   It is a condition that develops when the pancreas fails to produce insulin or body cells do not properly respond to insulin.

For Questions 13–19, write True if the statement is true. If the statement is false, change the underlined word or words to make the statement true.

True	**13.**	A major role of the <u>thyroid gland</u> is controlling the body's metabolism.
iodine	**14.**	The body needs <u>calcium</u> in order to produce thyroxine.
hypothyroidism	**15.**	Too little thyroxine leads to a condition called <u>hyperthyroidism</u>.
True	**16.**	<u>Calcitonin</u> is a hormone produced by the thyroid gland.
thyroid	**17.**	The parathyroid glands are located on the back of the <u>pituitary</u> gland.
True	**18.**	Parathyroid hormone promotes the proper functioning of <u>nerves and muscles</u>.
gonads	**19.**	The reproductive organs are referred to as <u>gametes</u>.

Control of the Endocrine System

20. What is feedback inhibition?

Feedback inhibition is a process in which an increase in a product slows or stops the process that produces the product.

21. Complete the flowchart to show how feedback controls regulate the thyroid gland.

Inhibition

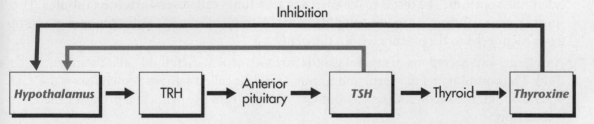

Hypothalamus → TRH → Anterior pituitary → TSH → Thyroid → Thyroxine

22. Explain how feedback control regulates the rate of metabolism.

The hypothalamus produces thyroid-releasing hormone (TRH), which stimulates the anterior pituitary to produce thyroid-stimulating hormone (TSH), which causes the thyroid gland to produce thyroxine, which increases the rate of metabolism. Rising levels of TSH and thyroxine in the blood both cause the hypothalamus to slow or stop production of TRH, which leads to the slowing of the metabolic rate.

Apply the Big idea

23. Which gland, the hypothalamus or the pituitary gland, should be given the title "master gland"? Explain your choice.

SAMPLE ANSWER: _The hypothalamus should really be called the "master gland." Even though the pituitary gland's hormones affect many of the body's organs and functions, the hypothalamus controls the secretions of the pituitary gland._

34.3 The Reproductive System

Lesson Objectives

☞ Describe the effects the sex hormones have on development.

☞ Name and discuss the structures of the male reproductive system.

☞ Name and discuss the structures of the female reproductive system.

☞ Describe some of the most common sexually transmitted diseases.

Lesson Summary

Sexual Development Hormones released by the ovaries and testes cause sexual development during **puberty**, a period of rapid growth and sexual maturation that usually starts between the ages of 9 and 15. At the end of puberty, the male and female reproductive organs are fully developed and become fully functional.

The Male Reproductive System The main role of the male reproductive system is to make and deliver sperm.

▶ The **testes** are the main organs of the male system. Two testes are held in an external sac called the **scrotum**. The testes make sperm in tiny tubes called **seminiferous tubules**. The sperm mature and are stored in an **epididymis**. A tube called a **vas deferens** carries sperm from each testis to the urethra within the penis.

▶ Along the way, secretions of several glands form a nutrient-rich fluid called seminal fluid. The combination of sperm and seminal fluids is called **semen**. Semen leaves the body through the urethra. Contractions eject semen from the penis in a process called ejaculation.

▶ A mature sperm cell consists of a head that contains the nucleus, a midpiece that is packed with mitochondria, and a flagellum that propels the sperm.

The Female Reproductive System The main roles of the female reproductive system are to make eggs and prepare the female body to nourish an embryo.

▶ The **ovary** is the main organ of the female system. Each ovary has thousands of follicles, which are clusters of cells that surround an egg. A mature egg moves through the Fallopian tube to the uterus, which is connected to the outside of the body by the vagina.

▶ Beginning in puberty, the female body goes through a **menstrual cycle**, a series of events that prepares the body to care for a fertilized egg. The menstrual cycle has four phases:

• Follicular phase: An egg matures in its follicle.

• **Ovulation**: The mature egg is released from the ovary.

• Luteal phase: The follicle develops into a structure called the **corpus luteum**.

• **Menstruation**: The lining of the uterus falls away and leaves the body through the vagina if the egg is not fertilized.

Sexually Transmitted Diseases A disease spread during sexual contact is called a **sexually transmitted disease** (STD). Bacteria and viruses can cause STDs. Chlamydia, syphilis, gonorrhea, and AIDS are STDs.

Sexual Development

For Questions 1–3, write the letter of the correct answer on the line at the left.

___B___ 1. Male and female embryos are nearly identical until the

    A. second week of development.   **C.** third month of development.

    B. seventh week of development.   **D.** fifth month of development.

___A___ 2. Which hormone, when produced in an embryo, triggers a male pattern of development?

    A. testosterone   **C.** estrogen

    B. progesterone   **D.** adrenalin

___D___ 3. The period of human development that includes rapid growth and sexual maturation is called

    A. adolescence.   **C.** maturity.

    B. childhood.   **D.** puberty.

The Male Reproductive System

For Questions 4–8, match each structure of the male reproductive system with its description.

Structure

___C___ 4. epididymis

___A___ 5. scrotum

___D___ 6. seminiferous tubule

___B___ 7. testis

___E___ 8. vas deferens

Description

A. External sac that holds male gonads

B. The primary male reproductive organ

C. Structure in which sperm mature

D. Structure in which meiosis occurs

E. The tube through which sperm travel to the urethra

For Questions 9–12, complete each statement by writing the correct word or words.

9. The seminal vesicles, ____prostate____ gland, and ____bulbourethral____ gland produce a nutrient-rich fluid called ____seminal____ fluid.

10. Sperm mixed with the seminal fluid is called ____semen____.

11. Signals from the ____autonomic____ nervous system cause sperm to be ejaculated.

12. The ____midpiece____ of a sperm cell contain mitochondria that supply energy to the ____flagellum____, which propels the sperm forward.

The Female Reproductive System

For Questions 13–16, complete each statement by writing the correct word or words.

13. The primary reproductive organs of females are the ____ovaries____.

14. The function of a(n) ____follicle____ is to help an egg mature.

15. Only about ____400____ of the 400,000 eggs a female is born with develop into a mature ovum.

16. The structure of the female reproductive system in which the embryo develops is called the ____uterus____.

For Questions 17–20, match each phase of the menstrual cycle with the correct event.

Phase

_____C_____ **17.** Follicular phase

_____D_____ **18.** Ovulation

_____B_____ **19.** Luteal phase

_____A_____ **20.** Menstruation

Event

A. An unfertilized egg leaves the body.

B. The egg travels through a Fallopian tube.

C. An egg within a follicle develops.

D. An egg is released from an ovary.

21. Complete the concept map to explain what the outcomes of a menstrual cycle can be.

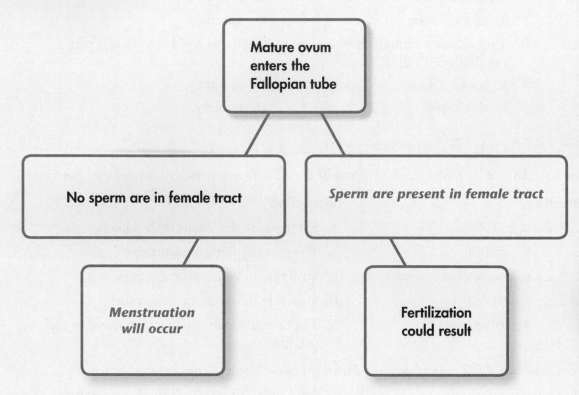

Sexually Transmitted Diseases

For Questions 22–24, write True if the statement is true. If the statement is false, change the underlined word or words to make the statement true.

Chlamydia **22.** <u>AIDS</u> is the most common bacterial STD.

True **23.** Chlamydia damages the reproductive tract and can cause <u>infertility</u>.

True **24.** <u>Hepatitis B</u> and genital herpes are viral STDs.

Apply the Big idea

25. How is the menstrual cycle an example of the body's use of negative feedback?

SAMPLE ANSWER: *The female body uses negative feedback during the menstrual cycle to maintain its readiness for reproduction. The presence of higher levels of hormones such as estrogens and progesterone causes their production to slow. In turn, the dropping levels of the hormones stimulate their increased production.*

34.4 Fertilization and Development

Lesson Objectives

▭ Describe fertilization and the early stages of development.

▭ Identify the major events of later stages of development.

Lesson Summary

Fertilization and Early Development Fertilization is the joining of a sperm and an egg. Following fertilization, a series of events called development begins.

▶ A fertilized egg is called a **zygote**. The zygote divides and undergoes repeated rounds of mitosis and develops into a hollow ball of cells called a **blastocyst**.

▶ About a week after fertilization, the blastocyst attaches to the wall of the uterus in the process of **implantation**. At the same time, cells of the blastocyst start to specialize through differentiation. Some cells migrate to form two cell layers—the ectoderm and the endoderm.

▶ A third layer of cells is produced by a process called **gastrulation**, in which cells from the ectoderm migrate to form the mesoderm. The three layers eventually develop into the different organs of the embryo.

▶ During **neurulation**, the notochord and the neural tube form. The neural tube eventually develops into the brain and spinal cord.

▶ As the embryo develops, membranes for protection and nourishment also form. Part of one membrane combines with the uterine lining to form the **placenta**. Mother and embryo/fetus exchange gases, food, and waste products across the placenta. The umbilical cord connects the embryo/fetus to the placenta.

▶ After eight weeks of development, the embryo is called a **fetus**. By the end of three months, most organs are fully formed.

Later Development Another six months of development occurs before birth.

▶ During months 4–6, the fetus's tissues become specialized and organs such as the heart begin to function.

▶ During months 7–9, the fetus's organ systems mature as the fetus grows in size and mass. The lungs and the central nervous system complete their development.

▶ Childbirth occurs about nine months after fertilization, when hormones cause contractions in the mother's uterus. The contractions first push the baby out through the vagina. Then, more contractions expel the placenta and amniotic sac from the uterus. Shortly after birth, the mother's breast tissue begins to produce milk that contains everything the baby needs for the first months of life.

▶ The placenta is a barrier to many harmful agents, but some are able to pass through it, such as viruses that cause AIDS and German measles. Alcohol, drugs, and smoking also have negative effects on embryos and fetuses. Prenatal care and advancements in medical technology have lowered the infant mortality rate.

Fertilization and Early Development

For Questions 1–4, complete each statement by writing the correct word or words.

1. The fusion of a sperm with an egg is called ___fertilization___ .

2. During implantation, the ___blastocyst___ embeds itself into the lining of the uterus.

3. Embryonic structures called ___chorionic villi___ combine with the uterine lining to form the ___placenta___ .

4. The embryo is surrounded by fluid called the ___amniotic___ fluid.

5. Complete the table by identifying events and structures of early development.

Event or Structure	What It Is
Fertilization	The process in which sperm joins an egg
Ectoderm	The layer of cells that develops into the skin and nervous system
Gastrulation	*Process that results in the formation of three cell layers*
Neurulation	Early stage in the development of the nervous system
Endoderm	*The innermost layer of cells in the early embryo that forms the lining of some organs*
Amniotic sac	Fluid-filled structure that cushions and protects the embryo
Placenta	Embryo's organ of respiration, nourishment, and excretion
Mesoderm	*Forms internal structures such as bones and muscles*
Umbilical cord	*Structure that connects the fetus to the placenta*

Later Development

6. What major changes occur in a developing fetus during months 4–6 of pregnancy?
The tissues of the fetus become more complex and specialized, and they begin to function. The heart becomes larger. Bone replaces cartilage.

7. What major changes occur in a developing fetus during months 7–9 of pregnancy?
The organ systems of the fetus mature, and the organs undergo changes that prepare them for life outside of the uterus. The fetus doubles in size. It begins to regulate its own body temperature. The nervous system and lungs complete development.

For Questions 8–13, write the letter of the correct answer on the line at the left.

___B___ 8. The contractions of labor before childbirth are triggered by
   A. the amniotic fluid.
   B. the hormone oxytocin.
   C. the umbilical cord.
   D. the uterine wall.

___C___ 9. The term "afterbirth" refers to the
   A. amnion and the chorion.
   B. clamping of the umbilical cord.
   C. placenta and amniotic sac.
   D. production of milk for the baby.

___B___ 10. What is a belly button?
   A. a structure with an unknown purpose
   B. a scar left from the umbilical cord
   C. remains of the notochord
   D. the point where implantation occurred

___D___ 11. Which hormone causes the mother's breast tissue to begin producing milk?
   A. estrogen
   B. oxytocin
   C. progesterone
   D. prolactin

___D___ 12. Using alcohol during pregnancy can harm a developing embryo, especially its
   A. reproductive system.
   B. circulatory system.
   C. endocrine system.
   D. nervous system.

___A___ 13. Which public health measure has decreased the incidence of spina bifida?
   A. the addition of folic acid to grain products
   B. the development of new types of baby formula
   C. the programs aimed at reducing smoking and alcohol use
   D. the use of a vaccine that prevents German measles

Apply the Big idea

14. Women with Type 1 diabetes may face challenges controlling blood sugar levels during pregnacy. Early in pregnancy, the developing fetus removes glucose from the mother's blood at a great rate. Would this raise or lower her need for insulin?

   This would lower her need for insulin. By removing a lot of glucose from her blood,

   the fetus would help keep her blood glucose levels at an appropriate level.

   _____

Chapter Vocabulary Review

On the lines provided, label the structures of the male reproductive system that correspond to the numbers in the diagram.

1. ___*Vas deferens*___

2. ___*Epididymis*___

3. ___*Testis*___

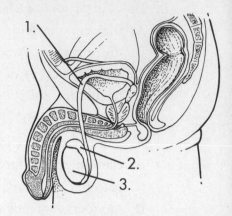

For Questions 4–10, match the term with its definition.

Term

___F___ 4. endocrine gland

___G___ 5. exocrine gland

___E___ 6. gastrulation

___D___ 7. hormone

___B___ 8. implantation

___C___ 9. menstruation

___A___ 10. semen

Definition

A. Mixture of sperm and seminal fluids

B. Attachment of the blastocyst to the uterine wall

C. Discharge of uterine tissue and blood from the vagina

D. Chemical made in one part of the body that travels in the bloodstream to other parts

E. The process that produces the three cell layers of the embryo

F. Type of gland that releases its chemicals directly into the bloodstream

G. Type of gland that releases its chemicals out of the body

For Questions 11–18, complete each statement by writing the correct word or words.

11. After eight weeks of development, an embryo is called a ___*fetus*___.

12. The gland that produces hormones that regulate the secretions of other glands is the ___*pituitary*___ gland.

13. Cells with receptors for a particular hormone are called ___*target*___ cells.

14. A fertilized egg is called a ___*zygote*___.

15. ___*Prostaglandins*___ are also known as "local hormones."

16. Oxygen and nutrients diffuse from the mother's blood to the embryo's blood through the ___*placenta*___.

17. The early stages of the brain and spinal cord form during ___*neurulation*___.

18. Sperm are produced in ducts called the ___*seminiferous*___ tubules.

CHAPTER MYSTERY

OUT OF STRIDE

In the Chapter Mystery, you learned about what happens when the body is not given everything it needs. Nonessential life processes, such as menstruation, may stop. In addition, the body may begin to take nutrients from organs and tissues.

21st Century Learning

Giving Your Body What It Needs

There are many diseases associated with undernutrition. In this country, most undernutrition diseases and disorders are associated with psychological issues rather than a lack of available nutrients. One of the most common of these diseases is anorexia nervosa. This is part of the FAQs page on a Web site about anorexia nervosa.

FAQS About Anorexia

Q: What is anorexia nervosa?
A: Anorexia nervosa is a medical condition that affects how a person thinks about food and about his or her own body.

[Return to Top]

Q: Does anorexia affect only girls and women?
A: It's true that 90–95% of anorexics are female, but that means that 5–10% are boys and men.

[Return to Top]

Q: What causes anorexia?
A: We don't know. We don't even know if there is one cause or many. But there are risk factors.

[Return to Top]

Q: What are the risk factors?

A: The first is culture. Anorexia almost exclusively affects people who grew up in or moved to Western cultures where they were exposed to images of the "ideal" body type for their sex. For example, Western media is full of images of flawless, thin women.

   Having a relative with anorexia makes it more likely a person will develop it. It's possible that personality traits and genetic factors are involved as well.

[Return to Top]

Q: What effect does anorexia have on the human body?
A: The symptoms of anorexia vary depending on the severity and length of time the person has suffered from the disease. Anorexia changes the brain chemistry, causing irritability, moodiness, and difficulty thinking. The hair and nails become brittle. The blood pressure goes down and the heart rate slows. The skin becomes dry and bruises easily. Bones lose mass and break more easily. Other symptoms include kidney stones and kidney failure, anemia, yellowing of the skin, and the growth of fine hairs over the entire body. In women, anorexia stops the menstrual cycle and increases the possibility of miscarriage and low birth weight.

[Return to Top]

Continued on next page ▶

21st Century Themes Science and Health Literacy

1. What percentage of anorexics are male?

5–10%

2. What parts of the body are affected by anorexia nervosa?

The brain, hair, nails, heart, skin, bones, kidneys, blood, and in women at least, the reproductive system

3. What symptoms are described both in this FAQ and in the solution to the Chapter Mystery?

Stopping of the menstrual cycle and bones losing mass and breaking more easily

4. What do you think some of the treatments for anorexia might be?

SAMPLE ANSWER: *First, the patient would be fed a nutrient-rich diet under supervision. The patient would then receive psychiatric care in order to treat the underlying causes of the disease.*

5. Suggest some ways in which the incidence of anorexia nervosa in the United States might be decreased.

SAMPLE ANSWER: *Encourage advertising agencies, magazine publishers, cosmetic and clothing companies to use models with a wide variety of body types. Have media give coverage to female athletes, politicians, businesswomen, and other role models that do not fit the mainstream idea of the ideal feminine form.*

21st Century Skills Help Wanted: Nutritionist

The skills used in this activity include **communication skills, creativity and intellectual curiosity, interpersonal and collaborative skills, accountability and adaptability,** and **social responsibility.**

An interest in nutrition could lead to a career as a nutritionist or a dietician. Nutritionists and dieticians work in hospitals, nursing homes, medical offices, schools, governmental agencies, and any number of other places. Use library or Internet resources to research the various job opportunities that involve nutrition. Then write up a help wanted ad that describes your ideal job.

Compare your ad with those of your classmates.

Students' ads should describe the job and the qualifications required for the job.

35 Immune System and Disease

 Homeostasis

Q: How does the body fight against invading organisms that may disrupt homeostasis?

WHAT I KNOW	WHAT I LEARNED
35.1 How do people catch infectious diseases?	SAMPLE ANSWER: *People catch infectious diseases from other people who are sick.*	SAMPLE ANSWER: *Infectious diseases are caused by microorganisms that can be spread through physical contact, body fluids, contaminated food and water, or animals.*
35.2 How does the body defend against infection?	SAMPLE ANSWER: *The body's immune system defends it against infection.*	SAMPLE ANSWER: *The immune system defends against infection with nonspecific defenses, such as the inflammatory response and interferons, and specific defenses that work together in the immune response.*
35.3 How do humans fight and prevent the spread of disease?	SAMPLE ANSWER: *Humans fight and prevent disease by keeping things clean and by going to the doctor and taking medicine.*	SAMPLE ANSWER: *Vaccinations, public health programs, and medications are all ways that humans fight and prevent the spread of disease.*
35.4 What happens when the immune system does not function properly?	SAMPLE ANSWER: *A person will get sick often if his or her immune system does not function properly.*	SAMPLE ANSWER: *Autoimmune diseases such as Type I diabetes, rheumatoid arthritis, and immunodeficiency diseases result from improper functioning of the immune system.*

35.1 Infectious Disease

Lesson Objectives

🔑 Identify the causes of infectious disease.

🔑 Explain how infectious diseases are spread.

Lesson Summary

Causes of Infectious Disease Changes to body physiology that disrupt normal body functions and are caused by microorganisms are called **infectious diseases**. This explanation, established by Louis Pasteur and Robert Koch, is called the **germ theory of disease**.

▶ Infectious diseases are caused by viruses, bacteria, fungi, protists, and parasitic worms. Disease-causing microorganisms are also called pathogens.

▶ Koch also developed a series of rules that help scientists identify which organism causes a specific disease. These rules are called **Koch's postulates**.

▶ Many microorganisms are symbionts that are either harmless or beneficial. Pathogens cause disease by destroying cells, disrupting body functions, or releasing toxins that kill cells or interfere with their normal functions.

How Diseases Spread Infectious diseases can be spread in several ways.

▶ Some infectious diseases are spread from person to person through coughing, sneezing, physical contact, or exchange of body fluids. Most infectious diseases are spread through indirect contact, such as pathogens that are carried through the air. These pathogens can be inhaled, or they can be picked up from surfaces.

▶ Some pathogens are spread by specific kinds of direct contact, such as sexual contact or drug use that involves shared syringes.

▶ Other infectious diseases are spread through contaminated water or food.

▶ Some infectious diseases spread from animals to humans. Such a disease is called a **zoonosis**. Often, the spread of zoonoses involves **vectors**, which are disease carriers that usually do not get sick from the pathogen.

Causes of Infectious Disease

1. What are infectious diseases, and what causes them?

Infectious diseases are changes to body physiology that disrupt normal body functions. They are caused by microorganisms.

2. How did the germ theory of disease get its name?

Microorganisms were once called germs; today the word "germ" has no scientific meaning

3. What is another name that scientists use for a disease-causing agent?

pathogen

For Questions 4–12, match each type of disease with the type of disease-causing agent that causes it. Some types of disease-causing agents may be used more than once.

Disease

Type of Disease-Causing Agent

_C_	**4.** African sleeping sickness	**A.** virus
_E_	**5.** athlete's foot	**B.** bacterium
_B_	**6.** botulism	**C.** protist
_A_	**7.** chicken pox	**D.** parasitic worm
_D_	**8.** hookworm	**E.** fungus
_A_	**9.** influenza	
_C_	**10.** malaria	
_D_	**11.** trichinosis	
_B_	**12.** tuberculosis	

13. What are Koch's postulates used for?

They are used to scientifically identify the microorganism that causes a specific

disease.

14. Complete the flowchart by numbering the steps to show the order in which a researcher applies Koch's postulates.

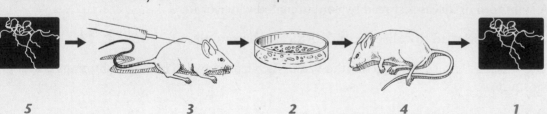

Same pathogen recovered from sick mouse	Pathogen injected into a healthy lab mouse	Pathogen grown in a pure culture	Healthy mouse becomes sick	Pathogen isolated from a dead mouse
_5_	_3_	_2_	_4_	_1_

15. Are microorganisms always harmful to the human body? Explain your answer, and give an example.

No. Most microorganisms that live in the human body are symbionts, which are either

harmless or even beneficial. For example, bacteria that live in the large intestine help

with digestion and also produce vitamins.

16. List two ways that bacteria can produce illness.

A. _by destroying cells_

B. _by producing poisons that kill cells or interfere with their normal functions_

17. List three ways that parasitic worms cause disease.

A. _by blocking blood flow in blood vessels and organs_____

B. _by taking up nutrients_____

C. _by disrupting body functions_____

How Diseases Spread

For Questions 18–26, complete each statement by writing the correct word or words.

18. Natural selection favors pathogens with ___adaptations___ that help them spread from host to host.

19. Symptoms of disease that can spread pathogens include ___coughing___ and ___sneezing___.

20. The best ways to prevent infections of the nose, throat, and respiratory tract are frequent and thorough ___hand washing___ and avoiding ___touching___ your mouth and nose.

21. ___Drug-resistant staphylococci___ that cause skin infections can be transmitted by any body contact or by contact with contaminated towels or equipment.

22. ___SAMPLE ANSWER: Chlamydia___ is spread from one host to another in body fluids exchanged during sexual activity.

23. Blood on shared syringes can spread certain forms of ___hepatitis___, as well as ___AIDS___.

24. A symptom of diseases spread by contaminated water or food is ___diarrhea___.

25. Lyme disease, mad cow disease, and SARS are all examples of ___zoonoses___.

26. The ___vector___ that carries the West Nile virus between birds and humans is a mosquito.

Apply the Big idea

27. Explain how coughing and sneezing can not only spread infection, but also help protect against invading organisms.

SAMPLE ANSWER: *Coughing and sneezing release thousands of droplets that could contain pathogens. Other people can breathe them in or touch where they land, thereby contracting the infection. However, coughing and sneezing also expel unwanted pathogens out of the body with great force. The fewer pathogens that are in the body, the easier it will be for the immune system to fight the infection.*

_____

_____

35.2 Defenses Against Infection

Lesson Objectives

🔑 Describe the body's nonspecific defenses against invading pathogens.

🔑 Describe the function of the immune system's specific defenses.

🔑 List the body's specific defenses against pathogens.

Lesson Summary

Nonspecific Defenses The body has many nonspecific defenses, which defend against a wide range of pathogens.

▶ The first line of defense is skin. Skin keeps pathogens out of the body by forming a barrier that few pathogens can get through. Mucus, saliva, and tears contain an enzyme that can kill bacteria. Mucus can also trap pathogens.

▶ When pathogens do enter the body, the second line of defense goes to work. These nonspecific defenses include:

- the **inflammatory response**, in which chemicals called **histamines** cause blood vessels near a wound to expand and phagocytes to move into the tissue to fight infection.
- the production of proteins called **interferons**, which help block the replication of viruses.
- the release of chemicals that produce a **fever**, an increase in normal body temperature, which may slow the growth of pathogens and speed up immune response.

Specific Defenses: The Immune System The function of the immune system is to fight infection by inactivating foreign substances or cells that have entered the body. The specific immune response works in several ways, including:

▶ recognizing "self," including cells and proteins that belong to the body.

▶ recognizing "nonself", or **antigens**, molecules found on foreign substances. Antigens stimulate the immune system to produce cells called lymohocytes that recognize, attack, destroy, and "remember" specific pathogens.

▶ producing specific lymphocytes that recognize specific antigens. They work by attacking infected cells or producing **antibodies**, proteins which tag antigens for destruction by immune cells.

The Immune System in Action The immune response works in two ways.

▶ In **humoral immunity**, white blood cells, called B lymphocytes (B cells), make antibodies that attack pathogens in the blood.

▶ In **cell-mediated immunity** white blood cells, called T lymphocytes (T cells), find and destroy abnormal or infected cells.

▶ After a pathogen is destroyed, memory B cells and memory T cells stay in the body. These cells help create a faster immune response if the same pathogen enters the body again.

Nonspecific Defenses

For Questions 1–8, write the letter of the definition that best matches each term.

Term

_H_ 1. skin

_C_ 2. lysozyme

_F_ 3. inflammatory response

_D_ 4. histamines

_G_ 5. interferons

_A_ 6. fever

_B_ 7. mucus

_E_ 8. nonspecific defenses

Definition

A. An increase in body temperature, which slows or stops pathogens

B. A secretion of the nose and throat that traps pathogens

C. An enzyme found in tears and saliva that breaks down bacterial cell walls

D. Chemicals that increase blood flow to tissues

E. Combination of physical and chemical barriers that defend against pathogens

F. Redness, pain, and swelling at the site of an injury

G. Proteins that fight viral growth

H. The body's most important nonspecific defense

Specific Defenses: The Immune System

For Questions 9–14, complete each statement by writing the correct word or words.

9. The ____immune____ response is the body's response to specific invaders.

10. A substance that triggers the immune response is known as a (n) ____antigen____.

11. The main role of ____antibodies____ is to tag ____antigens____ for destruction by immune-system cells.

12. The main working cells of the immune system are two types of ____lymphocytes____. Their specific types are determined by a person's ____genes____.

13. ____B lymphocytes/B cells____ discover antigens in body fluids.

14. ____T lymphocytes/T cells____ defend the body against pathogens that have infected body cells.

15. **THINK VISUALLY** In the space provided, draw an example of each type of lymphocyte indicated to show a basic difference between the two types of cells.

B Cell	T Cell
See the textbook for what this drawing should look like.	*See the textbook for what this drawing should look like.*

The Immune System in Action

For Questions 16–22, write True or False on the line provided.

_____True_____ 16. Humoral immunity is a response to pathogens in blood and lymph.

_____False_____ 17. The first response of humoral immunity to infection is much faster than the second response.

_____True_____ 18. Plasma cells are specialized B cells.

_____False_____ 19. Cell-mediated immunity involves antibodies.

_____True_____ 20. Cell-mediated immunity causes infected body cells to die.

_____False_____ 21. Cell-mediated immunity only works on viral diseases.

_____True_____ 22. Cytotoxic T cells are a cause of rejection of transplanted organs.

23. Complete the table to compare how humoral and cell-mediated immunity work after a virus invades the body for the first and second times.

Humoral Immunity vs. Cell-Mediated Immunity	
Action of Humoral Immunity	**Action of Cell-Mediated Immunity**
Primary response:	**Primary response:**
Antigens bind to antibodies.	Macrophages consume viruses and display their antigens on the cell surface. Helper T cells are activated.
Activated B cells grow and divide rapidly.	*Activated T cells divide.*
B cells produce plasma cells and memory B cells.	Helper T cells activate B cells and cytotoxic T cells and produce memory cells.
Plasma cells release antibodies that capture antigens and mark them for destruction.	*Cytotoxic T cells bind to infected body cells and destroy them.*
Secondary response:	**Secondary response:**
Memory B cells respond faster than B cells in the primary response.	*Memory T cells respond faster than helper T cells in the primary response.*

Apply the Big idea

24. A runny nose is a symptom of a cold. How is this evidence that the body's immune defenses are working?

SAMPLE ANSWER: *Mucus is one of the body's nonspecific defenses. It traps pathogens and removes then from the body. An increase in mucus would prove the body's defenses were working to fight pathogens.*

35.3 Fighting Infectious Disease

Lesson Objectives

- 🔑 Distinguish between active immunity and passive immunity.
- 🔑 Describe how public health measures and medications fight disease.
- 🔑 Describe why patterns of infectious disease have changed.

Lesson Summary

Acquired Immunity You can acquire immunity without having a disease.

▶ **Vaccination** is the injection of a weakened or mild form of a pathogen to cause immunity.

▶ **Active immunity** results from vaccines or natural exposure to an antigen.

▶ **Passive immunity** forms when antibodies are introduced into the body. It lasts only until the immune system destroys the foreign antibodies.

Public Health and Medications In 2005, less than 5 percent of human deaths were caused by infectious diseases. This statistic is the result of two major factors.

▶ The field of public health provides services that help monitor food and water supplies and promote vaccinations and healthy behavior.

▶ The development and use of many new medications, particularly antibiotics and antiviral drugs, has saved many lives by helping to cure infectious diseases.

New and Re-Emerging Diseases Since 1980, many new diseases have appeared and several diseases once thought to have been eradicated have recurred. There are two main reasons for these changes.

▶ Interactions with exotic animals have increased.

▶ The misuse of medications has caused diseases that were once under control, such as tuberculosis and malaria, to evolve resistance to many antibiotics.

Acquired Immunity

1. What was the origin of the term *vaccination*? Explain why this name was given.

The term comes from the Latin word vacca *that means "cow." The name was given to*

honor the work of English physician Edward Jenner who used fluid from cowpox sores

to produce immunity to smallpox in humans.

_____

2. How does a vaccine work?

A vaccine stimulates the body to make memory B cells and memory T cells for a

specific antigen to strengthen and quicken the body's response to repeated infections.

_____

_____

3. What type of immunity do vaccinations produce?

active immunity

4. What type of immunity does a mother pass on to her infant while breastfeeding?

passive immunity

5. Why is passive immunity only temporary?

The body's immune system destroys the antibodies because it sees them as foreign.

6. Complete the Venn diagram comparing the two types of immunity and writing the correct word or words on the lines provided.

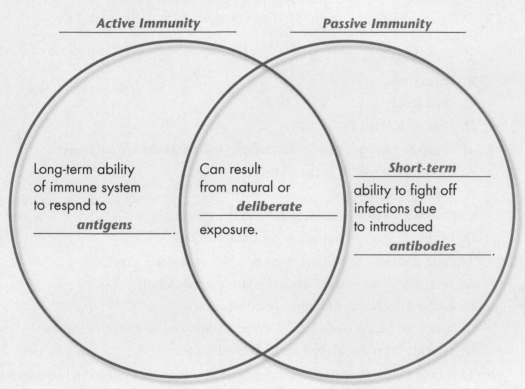

Active Immunity

Passive Immunity

Long-term ability of immune system to respnd to ____*antigens*____.

Can result from natural or ____*deliberate*____ exposure.

____*Short-term*____ ability to fight off infections due to introduced ____*antibodies*____.

Public Health and Medications

For Questions 7–11, complete each statement by writing the correct word or words.

7. Promoting childhood ___*vaccinations*___ and providing clean drinking water are two ___*public health*___ activities that have greatly reduced the spread of many infectious diseases.

8. Compounds that kill bacteria without harming the host cells are called ___*antibiotics*___.

9. The first antibiotic to be discovered was ___*penicillin*___.

10. ___*Antiviral*___ drugs inhibit the ability of viruses to invade cells or multiply within cells.

11. How did Alexander Fleming discover the first antibiotic?

Fleming saw that the growth of bacteria was inhibited by a mold called Penicillium notatum. He isolated a compound made by the mold and determined that it killed the bacteria.

New and Re-Emerging Diseases

For Questions 12–16, write the letter of the correct answer on the line at the left.

_____C_____ 12. Which of the following is NOT considered to be a major cause of new or re-emerging diseases?

    A. misuse of medications

    B. merging of human and animal habitats

    C. vaccination

    D. trade in exotic animals

_____C_____ 13. Which is an example of an infectious disease that was eliminated by public health measures?

    A. avian influenza

    B. hantavirus

    C. smallpox

    D. West Nile virus

_____A_____ 14. How are monkeypox and SARS thought to have started in humans?

    A. by animal trade for pets and food

    B. antibiotic resistance

    C. the clearing of new areas of land in the tropics

    D. by the merging of human and animal habitats

_____B_____ 15. Malaria and tuberculosis are two examples of diseases that have

    A. been totally eliminated from the human population.

    B. evolved resistance to many antibiotics.

    C. increased because of a lack of understanding of how vaccines work.

    D. recently been discovered in the United States.

_____D_____ 16. Failing to follow vaccination recommendations are thought to be responsible for the comeback of

    A. Ebola.

    B. influenza.

    C. Lyme disease.

    D. measles.

Apply the Big idea

17. After being vaccinated, many children are treated for fever. This is not considered a danger or problem. Why might this happen?

    SAMPLE ANSWER: *Vaccines are often weakened forms of an antigen. The body reacts to it by attacking it. Vaccination depends on the body recognizing, attacking, and remembering the antigen. Fever is one of the first immune responses. So, a fever after vaccination is evidence that the body is reacting strongly to the antigen.*

35.4 Immune System Disorders

Lesson Objectives

⚏ Explain what happens when the immune system overreacts to harmless pathogens.

⚏ Describe how HIV is transmitted and how it affects the immune system.

Lesson Summary

When the Immune System "Misfires" Sometimes, the immune system overreacts to otherwise harmless antigens. Three types of disorders are caused in this way.

▶ The most common immune-system disorders are **allergies**, which occur when antigens enter the body and bind to mast cells. The mast cells release histamines, which increase the flow of blood and fluids to the area. This causes allergy symptoms.

▶ Allergic reactions in the respiratory system can cause **asthma**, a dangerous chronic disease in which the air passages narrow and breathing becomes difficult.

▶ When the immune system makes a mistake and attacks the body's own cells, an autoimmune disease results. Autoimmune diseases include Type I diabetes, rheumatoid arthritis, and lupus.

HIV and AIDS In the 1970s, clusters of cases of opportunistic diseases—diseases that attack people with weakened immune systems—led to the discovery of a new disease called acquired immunodeficiency syndrome (AIDS).

▶ Research revealed that AIDS is an infectious disease caused by human immunodeficiency virus (HIV). HIV attaches to receptors on helper T cells. Once inside the cells, HIV copies itself and the new viruses infect more helper T cells.

▶ HIV infection gradually leads to the death of more and more T cells. When a person's T cell count drops to about one-sixth the normal level, the person has AIDS.

▶ HIV can only be transmitted through contact with infected blood, semen, vaginal secretions, or breast milk.

When the Immune System "Misfires"

For Questions 1–5, complete each statement by writing the correct word or words.

1. An overreaction of the immune system to antigens of pollen and other harmless substances is called a(n) ____allergy____.

2. Sneezing, a runny nose, and watery eyes are symptoms of the ___inflammatory___ response in the respiratory system.

3. Drugs called ___antihistamines___ counteract the effects of ___histamines___ produced by mast cells.

4. A dangerous condition that affects the respiratory system and can be caused by allergies is called ___asthma___.

5. Examples of ___environmental___ triggers for allergic reactions include tobacco smoke, pollution, molds, and pet dander.

6. What is an autoimmune disease?

It is a disease in which the body's immune system fails to recognize "self" and attacks cells and compounds in the body as if they were pathogens.

7. Describe the advantage and disadvantage of treating an autoimmune illness such as lupus.

Treatment of lupus with an immunosuppressant medication can help alleviate symptoms, because it suppresses the immune response. However, because the medications suppress the body's normal immune response, they make the body more vulnerable to infections.

8. Complete the table about autoimmune diseases.

Autoimmune Diseases	
Autoimmune Disease	**Organ or Tissue That Is Attacked**
Type I diabetes	*Insulin-producing cells of the pancreas*
Rheumatoid arthritis	Connective tissues around the joints
Lupus	*Organs and tissues throughout the body*

HIV and AIDS

9. What does AIDS stand for?

It stands for "acquired immunodeficiency syndrome."

10. What is the term that describes diseases that attack people with a weakened immune system?

opportunistic diseases

11. List four body fluids that can transmit AIDS.

A. *blood*

B. *semen*

C. *vaginal secretions*

D. *breast milk*

12. What behaviors prevent people from being infected with HIV?

Abstinence from sexual activity and abstinence from intravenous drug use prevent infection by HIV.

13. Why is curing HIV infection so challenging? Explain your answer.

HIV can be treated, making it possible to survive with the infection for many years. However, a vaccine that can prevent HIV infection has not been developed yet because HIV mutates and evolves so rapidly.

14. Complete the flowchart that summarizes the HIV infection process.

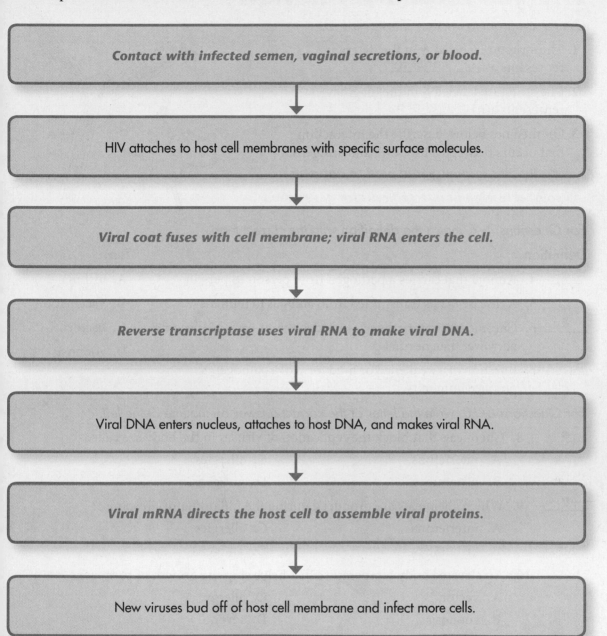

Contact with infected semen, vaginal secretions, or blood.

HIV attaches to host cell membranes with specific surface molecules.

Viral coat fuses with cell membrane; viral RNA enters the cell.

Reverse transcriptase uses viral RNA to make viral DNA.

Viral DNA enters nucleus, attaches to host DNA, and makes viral RNA.

Viral mRNA directs the host cell to assemble viral proteins.

New viruses bud off of host cell membrane and infect more cells.

Apply the Big idea

15. What is the key difference between an immunodeficiency disease and an autoimmune disease? Provide an example of both types of disease in your response.

SAMPLE ANSWER: *In an immunodeficiency disease, such as AIDS, the immune system itself is damaged or destroyed. While, in autoimmune disease, such as type 1 diabetes, it's the immune system that damages or destroys organs or tissues.*

Chapter Vocabulary Review

Use the diagram to answer Questions 1–3.

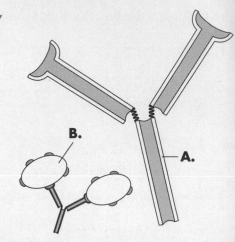

1. The structure labeled A in the diagram represents a(n) ___antibody___.

2. The structure labeled B in the diagram represents a(n) ___antigen___.

3. On the lines below, describe the interaction that occurs between antibodies and antigens.

   Antibodies recognize and bind to antigens

   tolabel foreign or infected cells for destruction.

For Questions 4–7, match the definition with the correct term.

Definition

___C___ 4. Animal that carries a pathogen from person to person

___D___ 5. A disease that is transmitted from animals to humans

___A___ 6. Chronic respiratory disease in which the air passages become narrower than normal

___B___ 7. Injection of a weakened or mild form of a pathogen to produce immunity

Term

A. asthma

B. vaccination

C. vector

D. zoonosis

For Questions 8–10, write the letter of the correct answer on the line at the left.

___A___ 8. Chemicals that block the replication of viruses in the body are called

    A. interferons.   C. allergies.

    B. histamines.   D. antigens.

___B___ 9. Which chemicals are produced during the inflammatory response?

    A. interferons   C. allergies

    B. histamines   D. antigens

___D___ 10. An elevated body temperature that helps stop the growth of pathogens is a(n)

    A. vector.   C. allergy.

    B. zoonosis.   D. fever.

For Questions 11–13, complete each statement by writing the correct word or words.

11. A change to the physiology that disrupts normal body functions and is caused by a microorganism is called a(n) ___infectious___ ___disease___.

12. The part of the immune response that depends on the action of macrophages and several types of T cells is called ___cell-mediated___ immunity.

13. The part of the immune response that depends on the action of B cells and antibodies circulating in the blood and lymph is called ___humoral___ immunity.

CHAPTER
MYSTERY

THE SEARCH FOR A CAUSE

21st Century Learning

In the Chapter Mystery, you learned about a group of people in one part of Connecticut who came down with Lyme disease. Lyme disease is spread by certain kinds of ticks. But many infectious diseases are spread directly from person to person.

Infectious Diseases in History

Smallpox is a deadly, highly-contagious disease that was once common throughout Europe, Asia, and North Africa. The war against smallpox began in the late 1700s when the British physician Edward Jenner developed a smallpox vaccine. In the 1900s, there was a worldwide effort to administer the vaccine on a global scale. By 1980, the disease had been effectively eradicated. One of the last serious smallpox outbreaks occurred in Eastern Europe in 1972. The following article describes what happened during one of the last battles against this devastatingly contagious disease.

SMALLPOX'S LAST STAND

Every year, millions of people travel to the city of Mecca in Saudi Arabia. In 1972, on his way back from the Middle East, one man traveled through an area known to have smallpox. He returned to his village in Kosovo, Yugoslavia with the smallpox virus.

Oddly enough, the pilgrim only became slightly sick. But he indirectly passed the virus along to a man named Ljatif Muzza, who lived in a neighboring town. When Muzza became sick, he went to the local hospital, where they could not diagnose what was wrong with him. (No one recognized smallpox because there had been no outbreaks for many years.) The local hospital sent him to a larger facility, which then sent him to the main hospital in the capital city, Belgrade. Muzza died shortly thereafter. But in his journey from hospital to hospital, he had infected 38 other people with smallpox, eight of whom would die as well.

At this time, Yugoslavia was ruled by a Communist dictator named Josip Broz, who called himself "Tito." He used his dictatorial powers to take drastic measures to stop the smallpox outbreak. He declared martial law and the province in which Muzza had lived was blocked off; no one was allowed in or out. People who had been infected were quarantined in special hospitals. Anyone who had come into contact with infected individuals—10,000 people in all—were given smallpox vaccinations and quarantined in hotels, under army guard. Around the country, public events were banned and barbed wire and barricades were used to stop people from traveling— and from spreading the disease. The outbreak died out after a few weeks, and only 35 people died.

Continued on next page ▶

21st Century Themes Science and Health Literacy

1. How was smallpox eradicated from the global population?

   The development of a smallpox vaccine and the worldwide effort to administer the
   vaccine effectively eradicated the disease on a global scale.

2. Why did it take so long for doctors to recognize Muzza's disease as smallpox?

   The doctors were not familiar with smallpox; there had been no outbreaks in many
   years.

3. What information in the article indicates that smallpox is spread directly from person to person?

   The fact that so many people whom Muzza came in contact with got sick, indicates
   that smallpox is spread from person to person.

4. What drastic measures were taken to control the outbreak?

   Sick people were quarantined; those who came in contact with them were vaccinated
   and also quarantined; travel was restricted.

5. In the United States, children are no longer given the smallpox vaccine. Why do you think this is the case?

   SAMPLE ANSWER: *Smallpox is spread from person to person. Because the disease has been*
   eradicated, there is little chance that the disease can spread from person to person.

21st Century Skills Controlling an Epidemic

The skills used in this activity include **information and media literacy, communication skills, creativity and intellectual curiosity,** and **social responsibility.**

Epidemic diseases are on people's minds much more today than they were in 1972. Smallpox has been eliminated, but others, such as avian flu and SARS, are possible threats. Your state government most likely has plans in place to deal with possible epidemics or pandemics. If you live in a large city, municipal officials may have been planning as well. Interview the appropriate officials to find out what plans and procedures are in place to protect the public in the event of an epidemic. Then use the information to write a magazine article describing your government's plans.

Students' articles should provide detailed descriptions of plans in place and should
contain quotes from state and/or local officials.

Appendix: Differentiated Instruction Teaching Strategies

The following list of teaching strategies can help you differentiate the content of *Miller & Levine Biology* for students at all learning levels. While the Teacher's Edition has identified places where these strategies may be particularly useful, you will likely find many other opportunities to apply them in your class.

There are four basic types of strategies:

1. **Previewing/Reviewing Strategies** Previewing strategies are implemented before the lesson begins. They help engage students, activate their prior knowledge, and guide them to predict what they will learn in the lesson. Often, these strategies contain a reviewing step in which students revisit their predictions.
2. **Active Learning Strategies** These strategies encourage students to interact with the text and lesson concepts.
3. **Peer Learning Strategies** These strategies promote cooperative learning. Struggling students hear and see concepts presented in different ways, while more advanced students benefit by teaching lesson concepts.
4. **Organizing Information Strategies** These strategies provide students with a scaffolded way to organize the information in the lesson. Often, the strategies involve using a graphic organizer.

The teaching strategies listed in this appendix have broad applications for all learner levels. Please note though, that when applicable, the strategies also include modification suggestions to help to make them more useful for particular learner groups. Refer to the Differentiated Instruction Key at the right to identify which learner group a strategy has been modified for.

Differentiated Instruction Key
- **L1** Special Needs or Struggling Students
- **ELL** English Language Learners
- **LPR** Less Proficient Readers
- **L2** On-Level Students
- **L3** Advanced Students

Strategy 1 (S1) ANTICIPATION/REACTION GUIDE

Previewing/Reviewing Before starting a lesson, ask the class questions that focus on lesson topics. While the questions can address topics you have not yet covered, make sure they require students to access some prior knowledge. After the lesson, have students re-answer the questions and compare how their answers have changed.

ELL Accept short phrases or statements from English language learners. Encourage students to say their answers out loud so that they can practice using the English language.

Strategy 2 (S2) CLOZE PROMPTS

Active Learning Provide the class with sentences in which key words or phrases have been replaced with blanks. As students work through the lesson, they should fill in the blanks with the correct terms or phrases.

L2 **L3** Challenge on-level and advanced students to create their own cloze prompt sentences. Students can then trade sentences to help them review lesson concepts.

Strategy 3 (S3) CORE CONCEPT DISCUSSION

Peer Learning Divide the class into small groups. Have each student identify a core concept—a main idea or lesson topic—to discuss within his or her group. After small-group discussions, have the class talk about at least one core concept from each group.

ELL Make sure English language learners take an active role in group and class discussions.

L3 Encourage advanced students to take a leadership role in group discussions.

Strategy 4 (S4) DEBATE

Peer Learning Divide the class into two groups. Assign each group a position to argue regarding a discussion topic. If desired, give groups time to research and plan their arguments.

Strategy 5 (S5) DIRECTED READING-THINKING ACTIVITY (DR-TA)

Previewing/Reviewing This strategy teaches students to make predictions, read to acquire lesson concepts, and then follow up with a review. Have students follow these steps:

• Skim the headings, images, and vocabulary in the text.

• Make a prediction of what the reading is about.

• Read the text.

• At teacher-defined stopping points, compare predictions with concepts and information learned in the lesson.

• Revise predictions.

LPR For less proficient readers, stop more frequently to compare predictions with what students have learned. You may also have them work in pairs or give them additional opportunities to discuss what they have read.

Strategy 6 (S6) GALLERY WALK

Peer Learning Post chart-paper stations around the classroom, each displaying a concept or question for groups to respond to. Divide the class into groups and assign each group a different color to write with. The number of groups should equal the number of stations.

Have each group walk to a station and respond to the posted question or prompt. Groups should then circulate through the stations, or "gallery." At each station, have them evaluate the previous groups' answers, making any necessary corrections or comments, and add any additional information they know. When groups return to their original stations, have them work together to summarize the information on the chart.

Strategy 7 (S7) JIGSAW REVIEW

Peer Learning In a jigsaw review, each student is responsible for teaching a concept to a small group of students.

• Divide the class into learning circles. The number of students in each learning circle should equal the number of concepts you will assign students to review.

• Assign each student in a learning circle a number.

• Have students with the same number join to form a study group. For example, all the 2s should work together.

• Assign each study group a different concept or topic to review. Study groups should then create a lesson plan to teach the concept.

• Have students return to their original learning circles and take turns teaching their lesson.

ELL Encourage English language learners who may be less proficient with spoken English to create visual aids to help them present information to their learning circles. If necessary, have them work in pairs to teach their lessons.

Strategy 8 (S8) LESSON PREVIEW

Previewing Have students preview the lesson by skimming topic headings, diagrams, pictures, vocabulary, and key concepts. Then, have students write down or discuss what they think the lesson will be about.

ELL **LPR** Give students additional time to discuss their predictions. Accept drawings and short phrases from beginning English language learners.

Strategy 9 (S9) PROBLEM AND SOLUTION

Peer Learning Present students with a problem. Have small groups discuss the problem and propose a solution. Each group should share their solution with the class. Have the class compare and contrast the different solutions.

Strategy 10 (S10) QUESTION-ANSWER RELATIONSHIPS (QAR)

Active Learning Students learn to recognize four different types of questions so that they can better answer them. After working through a lesson, have students answer and/or write questions of each type.

- *Right There:* answers are found directly in the text.
- *Think and Search:* answers come from finding information in different parts of the text and fitting these ideas together.
- *Author and You:* answers are inferred—they are a mix of students' own knowledge and the author's writing.
- *On My Own:* answers are composed of students' own knowledge.

Strategy 11 (S11) QUICK WRITE

Active Learning Give students a short period of time (one, five, or ten minutes) to write everything they know about a topic. Encourage them to write continuously about the topic for the entire time, even if they have to repeat a fact several times.

ELL Accept drawings and/or bulleted lists from beginning English language learners.

Strategy 12 (S12) READER-WRITER-SPEAKER RESPONSE

Peer Learning In this strategy, students discuss a question or topic in groups of three. Each group member plays a different role. The *Reader* reads about the topic, the *Writer* records the discussion, and the *Speaker* shares the group's comments with the rest of the class.

Strategy 13 (S13) STOP AND ANSWER

Active Learning Write a list of sequential questions on the board. Next to the question, indicate when each question should be answered. As students read the lesson or discuss a concept, stop them at the specified points and have them answer the questions.

Strategy 14 (S14) THINK-PAIR-SHARE

Peer Learning Give students a question or topic to think about individually. Next, have pairs of students discuss the topic. Pairs should then share their comments with the class.

ELL If possible, pair beginning and intermediate English language learners with more advanced or native English speakers.

Strategy 15 (S15) TIMELINE

Organizing Information Have students create a timeline to display events that occurred in a sequential order. Suggest they show the passage of time as a straight line with important events and discoveries marked along the way, in the order in which they occurred.

Strategy 16 (S16) TOPIC CIRCLES

Peer Learning Arrange the class in small-group circles. Introduce a topic or idea. Then, have one member of each circle give a fact or detail about the topic being discussed. The student to their right should then provide a different fact or detail. The cycle should continue until there is no more new information to share.

Strategy 17 (S17) WORD WALL

Previewing/Reviewing Designate a wall in your classroom to be used as a word wall. Add key vocabulary and difficult words, along with their definitions, for the entire class to reference. Encourage students to contribute to the word wall.

ELL **LPR** Suggest students add any terms they are unfamiliar with to the word wall for future reference. If they hesitate to add words themselves, suggest they write down words for you to define and post.

Strategy 18 (S18) CAUSE AND EFFECT DIAGRAM

Organizing Information To visually represent cause-and-effect relationships, suggest students make and fill out cause-and-effect diagrams. Reinforce that a single cause can have multiple effects, just as several causes can contribute to a single effect.

ELL Accept short phrases or drawings for cause-and-effect descriptions from beginning and intermediate English language learners.

Use the graphic organizer (GO1) in the ***Transparencies*** *book to present this strategy.*

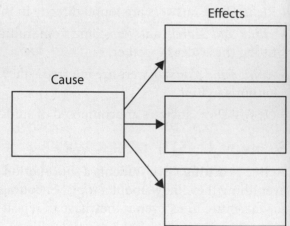

Strategy 19 (S19) CLUSTER DIAGRAM

Organizing Information Have students show how concepts are related to one another by making a cluster diagram.

To create a cluster diagram:

- Write the main idea or topic in the center of a sheet of paper. Circle it.
- Draw lines branching off the main idea, connected to ovals that contain concepts or characteristics related to the main topic.
- Continue adding facts and details in a branching pattern, connecting related ideas and facts.

Use the graphic organizer (GO2) in the ***Transparencies*** *book to present this strategy.*

Strategy 20 (S20) COMPARE/CONTRAST TABLE

Organizing Information A compare/contrast table helps students organize the similarities and differences between two or more concepts, objects, or processes.

To create a compare/contrast table:

• Draw a table.

• Label the columns with the items being compared.

• Label the rows with the characteristics being examined.

• Fill in the boxes with the characteristics of each item.

*Use the graphic organizer (GO3) in the **Transparencies** book to present this strategy.*

Strategy 21 (S21) CONCEPT MAP

Organizing Information A concept map helps students organize concepts using visual relationships and linking words. Mapping out these connections helps students think about how information fits together.

To create a concept map:

• Draw a box and write the main concept inside it.

• Below, draw arrows to additional boxes. Use linking words along the arrow lines to describe the relationships between connected boxes.

• In the second set of boxes, write details that support the main concept.

• Continue to add boxes and linking words as necessary to further organize details and facts.

*Use the graphic organizer (GO4) in the **Transparencies** book to present this strategy.*

Strategy 22 (S22) CORNELL NOTES

Organizing Information Cornell notes is a note-taking strategy. In addition to outlining lesson concepts, students use the Cornell note format to identify and list key words as well as briefly summarize lesson concepts.

ELL **LPR** Encourage less proficient readers and English language learners to list any terms that they are unfamiliar with in the left-hand column. Suggest they write a definition for each listed term.

*Use the graphic organizer (GO5) in the **Transparencies** book to present this strategy.*

Strategy 23 (S23) CYCLE DIAGRAM

Organizing Information Have students use a cycle diagram to show the steps involved in a repeating process.

To create a cycle diagram:

• Draw a box and fill in the first step of the cycle.

• Draw an arrow to a second box with the next step of the cycle.

• Continue adding boxes in a circular pattern for every step of the cycle. Connect the steps with arrows.

• The last box of the cycle should have an arrow connecting it to the first step.

L1 **ELL** **LPR** Encourage students to use drawings and other visual aids in their cycle diagrams.

*Use the graphic organizer (GO6) in the **Transparencies** book to present this strategy.*

Strategy 24 (S24) FISHBONE MAP

Organizing Information A fishbone map helps students organize complex topics into main ideas and supporting details.

To create a fishbone map:

- Draw a "backbone," or set of horizontal lines, and fill them in with a topic.
- Draw diagonal lines that extend off of this backbone. Label each of these diagonals with a main idea related to the topic.
- Draw several lines branching off of each diagonal. Write details that support each main idea on these lines.

Use the graphic organizer (GO7) in the **Transparencies** *book to present this strategy.*

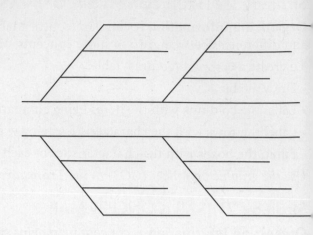

Strategy 25 (S25) FLOWCHART

Organizing Information Students can use a flowchart to show a sequence of steps or events involved in a process. Make sure students understand that a flowchart can have one or more paths.

To create a flowchart:

- Write the first step of a process inside a box.
- Use an arrow to connect this first box with a second box that contains the next step in the process.
- Continue connecting boxes until all steps of the process are represented.

L1 **ELL** **LPR** Encourage students to use drawings and other visual aids in their flowcharts.

Use the graphic organizer (GO8) in the **Transparencies** *book to present this strategy.*

Strategy 26 (S26) FRAYER MODEL

Organizing Information The Frayer model helps students understand a vocabulary term by noting its definition, characteristics, examples, and nonexamples.

To fill in a Frayer model:

- Write the vocabulary term in the center oval.
- Write the definition, characteristics, and examples of the term in the appropriate boxes.
- In the nonexample box, list things that are not examples of the term, but are similar in some way.

ELL The Frayer model can be modified for English language learners who are proficient in writing in their native language. Have these students use the bottom right box to list a translation of the definition in their native language.

Use the graphic organizers (GO9 Frayer Model and GO10 ELL Frayer Model) in the **Transparencies** *book to present this strategy.*

Strategy 27 (S27) KWL

Previewing/Reviewing KWL charts help students activate prior knowledge, gather information, and check for understanding.

To fill in a KWL chart:

- Before the lesson, have students fill in the K and W columns.